Applied Structural Design of Buildings

Applied Structural Design of Buildings

THOMAS H. McKAIG

B. Arch., C. E.
Consulting Architectural Engineer

SECOND EDITION

F. W. Dodge Corporation, New York

PREFACE

This book had its inception as a series of notes used in the instruction of a group of engineers and architects preparing for state license examinations. The notes were then expanded and published by the author in book form in 1949. In this second edition, the book has been revised to reflect changes in technology, such as the 1951 revision of the ACI Code for reinforced concrete, and also the suggestions for change made by users of the first edition.

In its present form the book is intended primarily for the use of architects, structural engineers, plant engineers, license applicants, and draftsmen. It is not strictly a textbook, but rather a handbook, in which the structural engineer will find in simple, practical form the working tools he needs. The presentation is based on the assumption that the person using it has a knowledge of the elements of physics, mechanics, materials of construction, and structural theory. No attempt is therefore made to develop the theory of these subjects, which is obtainable in any textbook. However, the book has been designed to be helpful even if the user's theoretical background was obtained some time ago, and has not been reviewed or brought up to date since.

Certain generally accepted code regulations of various authorities have been used. For structural steel, the AISC Code as adopted in 1946 (20,000 psi basic stress) has been most generally accepted, although some cities still use the AISC 1925 Code (18,000 psi basic stress). For reinforced concrete, the ACI 1951 Code has been used, although again many local codes do not recognize it.

Included in this book are tables which the author has most frequently used in his office practice. If the requirements of a specialized problem are beyond the limits of these tables, more complete ones may be found in the various handbooks.

The methods have been taken from good office practice and have proved to be efficient and at the same time acceptable to various building departments and other authorities. Short-cut methods have generally been derived from pure theory. They are recommended, not only to save time, but also to eliminate many sources of error.

Lest it be feared that short cuts sacrifice accuracy, it should be observed that factors of safety both in recommended loads and suggested stresses are more than adequate protection against any lack of refinement in the methods. In addition, the strength of the materials with which the designer is working may vary through a range far greater than the possible variation or error resulting from the short-cut methods.

The author wishes to acknowledge his indebtedness to many sources for his material, including those tables, formulae, and drawings that are reproduced here because they have been especially useful in office practice. Attempt has been made to acknowledge the source of such material wherever it appears, but the following additional acknowledgments, general and specific, are also due:

American Institute of Steel Construction, for much material drawn from recent editions of its manual, *Steel Construction*, and other publications

v

Bethlehem Steel Company, particularly for
Tables 4.16 and 10.1, and Fig. 9.12 to 9.32

Detroit Steel Products Company, Fig. 10.43
and 10.44, and Table 10.10

Engineering News-Record, Art. 8.11*d*

Factory Mutual Fire Insurance Companies,
Fig. 10.23

National Lumber Manufacturers Association, Art. 7.30, Table 9.10

Portland Cement Association, Fig. 5.13,
Art. 7.20, and part of Art. 11.50, in addition to much material specifically credited

Practical Builder, Table 7.14 and Fig. 11.3

Timber Engineering Company, for Tables
9.11 and 9.12 as well as other material
credited in Chapter 9, and also Art. 10.12

Weiskopf and Pickworth, Tables 4.12 and
4.17 to 4.19

CONTENTS

vii

1

General Principles

1.10 NOMENCLATURE

Nomenclature used in this book is generally that used in common practice, although it may not be used in college textbooks. In general, with a few exceptions, the nomenclature used in the steel handbooks agrees with that used here. Much of it has been agreed upon by a committee of the American Society of Civil Engineers and the American Concrete Institute.

Many subscripts will be used, and, if they are not self-explanatory, they will be defined as they appear. The general nomenclature is as follows:

A area of section in square inches.

a distance measured along the beam; length of beam bearing in inches; length of concentrated load on beam in inches. (See also Tables 4.17 and 4.18 for special use.)

ACI   American Concrete Institute.

AISC   American Institute of Steel Construction.

B bearing at end of beam, inches; bending factor of a column; width of combined footing.

b width in inches; in a concrete beam, width of rectangular beam.

b' width of flange of concrete T beam, in inches.

C constant for use in various formulae; carry over factor; coefficient.

c extreme fiber distance in inches, length of segment in inches.

D diameter; distance; depth in feet; design dead load; deflection factor.

d depth in inches; in concrete, net depth or depth to tension steel; direct stress coefficient (Art. 10.22); diameter.

D.S.   direct stress (Art. 10.22).

E modulus of elasticity in psi (subscript indicates material); effective width.

e eccentricity in inches.

F deflection coefficient, coefficient for two-way slabs; semirigid-construction redesign coefficient.

f fiber stress in psi, subscript designates material or nature of stress; coefficient for fixed end moment (see Figs. 3.27 to 3.29).

f' ultimate unit compressive stress in concrete.

fem   fixed end moment.

G reaction load per inch of bearing in a steel beam (see Art. 1.32).

g gage of rivets.

H horizontal thrust; altitude.

h gross depth of concrete beam in inches; height of wall, rigid frame, or column in feet.

I   American Standard beam.

I moment of inertia.

j ratio of lever arm of resisting couple to total depth d.

K constant for use in concrete beam problems; net diameter of screw thread; stiffness factor; material factor for grillage.

1

k ratio of depth of neutral axis to depth d (concrete); kips; distance, back of flange to toe of fillet (steel beam); decimal portion of length (Art. 2.30).

L length in feet; designation for structural angle; design live load.

l length in inches.

L.L.O.   longer leg outstanding.

L.L.V.   longer leg vertical.

M bending moment, expressed as inch-pounds or foot-pounds, kip-inches or kip-feet.

M_s static moment of section.

m ratio f_s/f_c in reinforced concrete beam; overhang of base plate; beam moment coefficient (Art. 10.22).

N number of loads, rivets, etc.; distance from edge of flange to face of web; external load on column; unit stress (Fig. 9.33).

n ratio E_s/E_c; number of rivets in group; span/rise of a truss; cantilever span of bearing plate.

o circumference or perimeter of bar; offset of footing.

o.c.   on centers.

P concentrated load.

p steel ratio in a concrete beam.

psf   pounds per square foot.

psi   pounds per square inch.

Q static moment beyond the plane under investigation; unit stress (Fig. 9.33).

R reactions in pounds (or kips); radius; reduction of column load in percent; rise of arch.

r radius of gyration; rise; ratio.

S section modulus.

s stirrup spacing; longitudinal rivet spacing; pitch of hooping; in rigid frame, slope length of beam.

S.L.O.   shorter leg outstanding.

S.L.V.   shorter leg vertical.

t thickness of steel beam web in inches; thickness of wall; thickness of flange of concrete T beam.

U factor for laterally unsupported beam.

u unit bond stress in concrete.

V total shear in pounds (or kips).

v unit shearing stress; shear coefficient (Art. 10.22).

W total uniform load.

w load per unit length or area.

WF   wide-flange beam.

X horizontal axis.

x distance, back of angle to axis 1-1; distance from end to point of zero shear.

x center of gravity or distance to neutral axis, horizontally.

Y vertical axis.

y distance back of angle to axis 2-2.

$\bar{y}$ center of gravity or distance to neutral axis, vertically.

z depth below top of beam to resultant of compressive stresses in a concrete beam.

α angle of neutral axis (see Art. 1.32); angle of slope of ground.

Δ total deformation; deflection of beams.

δ unit deformation.

θ slope deflection.

ϕ round bar (reinforcement); angle of repose.

Σ sum of.

Σ_o sum of bar perimeters.

$\square$ square bar (reinforcement).

1.11 Definitions

It may be advisable to state a few definitions, not always within the scope of elementary textbooks, that are the result of common usage rather than technical dictation. Some of these may seem elementary, but they have been included either because they have not always been elementary, or because they mean a certain specific thing in this text.

Ashlar Masonry composed of cut stone with proper bond.

Beam, continuous A beam which is continuous and capable of carrying moment over an interior support.

Beam, restrained A beam of which one or both ends are fixed or continuous over a support.

Beam, simple A beam freely supported at both ends, theoretically with no restraint. The restraint of a wall is considered to be insufficient to change the beam from "simple" to "restrained."

Beam, spandrel A beam from column to column, carrying an exterior wall in a skeleton building.

Girder As distinguished from "beam," the heavier supporting member which carries the load of the beams into the column, as in "beam and girder construction."

Girt A secondary horizontal member in a side wall, designed to resist wind pressure.

Kip A word used to denote a load of 1,000 lb, derived from "kilo-pound."

Lintel A beam especially provided over an opening for a door, window, or the like, to carry the wall over the opening.

Load, dead The weight of walls, partitions, framing, floors, roofs, and all other permanent stationary construction entering into a building.

Load, live All loads other than dead loads and wind pressure.

Modulus of rupture The unit fiber stress calculated from the beam formula $f = M/S$. In this text it is used as an extreme fiber stress in bending for a material such as plain concrete, which has a different strength in tension and in compression, and for which, because of certain phenomena in change of location of neutral axis, the fiber stress in neither tension nor compression can be used in figuring bending.

Mullion A vertical member between two sections of window sash, usually designed merely to carry wind load and not vertical load (not to be confused with *muntin*, the small member which separates lights of glass within the sash).

Redundant member A member in any frame or truss which may be omitted in the structure without affecting the ability to analyze the frame or truss by ordinary static methods (such as a counterdiagonal in a truss).

Rigid frame Any structure in a plane, made up of beams and columns, so constructed that the joints are rigidly fixed to transmit moment, and thus to reduce moment in other parts of the frame.

Skeleton construction Construction in which the load from all parts of the structure are carried to the foundation by means of beams and columns and not by walls.

Statically determinate structure A structure in which all elements may be computed by ordinary static methods of computation.

Statically indeterminate structure A structure in which all elements cannot be computed by ordinary static methods of computation.

Wall, apron That part of a skeleton building below a window sill and supported on a spandrel beam. (Used principally in reinforced-concrete buildings where the entire panel from column to column is filled with window sash.)

Wall, bearing Any wall which supports any vertical load in addition to its own weight.

Wall, nonbearing A wall which carries no load other than its own weight.

Wall, panel A nonbearing wall in skeleton construction, built between columns or piers and wholly supported at each story.

Wall, party A wall used or adapted for joint service between two buildings.

Wall, veneered A wall having a masonry facing which is not attached and bonded to the backing, and so does not form an integral part of the wall for purposes of load bearing and stability.

1.20　PROPERTIES OF MATERIALS

The design of any structural member or detail involves the consideration of two components—one a function of the material and the other a function of the shape and size of the member. Each is independent of the other. A tabulation of the properties of the various materials which go into structures is, therefore, a necessary part of any structural handbook (see Table 1.1).

The properties of materials include weight per cubic foot, allowable working stresses in tension, compression, or bearing, shear and bending, modulus of elasticity, and coefficient of expansion.

1.21　AISC CODE

As structural steel is a basic structural material, it has seemed desirable to include under the general heading of Properties of Materials those portions of the American Institute of

Table 1.1 Properties of Materials

Material	Weight, lb, per cu ft	Allowable stresses				E (000,000 omitted)	Coef. of expansion per deg F
		Tension f_t	Compression f_c	Shear f_v	Bending f		
Structural steel	490	20,000	17,000[a]	[b]	20,000	30	.0000067
High-carbon steel (rails)	490						.0000073
Drawn steel (wire)	490	20,000–40,000					.0000069
Rivet steel	490	15,000		15,000	15,000	30	.0000061
Cast steel	490	16,000	16,000	12,000	16,000	30	.0000061
Wrought iron	485	12,000	12,000	10,000	12,000	28	.0000067
Cast iron	450		10,000		3,000	12	.0000059
Aluminum	145	13,000	13,000	8,800	13,000	10	.0000125
Brass	534	3,000–9,000				9–14	.0000104
Bronze	509	20,000				4.5	.0000101
Copper	556	5,000					.0000093
Granite ashlar	165		[c]			7	.0000035
Limestone ashlar	160		[c]			7	.0000035
Sandstone ashlar	140		[c]			7	.0000035
Rubble	150						.0000035
Brick masonry	120						.0000031
Concrete (stone or gravel aggregate)	150		[d]				.0000079
Cast stone	160		400				
Structural clay tile (cells horiz. gross area)	[e]	[c]	70				
Concrete block (gross)	[e]	[c]	80				
Gypsum	48		165	25		0.6[f]	
Douglas fir, structural	32		400–1,400	100	1,600	1.6	.000032–.0000021
Hemlock, common	29		360–650	60	1,040	1.4	
Oak, red or white, commercial	45		600–950	120	1,200	1.5	.000030–.0000027
Longleaf yellow pine, merchantable structural	44		455–1,300	120	1,600	1.6	.000019–.0000030
Longleaf yellow pine, common	44		455–1,025	100	1,200	1.6	.000019–.0000030
Shortleaf yellow pine, structural	38		455–1,150	120	1,600	1.6	.000019–.0000030
Shortleaf yellow pine, common	38		390–1,200	120	1,200	1.6	.000019–.0000030
White pine, Norway pine, #1 common	30		360–775	75	1,100	1.2	.000019–.0000030
Redwood, select structural	26		320–1,450	110	1,700	1.2	
Redwood, heart structural	26		320–1,100	95	1,300	1.2	
Spruce, #1 common	27		300–900	95	1,200	1.2	

[a]See Art. 7.10.

[b]See Art. 1.21.

[c]See Art. 8.20.

[d]See Art. 1.22.

[e]Varies with design of block.

[f]I.e., $E = 600,000$.

Steel Construction Code which have to do with the design properties of the material. Particular portions of the code which apply to specific design problems are quoted and referred to in connection with the section to which they apply. The balance of this section is therefore quoted directly from the AISC Code, as revised in 1946.

Section 15. Allowable Unit Stresses

Except as provided in this Section under "Bending," under "Wind Only" and under "Wind and Other Forces" and as provided in Section 1, final paragraph, all parts of the structure shall be so proportioned that the unit stress in pounds per square inch shall not exceed the following values:

(*a*) Structural Steel, Rivets, Bolts, and Weld Metal.

(1) Tension.

Structural steel, net section	20,000
Butt welds, section through throat	20,000
Rivets, on area based on nominal diameter	20,000
Bolts and other threaded parts, on nominal area at root of thread	20,000

(2) Compression.

Columns, gross section

For axially loaded columns with values of l/r not greater than 120 . . . . . $17{,}000 - 0.485 \, (l^2/r^2)$

For axially loaded columns (bracing and other secondary members) with values of l/r greater than 120 . . . .

[for main members, see Section 16(*b*)] . . . . $\dfrac{18{,}000}{1 + \dfrac{l^2}{18{,}000 \, r^2}}$

In which l is the unbraced length of the column and r is the corresponding radius of gyration of the section, both in inches.

Plate Girder Stiffeners, gross section	20,000
Webs of Rolled Sections at toe of fillet.	24,000
Butt Welds—Section through throat (crushing)	20,000

(3) Bending.

Tension on extreme fibers of rolled sections, plate girders, and built-up members. [See Section 26(*a*)] 20,000

Compression on extreme fibers of rolled sections plate girders, and built-up members.

With ld/bt not in excess of 600 20,000

With ld/bt in excess of 600 . . . . $\dfrac{12{,}000{,}000}{ld/bt}$

In which l is the unsupported length and d the depth, of the member; b is the width, and t the thickness, of its compression flange; all in inches; except that l shall be taken as twice the length of the compression flange of a cantilever beam not fully stayed at its outer end against translation or rotation.

Stress on extreme fibers of pins 30,000

Fiber stresses in butt welds, due to bending, shall not exceed the values prescribed for tension and compression, respectively.

Fully continuous beams and girders may be proportioned for negative moments which are maximum at interior points of support, at a unit bending stress 20 percent higher than above stated; provided that the section modulus used over supports shall not be less than that required for the maximum positive moments in the same beam or girder, and provided that the compression flange shall be regarded as unsupported from the support to the point of contraflexure.

For columns proportioned for combined axial and bending stresses, the maximum unit bending stress may be taken at 24,000 pounds per square inch, when this stress is induced by the gravity loading of fully or partially restrained beams framing into the columns.

(4) Shearing.

Rivets	15,000
Pins, and turned bolts in reamed or drilled holes	15,000
Unfinished bolts	10,000
Webs of beams and plate girders, gross section	13,000
Weld metal	
On section through throat of fillet weld, or on faying surface area of plug or slot weld	13,600
On section through throat of butt weld	13,000

(Stress in a fillet weld shall be considered as shear on the throat, for any direction of applied stress. Neither plug nor slot welds shall be assigned any values in resistance to stresses other than shear.)

(5) Bearing.

	Double Shear	Single Shear
Rivets	40,000	32,000
Turned bolts in reamed or drilled holes	40,000	32,000
Unfinished bolts	25,000	20,000
Pins		32,000
Contact Area		
Milled Stiffeners and Other Milled Surfaces		30,000
Fitted Stiffeners		27,000
Expansion rollers and rockers (pounds per linear inch)		$600d$

in which d is diameter of roller or rocker in inches.

(b) Cast Steel.

Compression and Bearing, same as for Structural Steel. Other Unit Stresses, 75 percent of those for Structural Steel.

(c) Masonry Bearing.

Granite	800
Sandstone and Limestone	400
Portland Cement Concrete, unless otherwise specified	600
Hard Brick in Cement Mortar	250

(d) Wind Only.

Members subject only to stresses produced by wind forces may be proportioned for unit stresses $33\frac{1}{3}$ percent greater than those specified for dead and live load stresses. A corresponding increase may be applied to the allowable unit stresses in their connecting rivets, bolts or welds.

(e) Wind and Other Forces.

Members subject to stresses produced by a combination of wind and other loads may be proportioned for unit stresses $33\frac{1}{3}$ percent greater than those specified for dead and live load stresses, provided the section thus required is not less than that required for the combination of dead load, live load, and impact (if any). A corresponding increase may be applied to the allowable unit stresses in their connecting rivets, bolts or welds.

Section 16. Slenderness Ratio

(a) The ratio of unbraced length to least radius of gyration l/r for compression members and for tension members other than rods shall not exceed:

For main compression members	120
For bracing and other secondary members in compression	200
For main tension members	240
For bracing and other secondary members in tension	300

(b) The slenderness of a main compression member may exceed 120, but not 200, provided that it is not ordinarily subject to shock or vibratory loads and provided that its unit stress under full design loading shall not exceed the following fraction of that stipulated under Section 15(a)(2) for its actual ratio l/r:

$$1.6 - \frac{l}{200r}$$

Section 17. Depth Ratio

(*a*) Simple Spans.

The depth of beams and girders in floors shall if practicable be not less than $\frac{1}{24}$ of the span, and where subject to shocks or vibrations not less than $\frac{1}{20}$. If members of less depth are used, the unit stress in bending shall be decreased in the same ratio as the depth is decreased from the above recommended.

The depth of roof purlins shall if practicable be not less than $\frac{1}{24}$ of the span, and in no case less than $\frac{1}{30}$ of the span, except in the case of corrugated sheeting roofs, with a slope not less than $4\frac{3}{4}$ in 12.

Beams and girders supporting plastered ceilings shall if practicable be so proportioned that the maximum live load deflection will not exceed $\frac{1}{360}$ of the span.

(*b*) Restrained and Continuous Spans.

Minimum depth-ratios for restrained and continuous spans shall if practicable be such that the deflections at critical points will not be greater than those of simple spans of the minimum depth-ratio recommended under Paragraph (*a*).

(*c*) Secondary Tension Members.

The horizontal projection of the length of bracing and secondary members in tension, other than rods, shall if practicable not exceed 90 times the depth.

Table 1.2   Allowable Unit Stresses in Concrete

Stresses in pounds per square inch shall not exceed the following values, where f_c' equals the minimum compressive strength at 28 days.

Description	For any strength of concrete as fixed by test $n = \dfrac{30{,}000}{f_c'}$	Maximum value, psi	When strength of concrete is fixed by water content in accordance with Code			
			$f_c' = $ 2,000 psi, $n = 15$	$f_c' = $ 2,500 psi, $n = 12$	$f_c' = $ 3,000 psi, $n = 10$	$f_c' = $ 3,750 psi, $n = 8$
Flexure (f_c):						
Extreme fiber stress in compression	$0.45f_c'$		900	1,125	1,350	1,688
Extreme fiber stress in tension in plain concrete footings	$0.03f_c'$		60	75	90	113
Shear (as a measure of diagonal tension):						
Beams with no web reinforcement (v_c)	$0.03f_c'$		60	75	90	113
Beams with properly designed web reinforcement (v)	$0.12f_c'$		240	300	360	450
Flat slabs at distance d from edge of column capital or drop panel (v_c)	$0.03f_c'$		60	75	90	113
Footings (v_c)	$0.03f_c'$	75	60	75	75	75
Bond (u):						
Deformed bars:						
Top bars*	$0.07f_c'$	245	140	175	210	245
In two-way footings (except top bars)	$0.08f_c'$	280	160	200	240	280
All others	$0.10f_c'$	350	200	250	300	350
Plain bars (must be hooked):						
Top bars	$0.03f_c'$	105	60	75	90	105
In two-way footings (except top bars)	$0.036f_c'$	126	.72	90	108	126
All others	$0.045f_c'$	158	90	113	135	158
Bearing (f_c):						
On full area	$0.25f_c'$		500	625	750	938
On $\frac{1}{3}$ area or less†	$0.375f_c'$		750	938	1,125	1,405

*Top bars are horizontal bars so placed that more than 12 in. of concrete is cast in the member below the bar.

†The allowable bearing stress on an area greater than one-third but less than the full area shall be interpolated between the values given.

1.22 ACI CODE

As concrete is a basic structural material, it has seemed desirable to include under the general heading of Properties of Materials those portions of the American Concrete Institute Code which have to do with the design properties of the material. Particular portions of the code which apply to specific design problems are quoted and referred to in connection with the section to which they apply. The balance of this section and Table 1.2 are therefore quoted directly from the ACI Code, as revised and adopted in 1951.

(a) *Tension*

f_s = Tensile unit stress in longitudinal reinforcement

and

f_v = Tensile unit stress in web reinforcement

20,000 psi for Rail-Steel Concrete Reinforcement Bars, Billet-Steel Concrete Reinforcement Bars of intermediate and hard grades, Axle-Steel Concrete Reinforcement Bars of intermediate and hard grades, and Cold-Drawn Steel Wire for Concrete Reinforcement.

18,000 psi for Billet-Steel Concrete Reinforcement Bars of structural grade, and Axle-Steel Concrete Reinforcement Bars of structural grade.

(b) *Tension in one-way slabs of not more than 12-ft span*

f_s = Tensile unit stress in main reinforcement

For the main reinforcement, $\frac{3}{8}$ inch or less in diameter, in one-way slabs, 50 percent of the minimum yield point specified in the Standard Specifications of the American Society for Testing Materials for the particular kind and grade of reinforcement used, but in no case to exceed 30,000 psi.

Under current specifications this permits bars to be used at 20,000 psi and welded wire mesh at 30,000 psi.

(c) *Compression, vertical column reinforcement*

f_s = Nominal allowable stress in vertical column reinforcement

Forty percent of the minimum yield point specified in the Standard Specifications of the American Society for Testing Materials for the particular kind and grade of reinforcement used, but in no case to exceed 30,000 psi.

f_r = Allowable unit stress in the metal core of composite and combination columns

Structural steel sections . . . 16,000 psi
Cast iron sections . . . . . 10,000 psi

1.30 PROPERTIES OF SECTIONS

As has already been stated, the design of any structural member or detail involves the consideration of two components—the shape and size of the member and the material. Some of the functions of shape and size are simple to compute, such as the properties of squares or rectangles, which may be computed from the formulae in Table 1.3. Others, such as the properties of rolled-steel members, are obtainable directly from Tables 1.5 to 1.10. Still others must be computed by the more complex methods presented in Art. 1.31.

The elements or properties of sections are certain mathematical functions of the dimensions and shape of a homogeneous section, commonly used in structural calculations. The functions usually listed as elements or properties are (1) area, (2) position of neutral axis or center of gravity, (3) moment of inertia, (4) section modulus, and (5) radius of gyration. The properties of sections commonly used are shown in Table 1.3, taken from the handbook of the American Institute of Steel Construction.

1.31 Properties of compound sections

It is frequently necessary in structural design to compute the functions of compound sections. This consists of the application of several simple formulae to the elements of simple sections and is always best performed by means of a tabulation.

a The computation of position of neutral axis, or center of gravity of a composite cross-section, such as an angle, may be found from the following formula (Fig. 1.1):

$$\bar{y} = \frac{A_1 y_1 + A_2 y_2 + A_3 y_3 + \cdots A_n y_n}{A_1 + A_2 + A_3 + \cdots A_n} \quad (1.1)$$

where A_1, A_2, A_3, etc., are the component areas involved, and y_1, y_2, y_3, etc., are the distances from the various neutral axes of the component areas to a known reference line

Table 1.3   Properties of Sections

SQUARE

Axis of moments through center

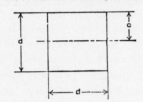

$A = d^2$

$c = \dfrac{d}{2}$

$I = \dfrac{d^4}{12}$

$S = \dfrac{d^3}{6}$

$r = \dfrac{d}{\sqrt{12}} = .288675\, d$

SQUARE

Axis of moments on base

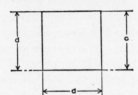

$A = d^2$

$c = d$

$I = \dfrac{d^4}{3}$

$S = \dfrac{d^3}{3}$

$r = \dfrac{d}{\sqrt{3}} = .577350\, d$

SQUARE

Axis of moments on diagonal

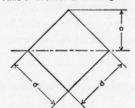

$A = d^2$

$c = \dfrac{d}{\sqrt{2}} = .707107\, d$

$I = \dfrac{d^4}{12}$

$S = \dfrac{d^3}{6\sqrt{2}} = .117851\, d^3$

$r = \dfrac{d}{\sqrt{12}} = .288675\, d$

RECTANGLE

Axis of moments through center

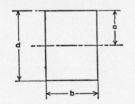

$A = bd$

$c = \dfrac{d}{2}$

$I = \dfrac{bd^3}{12}$

$S = \dfrac{bd^2}{6}$

$r = \dfrac{d}{\sqrt{12}} = .288675\, d$

Table 1.3   Properties of Sections (*Continued*)

RECTANGLE

Axis of moments on base

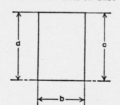

$A = bd$

$c = d$

$I = \dfrac{bd^3}{3}$

$S = \dfrac{bd^2}{3}$

$r = \dfrac{d}{\sqrt{3}} = .577350\, d$

RECTANGLE

Axis of moments on diagonal

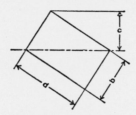

$A = bd$

$c = \dfrac{bd}{\sqrt{b^2 + d^2}}$

$I = \dfrac{b^3 d^3}{6\,(b^2 + d^2)}$

$S = \dfrac{b^2 d^2}{6\sqrt{b^2 + d^2}}$

$r = \dfrac{bd}{\sqrt{6\,(b^2 + d^2)}}$

RECTANGLE

Axis of moments any line
through center of gravity

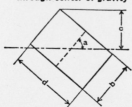

$A = bd$

$c = \dfrac{b \sin a + d \cos a}{2}$

$I = \dfrac{bd\,(b^2 \sin^2 a + d^2 \cos^2 a)}{12}$

$S = \dfrac{bd\,(b^2 \sin^2 a + d^2 \cos^2 a)}{6\,(b \sin a + d \cos a)}$

$r = \sqrt{\dfrac{b^2 \sin^2 a + d^2 \cos^2 a}{12}}$

HOLLOW RECTANGLE

Axis of moments through center

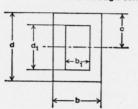

$A = bd - b_1 d_1$

$c = \dfrac{d}{2}$

$I = \dfrac{bd^3 - b_1 d_1^3}{12}$

$S = \dfrac{bd^3 - b_1 d_1^3}{6d}$

$r = \sqrt{\dfrac{bd^3 - b_1 d_1^3}{12\,A}}$

Copyright 1947 American Institute of Steel Construction

Table 1.3   Properties of Sections (*Continued*)

EQUAL RECTANGLES

Axis of moments through
center of gravity

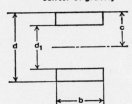

$A = b(d - d_1)$

$c = \dfrac{d}{2}$

$I = \dfrac{b(d^3 - d_1^3)}{12}$

$S = \dfrac{b(d^3 - d_1^3)}{6d}$

$r = \sqrt{\dfrac{d^3 - d_1^3}{12(d - d_1)}}$

UNEQUAL RECTANGLES

Axis of moments through
center of gravity

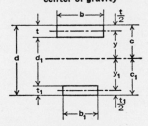

$A = bt + b_1 t_1$

$c = \dfrac{\frac{1}{2} bt^2 + b_1 t_1 (d - \frac{1}{2} t_1)}{A}$

$I = \dfrac{bt^3}{12} + bty^2 + \dfrac{b_1 t_1^3}{12} + b_1 t_1 y_1^2$

$S = \dfrac{I}{c} \qquad S_1 = \dfrac{I}{c_1}$

$r = \sqrt{\dfrac{I}{A}}$

TRIANGLE

Axis of moments through
center of gravity

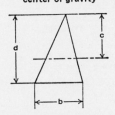

$A = \dfrac{bd}{2}$

$c = \dfrac{2d}{3}$

$I = \dfrac{bd^3}{36}$

$S = \dfrac{bd^2}{24}$

$r = \dfrac{d}{\sqrt{18}} = .235702\,d$

TRIANGLE

Axis of moments on base

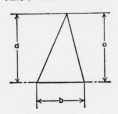

$A = \dfrac{bd}{2}$

$c = d$

$I = \dfrac{bd^3}{12}$

$S = \dfrac{bd^2}{12}$

$r = \dfrac{d}{\sqrt{6}} = .408248\,d$

Table 1.3 Properties of Sections (*Continued*)

TRAPEZOID

Axis of moments through center of gravity

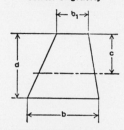

$$A = \frac{d(b + b_1)}{2}$$

$$c = \frac{d(2b + b_1)}{3(b + b_1)}$$

$$I = \frac{d^3 (b^2 + 4 bb_1 + b_1^2)}{36 (b + b_1)}$$

$$S = \frac{d^2 (b^2 + 4 bb_1 + b_1^2)}{12 (2b + b_1)}$$

$$r = \frac{d}{6(b + b_1)} \sqrt{2 (b^2 + 4 bb_1 + b_1^2)}$$

CIRCLE

Axis of moments through center

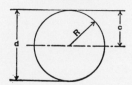

$$A = \frac{\pi d^2}{4} = \pi R^2 = .785398\, d^2 = 3.141593\, R^2$$

$$c = \frac{d}{2} = R$$

$$I = \frac{\pi d^4}{64} = \frac{\pi R^4}{4} = .049087\, d^4 = .785398\, R^4$$

$$S = \frac{\pi d^3}{32} = \frac{\pi R^3}{4} = .098175\, d^3 = .785398\, R^3$$

$$r = \frac{d}{4} = \frac{R}{2}$$

HOLLOW CIRCLE

Axis of moments through center

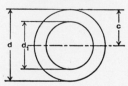

$$A = \frac{\pi (d^2 - d_1^2)}{4} = .785398\, (d^2 - d_1^2)$$

$$c = \frac{d}{2}$$

$$I = \frac{\pi (d^4 - d_1^4)}{64} = .049087\, (d^4 - d_1^4)$$

$$S = \frac{\pi (d^4 - d_1^4)}{32d} = .098175\, \frac{d^4 - d_1^4}{d}$$

$$r = \frac{\sqrt{d^2 + d_1^2}}{4}$$

HALF CIRCLE

Axis of moments through center of gravity

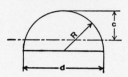

$$A = \frac{\pi R^2}{2} = 1.570796\, R^2$$

$$c = R \left(1 - \frac{4}{3\pi} \right) = .575587\, R$$

$$I = R^4 \left(\frac{\pi}{8} - \frac{8}{9\pi} \right) = .109757\, R^4$$

$$S = \frac{R^3}{24} \frac{(9\pi^2 - 64)}{(3\pi - 4)} = .190687\, R^3$$

$$r = R \frac{\sqrt{9\pi^2 - 64}}{6\pi} = .264336\, R$$

Table 1.3　Properties of Sections (*Continued*)

PARABOLA

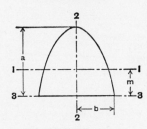

$$A = \frac{4}{3}ab$$

$$m = \frac{2}{5}a$$

$$I_1 = \frac{16}{175}a^3b$$

$$I_2 = \frac{4}{15}ab^3$$

$$I_3 = \frac{32}{105}a^3b$$

HALF PARABOLA

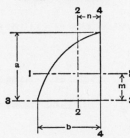

$$A = \frac{2}{3}ab$$

$$m = \frac{2}{5}a$$

$$n = \frac{3}{8}b$$

$$I_1 = \frac{8}{175}a^3b$$

$$I_2 = \frac{19}{480}ab^3$$

$$I_3 = \frac{16}{105}a^3b$$

$$I_4 = \frac{2}{15}ab^3$$

COMPLEMENT OF HALF PARABOLA

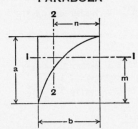

$$A = \frac{1}{3}ab$$

$$m = \frac{7}{10}a$$

$$n = \frac{3}{4}b$$

$$I_1 = \frac{37}{2100}a^3b$$

$$I_2 = \frac{1}{80}ab^3$$

PARABOLIC FILLET IN RIGHT ANGLE

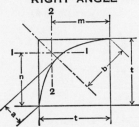

$$a = \frac{t}{2\sqrt{2}}$$

$$b = \frac{t}{\sqrt{2}}$$

$$A = \frac{1}{6}t^2$$

$$m = n = \frac{4}{5}t$$

$$I_1 = I_2 = \frac{11}{2100}t^4$$

Table 1.3   Properties of Sections (*Continued*)

REGULAR POLYGON

Axis of moments
through center

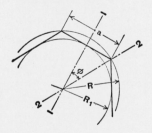

$n = $ Number of sides

$$\phi = \frac{180°}{n}$$

$$a = 2\sqrt{R^2 - R_1^2}$$

$$R = \frac{a}{2 \sin \phi}$$

$$R_1 = \frac{a}{2 \tan \phi}$$

$$A = \frac{1}{4} n a^2 \cot \phi = \frac{1}{2} n R^2 \sin 2\phi = n R_1^2 \tan \phi$$

$$I_1 = I_2 = \frac{A(6R^2 - a^2)}{24} = \frac{A(12R_1^2 + a^2)}{48}$$

$$r_1 = r_2 = \sqrt{\frac{6R^2 - a^2}{24}} = \sqrt{\frac{12R_1^2 + a^2}{48}}$$

ANGLE

Axis of moments through
center of gravity

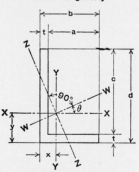

Z-Z is axis of minimum I

$$\tan 2\theta = \frac{2K}{I_Y - I_X}$$

$$A = t(b + c) \quad x = \frac{b^2 + ct}{2(b + c)} \quad y = \frac{d^2 + at}{2(b + c)}$$

$K = $ Product of Inertia about X-X & Y-Y

$$= \mp \frac{abcdt}{4(b + c)}$$

$$I_X = \frac{1}{3}\left(t(d - y)^3 + by^3 - a(y - t)^3 \right)$$

$$I_Y = \frac{1}{3}\left(t(b - x)^3 + dx^3 - c(x - t)^3 \right)$$

$$I_Z = I_X \sin^2\theta + I_Y \cos^2\theta + K \sin 2\theta$$

$$I_W = I_X \cos^2\theta + I_Y \sin^2\theta - K \sin 2\theta$$

K is negative when heel of angle, with respect
to c. g., is in 1st or 3rd quadrant, positive
when in 2nd or 4th quadrant.

BEAMS AND CHANNELS

Transverse force oblique
through center of gravity

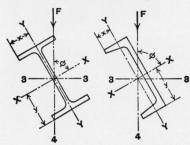

$$I_3 = I_X \sin^2\phi + I_Y \cos^2\phi$$

$$I_4 = I_X \cos^2\phi + I_Y \sin^2\phi$$

$$f = M\left(\frac{y}{I_X} \sin\phi + \frac{x}{I_Y} \cos\phi \right)$$

where M is bending moment due to force F.

Table 1.4   Properties of Pipes

	DIMENSIONS						COUPLINGS			PROPERTIES		
Nom. Dia. In.	Outside Dia. In.	Inside Dia. In.	Thickness In.	Weight per Foot Lb. Plain Ends	Weight per Foot Lb. Thread & Cplg.	Threads per Inch	Outside Dia. In.	Length In.	Weight Lb.	I In.⁴	A In.²	r In.
STANDARD												
⅛	.405	.269	.068	.24	.25	27	.562	⅞	.03	.001	.072	.12
¼	.540	.364	.088	.42	.43	18	.685	1	.04	.003	.125	.16
⅜	.675	.493	.091	.57	.57	18	.848	1⅛	.07	.007	.167	.21
½	.840	.622	.109	.85	.85	14	1.024	1⅜	.12	.017	.250	.26
¾	1.050	.824	.113	1.13	1.13	14	1.281	1⅝	.21	.037	.333	.33
1	1.315	1.049	.133	1.68	1.68	11½	1.576	1⅞	.35	.087	.494	.42
1¼	1.660	1.380	.140	2.27	2.28	11½	1.950	2⅛	.55	.195	.669	.54
1½	1.900	1.610	.145	2.72	2.73	11½	2.218	2⅜	.76	.310	.799	.62
2	2.375	2.067	.154	3.65	3.68	11½	2.760	2⅝	1.23	.666	1.075	.79
2½	2.875	2.469	.203	5.79	5.82	8	3.276	2⅞	1.76	1.530	1.704	.95
3	3.500	3.068	.216	7.58	7.62	8	3.948	3⅛	2.55	3.017	2.228	1.16
3½	4.000	3.548	.226	9.11	9.20	8	4.591	3⅝	4.33	4.788	2.680	1.34
4	4.500	4.026	.237	10.79	10.89	8	5.091	3⅝	5.41	7.233	3.174	1.51
5	5.563	5.047	.258	14.62	14.81	8	6.296	4⅛	9.16	15.16	4.300	1.88
6	6.625	6.065	.280	18.97	19.19	8	7.358	4⅛	10.82	28.14	5.581	2.25
8	8.625	8.071	.277	24.70	25.00	8	9.420	4⅝	15.84	63.35	7.265	2.95
8	8.625	7.981	.322	28.55	28.81	8	9.420	4⅝	15.84	72.49	8.399	2.94
10	10.750	10.192	.279	31.20	32.00	8	11.721	6⅛	33.92	125.9	9.178	3.70
10	10.750	10.136	.307	34.24	35.00	8	11.721	6⅛	33.92	137.4	10.07	3.69
10	10.750	10.020	.365	40.48	41.13	8	11.721	6⅛	33.92	160.7	11.91	3.67
12	12.750	12.090	.330	43.77	45.00	8	13.958	6⅛	48.27	248.5	12.88	4.39
12	12.750	12.000	.375	49.56	50.71	8	13.958	6⅛	48.27	279.3	14.58	4.38
EXTRA STRONG												
⅛	.405	.215	.095	.31	.32	27	.582	1⅛	.05	.001	.093	.11
¼	.540	.302	.119	.54	.54	18	.724	1⅜	.07	.004	.157	.15
⅜	.675	.423	.126	.74	.75	18	.898	1⅝	.13	.009	.217	.20
½	.840	.546	.147	1.09	1.10	14	1.085	1⅞	.22	.020	.320	.25
¾	1.050	.742	.154	1.47	1.49	14	1.316	2⅛	.33	.045	.433	.32
1	1.315	.957	.179	2.17	2.20	11½	1.575	2⅜	.47	.106	.639	.41
1¼	1.660	1.278	.191	3.00	3.05	11½	2.054	2⅞	1.04	.242	.881	.52
1½	1.900	1.500	.200	3.63	3.69	11½	2.294	2⅞	1.17	.391	1.068	.61
2	2.375	1.939	.218	5.02	5.13	11½	2.870	3⅝	2.17	.868	1.477	.77
2½	2.875	2.323	.276	7.66	7.83	8	3.389	4⅛	3.43	1.924	2.254	.92
3	3.500	2.900	.300	10.25	10.46	8	4.014	4⅛	4.13	3.894	3.016	1.14
3½	4.000	3.364	.318	12.51	12.82	8	4.628	4⅝	6.29	6.280	3.678	1.31
4	4.500	3.826	.337	14.98	15.39	8	5.233	4⅝	8.16	9.610	4.407	1.48
5	5.563	4.813	.375	20.78	21.42	8	6.420	5⅛	12.87	20.67	6.112	1.84
6	6.625	5.761	.432	28.57	29.33	8	7.482	5⅛	15.18	40.49	8.405	2.20
8	8.625	7.625	.500	43.39	44.72	8	9.596	6⅛	26.63	105.7	12.76	2.88
10	10.750	9.750	.500	54.74	56.94	8	11.958	6⅝	44.16	211.9	16.10	3.63
12	12.750	11.750	.500	65.42	68.02	8	13.958	6⅝	51.99	361.5	19.24	4.34
DOUBLE—EXTRA STRONG												
½	.840	.252	.294	1.71	1.73	14	1.085	1⅞	.22	.024	.504	.22
¾	1.050	.434	.308	2.44	2.46	14	1.316	2⅛	.33	.058	.718	.28
1	1.315	.599	.358	3.66	3.68	11½	1.575	2⅜	.47	.140	1.076	.36
1¼	1.660	.896	.382	5.21	5.27	11½	2.054	2⅞	1.04	.341	1.534	.47
1½	1.900	1.100	.400	6.41	6.47	11½	2.294	2⅞	1.17	.568	1.885	.55
2	2.375	1.503	.436	9.03	9.14	11½	2.870	3⅝	2.17	1.311	2.656	.70
2½	2.875	1.771	.552	13.70	13.87	8	3.389	4⅛	3.43	2.871	4.028	.84
3	3.500	2.300	.600	18.58	18.79	8	4.014	4⅛	4.13	5.992	5.466	1.05
3½	4.000	2.728	.636	22.85	23.16	8	4.628	4⅝	6.29	9.848	6.721	1.21
4	4.500	3.152	.674	27.54	27.95	8	5.233	4⅝	8.16	15.28	8.101	1.37
5	5.563	4.063	.750	38.55	39.20	8	6.420	5⅛	12.87	33.64	11.34	1.72
6	6.625	4.897	.864	53.16	53.92	8	7.482	5⅛	15.18	66.33	15.64	2.06
8	8.625	6.875	.875	72.42	73.76	8	9.596	6⅛	26.63	162.0	21.30	2.76

LARGE O. D. PIPE

Pipe 14″ and larger is sold by actual O. S. diameter and thickness.
Sizes, 14″, 15″, and 16″ are available regularly in thicknesses varying by 1⁄16″ from ¼″ to 1″, inclusive.

All pipe is furnished random length unless otherwise ordered, viz: 12 to 22 feet with privilege of furnishing 5 per cent in 6 to 12 feet lengths. Pipe railing is most economically detailed with slip joints and random lengths between couplings.

(such as the bottom leg of an angle). Then the value of $\bar{y}$ calculated from this formula is

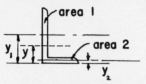

Fig. 1.1   Center of Gravity of Angles

the distance from this *same reference line* to the center of gravity of the compound section.

Problem   Find the distance of the center of gravity from the back of the short leg of a $6 \times 4 \times \frac{1}{2}$-in. L, disregarding all fillets.

Area A	y	Product Ay
$6 \times \frac{1}{2} = 3.00$	3.00	9.00
$3\frac{1}{2} \times \frac{1}{2} = 1.75$	0.25	0.44
4.75		9.44

$$\bar{y} = \frac{9.44}{4.75} = 1.99 \text{ in.}$$

This checks exactly the figure y for this angle from Table 1.10.

b   Ordinarily the center of gravity required is much more complex than indicated by the above problem, and it may involve the use of negative as well as positive areas. In using the above formula for $\bar{y}$, any hole is treated as a minus area; that is, area that is not present, area subtracted from the whole. A simple application of this principle would be to the problem just given. Instead of two small positive areas as shown, the cross-section might be assumed to consist of one large (6×4-in.) *positive* rectangle and one smaller ($3\frac{1}{2} \times 5\frac{1}{2}$-in.) *negative* rectangle, yielding the same result. Since the position of the reference line is an arbitrary one, some areas may extend below it, in which case y distances to the neutral axes of these areas are minus. It should be noted that the conventional rules

for multiplication of sign are to be followed in computing the products $A_1 y_1$, $A_2 y_2$, etc.; that is, minus A_1 times minus y_1 distance becomes $A_1 y_1$, etc.

Problem   To illustrate the use of Formula (1.1) in a more complex case, locate the center of gravity of the crane girder section shown in Fig. 1.2. As a reference axis we shall use a horizontal line through the center of the I beam.

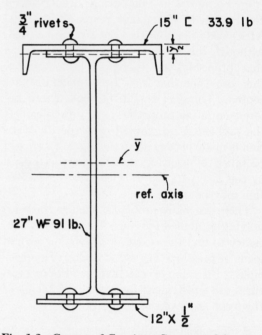

Fig. 1.2   Center of Gravity—Compound Section

Item	A	y	Ay
1. Beam	27.65	0	0
2. Channel	9.90	13.06	129.3
3. Bottom plate	6.00	− 13.7	− 82.2
4. Top holes	− 2.01	+ 13.28	− 26.7
5. Bottom holes	− 2.18	− 13.33	+ 29.1
	+ 39.36		+ 49.5

Therefore, $\bar{y} = 49.5/39.36 = 1.28$ in. (above reference line).

Explanation of terms:

$$y_2 = \frac{\text{beam depth}}{2} + (\text{web of channel} - x \text{ of channel}) = 13.45 + 0.4 - 0.79$$

$$y_3 = \frac{\text{beam depth}}{2} + \frac{\text{plate thickness}}{2} = 13.45 + .25$$

$$y_4 = \frac{\text{beam depth}}{2} + \text{web of channel} - \frac{\text{rivet length}}{2} = 13.85 - 0.57$$

$$y_5 = \frac{\text{beam depth}}{2} + \text{plate thickness} - \frac{\text{rivet length}}{2} = 13.95 - 0.62$$

$$A_4 = 2 \times 0.875 \times 1.147 = 2.01 \text{ sq in. (see Art. 2.13}a)$$

$$A_5 = 2 \times 0.875 \times 1.247 = 2.18 \text{ sq in. (see Art. 2.13}a)$$

Therefore, the center of gravity of the compound section is 1.28 in. *above* the center of the 27-in. beam.

c Formerly in computing properties of cover plated beams and plate girders, the AISC Code required that net section be used. Although this Code has now been revised so that properties are based on gross section, this provision has not been generally accepted. This fact should be looked into before computing properties in any problem. If the problem is so worded that specific mention is made of "net section," the holes should be taken as negative areas, as has been done in the last paragraph. Otherwise gross section may be used.

There are many problems, such as those involving combined footings, in which it is necessary to find the center of gravity of several loads or pressures instead of areas. The principle is the same except that weights or pressures are substituted for areas. Problems of this type are given in Art. 8.12.

d The computation of the moment of inertia of a compound section about any reference axis is an additive process, taking into account all component areas. The moment of inertia of any single component area about the reference axis is the sum of two terms: the moment of inertia of the area about its own centroidal axis parallel to the reference line; and a "transfer" term equal to Ad^2, in which A is the area of the component part and d is the distance between the reference axis and the centroidal axis of the area in question. This summation including all components is expressed algebraically:

$$I = (I_1 + A_1 d_1{}^2) + (I_2 + A_2 d_2{}^2) + \cdots (I_n + A_n d_n{}^2) \quad (1.2)$$

e The moment of inertia may be taken about any line as an axis, but ordinarily the only moment of inertia in which we are interested is about the centroidal or center of gravity axis. The moment of inertia about the gravity axis of any cross-section is the least moment of inertia for that section, and may be determined by application of the fundamental principles expressed by Formulae (1.1) and (1.2). The center of gravity is first determined as in the preceding problem, then a horizontal line through this point is arbitrarily taken as the reference axis, and Formula (1.2) is applied as shown in the following section.

f The solution of an unsymmetrical member, a rather common type of problem frequently given in state license examinations, is given below. Because of the complexity of the problem, it should always be tabulated following the procedure outlined above.

Problem The top chord of a truss is made up of two 15-in. channels 40, each with a side plate $12 \times \frac{3}{8}$ in., and with one cover plate $22 \times \frac{1}{2}$ in. Disregarding rivet holes, compute the moment of inertia through the center of gravity. (From a state license examination. Refer to Art. 1.32 for properties of steel beams and see Fig. 1.3.)

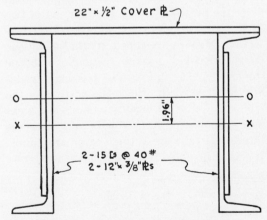

Fig. 1.3   **Top Chord of Bridge Truss**

The problem resolves itself into two steps, the determination of the center of gravity of the compound section, and the computation of

Item	Area A	y	Product Ay	I of member	Ay^2
Two 15-in. channels 40	23.4	0	0	692.6	0
Two plates 12 × $\frac{3}{8}$ in.	9.0	0	0	108	0
Cover plate 22 × $\frac{1}{2}$ in.	11.0	7.75	85.25	0.23	660.69
	43.4		85.25	800.83	660.69

$$\bar{y} = +\frac{85.25}{43.4} = +1.96$$

Total I about reference axis $= 660.69 + 800.83 = 1{,}461.52$

Transfer term $A\bar{y}^2 = 85.25 \times 1.96 = \underline{167.09}$

$I - A\bar{y}^2 = 1{,}294.43$

moment of inertia, first through a given reference axis, and then translated to the computed gravity axis.

The entire problem may be set up in one tabulation. We will use the center line of the 15-in. channels as the given reference axis.

g The section modulus is a property of the section used in the computation of a beam. Its definition is best stated by formula

$$S = \frac{I}{c}$$

in which c is the distance from the neutral axis to the extreme outermost fiber, the fiber farthest from the neutral axis. In a completely symmetrical beam this distance c is half the depth.

For the preceding problem, c is either

$$7.5 + 1.96 = 9.46$$

or

$$15.5 - 9.46 = 6.04$$

Therefore, $c = 9.46$, the greater of the two, and the section modulus

$$S = \frac{1{,}294.43}{9.46} = 136.83$$

h The radius of gyration is a property of the section used in computing its stiffness as a column and may be defined by the formula

$$r = \sqrt{\frac{I}{A}}$$

For the section about the x axis in the preceding problem,

$$r = \sqrt{\frac{1{,}294.43}{43.4}} = \sqrt{29.82} = 5.46$$

1.32 Steel-beam tables

The steel-beam tables, Tables 1.5 to 1.8, combine in one series the properties of rolled-steel beam, column, and channel sections in which the designer is interested, but they omit some of the dimensions pertaining primarily to steel detailing.

The even-numbered pages of the table give dimensions and end-reaction capacities, the odd-numbered pages list properties having to do with bending. The figures given in most of the columns are self-explanatory. The distance k is measured from the outside face of the flange to the point at which the curve of the fillet breaks from the web, so that the depth minus $2k$ represents the flat face of the web. This distance is used in determining the crippling value of the web as described in Art. 4.10i.

V kips is the maximum allowable end shear, and R kips is the maximum allowable end reaction for 3$\frac{1}{2}$-in. bearing based on crippling of the web, as indicated in Fig. 4.2. G is the increase in allowable R for each additional inch of bearing.

I and S are used in steel beams and plate-girder design—S usually for simple beam design as described in Art. 4.10, and I for plate-girder design as described in Art. 4.20.

The radius of gyration about axis x-x and axis y-y are used when these sections act as struts or columns, as described in Art. 7.10. The three columns under the heading "Laterally unsupported beams" are used in connection with Art. 4.10h, and "Composite equivalent S_E" is used in connection with the design of composite beams, Art. 6.50.

1.40 SELECTION OF SYSTEM

a The selection of the various systems of construction to be used is dependent on a number of factors. Frequently the whole matter is dictated to the structural designer, but certain phases of the design may be left for his recommendation, and it is well to consider the various factors which would influence the selection. Among these are:

1. Location
   Building code limitations
   General nature of neighborhood

2. Economics
   First cost of building
   Relation of building to land value
   Maintenance cost
   Insurance cost

3. Use
   Building code limitations
   Effect of loads

4. Advertising value of the building

5. General policy of the owner

b Perhaps the best primary classification for types of construction is the generally accepted code classification. The Building Code of the National Board of Fire Underwriters makes a standard classification as follows:

"Fireproof construction," as applied to buildings, means that in which the structural members are of approved noncombustible construction having the necessary strength and stability and having the fire resistance ratings of not less than 4 hours for exterior nonbearing walls and for wall panels, for columns, and for wall-supporting girders, and trusses, and not less than 3 hours for floors, for roofs, and for floor and roof supporting beams, girders and trusses; and in which exterior bearing walls and interior bearing walls, if any, are of approved masonry or of reinforced concrete.

This type of construction corresponds generally with that sometimes called "fully protected" or "fire-resistive" construction. Because of the long, well-established, and almost universal use of the term "fireproof," it is thought best to retain that term for the type of construction here defined.

"Semifireproof construction," as applied to buildings, means that in which the structural members are of approved noncombustible construction

having the necessary strength and stability, and having fire resistance ratings of not less than 4 hours for exterior walls and for wall panels; not less than 3 hours for columns, and for wall-supporting girders and trusses; not less than 2 hours for floors, for roofs, and for floor and roof supporting beams, girders and trusses; and in which exterior bearing walls and interior bearing walls, if any, are of approved masonry or reinforced concrete.

This type of construction corresponds generally with that sometimes called "protected" or "fire safe."

"Heavy timber construction," as applied to buildings, means that in which walls are of approved masonry or reinforced concrete; and in which the interior structural elements, including columns, floors and roof construction, consist of heavy timbers with smooth, flat surfaces assembled to avoid thin sections, sharp projections and concealed or inaccessible spaces; and in which all structural members which support masonry walls shall have a fire resistance rating of not less than 3 hours; and other structural members of steel or reinforced concrete, if used in lieu of timber construction, shall have a fire resistance rating of not less than 1 hour.

This type of construction is the same as that called "mill construction" for many years, and sometimes called "slow burning construction."

"Ordinary construction," as applied to buildings, means that in which exterior walls and bearing walls are of approved masonry or reinforced concrete, and in which the structural elements are wholly or partly of wood of smaller dimensions than required for heavy timber construction, or of steel or iron not protected as required for fireproof construction or semi-fireproof construction.

The term "ordinary construction" corresponds generally with that variously called "nonfireproof," "masonry walls and wooden joists," or "ordinary masonry" construction.

"Light noncombustible construction," as applied to buildings, means that in which all structural members including walls, floors, roofs and their supports are of steel, iron, concrete, or of other noncombustible materials, and in which the exterior enclosure walls are of masonry or concrete, or are of other fire resistive materials or assemblies of materials which have not less than 2-hour fire resistance ratings.

Structures similar to all-metal gasoline service stations would be included under this classification.

Table 1.5   Steel Beams—WF Sections

Nominal size	Weight per ft, lb	Area, sq in.	Depth, in.	Flange Width, in.	Flange Thickness, in.	Web thickness, in.	Distance k, in.	V, kips	R, kips	G, kips
$36 \times 16\frac{1}{2}$	300	88.17	36.72	16.655	1.680	.945	$2\frac{13}{16}$	451	143	22.7
	280	82.32	36.50	16.595	1.570	.885	$2\frac{11}{16}$	420	132	21.2
	260	76.56	36.24	16.555	1.440	.845	$2\frac{9}{16}$	398	123	20.3
	245	72.03	36.06	16.512	1.350	.802	$2\frac{7}{16}$	376	114	19.2
	230	67.73	35.88	16.475	1.260	.765	$2\frac{3}{8}$	357	108	18.4
36×12	194	57.11	36.48	12.117	1.260	.770	$2\frac{1}{8}$	365	104	18.5
	182	53.54	36.32	12.072	1.180	.725	$2\frac{1}{16}$	342	97	17.4
	170	49.98	36.16	12.027	1.100	.680	$1\frac{15}{16}$	320	89	16.3
	160	47.09	36.00	12.000	1.020	.653	$1\frac{7}{8}$	306	84	15.7
	150	44.16	35.84	11.972	.940	.625	$1\frac{13}{16}$	291	80	15.0
$33 \times 15\frac{3}{4}$	240	70.52	33.50	15.865	1.400	.830	$2\frac{7}{16}$	362	118	19.9
	220	64.73	33.25	15.810	1.275	.775	$2\frac{5}{16}$	335	108	18.6
	200	58.79	33.00	15.750	1.150	.715	$2\frac{3}{16}$	307	98	17.2
$33 \times 11\frac{1}{2}$	152	44.71	33.50	11.565	1.055	.635	$1\frac{7}{8}$	277	82	15.2
	141	41.51	33.31	11.535	.960	.605	$1\frac{3}{4}$	262	76	14.5
	130	38.26	33.10	11.510	.855	.580	$1\frac{11}{16}$	249	72	13.9
30×15	210	61.78	30.38	15.105	1.315	.775	$2\frac{5}{16}$	306	108	18.6
	190	55.90	30.12	15.040	1.185	.710	$2\frac{3}{16}$	278	97	17.0
	172	50.65	29.88	14.985	1.065	.655	$2\frac{1}{16}$	254	87	15.7
$30 \times 10\frac{1}{2}$	132	38.83	30.30	10.551	1.000	.615	$1\frac{11}{16}$	242	77	14.8
	124	36.45	30.16	10.521	.930	.585	$1\frac{5}{8}$	229	72	14.0
	116	34.13	30.00	10.500	.850	.564	$1\frac{9}{16}$	220	69	13.5
	108	31.77	29.82	10.484	.760	.548	$1\frac{1}{2}$	212	66	13.2
27×14	177	52.10	27.31	14.090	1.190	.725	$2\frac{1}{8}$	257	98	17.4
	160	47.04	27.08	14.023	1.075	.658	$2\frac{1}{16}$	232	88	15.8
	145	42.68	26.88	13.965	.975	.600	$1\frac{15}{16}$	210	78	14.4
27×10	114	33.53	27.28	10.070	.932	.570	$1\frac{5}{8}$	202	70	13.7
	102	30.01	27.07	10.018	.827	.518	$1\frac{9}{16}$	182	63	12.4
	94	27.65	26.91	9.990	.747	.490	$1\frac{7}{16}$	172	58	11.8
24×14	160	47.04	24.72	14.091	1.135	.656	2	211	87	15.7
	145	42.62	24.49	14.043	1.020	.608	$1\frac{7}{8}$	194	78	14.6
	130	38.21	24.25	14.000	.900	.565	$1\frac{3}{4}$	178	71	13.6
24×12	120	35.29	24.31	12.088	.930	.556	$1\frac{11}{16}$	176	69	13.3
	110	32.36	24.16	12.042	.855	.510	$1\frac{5}{8}$	160	63	12.2
	100	29.43	24.00	12.000	.775	.468	$1\frac{9}{16}$	146	57	11.2
24×9	94	27.63	24.29	9.061	.872	.516	$1\frac{7}{16}$	163	61	12.4
	84	24.71	24.09	9.015	.772	.470	$1\frac{3}{8}$	147	55	11.3
	76	22.37	23.91	8.985	.682	.440	$1\frac{1}{4}$	137	50	10.6
21×13	142	41.76	21.46	13.132	1.095	.659	$1\frac{7}{8}$	184	85	15.8
	127	37.34	21.24	13.061	.985	.588	$1\frac{3}{4}$	163	74	14.1
	112	32.93	21.00	13.000	.865	.527	$1\frac{5}{8}$	144	65	12.7
21×9	96	28.21	21.14	9.038	.935	.575	$1\frac{9}{16}$	158	70	13.8
	82	24.10	20.86	8.962	.795	.499	$1\frac{7}{16}$	135	59	12.0
$21 \times 8\frac{1}{4}$	73	21.46	21.24	8.295	.740	.455	$1\frac{5}{16}$	126	53	10.9
	68	20.02	21.13	8.270	.685	.430	$1\frac{1}{4}$	118	49	10.3
	62	18.23	20.99	8.240	.615	.400	$1\frac{3}{16}$	109	45	9.6

Table 1.5 Steel Beams—WF Sections (*Continued*)

Nominal size	Weight per ft, lb	Axis x-x			Axis y-y, r, in.	Laterally unsupported beams			Composite equivalent S_E
		I, in.^{4}	S, in.^{3}	r, in.		d/bt	L_u	U	
$36 \times 16\frac{1}{2}$	300	20,290.2	1,105.1	15.17	3.73	1.31	38.0	42,180	1,181
	280	18,819.3	1,031.2	15.12	3.70	1.40	35.5	36,829	1,104
	260	17,233.8	951.1	15.00	3.65	1.52	32.5	31,286	1,022
	245	16,092.2	892.5	14.95	3.62	1.62	30.5	27,546	961
	230	14,988.4	835.5	14.88	3.59	1.73	28.5	24,147	903
36×12	194	12,103.4	663.6	14.56	2.49	2.39	20.5	13,883	737.5
	182	11,281.5	621.2	14.52	2.47	2.55	19.5	12,180	683.7
	170	10,470.0	579.1	14.47	2.45	2.73	18.0	10,606	647.8
	160	9,738.8	541.0	14.38	2.42	2.94	17.0	9,203	604.9
	150	9,012.1	502.9	14.29	2.38	3.19	15.5	7,882	568.5
$33 \times 15\frac{3}{4}$	240	13,585.1	811.1	13.88	3.52	1.51	33.0	26,858	874.1
	220	12,312.1	740.6	13.79	3.48	1.65	30.0	22,442	801.0
	200	11,048.2	669.6	13.71	3.43	1.82	27.0	18,396	727.1
$33 \times 11\frac{1}{2}$	152	8,147.6	486.4	13.50	2.39	2.74	18.0	8,876	547.0
	141	7,442.2	446.8	13.39	2.35	3.01	16.5	7,253	503.6
	130	6,699.0	404.8	13.23	2.29	3.36	15.0	6,024	459.1
30×15	210	9,872.4	649.9	12.64	3.38	1.53	32.5	21,239	703.1
	190	8,825.9	586.1	12.57	3.34	1.69	29.5	17,341	636.4
	172	7,891.5	528.2	12.48	3.30	1.87	26.5	14,123	575.6
$30 \times 10\frac{1}{2}$	132	5,753.1	379.7	12.17	2.18	2.87	17.5	6,615	430.0
	124	5,347.1	354.6	12.11	2.16	3.08	16.0	5,757	403.0
	116	4,919.1	327.9	12.00	2.12	3.36	15.0	4,880	375.7
	108	4,461.0	299.2	11.85	2.06	3.74	13.0	4,000	345.6
27×14	177	6,728.6	492.8	11.36	3.16	1.63	30.5	15,117	537.2
	160	6,018.6	444.5	11.31	3.12	1.80	27.5	12,347	486.0
	145	5,414.3	402.9	11.26	3.09	1.97	25.0	10,226	437.3
27×10	114	4,080.5	299.2	11.03	2.11	2.91	17.0	5,141	341.0
	102	3,604.1	266.3	10.96	2.08	3.27	15.0	4,072	305.4
	94	3,266.7	242.8	10.87	2.04	3.61	13.5	3,363	280.2
24×14	160	5,110.3	413.5	10.42	3.23	1.55	32.0	13,339	449.6
	145	4,561.0	372.5	10.34	3.19	1.71	29.0	10,892	406.3
	130	4,009.5	330.7	10.24	3.13	1.93	26.0	8,567	350.0
24×12	120	3,635.3	299.1	10.15	2.68	2.16	23.0	6,924	331.6
	110	3,315.0	274.4	10.12	2.66	2.34	21.0	5,863	304.8
	100	2,987.3	248.9	10.08	2.63	2.58	19.0	4,824	277.2
24×9	94	2,683.0	220.9	9.85	1.92	3.07	16.0	3,598	253.1
	84	2,364.3	196.3	9.78	1.89	3.47	14.5	2,829	231.9
	76	2,096.4	175.4	9.68	1.85	3.90	12.5	2,249	203.6
21×13	142	3,403.1	317.2	9.03	3.04	1.49	33.5	10,644	347.1
	127	3,017.2	284.1	8.99	3.01	1.65	30.0	8,611	310.7
	112	2,620.6	249.6	8.92	2.96	1.87	27.0	6,674	274.5
21×9	96	2,088.9	197.6	8.60	1.97	2.50	20.0	3,952	225.6
	82	1,752.4	168.0	8.53	1.93	2.93	17.0	2,867	192.8
$21 \times 8\frac{1}{4}$	73	1,600.3	150.7	8.64	1.76	3.46	14.5	2,178	174.7
	68	1,478.3	139.9	8.59	1.74	3.73	13.5	1,875	162.8
	62	1,326.8	126.4	8.53	1.71	4.15	12.0	1,523	147.9

Table 1.5   Steel Beams—WF Sections (*Continued*)

Nominal size	Weight per ft, lb	Area, sq in.	Depth in.	Flange Width, in.	Flange Thickness, in.	Web thickness, in.	Distance k, in.	V, kips	R, kips	G, kips
$18 \times 11\frac{3}{4}$	114	33.51	18.48	11.833	.991	.595	$1\frac{11}{16}$	143	74	14.3
	105	30.86	18.32	11.792	.911	.554	$1\frac{5}{8}$	132	68	13.3
	96	28.22	18.16	11.750	.831	.512	$1\frac{1}{2}$	121	62	12.3
$18 \times 8\frac{3}{4}$	85	24.97	18.32	8.838	.911	.526	$1\frac{1}{2}$	125	63	12.6
	77	22.63	18.16	8.787	.831	.475	$1\frac{3}{8}$	112	56	11.4
	70	20.56	18.00	8.750	.751	.438	$1\frac{5}{16}$	103	51	10.5
	64	18.80	17.87	8.715	.686	.403	$1\frac{1}{4}$	94	46	9.7
$18 \times 7\frac{1}{2}$	60	17.64	18.25	7.558	.695	.416	$1\frac{3}{16}$	99	47	10.0
	55	16.19	18.12	7.532	.630	.390	$1\frac{1}{8}$	92	43	9.4
	50	14.71	18.00	7.500	.570	.358	$1\frac{1}{16}$	84	39	8.6
$16 \times 11\frac{1}{2}$	96	28.22	16.32	11.533	.875	.535	$1\frac{5}{8}$	114	66	12.8
	88	25.87	16.16	11.502	.795	.504	$1\frac{1}{2}$	106	61	12.1
$16 \times 8\frac{1}{2}$	78	22.92	16.32	8.586	.875	.529	$1\frac{1}{2}$	112	64	12.7
	71	20.86	16.16	8.543	.795	.486	$1\frac{3}{8}$	102	57	11.7
	64	18.80	16.00	8.500	.715	. 443	$1\frac{5}{16}$	92	51	10.6
	58	17.04	15.86	8.464	.645	.407	$1\frac{1}{4}$	84	46	9.8
16×7	50	14.70	16.25	7.073	.628	.380	$1\frac{1}{8}$	80	42	9.1
	45	13.24	16.12	7.039	.563	.346	$1\frac{1}{16}$	73	38	8.3
	40	11.77	16.00	7.000	.503	.307	1	64	33	7.4
	36	10.59	15.85	6.992	.428	.299	$\frac{15}{16}$	62	32	7.2
14×16	426	125.25	18.69	16.695	3.033	1.875	$3\frac{5}{8}$	455	320	45.0
	398	116.98	18.31	16.590	2.843	1.770	$3\frac{7}{16}$	423	295	42.8
	370	108.78	17.94	16.475	2.658	1.655	$3\frac{1}{4}$	386	268	39.7
	342	100.59	17.56	16.365	2.468	1.545	$3\frac{1}{16}$	352	243	37.1
	314	92.30	17.19	16.235	2.283	1.415	$2\frac{7}{8}$	314	217	34.0
	287	84.37	16.81	16.130	2.093	1.310	$2\frac{11}{16}$	286	194	31.4
	264	77.63	16.50	16.025	1.938	1.205	$2\frac{9}{16}$	258	175	28.9
	246	72.33	16.25	15.945	1.813	1.125	$2\frac{7}{16}$	238	160	27.0
	237	69.69	16.12	15.910	1.748	1.090	$2\frac{3}{8}$	230	154	26.2
	228	67.06	16.00	15.865	1.688	1.045	$2\frac{5}{16}$	217	146	25.1
	219	64.36	15.87	15.825	1.623	1.005	$2\frac{1}{4}$	208	139	24.1
	211	62.07	15.75	15.800	1.563	.980	$2\frac{3}{16}$	201	134	23.5
	202	59.39	15.63	15.750	1.503	.930	$2\frac{1}{8}$	189	125	22.3
	193	56.73	15.50	15.710	1.438	.890	$2\frac{1}{16}$	179	119	21.4
	184	54.07	15.38	15.660	1.378	.840	2	168	111	20.2
	176	51.73	15.25	15.640	1.313	.820	$1\frac{15}{16}$	163	107	19.7
	167	49.09	15.12	15.600	1.248	.780	$1\frac{7}{8}$	154	100	18.7
	158	46.47	15.00	15.550	1.188	.730	$1\frac{13}{16}$	142	93	17.5
	150	44.08	14.88	15.515	1.128	.695	$1\frac{3}{4}$	135	88	16.7
	142	41.85	14.75	15.500	1.063	.680	$1\frac{11}{16}$	130	84	16.1
	320	94.12	16.81	16.710	2.093	1.890	$2\frac{11}{16}$			
$14 \times 14\frac{1}{2}$	136	39.98	14.75	14.740	1.063	.660	$1\frac{11}{16}$	126	82	15.8
	127	37.33	14.62	14.690	.998	.610	$1\frac{5}{8}$	116	75	14.6
	119	34.99	14.50	14.650	.938	.570	$1\frac{9}{16}$	107	69	13.7
	111	32.65	14.37	14.620	.873	.540	$1\frac{1}{2}$	101	65	13.0
	103	30.26	14.25	14.575	.813	.495	$1\frac{7}{16}$	92	59	11.9
	95	27.94	14.12	14.545	.748	.465	$1\frac{3}{8}$	85	55	11.2
	87	25.56	14.00	14.500	.688	.420	$1\frac{5}{16}$	76	49	10.1
14×12	84	24.71	14.18	12.023	.778	.451	$1\frac{3}{8}$	83	53	10.8
	78	22.94	14.06	12.000	.718	.428	$1\frac{5}{16}$	78	49	10.3

Table 1.5   Steel Beams—WF Sections (*Continued*)

Nominal size	Weight per ft, lb	Axis x-x			Axis y-y, r, in.	Laterally unsupported beams			Composite equivalent S_E
		$I,$ in.^{4}	$S,$ in.^{3}	$r,$ in.		d/bt	L_u	U	
$18 \times 11\frac{3}{4}$	114	2,033.8	220.1	7.79	2.76	1.58	31.5	6,965	242.3
	105	1,852.5	202.2	7.75	2.73	1.71	29.0	5,912	223.7
	96	1,674.7	184.4	7.70	2.71	1.86	27.0	4,957	204.3
$18 \times 8\frac{3}{4}$	85	1,429.9	156.1	7.57	2.00	2.28	22.0	3,423	177.4
	77	1,286.8	141.7	7.54	1.98	2.49	20.0	2,845	161.2
	70	1,153.9	128.2	7.49	1.95	2.74	18.0	2,340	147.3
	64	1,045.8	117.0	7.46	1.93	2.99	16.5	1,955	133.9
$18 \times 7\frac{1}{2}$	60	984.0	107.8	7.47	1.63	3.48	14.5	1,549	125.8
	55	889.9	98.2	7.41	1.61	3.82	13.0	1,285	115.0
	50	800.6	89.0	7.38	1.59	4.22	12.0	1,054	104.5
$16 \times 11\frac{1}{2}$	96	1,355.1	166.1	6.93	2.71	1.62	31.0	5,127	184.0
	88	1,222.6	151.3	6.87	2.67	1.77	28.0	4,274	179.4
$16 \times 8\frac{1}{2}$	78	1,042.6	127.8	6.74	1.95	2.17	23.0	2,945	146.2
	71	936.9	115.9	6.70	1.93	2.38	21.0	2,435	129.7
	64	833.8	104.2	6.66	1.91	2.63	19.0	1,981	119.5
	58	746.4	94.1	6.62	1.88	2.91	17.0	1,617	108.3
16×7	50	655.4	80.7	6.68	1.54	3.66	13.5	1,102	92.6
	45	583.3	72.4	6.64	1.52	4.07	12.0	889.4	85.2
	40	515.5	64.4	6.62	1.50	4.54	11.0	709.3	76.0
	36	446.3	56.3	6.49	1.45	5.30	9.5	531.1	67.5
14×16	426	6,610.3	707.4	7.26	4.34	.37	135.0		
	398	6,013.7	656.9	7.17	4.31	.39	128.0		
	370	5,454.2	608.1	7.08	4.27	.41	122.0		
	342	4,911.5	559.4	6.99	4.24	.44	114.0		
	314	4,399.4	511.9	6.90	4.20	.46	109.0		
	287	3,912.1	465.5	6.81	4.17	.50	100.0		
	264	3,526.0	427.4	6.74	4.14	.53	93.0		
	246	3,228.9	397.4	6.68	4.12	.56	89.0		
	237	3,080.9	382.2	6.65	4.11	.58	85.0		
	228	2,942.4	367.8	6.62	4.10	.60	83.0		
	219	2,798.2	352.6	6.59	4.08	.62	81.0		
	211	2,671.4	339.2	6.56	4.07	.64	78.0		
	202	2,538.8	324.9	6.54	4.06	.66	76.0		
	193	2,402.4	310.0	6.51	4.05	.69	72.0		
	184	2,274.8	295.8	6.49	4.04	.71	70.0		
	176	2,149.6	281.9	6.45	4.02	.74	68.0		
	167	2,020.8	267.3	6.42	4.01	.78	64.0		
	158	1,900.6	253.4	6.40	4.00	.81	62.0		
	150	1,786.9	240.2	6.37	3.99	.85	59.0		
	142	1,672.2	226.7	6.32	3.97	.90	56.0		
	320	4,141.7	492.8	6.63	4.17				
$14 \times 14\frac{1}{2}$	136	1,593.0	216.0	6.31	3.77	.94	53.0		
	127	1,476.7	202.0	6.29	3.76	1.00	50.0		
	119	1,373.1	189.4	6.26	3.75	1.06	47.0		
	111	1,266.5	176.3	6.23	3.73	1.13	44.0		
	103	1,165.8	163.6	6.21	3.72	1.20	41.0		
	95	1,063.5	150.6	6.17	3.71	1.30	38.0		
	87	966.9	138.1	6.15	3.70	1.40	35.5		
14×12	84	928.4	130.9	6.13	3.02	1.52	33.0		
	78	851.2	121.1	6.09	3.00	1.63	30.5		

Table 1.5 Steel Beams—WF Sections (*Continued*)

Nominal size	Weight per ft, lb	Area, sq in.	Depth, in.	Flange Width, in.	Flange Thickness, in.	Web thickness, in.	Distance k, in.	V, kips	R, kips	G, kips
14 × 10	74	21.76	14.19	10.072	.783	.450	$1\frac{3}{8}$	83	53	10.8
	68	20.00	14.06	10.040	.718	.418	$1\frac{5}{16}$	76	48	10.0
	61	17.94	13.91	10.000	.643	.378	$1\frac{1}{4}$	68	43	9.1
14 × 8	53	15.59	13.94	8.062	.658	.370	$1\frac{1}{4}$	67	42	8.9
	48	14.11	13.81	8.031	.593	.339	$1\frac{3}{16}$	61	38	8.1
	43	12.65	13.68	8.000	.528	.308	$1\frac{1}{8}$	55	34	7.4
14 × 6¾	38	11.17	14.12	6.776	.513	.313	1	58	34	7.5
	34	10.00	14.00	6.750	.453	.287	$\frac{15}{16}$	52	31	6.9
	30	8.81	13.86	6.733	.383	.270	$\frac{7}{8}$	49	28	6.5
12 × 12	190	55.86	14.38	12.670	1.736	1.060	$2\frac{5}{16}$	198	148	25.4
	161	47.38	13.88	12.515	1.486	.905	$2\frac{1}{16}$	163	121	21.7
	133	39.11	13.38	12.365	1.236	.755	$1\frac{13}{16}$	131	96	18.1
	120	35.31	13.12	12.320	1.106	.710	$1\frac{11}{16}$	121	88	17.0
	106	31.19	12.88	12.230	.986	.620	$1\frac{9}{16}$	104	76	14.9
	99	29.09	12.75	12.190	.921	.580	$1\frac{1}{2}$	96	70	13.9
	92	27.06	12.62	12.155	.856	.545	$1\frac{7}{16}$	90	65	13.1
	85	24.98	12.50	12.105	.796	.495	$1\frac{3}{8}$	80	58	11.9
	79	23.22	12.38	12.080	.736	.470	$1\frac{5}{16}$	76	54	11.3
	72	21.16	12.25	12.040	.671	.430	$1\frac{1}{4}$	69	49	10.3
	65	19.11	12.12	12.000	.606	.390	$1\frac{3}{16}$	61	44	9.4
12 × 10	58	17.06	12.19	10.014	.641	.359	$1\frac{1}{4}$	57	41	8.6
	53	15.59	12.06	10.000	.576	.345	$1\frac{3}{16}$	54	39	8.3
12 × 8	50	14.71	12.19	8.077	.641	.371	$1\frac{1}{4}$	59	42	8.9
	45	13.24	12.06	8.042	.576	.336	$1\frac{3}{16}$	53	38	8.1
	40	11.77	11.94	8.000	.516	.294	$1\frac{1}{8}$	46	33	7.1
12 × 6½	36	10.59	12.24	6.565	.540	.305	$\frac{15}{16}$	49	33	7.3
	31	9.12	12.09	6.525	.465	.265	$\frac{7}{8}$	41	28	6.35
	27	7.97	11.95	6.500	.400	.240	$\frac{13}{16}$	37	25	5.75
10 × 10	112	32.92	11.38	10.415	1.248	.755	$1\frac{3}{4}$	111	95	18.1
	100	29.43	11.12	10.345	1.118	.685	$1\frac{5}{8}$	99	84	16.4
	89	26.19	10.88	10.275	.998	.615	$1\frac{1}{2}$	87	74	14.8
	77	22.67	10.62	10.195	.868	.535	$1\frac{3}{8}$	74	62	12.8
	72	21.18	10.50	10.170	.808	.510	$1\frac{5}{16}$	69	59	12.2
	66	19.41	10.38	10.117	.748	.457	$1\frac{1}{4}$	62	52	11.0
	60	17.66	10.25	10.075	.683	.415	$1\frac{3}{16}$	55	47	10.0
	54	15.88	10.12	10.028	.618	.368	$1\frac{1}{8}$	48	41	8.8
	49	14.40	10.00	10.000	.558	.340	$1\frac{1}{16}$	44	37	8.2
10 × 8	45	13.24	10.12	8.022	.618	.350	$1\frac{1}{8}$	46	39	8.4
	39	11.48	9.94	7.990	.528	.318	$1\frac{1}{16}$	41	35	7.65
	33	9.71	9.75	7.964	.433	.292	$\frac{15}{16}$	37	31	7.0
10 × 5¾	29	8.53	10.22	5.799	.500	.289	$\frac{7}{8}$	38	30	6.9
	25	7.35	10.08	5.762	.430	.252	$\frac{13}{16}$	33	26	6.05
	21	6.19	9.90	5.750	.340	.240	$\frac{11}{16}$	31	24	5.8
8 × 8	67	19.70	9.00	8.287	.933	.575	$1\frac{5}{16}$	67	66	13.8
	58	17.06	8.75	8.222	.808	.510	$1\frac{3}{16}$	58	53	12.2
	48	14.11	8.50	8.117	.683	.405	$1\frac{1}{16}$	45	44	9.7
	40	11.76	8.25	8.077	.558	.365	$\frac{15}{16}$	39	39	8.8
	35	10.30	8.12	8.027	.493	.315	$\frac{7}{8}$	33	33	7.6
	31	9.12	8.00	8.000	.433	.288	$\frac{13}{16}$	30	30	6.9
8 × 6½	28	8.23	8.06	6.540	.463	.285	$\frac{13}{16}$	30	30	6.85
	24	7.06	7.93	6.500	.398	.245	$\frac{3}{4}$	25	25	5.9
8 × 5¼	20	5.88	8.14	5.268	.378	.248	$\frac{11}{16}$	26	25	5.95
	17	5.00	8.00	5.250	.308	.230	$\frac{5}{8}$	24	23	5.5

24

Table 1.5   Steel Beams—WF Sections (*Continued*)

Nominal size	Weight per ft, lb	Axis x-x			Axis y-y, r, in.	Laterally unsupported beams			Composite equivalent S_E
		I, in.^{4}	S, in.^{3}	r, in.		d/bt	L_u	U	
14 × 10	74	796.8	112.3	6.05	2.84	1.80	28.0	3,119	125.9
	68	724.1	103.0	6.02	2.46	1.95	25.5	2,641	112.7
	61	641.5	92.2	5.98	2.45	2.16	23.0	2,134	103.4
14 × 8	53	542.1	77.8	5.90	1.92	2.63	19.0	1,479	89.0
	48	484.9	70.2	5.86	1.91	2.90	17.0	1,210	80.4
	43	429.0	62.7	5.82	1.89	3.24	15.5	967.6	72.0
14 × 6¾	38	385.3	54.6	5.87	1.49	4.06	12.5	672.4	64.4
	34	339.2	48.5	5.83	1.46	4.58	11.0	529.5	57.5
	30	289.6	41.8	5.73	1.41	5.37	9.5	389.8	50.3
12 × 12	190	1,892.5	263.2	5.82	3.25	.65	77.0		
	161	1,541.8	222.2	5.70	3.20	.75	66.5		
	133	1,221.2	182.5	5.59	3.16	.87	57.5		
	120	1,071.7	163.4	5.51	3.13	.96	52.0		
	106	930.7	144.5	5.46	3.11	1.06	47.0		
	99	858.5	134.7	5.43	3.09	1.14	44.0		
	92	788.9	125.0	5.40	3.08	1.20	41.5		
	85	723.3	115.7	5.38	3.07	1.29	38.0		
	79	663.0	107.1	5.34	3.05	1.39	36.0		
	72	597.4	97.5	5.31	3.04	1.52	33.0		
	65	533.4	88.0	5.28	3.02	1.67	30.0		
12 × 10	58	476.1	78.1	5.28	2.51	1.90	26.0		
	53	426.2	70.7	5.23	2.48	2.09	24.0		
12 × 8	50	394.5	64.7	5.18	1.96	2.35	21.0	1,377	74.2
	45	350.8	58.2	5.15	1.94	2.60	19.0	1,119	66.8
	40	310.1	51.9	5.13	1.94	2.89	17.5	897.9	59.7
12 × 6½	36	280.8	45.9	5.15	1.50	3.45	14.5	665.2	54.0
	31	238.4	39.4	5.11	1.47	3.98	12.5	495.0	46.6
	27	204.1	34.1	5.06	1.44	4.50	10.5	378.9	40.7
10 × 10	112	718.7	126.3	4.67	2.67	.88	57.0		
	100	625.0	112.4	4.61	2.65	.96	52.0		
	89	542.4	99.7	4.55	2.63	1.06	47.0		
	77	457.2	86.1	4.49	2.60	1.20	42.0		
	72	420.7	80.1	4.46	2.59	1.27	39.0		
	66	382.5	73.7	4.44	2.58	1.37	36.0		
	60	343.7	67.1	4.41	2.57	1.49	33.5		
	54	305.7	60.4	4.39	2.56	1.63	30.5		
	49	272.9	54.6	4.35	2.54	1.79	28.0		
10 × 8	45	248.6	49.1	4.33	2.00	2.04	24.5	1,204	56.8
	39	209.7	42.2	4.27	1.98	2.36	21.0	894.1	49.0
	33	170.9	35.0	4.20	1.94	2.83	17.5	618.4	41.2
10 × 5¾	29	157.3	30.8	4.29	1.34	3.52	14.0	437.5	37.3
	25	133.2	26.4	4.26	1.31	4.08	12.0	323.5	32.2
	21	106.3	21.5	4.14	1.25	5.07	10.0	212.0	26.9
8 × 8	67	271.8	60.4	3.71	2.12	1.17	43.0		
	58	227.3	52.0	3.65	2.10	1.31	38.0		
	48	183.7	43.2	3.61	2.08	1.53	33.0		
	40	146.3	35.5	3.53	2.04	1.83	27.0		42.2
	35	126.5	31.1	3.50	2.03	2.05	24.0		37.1
	31	109.7	27.4	3.47	2.01	2.31	21.5		32.9
8 × 6½	28	97.8	24.3	3.45	1.62	2.66	18.5	456.8	29.3
	24	82.5	20.8	3.42	1.61	3.07	16.0	338.8	27.6
8 × 5¼	20	69.2	17.0	3.43	1.20	4.08	12.0	208.3	21.9
	17	56.4	14.1	3.36	1.16	4.95	10.0	142.4	18.7

Table 1.6   Steel Beams—Miscellaneous Sections

Nominal size	Weight per ft, lb	Area, sq in.	Depth, in.	Flange		Web thick-ness, in.	Distance k, in.	V, kips	R, kips	G, kips
				Width, in.	Thick-ness, in.					
6 WF	25	7.37	6.37	6.080	.456	.320	$\frac{3}{4}$	26.5	32.7	7.7
6 × 6	20	5.90	6.20	6.018	.367	.258	$\frac{11}{16}$	20.8	25.9	6.2
	15.5	4.62	6.00	6.000	.269	.240	$\frac{9}{16}$	18.7	23.5	5.8
5 WF	18.5	5.45	5.12	5.025	.420	.265	$\frac{3}{4}$	17.6	27.2	6.4
5 × 5	16	4.70	5.00	5.000	.360	.240	$\frac{5}{8}$	15.6	23.9	5.8
4 WF	13	3.82	4.16	4.060	.345	.280	$\frac{5}{8}$	15.1	27.6	6.7
4 × 4	10	2.93	4.00	4.000	.265	.220	$\frac{9}{16}$	11.4	21.6	5.3
12 × 4	22	6.47	12.31	4.030	.424	.260	$\frac{3}{4}$	42	27	6.2
	19	5.62	12.16	4.010	.349	.240	$\frac{11}{16}$	38	24	5.8
	16.5	4.86	12.00	4.000	.269	.230	$\frac{5}{8}$	36	23	5.5
10 × 4	19	5.61	10.25	4.020	.394	.250	$\frac{11}{16}$	33	25	6.0
	17	4.98	10.12	4.010	.329	.240	$\frac{5}{8}$	32	24	5.8
	15	4.40	10.00	4.000	.269	.230	$\frac{9}{16}$	30	22	5.5
8 × 4	15	4.43	8.12	4.015	.314	.245	$\frac{5}{8}$	26	24	5.9
	13	3.83	8.00	4.000	.254	.230	$\frac{9}{16}$	24	22	5.5
6 × 4	16	4.72	6.25	4.030	.404	.260	$\frac{11}{16}$	21	26	6.2
	12	3.53	6.00	4.000	.279	.230	$\frac{9}{16}$	17.9	22	5.5
12 × 4	14	4.14	11.91	3.970	.224	.200	$\frac{9}{16}$	31	19.5	4.8
10 × 4	11.5	3.39	9.87	3.950	.204	.180	$\frac{1}{2}$	23	17.3	4.3
8 × 4	10	2.95	7.90	3.940	.204	.170	$\frac{1}{2}$	17.5	16.3	4.1
6 × 4	8.5	2.50	5.83	3.940	.194	.170	$\frac{7}{16}$	12.9	16.1	4.1

Junior Beams

12 × 3	11.8	3.45	12.00	3.063	.25	.175	$\frac{1}{2}$	27	16.8	4.2
11 × 2⅞	10.3	3.01	11.00	2.844	.1875	.165	$\frac{1}{2}$	24	15.8	4.0
10 × 2¾	9.0	2.64	10.00	2.688	.1875	.155	$\frac{7}{16}$	20	14.7	3.7
9 × 2⅜	7.5	2.20	9.00	2.375	.1875	.145	$\frac{7}{16}$	17.0	13.7	3.5
8 × 2¼	6.5	1.92	8.00	2.281	.1875	.135	$\frac{3}{8}$	14.0	12.6	3.2
7 × 2⅛	5.5	1.61	7.00	2.078	.1875	.126	$\frac{3}{8}$	11.5	11.7	3.0
6 × 1⅞	4.4	1.30	6.00	1.844	.1875	.114	$\frac{3}{8}$	8.9	10.6	2.7

"Frame construction," as applied to buildings, means that in which walls and interior construction are wholly or partly of wood.

Buildings of exterior masonry veneer, metal, or stucco on wooden frame, constituting wholly or in part the structural supports of the building or its loads, are frame buildings within the meaning of this definition.

"Unprotected metal construction," as applied to buildings, means that in which the structural supports are unprotected metal in which the roofing and walls or other enclosures are of sheet metal, or of other noncombustible materials, or of masonry deficient in thickness or otherwise not conforming to approved masonry.

c The second classification of construction is between skeleton and wall-bearing. Wall-bearing buildings are limited in height because of the thickness of walls required in buildings of over three stories. Even in buildings of less than three stories it may be advisable to use skeleton construction on some occasions. Skeleton construction permits greater overall speed of construction, because the framework can be completely erected for

Table 1.6   Steel Beams—Miscellaneous Sections (*Continued*)

Nominal size	Weight per ft, lb	Axis x-x			Axis y-y, r, in.	Laterally unsupported beams			Composite equivalent S_E
		I, in.^{4}	S, in.^{3}	r, in.		d/bt	L_u	U	
6 WF	25	53.5	16.8	2.69	1.52	2.31	21.65		
6 × 6	20	41.7	13.4	2.66	1.50	2.89	17.30		
	15.5	30.3	10.1	2.56	1.45	3.72	13.45		
5 WF	18.5	25.4	9.94	2.16	1.28	2.43	20.55		
5 × 5	16	21.3	8.53	2.13	1.26	2.78	18.00		
4 WF	13	11.3	5.45	1.72	.99	2.97	16.85		
4 × 4	10	8.31	4.16	1.68	.97	3.78	13.23		
12 × 4	22	155.7	25.3	4.91	.84	7.2	7.0	175.1	32.5
	19	130.1	21.4	4.81	.81	8.7	5.5	123.0	28.0
	16.5	105.3	17.5	4.65	.76	11.2	4.5	78.1	23.8
10 × 4	19	96.2	18.8	4.14	.86	6.5	7.5	144.6	24.5
	17	81.8	16.2	4.05	.83	7.7	6.5	105.2	21.6
	15	68.8	13.8	3.95	.80	9.3	5.5	74.2	19.0
8 × 4	15	48.0	11.8	3.29	.86	6.5	7.5	90.8	16.6
	13	39.5	9.88	3.21	.83	7.9	6.0	62.5	14.4
6 × 4	16	31.7	10.1	2.59	.96	3.8	13.0	132.9	15.0
	12	21.7	7.24	2.48	.90	5.4	9.0	67.0	11.8
12 × 4	14	88.2	14.8	4.61	.74	13.4	3.5		
10 × 4	11.5	51.9	10.5	3.92	.77	12.3	4.0		
8 × 4	10	30.8	7.79	3.23	.82	9.8	5.0		
6 × 4	8.5	14.8	5.07	2.43	.87	7.7	6.5		
Junior Beams									
12 × 3	11.8	72.2	12.0	4.57	.53	16	3.0		
11 × 2⅞	10.3	53.1	9.6	4.20	.50	20	2.5		
10 × 2¾	9.0	39.0	7.8	3.85	.48	20	2.5		
9 × 2⅝	7.5	26.2	5.8	3.45	.42	20	2.5		
8 × 2¼	6.5	18.7	4.7	3.12	.42	19	2.5		
7 × 2⅛	5.5	12.1	3.5	2.74	.39	18	2.5		
6 × 1⅞	4.4	7.3	2.4	2.37	.36	17	3.0		

walls and interior construction at the same time instead of slowing down steel erection to keep pace with the masonry walls. In factory buildings it is often necessary to use skeleton construction even for a one-story building, sometimes to provide for crane runways and sometimes to allow sufficient window area.

The chief advantages of wall-bearing construction, except for buildings using wood columns and beams, are slightly lower cost and freedom from breaks in the inside wall line, which are needed to cover up wall columns.

In any area subject to earthquakes, it is extremely advisable to use skeleton construction.

d   The third classification, and the one subject to most argument, distinguishes between structural-steel frame and reinforced concrete. Without going into too much detail, these general facts may be given pro and con:

1. For high buildings, structural steel has the advantage because of the lesser column areas and the greater simplicity of wind bracing.

Table 1.7 Steel Beams—American Standard

Nominal size	Weight per ft, lb	Area, sq in.	Depth, in.	Flange		Web thick-ness, in.	Distance k, in.	V, kips	R, kips	G, kips
				Width, in.	Thick-ness, in.					
$24 \times 7\frac{7}{8}$	120.0	35.13	24.00	8.048	1.102	.798	$1\frac{15}{16}$	249	104	19.2
	105.9	30.98	24.00	7.875	1.102	.625	$1\frac{15}{16}$	195	82	15.0
24×7	100.0	29.25	24.00	7.247	.871	.747	$1\frac{5}{8}$	233	92	17.9
	90.0	26.30	24.00	7.124	.871	.624	$1\frac{5}{8}$	195	77	15.0
	79.9	23.33	24.00	7.000	.871	.500	$1\frac{5}{8}$	156	62	12.0
20×7	95.0	27.74	20.00	7.200	.916	.800	$1\frac{3}{4}$	208	101	19.2
	85.0	24.80	20.00	7.053	.916	.653	$1\frac{3}{4}$	170	82	15.7
$20 \times 6\frac{1}{4}$	75.0	21.90	20.00	6.391	.789	.641	$1\frac{9}{16}$	167	78	15.4
	65.4	19.08	20.00	6.250	.789	.500	$1\frac{9}{16}$	130	61	12.0
18×6	70.0	20.46	18.00	6.251	.691	.711	$1\frac{3}{8}$	166	83	17.1
	54.7	15.94	18.00	6.000	.691	.460	$1\frac{3}{8}$	108	54	11.0
$15 \times 5\frac{1}{2}$	50.0	14.59	15.00	5.640	.622	.550	$1\frac{1}{4}$	107	63	13.2
	42.9	12.49	15.00	5.500	.622	.410	$1\frac{1}{4}$	80	47	9.8
$12 \times 5\frac{1}{4}$	50.0	14.57	12.00	5.477	.659	.687	$1\frac{5}{16}$	107	79	16.5
	40.8	11.84	12.00	5.250	.659	.460	$1\frac{5}{16}$	72	53	11.0
12×5	35.0	10.20	12.00	5.078	.544	.428	$1\frac{1}{8}$	67	48	10.3
	31.8	9.26	12.00	5.000	.544	.350	$1\frac{1}{8}$	55	39	8.4
$10 \times 4\frac{5}{8}$	35.0	10.22	10.00	4.944	.491	.594	1	77	64	14.3
	25.4	7.38	10.00	4.660	.491	.310	1	40	34	7.4
8×4	23.0	6.71	8.00	4.171	.425	.441	$\frac{7}{8}$	46	46	10.6
	18.4	5.34	8.00	4.000	.425	.270	$\frac{7}{8}$	28	28	6.5
$7 \times 3\frac{5}{8}$	20.0	5.83	7.00	3.860	.392	.450	$\frac{13}{16}$	41	47	10.8
	15.3	4.43	7.00	3.660	.392	.250	$\frac{13}{16}$	23	26	6.0
$6 \times 3\frac{3}{8}$	17.25	5.02	6.00	3.565	.359	.465	$\frac{3}{4}$	36	47	11.2
	12.5	3.61	6.00	3.330	.359	.230	$\frac{3}{4}$	17.9	24	6.5
5×3	14.75	4.29	5.00	3.284	.326	.494	$\frac{11}{16}$	32	30	11.9
	10.0	2.87	5.00	3.000	.326	.210	$\frac{11}{16}$	13.7	21	5.0
$4 \times 2\frac{5}{8}$	9.5	2.76	4.00	2.796	.293	.326	$\frac{5}{8}$	17.0	32	7.8
	7.7	2.21	4.00	2.660	.293	.190	$\frac{5}{8}$	9.9	18.8	4.6
$3 \times 2\frac{3}{8}$	7.5	2.17	3.00	2.509	.260	.349	$\frac{9}{16}$	13.6	34	8.4
	5.7	1.64	3.00	2.330	.260	.170	$\frac{9}{16}$	6.6	16.6	4.1

2. For buildings carrying heavy loads, the cost advantage is decidedly with reinforced concrete. No other form of construction for heavy loads can approach flat-slab reinforced concrete in cost when the spans are right.

3. For any type of factory where it will be necessary to change operations from time to time or where structural changes will be required, steel is better because it is easier to connect to.

4. Steel is usually better for long-span construction, although since the advent of rigid-frame construction the reinforced-concrete advocates can dispute this point.

5. Structural steel is more foolproof because the main supporting parts are shop-fabricated, and it is not so subject to weather changes, human failings, etc., as reinforced concrete.

The preference for one material over the other in many types of structures where the

Table 1.7   Steel Beams—American Standard (*Continued*)

Nominal size	Weight per ft, lb	Axis x-x			Axis y-y, r, in.	Laterally unsupported beams		
		I, in.^{4}	S, in.^{3}	r, in.		d/bt	L_u	U
24 × 7⅞	120.0	3,010.8	250.9	9.26	1.56	2.71	18.5	4,629
	105.9	2,811.5	234.3	9.53	1.60	2.76	18.0	4,245
24 × 7	100.0	2,371.8	197.6	9.05	1.29	3.81	13.0	2,593
	90.0	2,230.1	185.8	9.21	1.32	3.87	13.0	2,401
	79.9	2,087.2	173.9	9.46	1.36	3.94	12.5	2,207
20 × 7	95.0	1,599.7	160.0	7.59	1.35	3.03	16.5	2,640
	85.0	1,501.7	150.2	7.78	1.38	3.09	16.0	2,430
20 × 6¼	75.0	1,263.5	126.3	7.60	1.17	3.97	12.5	1,591
	65.4	1,169.5	116.9	7.83	1.21	4.05	12.0	1,443
18 × 6	70.0	917.5	101.9	6.70	1.09	4.17	12.0	1,222
	54.7	795.5	88.4	7.07	1.15	4.35	11.5	1,016
15 × 5½	50.0	481.1	64.2	5.74	1.05	4.28	11.5	750.0
	42.9	441.8	58.9	5.95	1.08	4.39	11.0	670.8
12 × 5¼	50.0	301.6	50.3	4.55	1.05	3.32	15.0	757.5
	40.8	268.9	44.8	4.77	1.08	3.47	14.5	645.5
12 × 5	35.0	227.0	37.8	4.72	.99	4.34	11.5	435.5
	31.8	215.8	36.0	4.83	1.01	4.41	11.5	408.2
10 × 4⅝	35.0	145.8	29.2	3.78	.91	4.12	12.0	354.4
	25.4	122.1	24.4	4.07	.97	4.37	11.5	279.2
8 × 4	23.0	64.2	16.0	3.09	.81	4.51	11.0	177.4
	18.4	56.9	14.2	3.26	.84	4.71	10.5	150.7
7 × 3⅝	20.0	41.9	12.0	2.68	.74	4.62	11.0	129.9
	15.3	36.2	10.4	2.86	.78	4.88	10.0	106.5
6 × 3⅜	17.25	26.0	8.7	2.28	.68	4.69	10.5	91.7
	12.5	21.8	7.3	2.46	.72	5.02	10.0	72.7
5 × 3	14.75	15.0	6.0	1.87	63	4.67	10.5	64.2
	10.0	12.1	4.8	2.05	.65	5.11	10.0	47.0
4 × 2⅝	9.5	6.7	3.3	1.56	.58	4.89	10.0	33.7
	7.7	6.0	3.0	1.64	.59	5.13	9.5	29.2
3 × 2⅜	7.5	2.9	1.9	1.15	.52	4.60	11.0	20.7
	5.7	2.5	1.7	1.23	.53	4.95	10.0	17.2

requirement is not self-evident is largely a question of minor factors like the current local market, the contractors available, and the attitude of the owner.

e It is permissible to change from one type of construction to another in various parts of the same building; for instance, in a two-story school where the structure in general is wall-bearing reinforced concrete, skeleton structural steel may be used over the auditorium because of the long span and light walls. However, it is inadvisable to use several systems of construction in the same job. It tends to increase the cost and slow down the work.

1.41   Floor systems

The selection of a floor system is largely independent of the various general systems of construction discussed in Art. 1.40. For in-

Table 1.8   Steel Beams—American Standard Channels

Nominal size	Weight per ft, lb	Area, sq in.	Depth, in.	Flange Width, in.	Flange Thickness, in.	Web thickness, in.	Distance k, in.	V, kips	R, kips	G, kips
18 × 4	58.0	16.98	18.00	4.200	.625	.700	$1\frac{5}{16}$	164	81	16.8
	51.9	15.18	18.00	4.100	.625	.600	$1\frac{5}{16}$	140	69	14.4
	45.8	13.38	18.00	4.000	.625	.500	$1\frac{5}{16}$	117	58	12.0
	42.7	12.48	18.00	3.950	.625	.450	$1\frac{5}{16}$	105	52	10.8
15 × 3⅜	50.0	14.64	15.00	3.716	.650	.716	$1\frac{5}{16}$	140	83	17.2
	40.0	11.70	15.00	3.520	.650	.520	$1\frac{5}{16}$	101	60	12.5
	33.9	9.90	15.00	3.400	.650	.400	$1\frac{5}{16}$	78	46	9.6
12 × 3	30.0	8.79	12.00	3.170	.501	.501	$1\frac{1}{16}$	80	56	12.2
	25.0	7.32	12.00	3.047	.501	.387	$1\frac{1}{16}$	60	42	9.3
	20.7	6.03	12.00	2.940	.501	.280	$1\frac{1}{16}$	44	31	6.7
10 × 2⅝	30.0	8.80	10.00	3.033	.436	.673	$\frac{15}{16}$	88	72	16.2
	25.0	7.33	10.00	2.886	.436	.526	$\frac{15}{16}$	68	56	12.6
	20.0	5.86	10.00	2.739	.436	.379	$\frac{15}{16}$	49	40	9.1
	15.3	4.47	10.00	2.600	.436	.240	$\frac{15}{16}$	31	26	5.8
9 × 2½	20.0	5.86	9.00	2.648	.413	.448	$\frac{7}{8}$	52	47	10.8
	15.0	4.39	9.00	2.485	.413	.285	$\frac{7}{8}$	33	30	6.8
	13.4	3.89	9.00	2.430	.413	.230	$\frac{7}{8}$	27	24	5.5
8 × 2¼	18.75	5.49	8.00	2.527	.390	.487	$\frac{13}{16}$	51	50	11.7
	13.75	4.02	8.00	2.343	.390	.303	$\frac{13}{16}$	32	31	7.3
	11.5	3.36	8.00	2.260	.390	.220	$\frac{13}{16}$	23	23	5.3
7 × 2⅛	14.75	4.32	7.00	2.299	.366	.419	$\frac{13}{16}$	38	43	10.1
	12.25	3.58	7.00	2.194	.366	.314	$\frac{13}{16}$	29	33	7.5
	9.8	2.85	7.00	2.090	.366	.210	$\frac{13}{16}$	19.1	22	5.0
6 × 2	13.0	3.81	6.00	2.157	.343	.437	$\frac{3}{4}$	34	45	10.5
	10.5	3.07	6.00	2.034	.343	.314	$\frac{3}{4}$	25	32	7.5
	8.2	2.39	6.00	1.920	.343	.200	$\frac{3}{4}$	15.6	20	4.8
5 × 1¾	9.0	2.62	5.00	1.885	.320	.325	$\frac{11}{16}$	21.0	33	7.8
	6.7	1.95	5.00	1.750	.320	.190	$\frac{11}{16}$	12.4	19.1	4.6
4 × 1⅝	7.25	2.12	4.00	1.720	.296	.320	$\frac{5}{8}$	16.6	32	7.7
	5.4	1.56	4.00	1.580	.296	.180	$\frac{5}{8}$	9.4	17.8	4.3
3 × 1½	6.0	1.75	3.00	1.596	.273	.356	$\frac{5}{8}$	13.9	35	8.5
	5.0	1.46	3.00	1.498	.273	.258	$\frac{5}{8}$	10.1	26	6.2
	4.1	1.19	3.00	1.410	.273	.170	$\frac{5}{8}$	6.6	16.9	4.1

stance, short-span concrete floors, concrete-joist floors, or two-way concrete floors may be used whether a building is wall-bearing or skeleton, fireproof or semifireproof, with a structural-steel or reinforced-concrete frame.

The number of floor systems using patented or specially manufactured materials is far too great to cover in any but a superficial manner. The general types of systems, how-ever, may be grouped briefly as to spans, materials, and theory of design:

1. Short-span systems, suitable for spans from 3 to 10 ft
    a. Concrete slabs,
        2,000-psi concrete or better
        Cinder concrete
    b. Gypsum systems

Table 1.8   Steel Beams—American Standard Channels (*Continued*)

Nominal size	Weight per ft, lb	Axis x-x			Axis y-y, x, in.	Laterally unsupported beam		
		I, in.^{4}	S, in.^{3}	r, in.		d/bt	L_u	U
18×4	58.0	670.7	74.5	6.29	.88	6.87	7.27	542.2
	51.4	622.1	69.1	6.40	.87	6.93	7.22	498.5
	45.8	573.5	63.7	6.55	.89	7.20	6.94	442.3
	42.7	549.2	61.0	6.64	.90	7.29	6.86	418.4
$15 \times 3\frac{3}{8}$	50.0	401.4	53.6	5.24	.80	6.20	8.05	432.3
	40.0	346.3	46.2	5.44	.78	6.56	7.56	352.1
	33.9	312.6	41.7	5.62	.79	6.79	7.37	307.1
12×3	30.0	161.2	26.9	4.28	.68	7.43	6.74	181.0
	25.0	143.5	23.9	4.43	.68	7.87	6.35	151.9
	20.7	128.1	21.4	4.61	.70	8.15	6.14	131.3
$10 \times 2\frac{5}{8}$	30.0	103.0	20.6	3.42	.65	7.58	6.60	135.9
	25.0	90.7	18.1	3.52	.62	7.92	6.31	114.3
	20.0	78.5	15.7	3.66	.61	8.40	5.95	93.5
	15.3	66.9	13.4	3.87	.64	8.82	5.67	76.0
$9 \times 2\frac{1}{2}$	20.0	60.6	13.5	3.22	.59	8.23	6.08	82.0
	15.0	50.7	11.3	3.40	.59	8.78	5.70	64.4
	13.4	47.3	10.5	3.49	.61	8.97	5.58	58.5
$8 \times 2\frac{1}{4}$	18.75	43.7	10.9	2.82	.57	8.13	6.23	67.0
	13.75	35.8	9.0	2.99	.56	8.80	5.68	51.2
	11.5	32.3	8.1	3.10	.58	9.09	5.50	44.5
$7 \times 2\frac{1}{8}$	14.75	27.1	7.7	2.51	.53	8.32	6.02	46.3
	12.25	24.1	9.6	2.59	.53	8.73	5.73	39.5
	9.8	21.1	6.0	2.72	.55	9.16	5.47	32.8
6×2	13.0	17.3	5.8	2.13	.52	8.12	6.17	35.7
	10.5	15.1	5.0	2.22	.50	8.60	5.82	29.1
	8.2	13.0	4.3	2.34	.52	9.12	5.49	23.6
$5 \times 1\frac{3}{4}$	9.0	8.8	3.5	1.83	.48	8.30	6.03	21.1
	6.7	7.4	3.0	1.95	.49	11.20	4.46	13.4
$4 \times 1\frac{5}{8}$	7.25	4.5	2.3	1.47	.46	7.88	6.35	14.6
	5.4	3.8	1.9	1.56	.46	8.55	5.84	11.1
$3 \times 1\frac{1}{2}$	6.0	2.1	1.4	1.08	.46	6.88	7.27	10.2
	5.0	1.8	1.2	1.12	.44	7.34	6.81	8.2
	4.1	1.6	1.1	1.17	.44	7.80	6.41	7.0

Cast in place or monolithic

Precast

c. Arch systems (seldom used nowadays because of cost and dead weight)

Brick arch

Tile arch

2. Long-span one-way systems, suitable from about 9 to 30 ft

a. Concrete joists

Tile fillers

Metal fillers

b. Steel joists

Bar joists

Junior beams

3. Two-way systems

a. Two-way slabs on steel or concrete beams

Solid concrete

Table 1.9 Steel Angles—Equal Legs

Size	Thickness, in.	Weight per ft	Area, in.²	Axis x-x and axis y-y				Axis z-z, r, in.
				I, in.⁴	S, in.³	r, in.	x or y, in.	
8 × 8	1⅛	56.9	16.73	98.0	17.5	2.42	2.41	1.56
	1	51.0	15.00	89.0	15.8	2.44	2.37	1.56
	⅞	45.0	13.23	79.6	14.0	2.45	2.32	1.57
	¾	38.9	11.44	69.7	12.2	2.47	2.28	1.57
	⅝	32.7	9.61	59.4	10.3	2.49	2.23	1.58
	9/16	29.6	8.68	54.1	9.3	2.50	2.21	1.58
	½	26.4	7.75	48.6	8.4	2.50	2.19	1.59
6 × 6	1	37.4	11.00	35.5	8.6	1.80	1.86	1.17
	⅞	33.1	9.73	31.9	7.6	1.81	1.82	1.17
	¾	28.7	8.44	28.2	6.7	1.83	1.78	1.17
	⅝	24.2	7.11	24.2	5.7	1.84	1.73	1.18
	9/16	21.9	6.43	22.1	5.1	1.85	1.71	1.18
	½	19.6	5.75	19.9	4.6	1.86	1.68	1.18
	7/16	17.2	5.06	17.7	4.1	1.87	1.66	1.19
	⅜	14.9	4.36	15.4	3.5	1.88	1.64	1.19
	5/16	12.5	3.66	13.0	3.0	1.89	1.61	1.19
5 × 5	⅞	27.2	7.98	17.8	5.2	1.49	1.57	.97
	¾	23.6	6.94	15.7	4.5	1.51	1.52	.97
	⅝	20.0	5.86	13.6	3.9	1.52	1.48	.98
	½	16.2	4.75	11.3	3.2	1.54	1.43	.98
	7/16	14.3	4.18	10.0	2.8	1.55	1.41	.98
	⅜	12.3	3.61	8.7	2.4	1.56	1.39	.99
	5/16	10.3	3.03	7.4	2.0	1.57	1.37	.99
4 × 4	¾	18.5	5.44	7.7	2.8	1.19	1.27	.78
	⅝	15.7	4.61	6.7	2.4	1.20	1.23	.78
	½	12.8	3.75	5.6	2.0	1.22	1.18	.78
	7/16	11.3	3.31	5.0	1.8	1.23	1.16	.78
	⅜	9.8	2.86	4.4	1.5	1.23	1.14	.79
	5/16	8.2	2.40	3.7	1.3	1.24	1.12	.79
	¼	6.6	1.94	3.0	1.1	1.25	1.09	.80
3½ × 3½	½	11.1	3.25	3.6	1.5	1.06	1.06	.68
	7/16	9.8	2.87	3.3	1.3	1.07	1.04	.68
	⅜	8.5	2.48	2.9	1.2	1.07	1.01	.69
	5/16	7.2	2.09	2.5	.98	1.08	.99	.69
	¼	5.8	1.69	2.0	.79	1.09	.97	.69
3 × 3	½	9.4	2.75	2.2	1.1	.90	.93	.58
	7/16	8.3	2.43	2.0	.95	.91	.91	.58
	⅜	7.2	2.11	1.8	.83	.91	.89	.58
	5/16	6.1	1.78	1.5	.71	.92	.87	.59
	¼	4.9	1.44	1.2	.58	.93	.84	.59
	3/16	3.71	1.09	.96	.44	.94	.82	.59
2½ × 2½	½	7.7	2.25	1.2	.72	.74	.81	.49
	⅜	5.9	1.73	.98	.57	.75	.76	.49
	5/16	5.0	1.47	.85	.48	.76	.74	.49
	¼	4.1	1.19	.70	.39	.77	.72	.49
	3/16	3.07	.90	.55	.30	.78	.69	.49
2 × 2	⅜	4.7	1.36	.48	.35	.59	.64	.39
	5/16	3.92	1.15	.42	.30	.60	.61	.39
	¼	3.19	.94	.35	.25	.61	.59	.39
	3/16	2.44	.71	.27	.19	.62	.57	.39
	⅛	1.65	.48	.19	.13	.63	.55	.40

Table 1.9 Steel Angles—Equal Legs (*Continued*)

Size	Thickness, in.	Weight per ft	Area, in.²	Axis x-x and axis y-y				Axis z-z, r, in.
				I, in.⁴	S, in.³	r, in.	x or y, in.	
$1\frac{3}{4} \times 1\frac{3}{4}$	$\frac{1}{4}$	2.77	.81	.23	.19	.53	.53	.34
	$\frac{3}{16}$	2.12	.62	.18	.14	.54	.51	.34
	$\frac{1}{8}$	1.44	.42	.13	.10	.55	.48	.35
$1\frac{1}{2} \times 1\frac{1}{2}$	$\frac{1}{4}$	2.34	.69	.14	.13	.45	.47	.29
	$\frac{3}{16}$	1.80	.53	.11	.10	.46	.44	.29
	$\frac{1}{8}$	1.23	.36	.08	.07	.47	.42	.30
$1\frac{1}{4} \times 1\frac{1}{4}$	$\frac{1}{4}$	1.92	.56	.08	.09	.37	.40	.24
	$\frac{3}{16}$	1.48	.43	.06	.07	.38	.38	.24
	$\frac{1}{8}$	1.01	.30	.04	.05	.38	.36	.25
1×1	$\frac{1}{4}$	1.49	.44	.04	.06	.29	.34	.20
	$\frac{3}{16}$	1.16	.34	.03	.04	.30	.32	.19
	$\frac{1}{8}$	.80	.23	.02	.03	.30	.30	.20

Concrete with tile fillers (Shuster system)

Concrete with concrete-block fillers (Republic system)

Concrete with metal-dome fillers (grid system)

b. Flat slab

The various factors which might influence the selection of the floor system to be used are as follows:

1. Use of floor
   a. Loading
      Light or heavy
      Uniform or concentrated
   b. Span
      Long or short
      Regularity of support arrangement
   c. Freedom from obstruction
      Columns
      Beams or girders
      Incorporation of pipes, conduits, or vent shafts
   d. Rigidity and resistance to:
      Machinery shocks
      Outside vibrations
      Wind stresses or earthquakes
   e. Adaptability to alteration
      Main members
      Secondary members
   f. Conformity to code

City or other local codes
Fire or other insurance codes
   g. Insulation
      Sound
      Heat or cold
   h. Acoustical properties
2. Cost of floor
   a. First cost
   b. Maintenance cost
   c. Indirect cost (affecting cost of remainder of building)
      Ability to "tie in" to structure
      Difference in weight and story height as affecting size and cost of supporting columns and foundations
   d. Royalty costs of patented types
   e. Salvage of form work
3. Appearance of floor
   a. Floor finish
      Integral concrete
      Any finish applied later
   b. Ceiling finish
      Exposed and untreated
      Plaster
      Paint
4. Local building conditions
   a. Material
      Supply, including freight rate
      Handling on the job
      Storage space

Table 1.10 Steel Angles—Unequal Legs

Size	Thickness, in.	Weight per ft	Area, in.²	Axis x-x				Axis y-y				Axis z-z	
				I, in.⁴	S, in.³	r, in.	y, in.	I, in.⁴	S, in.³	r, in.	x, in.	r, in.	Tan α
9×4	1	40.8	12.00	97.0	17.6	2.84	3.50	12.0	4.0	1.00	1.00	.83	.203
	$\frac{7}{8}$	36.1	10.61	86.8	15.7	2.86	3.45	10.8	3.6	1.01	.95	.84	.208
	$\frac{3}{4}$	31.3	9.19	76.1	13.6	2.88	3.41	9.6	3.1	1.02	.91	.84	.212
	$\frac{5}{8}$	26.3	7.73	64.9	11.5	2.90	3.36	8.3	2.6	1.04	.86	.85	.216
	$\frac{9}{16}$	23.8	7.00	59.1	10.4	2.91	3.33	7.6	2.4	1.04	.83	.85	.218
	$\frac{1}{2}$	21.3	6.25	53.2	9.3	2.92	3.31	6.9	2.2	1.05	.81	.85	.220
8×6	1	44.2	13.00	80.8	15.1	2.49	2.65	38.8	8.9	1.73	1.65	1.28	.543
	$\frac{7}{8}$	39.1	11.48	72.3	13.4	2.51	2.61	34.9	7.9	1.74	1.61	1.28	.547
	$\frac{3}{4}$	33.8	9.94	63.4	11.7	2.53	2.56	30.7	6.9	1.76	1.56	1.29	.551
	$\frac{5}{8}$	28.5	8.36	54.1	9.9	2.54	2.52	26.3	5.9	1.77	1.52	1.29	.554
	$\frac{9}{16}$	25.7	7.56	49.3	9.0	2.55	2.50	24.0	5.3	1.78	1.50	1.30	.556
	$\frac{1}{2}$	23.0	6.75	44.3	8.0	2.56	2.47	21.7	4.8	1.79	1.47	1.30	.558
	$\frac{7}{16}$	20.2	5.93	39.2	7.1	2.57	2.45	19.3	4.2	1.80	1.45	1.31	.560
8×4	1	37.4	11.00	69.6	14.1	2.52	3.05	11.6	3.9	1.03	1.05	.85	.247
	$\frac{7}{8}$	33.1	9.73	62.5	12.5	2.53	3.00	10.5	3.5	1.04	1.00	.85	.253
	$\frac{3}{4}$	28.7	8.44	54.9	10.9	2.55	2.95	9.4	3.1	1.05	.95	.85	.258
	$\frac{5}{8}$	24.2	7.11	46.9	9.2	2.57	2.91	8.1	2.6	1.07	.91	.86	.262
	$\frac{9}{16}$	21.9	6.43	42.8	8.4	2.58	2.88	7.4	2.4	1.07	.88	.86	.265
	$\frac{1}{2}$	19.6	5.75	38.5	7.5	2.59	2.86	6.7	2.2	1.08	.86	.86	.267
	$\frac{7}{16}$	17.2	5.06	34.1	6.6	2.60	2.83	6.0	1.9	1.09	.83	.87	.269
7×4	$\frac{7}{8}$	30.2	8.86	42.9	9.7	2.20	2.55	10.2	3.5	1.07	1.05	.86	.318
	$\frac{3}{4}$	26.2	7.69	37.8	8.4	2.22	2.51	9.1	3.0	1.09	1.01	.86	.324
	$\frac{5}{8}$	22.1	6.48	32.4	7.1	2.24	2.46	7.8	2.6	1.10	.96	.86	.329
	$\frac{9}{16}$	20.0	5.87	29.6	6.5	2.24	2.44	7.2	2.4	1.11	.94	.87	.332
	$\frac{1}{2}$	17.9	5.25	26.7	5.8	2.25	2.42	6.5	2.1	1.11	.92	.87	.335
	$\frac{7}{16}$	15.8	4.62	23.7	5.1	2.26	2.39	5.8	1.9	1.12	.89	.88	.337
	$\frac{3}{8}$	13.6	3.98	20.6	4.4	2.27	2.37	5.1	1.6	1.13	.87	.88	.339
6×4	$\frac{7}{8}$	27.2	7.98	27.7	7.2	1.86	2.12	9.8	3.4	1.11	1.12	.86	.421
	$\frac{3}{4}$	23.6	6.94	24.5	6.3	1.88	2.08	8.7	3.0	1.12	1.08	.86	.428
	$\frac{5}{8}$	20.0	5.86	21.1	5.3	1.90	2.03	7.5	2.5	1.13	1.03	.86	.435
	$\frac{9}{16}$	18.1	5.31	19.3	4.8	1.90	2.01	6.9	2.3	1.14	1.01	.87	.438
	$\frac{1}{2}$	16.2	4.75	17.4	4.3	1.91	1.99	6.3	2.1	1.15	.99	.87	.440
	$\frac{7}{16}$	14.3	4.18	15.5	3.8	1.92	1.96	5.6	1.9	1.16	.96	.87	.443
	$\frac{3}{8}$	12.3	3.61	13.5	3.3	1.93	1.94	4.9	1.6	1.17	.94	.88	.446
	$\frac{5}{16}$	10.3	3.03	11.4	2.8	1.94	1.92	4.2	1.4	1.17	.92	.88	.449
$6 \times 3\frac{1}{2}$	$\frac{1}{2}$	15.3	4.50	16.6	4.2	1.92	2.08	4.3	1.6	.97	.83	.76	.344
	$\frac{3}{8}$	11.7	3.42	12.6	3.2	1.94	2.04	3.3	1.2	.99	.79	.77	.350
	$\frac{5}{16}$	9.8	2.87	10.9	2.7	1.95	2.01	2.9	1.0	1.00	.76	.77	.352
	$\frac{1}{4}$	7.9	2.31	8.9	2.2	1.96	1.99	2.3	0.85	1.01	.74	.78	.355
$5 \times 3\frac{1}{2}$	$\frac{3}{4}$	19.8	5.81	13.9	4.3	1.55	1.75	5.6	2.2	.98	1.00	.75	.464
	$\frac{5}{8}$	16.8	4.92	12.0	3.7	1.56	1.70	4.8	1.9	.99	.95	.75	.472
	$\frac{1}{2}$	13.6	4.00	10.0	3.0	1.58	1.66	4.1	1.6	1.01	.91	.75	.479
	$\frac{7}{16}$	12.0	3.53	8.9	2.6	1.59	1.63	3.6	1.4	1.01	.88	.76	.482
	$\frac{3}{8}$	10.4	3.05	7.8	2.3	1.60	1.61	3.2	1.2	1.02	.86	.76	.486
	$\frac{5}{16}$	8.7	2.56	6.6	1.9	1.61	1.59	2.7	1.0	1.03	.84	.76	.489
	$\frac{1}{4}$	7.0	2.06	5.4	1.6	1.61	1.56	2.2	.83	1.04	.81	.76	.492
5×3	$\frac{1}{2}$	12.8	3.75	9.5	2.9	1.59	1.75	2.6	1.1	.83	.75	.65	.357
	$\frac{7}{16}$	11.3	3.31	8.4	2.6	1.60	1.73	2.3	1.0	.84	.73	.65	.361
	$\frac{3}{8}$	9.8	2.86	7.4	2.2	1.61	1.70	2.0	.89	.84	.70	.65	.364
	$\frac{5}{16}$	8.2	2.40	6.3	1.9	1.61	1.68	1.8	.75	.85	.68	.66	.368
	$\frac{1}{4}$	6.6	1.94	5.1	1.5	1.62	1.66	1.4	.61	.86	.66	.66	.371

34

Table 1.10   Steel Angles—Unequal Legs (*Continued*)

Size	Thickness, in.	Weight per ft	Area, in.^{2}	Axis x-x				Axis y-y				Axis z-z	
				I, in.^{4}	S, in.^{3}	r, in.	y, in.	I, in.^{4}	S, in.^{3}	r, in.	x, in.	r, in.	Tan α
$4 \times 3\frac{1}{2}$	$\frac{5}{8}$	14.7	4.30	6.4	2.4	1.22	1.29	4.5	1.8	1.03	1.04	.72	.745
	$\frac{1}{2}$	11.9	3.50	5.3	1.9	1.23	1.25	3.8	1.5	1.04	1.00	.72	.750
	$\frac{7}{16}$	10.6	3.09	4.8	1.7	1.24	1.23	3.4	1.4	1.05	.98	.72	.753
	$\frac{3}{8}$	9.1	2.67	4.2	1.5	1.25	1.21	3.0	1.2	1.06	.96	.73	.755
	$\frac{5}{16}$	7.7	2.25	3.6	1.3	1.26	1.18	2.6	1.0	1.07	.93	.73	.757
	$\frac{1}{4}$	6.2	1.81	2.9	1.0	1.27	1.16	2.1	.81	1.07	.91	.73	.759
4×3	$\frac{5}{8}$	13.6	3.98	6.0	2.3	1.23	1.37	2.9	1.4	.85	.87	.64	.534
	$\frac{1}{2}$	11.1	3.25	5.1	1.9	1.25	1.33	2.4	1.1	.86	.83	.64	.543
	$\frac{7}{16}$	9.8	2.87	4.5	1.7	1.25	1.30	2.2	1.0	.87	.80	.64	.547
	$\frac{3}{8}$	8.5	2.48	4.0	1.5	1.26	1.28	1.9	.87	.88	.78	.64	.551
	$\frac{5}{16}$	7.2	2.09	3.4	1.2	1.27	1.26	1.7	.73	.89	.76	.65	.554
	$\frac{1}{4}$	5.8	1.69	2.8	1.0	1.28	1.24	1.4	.60	.90	.74	.65	.558
$3\frac{1}{2} \times 3$	$\frac{1}{2}$	10.2	3.00	3.5	1.5	1.07	1.13	2.3	1.1	.88	.88	.62	.714
	$\frac{7}{16}$	9.1	2.65	3.1	1.3	1.08	1.10	2.1	.98	.89	.85	.62	.718
	$\frac{3}{8}$	7.9	2.30	2.7	1.1	1.09	1.08	1.9	.85	.90	.83	.62	.721
	$\frac{5}{16}$	6.6	1.93	2.3	.95	1.10	1.06	1.6	.72	.90	.81	.63	.724
	$\frac{1}{4}$	5.4	1.56	1.9	.78	1.11	1.04	1.3	.59	.91	.79	.63	.727
$3\frac{1}{2} \times 2\frac{1}{2}$	$\frac{1}{2}$	9.4	2.75	3.2	1.4	1.09	1.20	1.4	.76	.70	.70	.53	.486
	$\frac{7}{16}$	8.3	2.43	2.9	1.3	1.09	1.18	1.2	.68	.71	.68	.54	.491
	$\frac{3}{8}$	7.2	2.11	2.6	1.1	1.10	1.16	1.1	.59	.72	.66	.54	.496
	$\frac{5}{16}$	6.1	1.78	2.2	.93	1.11	1.14	.94	.50	.73	.64	.54	.501
	$\frac{1}{4}$	4.9	1.44	1.8	.75	1.12	1.11	.78	.41	.74	.61	.54	.506
$3 \times 2\frac{1}{2}$	$\frac{1}{2}$	8.5	2.50	2.1	1.0	.91	1.00	1.3	.74	.72	.75	.52	.667
	$\frac{7}{16}$	7.6	2.21	1.9	.93	.92	.98	1.2	.66	.73	.73	.52	.672
	$\frac{3}{8}$	6.6	1.92	1.7	.81	.93	.96	1.0	.58	.74	.71	.52	.676
	$\frac{5}{16}$	5.6	1.62	1.4	.69	.94	.93	.90	.49	.74	.68	.53	.680
	$\frac{1}{4}$	4.5	1.31	1.2	.56	.95	.91	.74	.40	.75	.66	.53	.684
3×2	$\frac{1}{2}$	7.7	2.25	1.9	1.0	.92	1.08	.67	.47	.55	.58	.43	.414
	$\frac{7}{16}$	6.8	2.00	1.7	.89	.93	1.06	.61	.42	.55	.56	.43	.421
	$\frac{3}{8}$	5.9	1.73	1.5	.78	.94	1.04	.54	.37	.56	.54	.43	.428
	$\frac{5}{16}$	5.0	1.47	1.3	.66	.95	1.02	.47	.32	.57	.52	.43	.435
	$\frac{1}{4}$	4.1	1.19	1.1	.54	.95	.99	.39	.26	.57	.49	.43	.440
	$\frac{3}{16}$	3.07	.90	.84	.41	.97	.97	.31	.20	.58	.47	.44	.446
$2\frac{1}{2} \times 2$	$\frac{3}{8}$	5.3	1.55	.91	.55	.77	.83	.51	.36	.58	.58	.42	.614
	$\frac{5}{16}$	4.5	1.31	.79	.47	.78	.81	.45	.31	.58	.56	.42	.620
	$\frac{1}{4}$	3.62	1.06	.65	.38	.78	.79	.37	.25	.59	.54	.42	.626
	$\frac{3}{16}$	2.75	.81	.51	.29	.79	.76	.29	.20	.60	.51	.43	.631
$2\frac{1}{2} \times 1\frac{1}{2}$	$\frac{3}{8}$	4.7	1.36	.82	.52	.78	.92	.22	.20	.40	.42	.32	.340
	$\frac{5}{16}$	3.92	1.15	.71	.44	.79	.90	.19	.17	.41	.40	.32	.349
	$\frac{1}{4}$	3.19	.94	.59	.36	.79	.88	.16	.14	.41	.38	.32	.357
	$\frac{3}{16}$	2.44	.72	.46	.28	.80	.85	.13	.11	.42	.35	.33	.364
$2 \times 1\frac{1}{2}$	$\frac{1}{4}$	2.77	.81	.32	.24	.62	.66	.15	.14	.43	.41	.32	.543
	$\frac{3}{16}$	2.12	.62	.25	.18	.63	.64	.12	.11	.44	.39	.32	.551
	$\frac{1}{8}$	1.44	.42	.17	.13	.64	.62	.09	.08	.45	.37	.33	.558
$1\frac{3}{4} \times 1\frac{1}{4}$	$\frac{1}{4}$	2.34	.69	.20	.18	.54	.60	.09	.10	.35	.35	.27	.486
	$\frac{3}{16}$	1.80	.53	.16	.14	.55	.58	.07	.08	.36	.33	.27	.496
	$\frac{1}{8}$	1.23	.36	.11	.09	.56	.56	.05	.05	.37	.31	.27	.506

b. Labor
Type available
Possibility of importation
Labor restrictions
c. Special conditions of bidding by contractors
d. Climatic conditions
5. Time requirements
a. Speed of construction as affecting revenue of the building
b. Delays caused by purchase of special materials not available locally
6. Supervision
a. Normal
b. Extra rigid, due to unusual or new system involved
c. Ease of repairing the result of slight errors or omissions, without reducing factor of safety

Another thing to avoid is the use of any system of construction which requires that the rest of the building be built to fit the floor system. What advantage is there in saving 3¢ per sq ft in the floor construction and spending $3\frac{1}{2}$¢ extra in electric and heating contracts?

Further discussion which may influence the selection of a floor system may be found in connection with the sections dealing with the design of floors, as follows:

1. Short-span systems
Concrete slabs—Art. 5.40
Gypsum systems—Art. 5.60
Arch systems—Art. 5.70
2. Long-span one-way systems
Concrete joists—Art. 5.41
Steel joists—Art. 4.30
3. Two-way systems
Two-way slabs—Art. 5.50
Flat slabs—Art. 5.51

1.42 Fire-resistance ratings

It has been stated in Art. 1.40 that one of the chief criteria for the use of any construction system or detail of construction is based on the fire-resistance rating, or, as it is frequently called, the fire rating. This rating is being adopted by building codes throughout the country as the standard of measurement

Table 1.11 Properties of Wood Sections

Nominal size	Actual size	A	S	Weight per ft	fbm per lin ft
2 × 4	$1\frac{5}{8} \times 3\frac{5}{8}$	5.89	3.56	1.64	.67
2 × 6	$1\frac{5}{8} \times 5\frac{5}{8}$	9.14	8.57	2.54	1.0
2 × 8	$1\frac{5}{8} \times 7\frac{1}{2}$	12.2	15.3	3.39	1.33
2 × 10	$1\frac{5}{8} \times 9\frac{1}{2}$	15.4	24.4	4.29	1.67
2 × 12	$1\frac{5}{8} \times 11\frac{1}{2}$	18.7	35.8	5.19	2.0
2 × 14	$1\frac{5}{8} \times 13\frac{1}{2}$	21.9	49.4	6.09	2.33
3 × 8	$2\frac{5}{8} \times 7\frac{1}{2}$	19.7	24.6	5.47	2.0
3 × 10	$2\frac{5}{8} \times 9\frac{1}{2}$	24.9	39.5	6.93	2.5
3 × 12	$2\frac{5}{8} \times 11\frac{1}{2}$	30.2	57.9	8.39	3.0
3 × 14	$2\frac{5}{8} \times 13\frac{1}{2}$	35.4	79.7	9.84	3.5
4 × 6	$3\frac{5}{8} \times 5\frac{5}{8}$	20.4	19.1	5.66	2.0
4 × 8	$3\frac{5}{8} \times 7\frac{1}{2}$	27.2	34.0	7.55	2.67
4 × 10	$3\frac{5}{8} \times 9\frac{1}{2}$	34.4	54.5	9.57	3.33
4 × 12	$3\frac{5}{8} \times 11\frac{1}{2}$	41.7	79.5	11.6	4.0
4 × 14	$3\frac{5}{8} \times 13\frac{1}{2}$	48.9	110.0	13.6	4.67
4 × 16	$3\frac{5}{8} \times 15\frac{1}{2}$	56.2	145.0	15.6	5.33
6 × 6	$5\frac{1}{2} \times 5\frac{1}{2}$	30.3	27.7	8.4	3.0
6 × 8	$5\frac{1}{2} \times 7\frac{1}{2}$	41.3	51.6	11.4	4.0
6 × 10	$5\frac{1}{2} \times 9\frac{1}{2}$	52.3	82.7	14.5	5.0
6 × 12	$5\frac{1}{2} \times 11\frac{1}{2}$	63.3	121.0	17.5	6.0
6 × 14	$5\frac{1}{2} \times 13\frac{1}{2}$	74.3	167.0	20.6	7.0
6 × 16	$5\frac{1}{2} \times 15\frac{1}{2}$	85.3	220.0	23.6	8.0
8 × 6	$7\frac{1}{2} \times 5\frac{1}{2}$	41	51.56	11.4	4.0
8 × 8	$7\frac{1}{2} \times 7\frac{1}{2}$	56	70.31	15.7	5.33
8 × 10	$7\frac{1}{2} \times 9\frac{1}{2}$	71	112.8	19.8	6.67
8 × 12	$7\frac{1}{2} \times 11\frac{1}{2}$	86	165.3	24.0	8.0
8 × 14	$7\frac{1}{2} \times 13\frac{1}{2}$	101	227.8	28.0	9.33
8 × 16	$7\frac{1}{2} \times 15\frac{1}{2}$	116	300.3	32.5	10.67
10 × 10	$9\frac{1}{2} \times 9\frac{1}{2}$	90.3	143	25.0	8.33
10 × 12	$9\frac{1}{2} \times 11\frac{1}{2}$	109	209	30.3	10.0
10 × 14	$9\frac{1}{2} \times 13\frac{1}{2}$	128	289	35.6	11.67
10 × 16	$9\frac{1}{2} \times 15\frac{1}{2}$	147	380	40.9	13.33
10 × 18	$9\frac{1}{2} \times 17\frac{1}{2}$	166	485	46.1	15.0
12 × 1	$11\frac{1}{2} \times \frac{25}{32}$	9.04	1.17	2.5	1
12 × 1¼	$11\frac{1}{2} \times 1\frac{1}{16}$	12.4	2.23	3.44	1.25
12 × 1½	$11\frac{1}{2} \times 1\frac{5}{16}$	15.0	3.3	4.16	1.5
12 × 2	$11\frac{1}{2} \times 1\frac{5}{8}$	18.6	5.07	5.17	2
12 × 2½	$11\frac{1}{2} \times 2\frac{1}{8}$	24.4	8.61	6.78	2.5
12 × 3	$11\frac{1}{2} \times 2\frac{5}{8}$	30.2	13.24	8.38	3
12 × 4	$11\frac{1}{2} \times 3\frac{5}{8}$	41.6	25.1	11.57	4
12 × 6	$11\frac{1}{2} \times 5\frac{5}{8}$	64.6	60.6	18.0	6
12 × 8	$11\frac{1}{2} \times 7\frac{1}{2}$	86	108	23.9	8
12 × 10	$11\frac{1}{2} \times 9\frac{1}{2}$	109	172.5	30.3	10
12 × 12	$11\frac{1}{2} \times 11\frac{1}{2}$	132	253	36.7	12
12 × 14	$11\frac{1}{2} \times 13\frac{1}{2}$	155	349	43.1	14
12 × 16	$11\frac{1}{2} \times 15\frac{1}{2}$	178	460	49.5	16
14 × 14	$13\frac{1}{2} \times 13\frac{1}{2}$	182	410	50.6	16.33
14 × 16	$13\frac{1}{2} \times 15\frac{1}{2}$	209	541	58.1	18.66
14 × 18	$13\frac{1}{2} \times 17\frac{1}{2}$	236	680	65.6	21
16 × 16	$15\frac{1}{2} \times 15\frac{1}{2}$	240	621	66.7	21.33
16 × 18	$15\frac{1}{2} \times 17\frac{1}{2}$	270	791	75.3	24

Table 1.12 Fire-Resistance Ratings of Walls and Partitions

Minimum wall thickness, in.

Type	Details of construction	Combustible members framed in wall				Members framed in wall—none or noncombustible			
		4 hr	3 hr	2 hr	1 hr	4 hr	3 hr	2 hr	1 hr
Brick (clay, shale, concrete, or sand lime)	Solid walls, unplastered	12	12	8	8	8	8	8	4
	Solid walls, plastered both sides with ½-in. gypsum or portland-cement plaster (except as below)	12	12	8	8	8	8	4	4
	Hollow "Rolok" walls, unplastered		12	12	8	12	12	8	8
	Hollow "Rolok" walls, plastered (as above)	12	12	12	8	8	8	8	8
	Hollow cavity-type walls, ¼-in. round metal ties, 2 ft o.c. every sixth course			9	9	9	9	9	9
	Solid walls, concrete or sand lime, plastered both sides	12	12	8	8	8	4	4	4
	Coved brick, 1 unit, 1 cell in thickness, 70% solid material, unplastered				8			8	8
	Same, plastered both sides				8	8	8	8	8
	Coved brick, 2 units, 2 cells thick, 87% solid material, un- or plastered both sides			8	8	8	8	8	8
	Poured concrete, unreinforced	12	12	8	8	7	7	5	4
	Solid stone masonry, plastered or not	16	16	12	12	12	12	12	8
Load-bearing walls of concrete, masonry, Haydite, limestone, slag, or cinder aggregate	1 cell thick, 52% solid unplastered					12		8	8
	1 cell thick, 52% solid, plastered both sides			12	8		8	8	8
	1 cell thick, 62% solid, unplastered			10	8	10	10	8	8
	1 cell thick, 62% solid, plastered both sides			10	8		8	8	8
	1 cell thick, 70% solid, unplastered				8		8	8	8
	1 cell thick, 70% solid, plastered both sides				8	8	8	8	8
	2 cells thick, 65% solid, unplastered				8		8	8	8
	2 cells thick, 65% solid, plastered both sides				8	8	8	8	8
	2 cells thick, 62% solid, 2-in. air space, unplastered				10		10	10	10
	2 cells thick, 62% solid, 2-in. air space, plastered both sides			10	10	10	10	10	10
Concrete masonry, expanded slag, or pumice aggregate	1 cell thick, 70% solid, plastered or not		6		6	6	6	6	6
	1 cell thick, 55% solid, unplastered				8		8	8	8
	1 cell thick, 55% solid, plastered both sides				8	8	8	8	8
	1 cell thick, 62% solid, unplastered			10	8	8	8	8	8
	1 cell thick, 62% solid, plastered both sides				8	8	8	8	8
	2 cells thick, 62% solid, 2-in. air space, unplastered				10	10	10	10	10
	2 cells thick, 62% solid, 2-in. air space, plastered both sides				10	10	10	10	10
Concrete masonry, calcareous sand and gravel	2 cells thick, 62% solid, 2-in. air space, unplastered				10				10
	2 cells thick, 62% solid, 2-in. air space, plastered both sides			12	12	10	10	10	10
Concrete masonry, siliceous sand and gravel	1 cell thick, 57% solid, plastered both sides					12	12	12	12
	2 cells thick, 55% solid, plastered or unplastered			12	12	12	12	12	12
Load-bearing clay tile	2 cells thick, 40% solid, unplastered								8
	2 cells thick, 40% solid, plastered both sides				8		8	8	8
	2 cells thick, 46% solid, unplastered				8				8
	2 cells thick, 49% solid, unplastered				8			8	8
	2 cells thick, 49% solid, plastered both sides			8	8	8	8	8	8
	3 or 4 cells thick, 43% solid, unplastered							8	8
	3 or 4 cells thick, 43% solid, plastered both sides				8	8	8	8	8

Table 1.12 Fire-Resistance Ratings of Walls and Partitions (*Continued*)

Type	Details of construction	Minimum wall thickness, in.			
		4 hr	3 hr	2 hr	1 hr
Nonbearing partitions, clay tile	1 cell thick, 40% solid, medium burned clay, plastered both sides				4
	1 cell thick, 40% solid, medium or hard burned clay, plastered both sides				4
	1 cell thick, 30% solid, medium or hard burned clay, plastered both sides				6
	2 cells thick, 50% solid, medium or hard burned clay, plastered both sides				4
	2 cells thick, 60% solid, hard burned clay, plastered both sides				4
	2 cells thick, 60% solid, medium burned clay, plastered both sides			4	4
	2 cells thick, 45% solid, hard burned clay, plastered both sides				6
	2 cells thick, 45% solid, medium burned clay, unplastered				6
	2 cells thick, 45% solid, medium burned clay, plastered both sides			6	6
Nonbearing partitions, gypsum tile	Solid, unplastered	5	5	5	2
	70% solid, unplastered				3
	70% solid, plastered both sides		4	3	3
Concrete masonry, expanded clay or pumice (all 1 cell thick)	49% solid, unplastered				6
	49% solid, plastered both sides			6	6
	62% solid, unplastered				4
Haydite, slag, and cinders except as noted below	62% solid, plastered both sides			4	4
	73% solid, unplastered		6	6	4
	73% solid, plastered both sides	6	6	3	3
Concrete masonry, Haydite, slag, and cinder aggregate (1 cell thick)	73% solid, unplastered			6	4
	73% solid, plastered both sides	6	6	4	3

of construction required. Ratings are based on standard fire tests as set up by the American Standards Association. The generally recognized authority for fire ratings is the "Technical Report on Building Materials 44" (commonly called "TRBM–44") and pamphlet BMS–92 of the National Bureau of Standards, although other tests conducted in the approved manner are also recognized. Tables 1.12–1.15 give the currently accepted standards for fire ratings.

Cast-in-place concrete should have a coarse aggregate consisting of limestone, calcareous gravel, traprock, blast furnace slag, burnt clay, or burnt shale.

The thicknesses in Table 1.13 refer to thicknesses of protective materials before the application of plaster. Such thicknesses are measured from the extreme outer edge of the member, except that the thickness of protective material required at the extreme edges of lugs, brackets, wind bracing, and other connections should not be less than 1 in.

All interior or reentrant spaces should be filled with concrete or with the same material as the protection. For gypsum-block protections, such filling may be omitted when the blocks are so anchored or tied together as to preserve the integrity of the protection for the required fire period. Pipes, conduits, wires,

Table 1.12 Fire-Resistance Ratings of Walls and Partitions (*Continued*)

Miscellaneous walls and partitions	Resistance, hr
Wood-stud load-bearing partitions (see TRBM–44 for details):	
With wood lath and mineral-wool bats or with gypsum plaster	1
With plaster on metal lath	up to 2
With filled stud space and various wallboards	up to 2
Steel-stud load-bearing partitions with plaster in metal lath (see TRBM–44 for details)	up to 2
Solid 2-in. plaster partitions on $\frac{3}{4}$-in. metal studs, wood-fibered gypsum plaster	2
Brick-veneer wall on metal lath, steel studs, $\frac{3}{4}$-in. sanded gypsum plaster inside (see BMS–92 for details)	4

cables, and other service equipment should not be placed within the required thickness of protective covering of any column.

Poured protection should have a minimum reinforcement of 4×4-in. wire mesh weighing not less than $1\frac{1}{2}$ lb per sq yd, or equivalent. Protective coverings of masonry units should be solidly bedded and laid in cement or lime-cement mortar, except that gypsum blocks should be laid in gypsum mortar. Block and tile protective coverings should be securely anchored or bonded by wall ties or metal mesh laid in the horizontal joints, by metal clips connecting one unit to another, by outside tie wires not smaller than 0.1 in. with at least one such tie around every course, or by means of specially designed units providing positive anchorage to the member or to other units. All outside tie wires should be protected by at least $\frac{1}{2}$ in. of plaster. Wherever plaster is required, gypsum or portland-cement plaster at least $\frac{1}{2}$ in. thick should be used; except that, on gypsum units, gypsum plaster only should be used.

Where fire-resistive covering on columns is exposed to damage from trucking or handling of merchandise, it should be jacketed for a height of at least 5 ft from the floor with a substantial covering.

For the ratings in Table 1.14, protective

Table 1.13 Fire-Resistance Ratings of Protected Steel and Cast-Iron Columns

Details of Construction	Thickness, in.		
	4 hr	3 hr	2 hr
Concrete cast in place, metal reinforcement	2	2	$1\frac{1}{2}$
Brick	$3\frac{3}{4}$	$3\frac{3}{4}$	$2\frac{1}{4}$
Structural clay tile	4	3	2
Structural clay tile, plastered	3	$2\frac{1}{2}$	
Concrete masonry units—hollow, plastered	4	3	3
Concrete masonry units—solid, aggregate of expanded slag, cinders, burned clay, or shale—plastered	3	2	
Concrete masonry units—solid, aggregate of expanded slag, cinders, burned clay, or shale—unplastered			2
Gypsum—cast in place, wire-mesh reinforcement	2	$1\frac{1}{2}$	$1\frac{1}{2}$
Gypsum—cast in place, wire-mesh reinforcement, plastered	2	$1\frac{1}{2}$	$1\frac{1}{2}$
Gypsum—solid block			2
Gypsum—solid block, plastered	2	2	
Gypsum—hollow block			3
Gypsum—hollow block, plastered	3	3	
Gypsum—perlite plaster over self-furring lath, wrapped around column	$1\frac{3}{4}$	$1\frac{3}{8}$	1
Gypsum—vermiculite or perlite plaster over metal lath, furred out $1\frac{1}{4}$ in., space filled with plaster	$1\frac{1}{2}$	1	
Gypsum—perlite plaster over metal lath, furred $\frac{7}{16}$ in. from column with $\frac{3}{4}$-in. channel brackets 2 ft o.c.	$1\frac{1}{2}$		
Gypsum—perlite plaster over metal lath, furred out $1\frac{1}{4}$ in. from column			1

Table 1.14   Fire-Resistance Ratings of Protected Steel Beams, Girders, and Trusses

	Thickness, in.			
	4 hr	3 hr	2 hr	1 hr
Concrete cast in place	2	2	$1\frac{1}{2}$	$1\frac{1}{2}$
Brick, back filled	$3\frac{3}{4}$	$3\frac{3}{4}$	$2\frac{1}{4}$	$2\frac{1}{4}$
Structural clay tile	4	3	2	2
Structural clay tile, plastered	3	$2\frac{1}{4}$	2	2
Concrete masonry units		3	2	2
Concrete masonry units—aggregate of expanded slag, cinders, burned clay, or shale—plastered	3	2		
Gypsum—cast in place		$1\frac{1}{2}$	1	
Gypsum—cast in place, plastered	2	$1\frac{1}{2}$	1	1
Gypsum—vermiculite plaster over metal lath with $2\frac{1}{2}$ in. air space, or perlite plaster on metal lath with 3 in. air space between lath and structural members	1			
Gypsum—perlite plaster on metal lath, $3\frac{1}{2}$ in. air space	$\frac{7}{8}$			
Gypsum—vermiculite plaster (plus $\frac{1}{2}$ in. vermiculite acoustical plaster over metal lath), $2\frac{1}{2}$ in. air space	$\frac{5}{8}$			
Sprayed asbestos fiber on metal lath, 2 in. air space		1		
Gypsum vermiculite on metal lath, in contact with steel	1	$\frac{3}{4}$		
Gypsum sanded plaster, 1:2, 1:3, on metal lath, contact			1	
Portland cement or sanded gypsum plaster, 1:2, 1:3, on metal lath				$\frac{3}{4}$

materials should individually encase lower flanges and portions of webs and members not otherwise protected by arches or slabs. All upper flanges should be protected by not less than $1\frac{1}{2}$ in. of protective materials. Thicknesses of masonry refer to thicknesses of protective materials before the application of plaster. Such thicknesses should be measured from the extreme outer edge of the member, except that the thickness of protective material required at the extreme edges of lugs, brackets, wind bracing, and other connections should not be less than 1 in.

Poured protections should be adequately reinforced with 4×4-in. wire mesh weighing not less than $1\frac{1}{2}$ lb per sq yd or equivalent reinforcement. Protective coverings of masonry units should be solidly bedded and laid in cement or lime-cement mortar. Block and tile protective coverings should be securely anchored or bonded by wall ties or metal mesh laid in the horizontal joints, by metal clips connecting one unit to another, by outside tie wires not smaller than 0.1 in. with at least one such tie around every course, or by means of specially designed units providing

Table 1.15   Fire-Resistance Ratings of Floor and Roof Panels

	Rating, hr
4-in. concrete slab, $\frac{3}{4}$ in. cover on reinforcement, free or partly restrained	$1\frac{1}{4}$
5-in. concrete slab, $\frac{3}{4}$ in. cover on reinforcement, free or partly restrained	$1\frac{1}{2}$
5-in. concrete slab, $\frac{3}{4}$ in. cover on reinforcement, fully restrained	1
6-in. concrete slab, 1 in. cover on reinforcement, fully restrained	$1\frac{1}{2}$
6-in. concrete slab, 1 in. cover on reinforcement, free or partly restrained	2
4- or 6-in. clay tile fillers, concrete joists, $1\frac{1}{2}$ to 2 in. top slab—unplastered	1
4-in. clay tile fillers, concrete joists, $1\frac{1}{2}$ to 2 in. top slab—plastered	$1\frac{1}{2}$
6-in. clay tile fillers, concrete joists, $1\frac{1}{2}$ in. top slab—plastered	2
Steel joists, 2-in. reinforced-concrete or mortar-covered gypsum top slab, $\frac{3}{4}$ in. gypsum plaster	2
Steel joists, $2\frac{1}{2}$-in. reinforced-concrete or $\frac{1}{2}$ in. mortar on 2-in.-gypsum slab, 1 in. vermiculite plaster	4

positive anchorage to the member or to other units. All outside tie wires should be protected by at least $\frac{1}{2}$ in. of plaster.

Wherever plaster is required and no thickness prescribed, gypsum or portland-cement plaster not less than $\frac{1}{2}$ in. thick should be used, except that on gypsum units, gypsum plaster only should be used. Pipes, conduits, wires, cables, and other service equipment should not be placed within the required thickness of protective covering.

The thicknesses in Table 1.15 refer to thickness of construction before the application of plaster and before the addition of any floor fill. Wherever plaster is required and no thickness prescribed, gypsum or portland-cement plaster not less than $\frac{1}{2}$ in. thick should be used, except that on gypsum units, gypsum plaster only should be used.

1.50 DESIGN LOADS

a Every part of a building or structure must be designed to support safely a prescribed live load plus the full dead load.

The dead load is the entire load of construction, including all carrying members, slabs, fill and finish, ceilings, and partitions. Live loads include all superimposed loads, machinery, furniture, moving loads, snow loads on roofs, occupants, and stored material. Unless it is known that the use of the building will require the use of heavier loads, the live load shall be in accordance with code requirements. It is well to check all city and state codes covering the requirements, but in the absence of any such code, the requirements of "Minimum Live Loads Allowable for Use in the Design of Buildings" compiled by the U.S. Department of Commerce (Table 1.16) are accepted as good engineering practice.

b The dead load of the floor slab is made up of

1. Finish
2. Fill
3. Slab
4. Ceiling
5. Partition

Some codes require the load of the partition to be spread out uniformly over the entire slab as a means of providing for possible relocation of partitions, as is frequently done in office buildings.

The New York City Code requires for office and public buildings where partitions are apt to be moved to different locations that an allowance of 20 psf shall be made as additional dead load on the floors in place of partition load. The U.S. Army requires for hospitals and similar structures, using short-span systems, that a load of 300 lb per lin ft be applied centrally concentrated on any slab, or on any beam or girder.

The weights of materials entering into the dead weight are given in Table 1.17.

The weight of the beam and haunching does not need to be taken into the slab, but to arrive at the design load for the beam, it must be added in.

If there is no haunching, the weight of a steel beam does not add much, and the beam can be estimated as 1 in. depth for 1.75 ft span, using the next commercial size above this; for a 17-ft span, 10 WF 21. If the beam is haunched, assume the beam as above, and estimate the weight of beam and haunching per foot to be $d(b + 4) + \frac{2}{3}w'$, where d is the depth of steel beam, b the width of flange of beam, and w' the weight of beam estimated. Thus a 10 WF 21 would be

$$10(5.75 + 4) + (\tfrac{2}{3} \times 21) =$$
$$97.5 + 14 = 111.5 \text{ psf}$$

This allows for the weight of stone or gravel concrete.

If the beams are spaced 7 ft o.c. this will add to the uniform floor load $111.5/7 = 16$ psf. Ordinarily, however, this weight of beam and haunching is merely added into the load per linear foot of beam for the design.

The load on the roof slab is made up of

1. Roofing
2. Fill (if required)
3. Slab
4. Ceiling

Spandrel beams carry their share of the interior load, and in addition they carry wall load. Solid brick wall may be estimated to weigh 10 psf per inch of nominal thickness—

an 8-in. wall, 80 psf. Four-inch brick with 8-in. tile backing, which is the common spandrel material for skeleton buildings, weighs 80 psf with plaster. Window openings are deducted, no allowance being made for the window itself. Loads from lintels are considered as spread uniformly over the piers supporting them to the beam below. Lintel beams in high brick walls are figured to carry a triangular load of masonry equal in height to the span of the lintel.

c For buildings over three stories high it is often permissible to reduce column loads as follows:

Roof and top story—full design load

Second story down—full dead load plus 95 per cent of live load

Third story down—full dead load plus 90 per cent of live load.

Continue this reduction of 5 percent per story till 50 percent of the live load is reached, and carry this same 50 percent reduction through the balance of the floors to the foundations. The U.S. Department of Commerce Code, which has been used by many cities, uses the full design load for the top story, then reduces by 10 percent jumps to the 50 per cent limitation. This load reduction is not usually permitted in warehouses and other buildings where the full load may be on all stories at the same time.

The approximate weight of the column and covering for any given story may be estimated as follows by the equation $w = 60 + 0.4P/1,000$, where w = weight per foot of height, and P is the total weight down to the section of column under consideration.

d The following extract and Table 1.16 are the U.S. Department of Commerce Minimum Design Loads in Building and Other Structures, from American Standard Building Code Requirements A58.1—1945, National Bureau of Standards, sponsor.

Uniformly Distributed Floor Loads

The live loads assumed for purposes of design shall be the greatest loads that probably will be produced by the intended occupancies or uses, provided that the live loads to be considered as uniformly distributed shall be not less than the values given in the following table [Table 1.16].

Provision for Partitions

In office buildings or other buildings where partitions might be subject to erection or rearrangement, provision for partition weight shall be made, whether or not partitions are shown on the plans, unless the specified live load exceeds 80 pounds per square foot.

Table 1.16   Minimum Design Loads

Occupancy or Use	Live Load Lb. per Sq. Ft.	Occupancy or Use	Live Load Lb. per Sq. Ft.
Apartment houses:		Hotels:	
Private apartments	40	Guest rooms	40
Public stairways	100	Corridors serving public rooms	100
Assembly halls:		Public rooms	100
Fixed seats	60	Loft buildings	125
Movable seats	100		
Corridors, upper floors	100	Manufacturing, light	125
Corridors:		Office buildings:	
First floor	100	Offices	80
Other floors, same as occupancy served except as indicated		Lobbies	100
		Schools:	
Courtrooms	80	Classrooms	40
Dance halls	100	Corridors	100
Dining rooms, public	100	Stores	125
Dwellings	40	Theatres:	
Hospitals and asylums:		Aisles, corridors, and lobbies	100
Operating rooms	60	Orchestra floor	60
Private rooms	40	Balconies	60
Wards	40	Stage floor	150
Public space	80		

Concentrated Loads

In the design of floors, consideration shall be given to the effects of known or probable concentrations of load to which they may be subjected. Floors shall be designed to carry the specified distributed loads, or the following minimum concentrations, whichever may produce the greater stresses. The indicated concentrations shall be assumed to occupy areas $2\frac{1}{2}$ feet square and to be so placed as to produce maximum stresses in the affected members.

Floor Space	Load
Office floors, including corridors	2,000 lb
Garages	Maximum wheel load
Trucking space within building	Maximum wheel load

Partial Loading

When the construction is such that the structural elements thereof act together in the nature of an elastic frame due to their continuity and the rigidity of the connections, and the live load exceeds 150 pounds per square foot or twice the dead load, the effect of partial live load such as will produce maximum stress in any member shall be provided for in the design.

Impact Loads

The live loads tabulated above may be assumed to include a sufficient allowance to cover the effects of ordinary impact. For special occupancies and loads involving unusual impacts, such as those resulting from moving machinery, elevators, craneways, vehicles, etc., provision shall be made by a suitable increase in the assumed live load.

Reduction of Live Load

(a) No reduction shall be applied to the roof live load.

(b) For live loads of 100 pounds or less per square foot, the design live load on any member supporting 150 square feet or more may be reduced at the rate of 0.08 percent per square foot of area supported by the member, except that no reduction shall be made for areas to be occupied as places of public assembly. The reduction shall exceed neither R as determined by the following formula, nor 60 percent:

$$R = 100 \times \frac{D + L}{4.33L}$$

in which R = reduction in percent
D = dead load per square foot of area supported by the member
L = design live load per square foot of area supported by the member

For live loads exceeding 100 pounds per square foot, no reduction shall be made, except that the design live loads on columns may be reduced 20 percent.

Roof Loads (Including Snow Loads)

(a) Ordinary roofs, either flat or pitched, shall be designed for a load of not less than 20 pounds per square foot of horizontal projection in addition to the dead load, and in addition to either the wind or the earthquake load, whichever produces the greater stresses.

(*Note:* The figure of 20 pounds per square foot is a minimum snow load and should be increased in many localities. A U.S. Weather Bureau map in the Appendix to A58.1–1945 indicates roughly that such an increase is in order north of the 40th parallel of latitude; attaining 40 pounds per square foot at the northeastern and north central boundaries of the United States and in parts of Washington, Oregon and Idaho.)

(b) Roofs to be used for promenades shall be designed for a minimum load of 60 pounds per square foot in addition to the dead load. Roofs to be used for other special purposes shall be designed for appropriate loads as directed or approved by the building official.

Other Live Loads

(a) Stair treads shall be designed to support a uniformly distributed load of 100 pounds per square foot, or concentrated loads of 300 pounds spaced 3 feet center to center, each occupying an area 1 foot wide by the depth of the tread, whichever will produce the greater stresses.

(b) Sidewalks shall be designed to support either a uniformly distributed load of 250 pounds per square foot, or a concentrated load of 8,000 pounds on an area $2\frac{1}{2}$ feet square placed in any position, whichever will produce the greater stresses.

(c) Driveways shall be designed to support a uniformly distributed load of 100 pounds per square foot for vehicles weighing less than 3 tons with load, 150 pounds per square foot for vehicles weighing 3 to 10 tons with load, 200 pounds per square foot for vehicles weighing over 10 tons with load, or a concentrated load equal to the maximum expected wheel load on an area $2\frac{1}{2}$ feet square placed in any position, whichever will produce the greater stresses.

(d) Accessible ceilings, scuttles, and ribs of skylights shall be designed to support a concentrated load of 200 pounds occupying an area $2\frac{1}{2}$ feet square and so placed as to produce maximum stresses in the affected members.

(e) Stairway and balcony railings, both exterior and interior, shall be designed to resist a horizontal thrust of 50 pounds per linear foot applied at the top of the railing.

Table 1.17   Weights of Building Materials

Materials	Weight Lb. per Sq. Ft.	Materials	Weight Lb. per Sq. Ft.
CEILINGS		**PARTITIONS**	
Gypsum ceiling block, 2″ thick, un-plastered	10	Channel studs, metal lath, cement plaster, solid, 2″ thick	20
Plaster board, unplastered	3	Studs, 2″ x 4″, wood or metal lath, ¾″ plaster both sides	18
Plaster, ¾″, and wood lath	8	Studs, 2″ x 4″ plaster board, ½″ plaster both sides	18
Plaster, ¾″, and metal lath	8	Plaster, ½″, on gypsum block or clay tile (one side)	4
Plaster, on tile or concrete	5	Hollow clay tile, 2″	13
Suspended, metal lath and plaster	10	Hollow clay tile, 3″	16
		Hollow clay tile, 4″	18
		Hollow clay tile, 5″	20
FLOORS		Hollow clay tile, 6″	25
		Hollow clay tile, 8″	30
Hardwood flooring, ⅞″ thick	4	Hollow clay tile, 10″	35
Sheathing, white, red and Oregon pine, spruce or hemlock, ⅞″ thick	2½	Hollow gypsum block, 3″	10
Sheathing, yellow pine, 1″ thick	4	Hollow gypsum block, 4″	13
Wood block, creosoted, 3″ thick	15	Hollow gypsum block, 5″	15½
Cement finish, per inch thick	12	Hollow gypsum block, 6″	16½
Cinder concrete, per inch thick	9	Solid gypsum block, 2″	9½
Cinder concrete fill, per inch thick	5	Solid gypsum block, 3″	13
Terrazzo, Tile, Mastic, Linoleum, per inch thick, including base	12	Steel partitions	4
Gypsum slab, per inch thick	5		
		WALLS	
		Brick, 9″ thick	84
ROOFS		Brick, 13″ thick	121
		Brick, 18″ thick	168
Corrugated metal	Page 143	Brick, 22″ thick	205
Roofing felt, 3 ply and gravel	5½	Brick, 26″ thick	243
Roofing felt, 5 ply and gravel	6½	Wall tile, 6″ thick	30
Roofing felt, 3 ply and slag	4½	Wall tile, 8″ thick	33
Roofing felt, 5 ply and slag	5½	Wall tile, 10″ thick	40
3-ply ready roofing	1	Wall tile, 12″ thick	45
Shingles, wood	2	Brick 4″, tile backing 4″	60
Tile or slate	5-20	Brick 4″, tile backing 8″	75
		Brick 9″, tile backing 4″	100
		Brick 9″, tile backing 8″	115
		Limestone 4″, brick 9″	140
		Limestone 4″, brick 13″	175
		Limestone 4″, tile 8″	90
		Limestone 4″, tile 12″	100
		Windows, glass, frame and sash	8

1.51   Heavy concentrated loads

a   A frequent problem concerns the distribution of a heavy concentrated load on a floor slab, such as an automobile or a truck, or of a heavy safe. The selection of the proper design load may be left up to the engineer or it may be specified by code. The Syracuse building code requires garages with doors not over 8 ft high to be designed to carry a 1,500-lb wheel load, (presumably because heavy trucks require over 8 ft clearance); and garages with doors over 8 ft high to carry

an 8,000-lb wheel concentration. This 8,000-lb wheel load represents a total truck load of 24,000 lb. This should be considered not only on garage floors, but on loading docks and sidewalk slabs. Moreover, modern codes require office-building floors to be designed to carry a load of 2,000 lb on an area 2.5 ft square of otherwise unloaded floor. This would seem to indicate a floor-load requirement of 320 psf instead of the 50-lb requirement elsewhere specified.

In neither of the above instances, however, is the concentration as serious as it might seem to be. The manner in which this load may be distributed should be investigated to determine whether the concentration will have any effect on the design load of any part of the floor system.

b Probably the most commonly accepted method of distributing any concentrated load is the method used by the highway departments for distributing loads on bridge floor

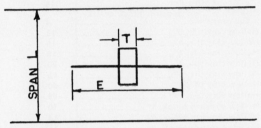

Fig. 1.4   Distribution of Concentrated Load

slabs. The load is considered as concentrated along a line at right angles to the span and along a width E. For the common condition, with a single load centered on the span (Fig. 1.4),

$$E = 0.7(L + T)$$

where T is the width of tire or lesser dimension of the load. The centrally concentrated load per unit width is then P/E. Where the load

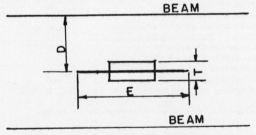

Fig. 1.5   Alternative Distribution of Concentrated Load

is placed at some given point on the span, as the concentrated load of a machine base, the width is (Fig. 1.5)

$$E = 0.7 (2D + T)$$

where D is the distance to the closest supporting beam.

Problem   Design and check an office-building floor panel with the following condi-

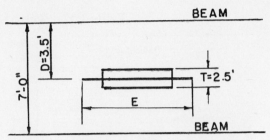

Fig. 1.6   Distribution of Concentrated Load

tions. Assume a beam and slab floor; beams on 7-ft spacing; live load 50 psf, or a 2,000-lb safe on a $2\frac{1}{2}$-ft square area (Fig. 1.6).

$$E = 0.7 (2D + T)$$
$$E = 0.7 (7 + 2.5)$$
$$E = 0.7 \times 9.5 = 6.65$$

Centrally concentrated load $= 2,000/6.65 = 302$ lb per linear foot. Therefore the design for live load must be based on 302 lb per linear foot centrally concentrated load, or 350 lb per foot of width of slab uniform load.

From the formulae given in Art. 3.11, for concentrated load,

$$M_{LL} = \frac{302 \times 7 \times 12}{8} = 3,180 \text{ in.-lb}$$

and for uniform load,

$$M_{LL} = \frac{350 \times 7 \times 12}{12} = 2,450 \text{ in.-lb}$$

Therefore the concentrated load of the safe would be the controlling factor. It will be found that for this commonly used code, the design for weight of safe will control the slab design for a span up to 8.1 ft, and the load of 50 psf beyond this slab span.

Similarly for a truck-wheel load of 8,000 lb against a uniform load of 100 psf, the concentration of the truck wheel will control for spans up to 7.6 ft, and the uniform load for greater spans. Where two loads overlap, as in adjoining traffic lanes, the maximum permissible width to design for is the traffic lane width of 9 ft.

c Some years ago M. Hirschthal, Concrete Engineer for the Lackawanna R.R., published in *Engineering News-Record* the method used by his office in the design of overhead bridges, which approximate a two-way slab in their shape. While most of their designs

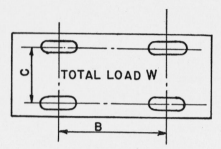

Fig. 1.7　Truck Load Diagram

are for a 20-ton truck (H-20 highway loading) with $\frac{2}{3}$ of the load on the rear axle, the method given is general.

Using the nomenclature shown in Figs. 1.7, 1.8, and 1.9, for longitudinal distribution the maximum moment occurs when the load is

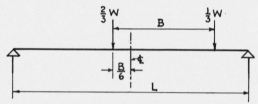

Fig. 1.8　Longitudinal Distribution of Truck Load

placed as shown in Fig. 1.8 and the equivalent uniform load longitudinally is

$$w = \frac{W}{3L^3}(3L^2 - 2bL + \tfrac{1}{3}b^2) \qquad (1.3)$$

With two trucks placed at a distance apart approximately equal to the transverse wheel base, the maximum transverse moment occurs when the load is placed as shown in

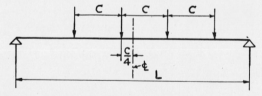

Fig. 1.9　Transverse Distribution of Truck Load

Fig. 1.9 and the equivalent uniform load, referring to the uniform load w already found for the longitudinal distribution, is

$$w_1 = \frac{8w}{L_1^3}(L_1^2 - 2cL_1 + \tfrac{1}{4}c^2) \qquad (1.4)$$

Thus w_1 is the uniform load to design for, and in the design of a two-way slab should be dis-

tributed in accordance with the method given in Art. 5.50. While the method and the formula apply to two-way reinforced slabs, the method may be applied to one-way slabs for any width decided on for distribution.

Problem　Assume a 20-ton truck, wheel base $b = 12$ ft, $c = 6$ ft;　panel, 30 ft long by 28 ft wide.　From Formula (1.3) above,

$$w = \frac{40,000}{3 \times 30^3}(3 \times 30^2 - 24 \times 30 + \tfrac{1}{3} \times 144)$$
$$= 0.494 \times 2,028 = 1,002$$
$$w_1 = \frac{8 \times 1,002}{28^3}(28^2 - 2 \times 6 \times 28 + \tfrac{1}{4} \times 6^2)$$
$$= 0.365 \times 457 = 167 \text{ psf　equivalent live load}$$

1.60　MATHEMATICAL PROBLEMS

There are several problems in structural design which require the use of geometry, algebra, or other mathematics which the engineer may not have used since he left college, or the use of some special geometric section.　Probably the most important of these is the parabola, and it is discussed here at some length.

a　Because the parabola is required for uniform-load–moment diagrams, two simple methods of construction are given here, a purely graphical method and a direct or ordinate method which involves a small amount of computation.　In the graphical method,

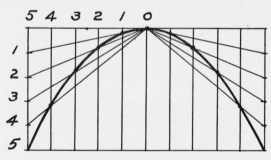

Fig. 1.10　Construction of Parabola— Ray Method

shown in Fig. 1.10, lay out the base line and the center height or maximum moment.　Then divide the height into any number of equal parts, marking these points on a side ordinate.　Divide the space from the center line of the parabola (the origin) to the side line, into the same number of equal spaces, and draw vertical lines through each of these points to the base, parallel with the side line. Then from the point of origin, draw rays to the points on the side lines. The point where ray 1 intersects vertical line 1 is a point on the parabola, etc., thus giving any required number of points.

The ordinate method is a correct mathematical method of construction, as shown in

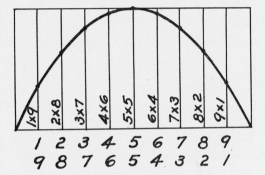

Fig. 1.11   Construction of Parabola— Ordinate Method

Fig. 1.11. Divide the base into an even number of equal parts and number them from left to right and again from right to left as shown. Then the height of the ordinate next to the center is $(4 \times 6)/(5 \times 5)$ of the center ordinate, the second ordinate is $(3 \times 7)/(5 \times 5)$ of the center ordinate, the third ordinate is

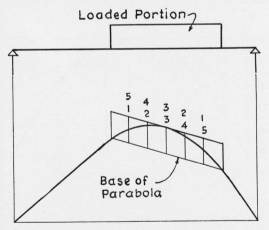

Fig. 1.12   Parabola on Part of Span

$(2 \times 8)/(5 \times 5)$ of the center ordinate. The method is identical, regardless of how many sections may be used, the denominator being

the square of the center ordinate. Figure 1.12 indicates the method of laying out a parabola on part of the span only, as mentioned in Art. 3.12d.

For simplicity in determining the area of any fractional part of a parabola, which is required in deflection problems by the moment-area theorem (Art. 2.31), Table 1.18 will be found useful.

Either Table 1.18 or the method of Fig. 1.11 may be used to determine the moment at any given point on a simple uniformly loaded beam. To determine from Table 1.18 the moment at a point 3.5 ft from the end of a beam 17 ft long,

$$\frac{A}{L} = \frac{3.5}{17} = 0.206$$

By interpolation between 0.6636 and 0.64, $M = 0.654$ of the center moment. By the method of Fig. 1.11,

$$M = \frac{3.5 \times 13.5}{8.5 \times 8.5} = 0.654 \text{ of the center moment}$$

b It is occasionally necessary to find the area of a parabolic segment such as the one

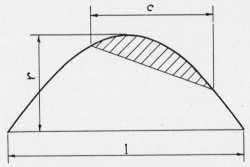

Fig. 1.13   Area of Parabolic Section

shown in Fig. 1.13. Given the span l, the rise r, and the segmental length c,

$$A = \frac{2}{3} \times \frac{r}{l^2} \times c^3$$

c Another common geometrical problem in structural design is the solution of a pressure trapezoid. If the load on any wall, buttress, footing, etc., is applied off center, the pressure is not uniform across the bearing, but varies uniformly from a maximum at the edge nearer the point of load to a minimum at the opposite edge.

Table 1.18   Altitude and Area of Section of Parabola

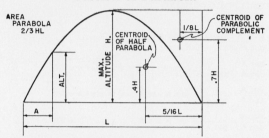

Area of parabola $= \frac{2}{3} HL$

For given altitude (expressed in table as decimal fraction of maximum altitude H), area of section equals decimal fraction given of rectangle HL.

A/L	Altitude ($\times H$)	Area ($\times HL$)	A/L	Altitude ($\times H$)	Area ($\times HL$)
.01	.0396	.000198	.26	.7696	.111754
.02	.0784	.000788	.27	.7884	.119544
.03	.1164	.001762	.28	.8064	.127518
.04	.1536	.003116	.29	.8236	.135668
.05	.19	.004834	.30	.84	.143986
.06	.2256	.006912	.31	.8556	.152464
.07	.2604	.009342	.32	.8704	.161094
.08	.2944	.012116	.33	.8844	.169868
.09	.3276	.015228	.34	.8976	.178778
.10	.36	.018666	.35	.91	.187816
.11	.3916	.022424	.36	.9216	.196974
.12	.4224	.026494	.37	.9324	.206244
.13	.4524	.030868	.38	.9424	.215618
.14	.4816	.035538	.39	.9516	.225088
.15	.51	.040496	.40	.96	.234636
.16	.5376	.045734	.41	.9676	.244274
.17	.5644	.051244	.42	.9744	.253984
.18	.5904	.057018	.43	.9804	.263758
.19	.6156	.063048	.44	.9856	.273588
.20	.64	.069326	.45	.99	.283466
.21	.6636	.075844	.46	.9936	.293384
.22	.6864	.082594	.47	.9964	.303334
.23	.7084	.089568	.48	.9984	.313308
.24	.7296	.096758	.49	.9996	.323298
.25	.75	.104156	.50	1.0	.333333

Graphically we may represent the resultant pressures by a trapezoid, as shown in Fig. 1.14. A unit length is represented by area A, for the sake of simplifying the problem. The pressure f increases and f_1 decreases very rapidly as the eccentricity of the load increases, until the eccentricity is $\frac{1}{6}A$, at which point f_1 becomes zero and f is double the average load. The unit pressure at the edge is obtained from the formula,

$$f = \frac{P}{A}\left(1 \pm \frac{6e}{A}\right) \qquad (1.5)$$

in which plus is used to compute f and minus to compute f_1.

Another typical trapezoidal problem is the design of a trapezoidal footing, as described in Art. 8.12e. In this instance the two ends of the trapezoid are the widths of the footing required. The eccentricity is determined by solving for center of gravity of the loads, as described in Art. 1.31a. Then referring to the properties of the trapezoid in Art. 1.30, knowing the required area of footing A, and the available length of footing d, the factor $(b + b_1)$ in the first equation may be determined. Referring to the second equation, c is known, d is known and the sum of $b + b_1$ is known, from which $2b + b_1$ may be computed. By solving the two simultaneous equations, b and b_1 may be obtained. For example, assume the maximum permissible length of footing to be 20 ft, with columns 18 ft o.c., each 1 ft from the end of the footing. The load at

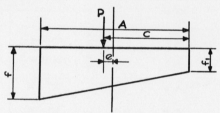

Fig. 1.14   Pressure Trapezoid

one end is 300 kips and at the other end 250 kips, and the allowable net soil pressure 5 kips per sq ft. The required $A = \frac{550}{5} = 110$ sq ft. From Table 1.3, the first equation is

$$110 = \frac{20(b + b_1)}{2} = 10(b + b_1)$$

$$b + b_1 = 11$$

The center of gravity of the column loads from the heavy-load column is $250 \times \frac{18}{550} = 8.18$ ft from the column, or 9.18 ft from the wall, and $c = 9.18$.

From the second equation,

$$9.18 = \frac{20(2b + b_1)}{3 \times 11}$$

from which

$$2b + b_1 = 15.1$$
$$\underline{b + b_1 = 11}$$
$$b \quad\quad = 4.1$$
$$b_1 \quad\quad = 6.9$$

Table 1.19   Trigonometric Formulae

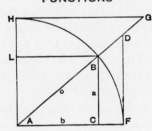

TRIGONOMETRIC FUNCTIONS

Radius AF $= 1$
$= \sin^2 A + \cos^2 A = \sin A \ \text{cosec} \ A$
$= \cos A \ \sec A = \tan A \ \cot A$

Sine A $= \dfrac{\cos A}{\cot A} = \dfrac{1}{\text{cosec} A} = \cos A \tan A = \sqrt{1 - \cos^2 A} = BC$

Cosine A $= \dfrac{\sin A}{\tan A} = \dfrac{1}{\sec A} = \sin A \cot A = \sqrt{1 - \sin^2 A} = AC$

Tangent A $= \dfrac{\sin A}{\cos A} = \dfrac{1}{\cot A} = \sin A \sec A$ $= FD$

Cotangent A $= \dfrac{\cos A}{\sin A} = \dfrac{1}{\tan A} = \cos A \ \text{cosec} \ A$ $= HG$

Secant A $= \dfrac{\tan A}{\sin A} = \dfrac{1}{\cos A}$ $= AD$

Cosecant A $= \dfrac{\cot A}{\cos A} = \dfrac{1}{\sin A}$ $= AG$

RIGHT ANGLED TRIANGLES

$a^2 = c^2 - b^2$
$b^2 = c^2 - a^2$
$c^2 = a^2 + b^2$

Known	Required					
	A	B	a	b	c	Area
a, b	$\tan A = \dfrac{a}{b}$	$\tan B = \dfrac{b}{a}$			$\sqrt{a^2 + b^2}$	$\dfrac{ab}{2}$
a, c	$\sin A = \dfrac{a}{c}$	$\cos B = \dfrac{a}{c}$		$\sqrt{c^2 - a^2}$		$\dfrac{a\sqrt{c^2 - a^2}}{2}$
A, a		$90° - A$		$a \cot A$	$\dfrac{a}{\sin A}$	$\dfrac{a^2 \cot A}{2}$
A, b		$90° - A$	$b \tan A$		$\dfrac{b}{\cos A}$	$\dfrac{b^2 \tan A}{2}$
A, c		$90° - A$	$c \sin A$	$c \cos A$		$\dfrac{c^2 \sin 2A}{4}$

OBLIQUE ANGLED TRIANGLES

$s = \dfrac{a + b + c}{2}$

$K = \sqrt{\dfrac{(s-a)(s-b)(s-c)}{s}}$

$a^2 = b^2 + c^2 - 2bc \cos A$
$b^2 = a^2 + c^2 - 2ac \cos B$
$c^2 = a^2 + b^2 - 2ab \cos C$

Known	Required					
	A	B	C	b	c	Area
a, b, c	$\tan \frac{1}{2} A =$ $\dfrac{K}{s-a}$	$\tan \frac{1}{2} B =$ $\dfrac{K}{s-b}$	$\tan \frac{1}{2} C =$ $\dfrac{K}{s-c}$			$\sqrt{s(s-a)(s-b)(s-c)}$
a, A, B			$180° - (A+B)$	$\dfrac{a \sin B}{\sin A}$	$\dfrac{a \sin C}{\sin A}$	
a, b, A		$\sin B = \dfrac{b \sin A}{a}$			$\dfrac{b \sin C}{\sin B}$	
a, b, C	$\tan A = \dfrac{a \sin C}{b - a \cos C}$				$\sqrt{a^2 + b^2 - 2ab \cos C}$	$\dfrac{ab \sin C}{2}$

Table 1.20   Properties of the Circle

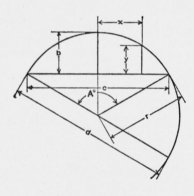

Circumference $= 6.28318 \, r = 3.14159 \, d$
Diameter $\quad\quad = 0.31831 \text{ circumference}$
Area $\quad\quad\quad = 3.14159 \, r^2$

Arc $\quad a \;\; = \dfrac{\pi r A^\circ}{180^\circ} = 0.017453 \, r A^\circ$

Angle $\; A^\circ = \dfrac{180^\circ a}{\pi r} = 57.29578 \dfrac{a}{r}$

Radius $r \;\; = \dfrac{4 b^2 + c^2}{8 b}$

Chord $\; c \;\; = 2\sqrt{2 br - b^2} = 2 r \sin \dfrac{A}{2}$

Rise $\quad b \;\; = r - \tfrac{1}{2}\sqrt{4 r^2 - c^2} = \dfrac{c}{2} \tan \dfrac{A}{4}$

$\quad\quad\quad\quad = 2 r \sin^2 \dfrac{A}{4} = r + y - \sqrt{r^2 - x^2}$

$\quad\quad y \;\; = b - r + \sqrt{r^2 - x^2}$

$\quad\quad x \;\; = \sqrt{r^2 - (r + y - b)^2}$

Diameter of circle of equal periphery as square $= 1.27324$ side of square
Side of square of equal periphery as circle $\quad\;\; = 0.78540$ diameter of circle
Diameter of circle circumscribed about square $= 1.41421$ side of square
Side of square inscribed in circle $\quad\quad\quad\quad = 0.70711$ diameter of circle

---

CIRCULAR SECTOR

r = radius of circle y = angle ncp in degrees
Area of Sector ncpo $= \frac{1}{2}$ (length of arc nop $\times r$)

$\quad\quad\quad\quad\quad\quad\quad\quad = \text{Area of Circle} \times \dfrac{y}{360}$

$\quad\quad\quad\quad\quad\quad\quad\quad = 0.0087266 \times r^2 \times y$

CIRCULAR SEGMENT

r = radius of circle x = chord b = rise
Area of Segment nop = Area of Sector ncpo — Area of triangle ncp

$\quad\quad\quad\quad = \dfrac{(\text{Length of arc nop} \times r) - x (r - b)}{2}$

Area of Segment nsp = Area of Circle — Area of Segment nop

VALUES FOR FUNCTIONS OF π

$\pi = 3.14159265359, \quad \log = 0.4971499$

$\pi^2 = 9.8696044, \log = 0.9942997 \quad \dfrac{1}{\pi} = 0.3183099, \log = \overline{1}.5028501 \quad \sqrt{\dfrac{1}{\pi}} = 0.5641896, \log = \overline{1}.7514251$

$\pi^3 = 31.0062767, \log = 1.4914496 \quad \dfrac{1}{\pi^2} = 0.1013212, \log = \overline{1}.0057003 \quad \dfrac{\pi}{180} = 0.0174533, \log = \overline{2}.2418774$

$\sqrt{\pi} = 1.7724539, \log = 0.2485749 \quad \dfrac{1}{\pi^3} = 0.0322515, \log = \overline{2}.5085500 \quad \dfrac{180}{\pi} = 57.2957795, \log = 1.7581226$

Therefore the footing is 20 ft long, 4.1 ft wide at the end nearest the light load, and 6.9 ft at the heavy end.

Perhaps a simple solution would be to solve by application of Formula (1.5). In this instance, the eccentricity is $10 - 9.18 = 0.82$. Then

$$\text{Width} = \frac{110}{20}\left[1 \pm 6 \times \frac{0.82}{20}\right]$$
$$= 5.5\,(1 \pm 0.246)$$
$$(= 1.246 \quad \text{or} \quad .754).$$

Then the width at the light end is $0.754 \times 5.5 = 4.1$, and at the heavy end $1.246 \times 5.5 = 6.9$ ft, which checks with the previous solution.

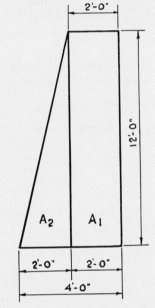

Fig. 1.15 Trapezoidal Retaining Wall

Problem A concrete wall is 12 ft high, 4 ft thick at the base, and 2 ft thick at the top. One face is vertical. What are the maximum and minimum pressures under the base due to the weight of concrete? (From a state license examination. See Fig. 1.15.)

The center of gravity of the wall, from the back face, is,

$$A_1x_1 = 24 \times 1 \quad = 24$$
$$A_2x_2 = 12 \times 2.67 = \underline{32}$$
$$A = 36 \qquad Ax = 56$$
$$x = \tfrac{56}{36} = 1.555$$
$$e = 2 - 1.555 = 0.445$$
$$P = 36 \times 150 \; = 5{,}400$$
$$f_1 = \frac{5{,}400}{4}\left(1 - 6 \times \frac{0.445}{4}\right) = \begin{array}{l}450 \text{ psf at} \\ \text{front of wall}\end{array}$$
$$f = \frac{5{,}400}{4}\left(1 + 6 \times \frac{0.445}{4}\right) = \begin{array}{l}2{,}250 \text{ psf at} \\ \text{back of wall}\end{array}$$

With the two end pressures known, determining the eccentricity is a problem in determining the center of gravity of a trapezoid. Referring to Fig. 1.14, the formula becomes

$$c = \frac{A\,(2f + f_1)}{3\,(f + f_1)}$$
$$e = c - \frac{A}{2}$$

d The solution of a simple quadratic equation is required in some cases in locating the point of zero shear in a beam with a uniformly increasing load, such as the design of a basement wall against earth pressure (see Art. 3.10o). For this problem in structural design, given the equation $x^2 + ax = b$,

$$x = \sqrt{b + \frac{a^2}{2}} - \frac{a}{2}$$

2

Simple Stresses and Elastic Theory

2.10 SIMPLE STRESSES

By simple stresses we mean tension, compression, or shear in the simple form—that is, without combination with bending, torsion, or any other stresses, and applied to a homogeneous material such as steel or plain concrete. This is the simplest form of structural computation, and may be solved by some variation of the formula

$$f = \frac{P}{A} \qquad (2.1)$$

2.11 Simple shear

a Vertical shear comes in almost entirely as part of some more complex design problem, such as the design of a concrete beam, a riveted joint, or a plate girder, and will be discussed under these headings. In any instance, the problem is solved by a direct application of Formula (2.1),

$$P_s = A f_s, \qquad \text{or} \qquad V = Av$$

Problem (from a state license examination) Compute the capacity of a $\frac{3}{4}$-in. power-driven rivet in single shear if the allowable stress is 13,500 psi.

$$V = Av = 0.4418 \times 13{,}500 = 5{,}960 \, \text{lb}$$

b Horizontal shear stress is caused by the tendency of horizontal layers or fibers to slip on each other because of the shortening of fibers on the compression side of a beam and the lengthening of the fibers on the tension side as a beam undergoes bending. It is therefore a more complex type of stress to determine.

Problems in horizontal shear are found in the design of riveting between flange angles and cover plates of a steel plate girder (see Art. 4.20) and in various wood-beam problems (see Art. 6.10).

The general formula for the determination of horizontal shear stress at any fiber distance from the neutral axis of any cross-section is

$$v_\text{H} = \frac{VM_s}{Ib} \qquad (2.2)$$

In this formula, v_H is the horizontal shear stress (psi), V is the total vertical shear force at the point along the span under consideration, M_s is the statical moment of the cross-sectional area beyond the fiber in question, taking the neutral axis as an axis of moments. In the denominator, I is the moment of inertia of the entire area about the neutral axis and b is the width of the beam.

Problem Derive an expression for the horizontal shear stress at the neutral axis of a rectangular cross-section.

From Fig. 2.1 the statical moment of the area above the neutral axis is

$$\frac{bd}{2} \times \frac{d}{4} = \frac{bd^2}{8}$$

From Art. 1.30, the moment of inertia of the rectangle is $bd^3/12$. Substituting in Formula (2.2) yields

$$v_\text{H} = \frac{V \, (bd^2/8)}{b \, (bd^3/12)} = 1.5 \frac{V}{bd}$$

or

$$v_\text{H} = 1.5 \frac{V}{A}$$

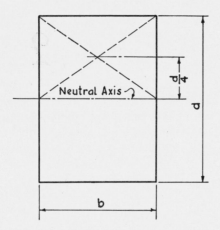

Fig. 2.1 Horizontal Shear

It might be noted that the value derived is 1.5 times the vertical shear stress acting across the entire cross-section. For other fibers than those at the neutral axis, different values will be found, varying parabolically from a maximum at the neutral axis to zero at the outermost fibers.

Another problem of this type is given in Art. 4.23.

2.12 Direct compression

Compression problems in the use of steel will be treated under the subject of columns in Art. 7.10, since they usually are not simple stress problems but are dependent on length and on secondary bending. Rivet holes are not deducted in the solution of compression problems, since the rivet or bolt is supposed to fill the hole sufficiently.

Except for the design of details which may be classed rather as bearing problems, compression in timber is ordinarily a problem in column design and will be considered in Art. 7.30. In compression problems using timber, remember that timber has two primary compression unit stresses (see Table 1.1)—on the side grain, or perpendicular to the grain, and on the end grain, or parallel with the grain—and any number of stresses on the diagonal grain, which will be treated in Art. 9.30.

Problems in bearing area may be classed as compression problems, as in the following example.

Problem The base plate of a column is 16 in. square. What is the unit bearing stress on the top of a concrete footing under a concentric load of 125,000 lb?

From Formula (2.1),

$$f = \frac{P}{A} = \frac{125,000 \text{ lb}}{256 \text{ sq in.}} = 488 \text{ psi}$$

Similar problems involve the determination of footing and foundation area (Arts. 8.10 and 8.12) and masonry piers (Art. 8.20).

2.13 Tension

a Problems in tension, although they may occur in other materials, are usually problems in steel design. In reinforced-concrete design, the tension value of the concrete is disregarded. In wood problems, because of the difficulty of obtaining proper connection, tension is seldom a controlling factor. Wood tension is discussed in Arts. 9.32, 9.33, and 10.12.

Direct tension in steel, as in hangers, truss members, and steel details, is subject to the following limits, in psi, in the AISC Code [Sec. 15(a), Allowable Unit Stresses, Tension].

Structural steel, net section	20,000
Butt welds, section through throat	20,000
Rivets, on area based on nominal diameter	20,000
Bolts and other threaded parts, on nominal area at root of thread	20,000

From Sec. 19(c) the net section can be determined by substituting for the gross width the net width, computed as follows:

Net Width—In the case of a chain of holes extending across a part in any diagonal or zigzag line, the net width of the part shall be obtained by deducting from the gross width the sum of the diameters of all the holes in the chain, and adding, for each gage space in the chain, the quantity

$$\frac{s^2}{4g}$$

where s = longitudinal spacing (pitch) in inches of any two successive holes.

g = transverse spacing (gage) in inches of the same two holes.

The critical net section of the part is obtained from that chain which gives the least net width.

Angles—For angles, the gross width shall be the sum of the widths of the legs less the thickness. The gage for holes in opposite legs shall be the sum of the gages from back of angle less the thickness.

Splice Members—For splice members, the thickness considered shall be only that part of the thickness of the member which has been developed by rivets or welds beyond the section considered.

Size of Holes—In computing net area the diameter of a rivet hole shall be taken as $\frac{1}{8}$ inch greater than the nominal diameter of the rivet.

Minimum Connections—Connections carrying calculated stresses, except for lacing, sag bars, and girts, shall be designed for not less than 10,000 pounds, if welded; or if riveted or bolted, shall have no fewer than two rivets or two bolts.

b If a rod is upset and threaded, the least section is in the body of the rod, since the area at the root of the thread is in excess of the area of the rod. The cost of work involved in upsetting, however, will ordinarily make it more economical to use a plain rod, threaded. With such rods, the area used in tension problems is the area at the root of thread (see Table 2.4). It is not good policy to use any threaded rod of less than $\frac{5}{8}$ in. diameter, because thin rods may easily be overstressed or even fractured at the root of the thread when the nut is pulled up. In building work, rods of diameters larger than $1\frac{3}{4}$ in. are seldom used. A satisfactory upset rod may be made by welding a threaded rod the size of upset to a base rod of the required size. This is only economical if the rod is long enough so that the resultant saving in the base rod is sufficient to offset the cost of the welding. In order to develop the strength of the rod, special design may be necessary in the weld detail. If stresses require more area than this, angles or flats are ordinarily used.

Problem A rod hanger is required to carry a load of 11,000 lb. Using a maximum tensile fiber stress of 20,000 psi, what size standard rod will be required? The rod will not be upset.

From Formula (2.1),

$$A = \frac{P}{f} = \frac{11,000}{20,000} = 0.55 \text{ sq in.}$$

Table 2.4 shows that a 1-in. round rod has the required area of 0.55 sq in. at root of thread.

If no allowable stress is mentioned, it is advisable to use the AISC Code, which allows 20,000 psi on the net section. Many

building codes, however, still hold to a maximum of 18,000 psi, and a few still require 16,000 psi.

c If a plate or angle is used, the holes are to be deducted. For bolts or rivets, the hole is ordinarily punched $\frac{1}{16}$ in. larger than the nominal size of bolt or rivet to allow easy insertion, and an additional allowance of $\frac{1}{16}$ in. diameter is deducted to allow for deformation of the plate or angle due to punching. Thus a $\frac{3}{4}$-in. rivet requires a $1\frac{3}{16}$-in. hole, and an allowance of $\frac{7}{8}$ in. will be deducted from the width in computing the net area of the plate or angle.

Problem Assume a flat bar hanger 4 in. wide with the required number of $\frac{3}{4}$-in. rivets in a vertical row to carry a load of 18,000 lb. What thickness will be required, allowing a unit fiber stress of 20,000 psi? (See Fig. 2.2.)

From Formula (2.1), $A = \dfrac{18,000}{20,000} = 0.9$

Net width of bar $= 4 - 0.875 = 3.125$

Thickness required $= \dfrac{0.9}{3.125} = 0.29$ in.

Use $4 \times \frac{5}{16}$-in. bar.

Further problems in tension on net sections of bars will be found in Art. 9.10, Riveting.

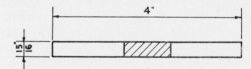

Allow $\frac{7}{8}$ in. for $\frac{3}{4}$-in. rivet in calculation

Fig. 2.2   Rivet Hole in Flat Bar

d The design of angle hangers is in accordance with the AISC Code, Sec. 19(d), as quoted in Art. 2.13a.

Table 2.2 will be found convenient by the many designers who consider "the effective net area" of the angles to be the net area of connected leg plus one-half the area of unconnected leg. The angles in Table 2.2 are arranged in order of their weights, increasing from the top of the table to the bottom. Entering the table in the proper column and reading from the top downward, the first section which will fill the given requirements is the most economical in weight. Other sections will appear in successive order of their economy. Angles of equal weight are arranged in order of their stiffness. Sections bearing an asterisk (*) beside the tabulated thickness have an outstanding leg greater than 12 times the thickness and should be used only for purely tension members unless investigated in regard to the specification requirement in this respect. Net areas are shown after the deduction of two full holes from all connected legs 5 in. and over in width, even though in some (for which the values are given in parentheses), two full holes will never actually be taken out. This permits an interpolation for staggered rivets with a deduction of one and a fraction holes.

Problem Required: the lightest single angle with a net area of 2.75 sq in. and minimum radius of gyration of 1.05 in. One $\frac{7}{8}$-in. hole has been made in the long leg.

Entering the eighth column from the right in Table 2.2 and reading downward, the first effective net area equal to or greater than 2.75 is 2.97. Reading to the left, the corresponding minimum radius of gyration is 0.88 in. This is inadequate. Reading downward in the column for minimum r, the first radius equal to or greater than 1.05 is 1.19. The corresponding angle is a $6 \times 6 \times \frac{3}{8}$ weighing 14.9 lb per ft. Checking back on the net area, it is found to be 2.98 sq in., which is greater than 2.75. Since the connected leg is 6 in. in width, the rivets may be staggered on two gage lines with $1\frac{1}{2}$ holes out. The net area for two holes out is 2.65 sq in., and interpolating between 2.98 and 2.65 gives 2.81 sq in., which is also greater than the 2.75 required. This angle fulfills, therefore, all the required conditions and is the lightest angle available. Other selections may be made by proceeding downward in the column for net area and checking back on the minimum radius of gyration, or vice versa.

e The usual gages for angles are given in Table 2.1 (Fig. 2.3). If two or more of the holes are in a line, their net area may be taken directly from Table 2.2. However, occasionally the holes are staggered, or in a diagonal or zigzag line, and the net width must be determined by means of Steinman's rule, as given in Sec. 19(c) of the AISC Code. The chart and problem indicating the use of this formula are given in Fig. 2.4.

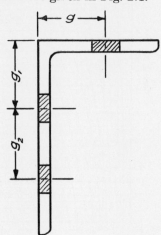

Fig. 2.3   Gage Lines in Angle Legs

2.20   SIMPLE STRESS–STRAIN PROBLEMS

a The fundamental formula for stress-strain problems is derived from the definition of the modulus of elasticity,

$$E = \frac{f}{\delta} \quad \text{or} \quad \frac{\text{Unit stress}}{\text{Unit deformation}} \quad (2.3)$$

Since $f = \frac{P}{A}$ and $\delta = \frac{\Delta}{l}$, the above formula may be written $E = \frac{Pl}{\Delta A}$.

Most stress-strain problems require either the deformation due to a given load or stress or the stress from a given deformation. The value of the modulus of elasticity of various

Table 2.1   Gage for Angle Legs

Leg	8 in.	7 in.	6 in.	5 in.	4 in.	3½ in.	3 in.	2½ in.	2 in.	1¾ in.	1½ in.	1⅜ in.	1¼ in.	1 in.
g	$4\frac{1}{2}$	4	$3\frac{1}{2}$	3	$2\frac{1}{2}$	2	$1\frac{3}{4}$	$1\frac{3}{8}$	$1\frac{1}{8}$	1	$\frac{7}{8}$	$\frac{7}{8}$	$\frac{3}{4}$	$\frac{5}{8}$
g_1	3	$2\frac{1}{2}$	$2\frac{1}{4}$	2										
g_2	3	3	$2\frac{1}{2}$	$1\frac{3}{4}$										

NET SECTION OF RIVETED TENSION MEMBERS

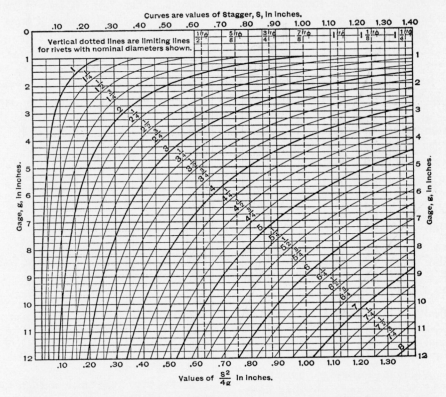

Curves are values of Stagger, S, in inches.

Vertical dotted lines are limiting lines for rivets with nominal diameters shown.

Gage, g, in inches.

Values of $\frac{s^2}{4g}$ in inches.

The above chart will simplify the application of the rule for net width, Section 19, Pars. (c) and (d) of the Institute Specifications. Entering the chart at left or right with the gauge "g" and proceeding horizontally to intersection with the curve for the pitch "s", thence vertically to top or bottom, the value of s²/4g may be read directly.

The example below illustrates the application of the rule, and the use of the chart.

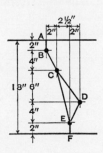

Chain A B C E F		
Deduct for 3 holes @ (¾ + ⅛)	=	—2.625
BC, g = 4, s = 2; add s²/4g	=	+0.25
CE, g = 10, s = 2½; add s²/4g	=	+0.16
Total Deduction	=	—2.215″
Chain A B C D E F		
Deduct for 4 holes @ (¾ + ⅛)	=	—3.50
BC, as above, add	=	+0.25
CD, g = 6, s = 4½; add s²/4g	=	+0.85
DE, g = 4, s = 2; add s²/4g	=	+0.25
Total Deduction	=	—2.15″

Net Width = 18.0 — 2.215 = 15.785″.

¾″ Rivets

In comparing the path CDE with the path CE, it is seen that if the sum of the two values of s²/4g for CD and DE exceed the single value of s²/4g for CE, by more than the deduction for one hole, then the path CDE is not critical as compared with CE.

Evidently if the value of s²/4g for one leg CD of the path CDE is greater than the deduction for one hole, the path CDE cannot be critical as compared with CE. The vertical dotted lines in the chart serve to indicate, for the respective rivet diameters noted at the top thereof, that any value of s²/4g to the right of such line is derived from a non-critical chain which need not be further considered.

Fig. 2.4   Net Section of Riveted Tension Members

Table 2.2 Effective Net Areas of Angles

Net Area in Sq. In.

Size	Weight per Foot	Min. r	Long Leg Connected						Short Leg Connected					
			1⅛"φ Holes		1"φ Holes		⅞"φ Holes		1⅛"φ Holes		1"φ Holes		⅞"φ Holes	
Inches	Lb.	In.	One	Two	One	Two	One	Two	One	Two	One	Two	One	Two
2½x2 x ¼	3.62	.42					0.62							
2½x2½x¼	4.1	.49					0.69							
3 x 2½x¼	4.5	.53					0.81						0.69	
2½x2 x 5⁄16	4.5	.42					0.77						0.75	
3 x 3 x ¼	4.9	.59					0.88						0.88	
2½x2½x5⁄16	5.0	.49					0.85						0.85	
2½x2 x ⅜	5.3	.42					0.92							
3½x3 x ¼*	5.4	.63			0.97		1.00						0.93	
3 x 2½x5⁄16	5.6	.53					1.00						0.93	
3½x3½x¼*	5.8	.69				1.03	1.06				1.03		1.06	
4 x 3 x ¼*	5.8	.65	1.06		1.10		1.13						1.00	
2½x2½x⅜	5.9	.49					1.00						1.00	
3 x 3 x 5⁄16	6.1	.59					1.09						1.09	
3½x3 x 5⁄16	6.6	.63				1.20	1.24						1.16	
3 x 2½x⅜	6.6	.52					1.19						1.10	
3½x3½x5⁄16	7.2	.69				1.28	1.32				1.28		1.32	
4 x 3 x 5⁄16*	7.2	.65	1.32		1.36		1.40						1.24	
3 x 3 x ⅜	7.2	.58					1.29						1.29	
3 x 2½x7⁄16	7.6	.52					1.38						1.27	
4 x 3½x5⁄16*	7.7	.73	1.40		1.44		1.48				1.36		1.40	
3½x3 x ⅜	7.9	.62				1.43	1.48						1.39	
4 x 4 x 5⁄16*	8.2	.79	1.47		1.51		1.55		1.47		1.51		1.55	
3 x 3 x 7⁄16	8.3	.58					1.49						1.49	
3½x3½x⅜	8.5	.69				1.52	1.57				1.52		1.57	
4 x 3 x ⅜	8.5	.64	1.57		1.61		1.66						1.47	
3 x 2½x½	8.5	.52					1.56						1.44	
5 x 3½x5⁄16*	8.7	.77	1.71	(1.36)	1.75	(1.44)	1.79	(1.51)			1.51		1.55	
4 x 3½x⅜	9.1	.73	1.66		1.71		1.76				1.62		1.66	
3½x3 x 7⁄16	9.1	.62				1.65	1.71						1.60	
5 x 4 x 5⁄16*	9.3	.86	1.78	(1.43)	1.82	(1.51)	1.86	(1.59)	1.63		1.66		1.70	
3 x 3 x ½	9.4	.58					1.69						1.69	
4 x 4 x ⅜	9.8	.79	1.76		1.81		1.85		1.76		1.81		1.85	
3¼x3½x7⁄16	9.8	.68				1.76	1.82				1.76		1.82	
4 x 3 x 7⁄16	9.8	.64	1.82		1.87		1.93						1.71	
3½x3 x ½	10.2	.62				1.87	1.94						1.81	
5 x 3½x⅜*	10.4	.76	2.04	(1.62)	2.09	(1.71)	2.14	(1.81)			1.81		1.85	
3 x 3 x 9⁄16	10.4	.58					1.88						1.88	
4 x 3½x7⁄16	10.6	.72	1.93		1.98		2.04				1.87		1.93	
5 x 4 x ⅜*	11.0	.85	2.13	(1.71)	2.18	(1.80)	2.22	(1.89)	1.94		1.99		2.03	
3½x3½x½	11.1	.68				2.00	2.06				2.00		2.06	
4 x 3 x ½	11.1	.64	2.06		2.12		2.19						1.94	

materials is given in Table 1.1. If the problem is an examination problem, both the total length and the gage length of the member may be given. The gage length is the length to use here.

b Probably the commonest form of stress-strain problem is that which requires the deformation under a given stress. This is a favorite type of problem in professional engineers' license examinations.

Problem What is the elongation of a steel rod ½ in. in diameter, 40 ft long, carrying a total suspended load of 6,000 lb?

Table 2.2   Effective Net Areas of Angles (*Continued*)

| Size | Weight per Foot | Min. r | Long Leg Connected | | | | | | Short Leg Connected | | | | | |
| | | | 1⅛"φ Holes | | 1"φ Holes | | ⅞"φ Holes | | 1⅛"φ Holes | | 1"φ Holes | | ⅞"φ Holes | |
Inches	Lb.	In.	One	Two	One	Two	One	Two	One	Two	One	Two	One	Two
4 x 4 x 7/16	11.3	.78	2.04		2.09		2.15		2.04		2.09		2.15	
3½x3 x 9/16	11.4	.62			2.09		2.16						2.02	
3 x 3 x 5/8	11.5	.58					2.07						2.07	
4 x 3½x½	11.9	.72	2.19		2.25		2.31				2.12		2.19	
5 x 3½x7/16	12.0	.76	2.37	(1.88)	2.42	(1.99)	2.48	(2.09)			2.09		2.15	
5 x 5 x 3/8*	12.3	.99	2.32	(1.90)	2.37	(1.99)	2.41	(2.09)	2.32	(1.90)	2.37	(1.99)	2.41	(2.09)
6 x 4 x 3/8*	12.3	.88	2.51	(2.09)	2.56	2.18	2.60	2.27	2.13		2.18		2.23	
3½x3½x9/16	12.4	.68			2.23		2.30				2.23		2.30	
4 x 3 x 9/16	12.4	.64	2.30		2.37		2.44						2.16	
3½x3 x 5/8	12.5	.62			2.30		2.38						2.22	
5 x 4 x 7/16	12.8	.85	2.48	(1.99)	2.53	(2.10)	2.59	(2.20)	2.26		2.31		2.37	
4 x 4 x ½	12.8	.78	2.31		2.37		2.44		2.31		2.37		2.44	
4 x 3½x9/16	13.3	.72	2.44		2.51		2.58				2.37		2.44	
7 x 4 x 3/8*	13.6	.88	2.88	2.46	2.93	2.55	2.97	2.64	2.32		2.36		2.41	
5 x 3½x½	13.6	.75	2.69	(2.12)	2.75	(2.25)	2.81	(2.37)			2.37		2.44	
3½x3½x5/8	13.6	.68			2.46		2.53				2.46		2.53	
4 x 3 x 5/8	13.6	.64	2.53		2.61		2.69						2.38	
3½x3 x 11/16	13.6	.62			2.52		2.60						2.43	
5 x 5 x 7/16	14.3	.98	2.69	(2.20)	2.74	(2.31)	2.80	(2.42)	2.69	(2.20)	2.74	(2.31)	2.80	(2.42)
6 x 4 x 7/16*	14.3	.87	2.91	(2.42)	2.96	2.53	3.02	2.63	2.47		2.53		2.58	
4 x 4 x 9/16	14.3	.78	2.58		2.65		2.72		2.58		2.65		2.72	
5 x 4 x ½	14.5	.85	2.81	(2.25)	2.87	(2.37)	2.94	(2.50)	2.56		2.62		2.69	
4 x 3½x5/8	14.7	.72	2.70		2.78		2.85				2.62		2.70	
3½x3 x 3/4	14.7	.62			2.72		2.81						2.62	
3½x3½x11/16	14.8	.68			2.69		2.77				2.69		2.77	
4 x 3 x 11/16	14.8	.64	2.77		2.86		2.94						2.60	
6 x 6 x 3/8*	14.9	1.19	2.88	(2.46)	2.93	2.56	2.98	2.65	2.88	(2.46)	2.93	2.56	2.98	2.65
5 x 3½x9/16	15.2	.75	3.01	(2.38)	3.08	(2.52)	3.15	(2.66)			2.66		2.73	
4 x 4 x 5/8	15.7	.78	2.85		2.93		3.01		2.85		2.93		3.01	
7 x 4 x 7/16*	15.8	.88	3.35	2.86	3.40	2.97	3.46	3.07	2.69		2.75		2.80	
4 x 3½x11/16	16.0	.72	2.94		3.03		3.11				2.85		2.94	
3½x3½x3/4	16.0	.68			2.91		3.00				2.91		3.00	
4 x 3 x 3/4	16.0	.64	3.00		3.10		3.19						2.81	
5 x 5 x ½	16.2	.98	3.06	(2.50)	3.12	(2.62)	3.19	(2.75)	3.06	(2.50)	3.12	(2.62)	3.19	(2.75)
6 x 4 x ½	16.2	.87	3.31	(2.75)	3.37	2.87	3.44	3.00	2.81		2.87		2.94	
5 x 4 x 9/16	16.2	.85	3.15	(2.52)	3.22	(2.66)	3.29	(2.80)	2.87		2.94		3.01	
5 x 3½x5/8	16.8	.75	3.32	(2.61)	3.40	(2.77)	3.47	(2.93)			2.93		3.01	
4 x 4 x 11/16	17.1	.78	3.12		3.20		3.29		3.12		3.20		3.29	
6 x 6 x 7/16*	17.2	1.19	3.35	(2.86)	3.41	2.97	3.46	3.08	3.35	(2.86)	3.41	2.97	3.46	3.08
8 x 4 x 7/16*	17.2	.87	3.79	3.30	3.84	3.41	3.90	3.51	2.91		2.97		3.02	
4 x 3½x3/4	17.3	.72	3.18		3.28		3.37				3.09		3.18	
5 x 4 x 5/8	17.8	.84	3.47	(2.77)	3.55	(2.92)	3.63	(3.08)	3.16		3.24		3.32	

For the solution of this problem, Formula (2.3) may be written

$$\Delta = \frac{Pl}{EA} =$$

$$\frac{6{,}000 \text{ lb} \times 40 \text{ ft} \times 12 \text{ in. per ft}}{30{,}000{,}000 \text{ psi} \times 0.1963 \text{ sq in.}} = 0.49 \text{ in.}$$

c   The above problem brings up another point—the units in any problem must cancel out properly. Note that in the problem the load is expressed in pounds, the length in feet multiplied by 12 in. per ft. The numerator above is therefore

$$\text{Pounds} \times \text{feet} \times \frac{\text{inches}}{\text{feet}}$$

which cancels out to pounds times inches. In the denominator, *E* is expressed in pounds per

Table 2.2 Effective Net Areas of Angles (*Continued*)

Size (Inches)	Weight per Foot (Lb.)	Min. r (In.)	Long Leg Connected — 1⅛"φ Holes One	Two	1"φ Holes One	Two	⅞"φ Holes One	Two	Short Leg Connected — 1⅛'φ Holes One	Two	1"φ Holes One	Two	⅞'φ Holes One	Two
7 x 4 x ½*	17.9	.87	3.81	3.25	3.87	3.37	3.94	3.50	3.06		3.12		3.19	
5 x 5 x 9⁄16	18.1	.98	3.43	(2.80)	3.50	(2.94)	3.57	(3.08)	3.43	(2.80)	3.50	(2.94)	3.57	(3.08)
6 x 4 x 9⁄16	18.1	.87	3.71	(3.08)	3.78	3.22	3.85	3.36	3.15		3.22		3.29	
5 x 3½x11⁄16	18.3	.75	3.63	(2.86)	3.72	(3.03)	3.80	(3.20)			3.20		3.29	
4 x 4 x ¾	18.5	.78	3.38		3.47		3.56		3.38		3.47		3.56	
5 x 4 x 11⁄16	19.5	.84	3.80	(3.02)	3.88	(3.20)	3.97	(3.37)	3.45		3.54		3.63	
6 x 6 x ½	19.6	1.18	3.81	(3.25)	3.87	3.37	3.94	3.50	3.81	(3.25)	3.87	3.37	3.94	3.50
8 x 4 x ½*	19.6	.86	4.31	3.75	4.37	3.87	4.44	4.00	3.31		3.37		3.44	
5 x 3½x¾	19.8	.75	3.93	(3.09)	4.03	(3.28)	4.12	(3.47)	3.47		3.47		3.56	
5 x 5 x ⅝	20.0	.98	3.79	(3.09)	3.87	(3.24)	3.95	(3.40)	3.79	(3.09)	3.87	(3.24)	3.95	(3.40)
7 x 4 x 9⁄16*	20.0	.87	4.27	3.64	4.34	3.78	4.41	3.92	3.43		3.50		3.57	
6 x 4 x ⅝	20.0	.86	4.10	(3.40)	4.18	3.55	4.26	3.71	3.48		3.55		3.63	
8 x 6 x 7⁄16*	20.2	1.31	4.22	3.73	4.28	3.84	4.33	3.95	3.78	(3.29)	3.84	3.40	3.89	3.51
5 x 4 x ¾	21.1	.84	4.13	(3.28)	4.22	(3.47)	4.31	(3.66)	3.75		3.85		3.94	
5 x 5 x 11⁄16	21.8	.98	4.14	(3.37)	4.23	(3.54)	4.32	(3.71)	4.14	(3.37)	4.23	(3.54)	4.32	(3.71)
6 x 4 x 11⁄16	21.8	.86	4.49	(3.71)	4.57	3.89	4.66	4.06	3.80		3.89		3.97	
6 x 6 x 9⁄16	21.9	1.18	4.27	(3.63)	4.34	3.78	4.41	3.92	4.27	(3.63)	4.34	3.78	4.41	3.92
8 x 4 x 9⁄16*	21.9	.86	4.83	4.20	4.90	4.34	4.97	4.48	3.71		3.78		3.85	
7 x 4 x ⅝	22.1	.86	4.72	4.02	4.80	4.17	4.88	4.33	3.78		3.86		3.94	
5 x 4 x 13⁄16	22.7	.84	4.44	(3.53)	4.54	(3.73)	4.64	(3.93)	4.03		4.14		4.24	
8 x 6 x ½*	23.0	1.30	4.81	4.25	4.87	4.37	4.94	4.50	4.31	(3.75)	4.37	3.87	4.44	4.00
5 x 5 x ¾	23.6	.97	4.50	(3.66)	4.60	(3.85)	4.69	(4.03)	4.50	(3.66)	4.60	(3.85)	4.69	(4.03)
6 x 4 x ¾	23.6	.86	4.88	(4.03)	4.97	4.22	5.06	4.41	4.13		4.22		4.31	
6 x 6 x ⅝	24.2	1.18	4.73	(4.03)	4.80	4.18	4.88	4.34	4.73	(4.02)	4.80	4.18	4.88	4.34
7 x 4 x 11⁄16	24.2	.86	5.18	4.40	5.26	4.58	5.35	4.75	4.15		4.23		4.32	
8 x 4 x ⅝*	24.2	.86	5.35	4.65	5.43	4.80	5.51	4.96	4.10		4.18		4.26	
5 x 4 x ⅞	24.2	.84	4.76	(3.77)	4.87	(3.99)	4.98	(4.21)	4.32		4.43		4.54	
5 x 5 x 13⁄16	25.4	.97	4.84	(3.93)	4.95	(4.13)	5.05	(4.34)	4.84	(3.93)	4.95	(4.13)	5.05	(4.34)
6 x 4 x 13⁄16	25.4	.86	5.26	(4.35)	5.36	4.55	5.46	4.75	4.45		4.55		4.65	
8 x 6 x 9⁄16*	25.7	1.30	5.40	4.76	5.47	4.91	5.54	5.05	4.84	(4.20)	4.91	4.34	4.98	4.48
7 x 4 x ¾	26.2	.86	5.63	4.78	5.72	4.97	5.81	5.16	4.50		4.60		4.69	
8 x 8 x ½*	26.4	1.59	5.31	4.75	5.37	4.87	5.44	5.00	5.31	4.75	5.37	4.87	5.44	5.00
6 x 6 x 11⁄16	26.5	1.17	5.18	(4.41)	5.27	4.58	5.35	4.75	5.18	(4.41)	5.27	4.58	5.35	4.75
8 x 4 x 11⁄16	26.5	.85	5.87	5.09	5.95	5.27	6.04	5.44	4.49		4.58		4.66	
5 x 5 x ⅞	27.2	.97	5.19	(4.21)	5.30	(4.43)	5.41	(4.64)	5.19	(4.21)	5.30	(4.43)	5.41	(4.64)
6 x 4 x ⅞	27.2	.86	5.63	(4.64)	5.74	4.86	5.85	5.08	4.75		4.86		4.97	
7 x 4 x 13⁄16	28.2	.86	6.07	5.16	6.17	5.36	6.27	5.56	4.85		4.95		5.05	

square inch and the area in square inches, so the denominator becomes,

$$\frac{\text{Pounds}}{\text{Square inches}} \times \text{square inches} = \text{pounds}$$

The problem is therefore

$$\Delta = \frac{\text{pounds} \times \text{inches}}{\text{pounds}} = \text{inches}$$

In complex problems, it is frequently advisable to set down and cancel out units to be sure of the final unit. Otherwise we are apt to run into the error of forgetting to reduce lengths or areas from feet to inch units, one of the most fruitful sources of error in engineering design.

Table 2.2 Effective Net Areas of Angles (*Continued*)

Net Area in Sq. In.

Size	Weight per Foot	Min. r	Long Leg Connected: 1 1/8″ϕ Holes, One	1 1/8″ϕ Holes, Two	1″ϕ Holes, One	1″ϕ Holes, Two	7/8″ϕ Holes, One	7/8″ϕ Holes, Two	Short Leg Connected: 1 1/8″ϕ Holes, One	1 1/8″ϕ Holes, Two	1″ϕ Holes, One	1″ϕ Holes, Two	7/8″ϕ Holes, One	7/8″ϕ Holes, Two
Inches	Lb.	In.												
8 x 6 x 5/8*	28.5	1.29	5.98	5.27	6.05	5.43	6.13	5.59	5.35	(4.65)	5.43	4.80	5.51	4.96
6 x 6 x 3/4	28.7	1.17	5.63	(4.78)	5.72	4.97	5.81	5.16	5.63	(4.78)	5.72	4.97	5.81	5.16
8 x 4 x 3/4	28.7	.85	6.38	5.53	6.47	5.72	6.56	5.91	4.88	......	4.97	......	5.06	......
5 x 5 x 15/16	28.9	.97	5.54	(4.49)	5.66	(4.72)	5.78	(4.96)	5.54	(4.49)	5.66	(4.72)	5.78	(4.96)
6 x 4 x 15/16	28.9	.86	6.01	(4.96)	6.13	5.19	6.24	5.42	5.07	......	5.19	......	5.31	......
8 x 8 x 9/16*	29.6	1.58	5.96	5.32	6.03	5.46	6.10	5.60	5.96	5.32	6.03	5.46	6.10	5.60
7 x 4 x 7/8	30.2	.86	6.51	5.52	6.62	5.74	6.73	5.96	5.20	......	5.31	......	5.41	......
5 x 5 x 1	30.6	.97	5.87	(4.75)	6.00	(5.00)	6.12	(5.25)	5.87	(4.75)	6.00	(5.00)	6.12	(5.25)
6 x 4 x 1	30.6	.86	6.37	(5.25)	6.50	5.50	6.62	5.75	5.37	......	5.50	......	5.62	......
6 x 6 x 13/16	31.0	1.17	6.07	(5.15)	6.17	5.36	6.27	5.56	6.07	(5.15)	6.17	5.36	6.27	5.56
8 x 4 x 13/16	31.0	.85	6.88	5.97	6.98	6.17	7.08	6.37	5.26	......	5.36	......	5.46	......
8 x 6 x 11/16	31.2	1.29	6.55	5.78	6.64	5.95	6.72	6.12	5.86	(5.09)	5.95	5.26	6.03	5.43
7 x 4 x 15/16	32.1	.86	6.94	5.89	7.06	6.12	7.17	6.35	5.53	......	5.65	......	5.77	......
8 x 8 x 5/8*	32.7	1.58	6.60	5.90	6.68	6.05	6.76	6.21	6.60	5.90	6.68	6.05	6.76	6.21
6 x 6 x 7/8	33.1	1.17	6.50	(5.52)	6.61	5.74	6.72	5.96	6.50	(5.52)	6.61	5.74	6.72	5.96
8 x 4 x 7/8	33.1	.85	7.38	6.39	7.49	6.61	7.60	6.83	5.63	......	5.74	......	5.85	......
8 x 6 x 3/4	33.8	1.29	7.13	6.28	7.22	6.47	7.31	6.66	6.38	(5.53)	6.47	5.72	6.56	5.91
7 x 4 x 1	34.0	.85	7.37	6.25	7.50	6.50	7.62	6.75	5.87	......	6.00	......	6.12	......
6 x 6 x 15/16	35.3	1.17	6.94	(5.89)	7.06	6.12	7.18	6.36	6.94	(5.89)	7.06	6.12	7.18	6.36
8 x 4 x 15/16	35.3	.85	7.88	6.83	8.00	7.06	8.11	7.29	6.00	......	6.12	......	6.24	......
8 x 8 x 11/16	35.8	1.58	7.24	6.47	7.33	6.64	7.41	6.81	7.24	6.47	7.33	6.64	7.41	6.81
8 x 6 x 13/16	36.5	1.28	7.70	6.78	7.80	6.99	7.90	7.19	6.89	(5.97)	6.99	6.17	7.09	6.38
6 x 6 x 1	37.4	1.17	7.37	(6.25)	7.50	6.50	7.62	6.75	7.37	(6.25)	7.50	6.50	7.62	6.75
8 x 4 x 1	37.4	.85	8.37	7.25	8.50	7.50	8.62	7.75	6.37	......	6.50	......	6.62	......
8 x 8 x 3/4	38.9	1.57	7.88	7.03	7.97	7.22	8.06	7.41	7.88	7.03	7.97	7.22	8.06	7.41
8 x 6 x 7/8	39.1	1.28	8.25	7.27	8.36	7.49	8.47	7.71	7.38	(6.39)	7.49	6.61	7.60	6.83
8 x 6 x 15/16	41.7	1.28	8.82	7.77	8.94	8.00	9.06	8.24	7.88	(6.83)	8.00	7.06	8.12	7.30
8 x 8 x 13/16	42.0	1.57	8.51	7.59	8.61	7.79	8.71	8.00	8.51	7.59	8.61	7.79	8.71	8.00
8 x 6 x 1	44.2	1.28	9.37	8.25	9.50	8.50	9.62	8.75	8.37	(7.25)	8.50	7.50	8.62	7.75
8 x 8 x 7/8	45.0	1.57	9.13	8.14	9.24	8.36	9.35	8.58	9.13	8.14	9.24	8.36	9.35	8.58
8 x 6 x 1 1/16	46.8	1.28	9.93	8.74	10.06	9.00	10.20	9.27	8.87	(7.67)	9.00	7.94	9.13	8.20
8 x 8 x 15/16	48.1	1.56	9.75	8.70	9.87	8.93	9.99	9.17	9.75	8.70	9.87	8.93	9.99	9.17
8 x 6 x 1 1/8	49.3	1.28	10.47	9.21	10.61	9.49	10.75	9.77	9.35	(8.08)	9.49	8.36	9.63	8.64
8 x 8 x 1	51.0	1.56	10.37	9.25	10.50	9.50	10.62	9.75	10.37	9.25	10.50	9.50	10.62	9.75
8 x 8 x 1 1/16	54.0	1.56	19.99	9.79	11.12	10.06	11.25	10.32	10.99	9.79	11.12	10.06	11.25	10.32
8 x 8 x 1 1/8	56.9	1.56	11.60	10.33	11.74	10.61	11.88	10.89	11.60	10.33	11.74	10.61	11.88	10.89

d A very common stress-strain problem is the computation of temperature stresses. In this type of problem, neither total length nor area is necessary. It is necessary to compute what the change in unit length would be if the member were free to expand or contract—then to translate this directly into a unit stress.

Problem A piece of medium steel 40 ft long is rigidly fixed so that it cannot expand. If temperature increases 30°F, what change in unit stress results? From formula (2.3)

$$f = E\delta = 30{,}000{,}000 \text{ psi} \times 0.0000067 \text{ in. per deg} \times 30° = 6{,}000 \text{ psi}$$

Refer to Table 1.1 for the properties of steel.

Table 2.3   Reduction of Area for Rivet Holes

REDUCTION OF AREA FOR RIVET HOLES

AREA IN SQUARE INCHES = ASSUMED DIAMETER OF HOLE BY THICKNESS OF METAL FOR COMPUTATION PURPOSES RIVET HOLES SHALL BE TAKEN AT THE NOMINAL DIAMETER OF THE RIVET PLUS ⅛ INCH

Thickness of Metal Inches	Diameter of Hole, Inches								
	⅝	¾	⅞	1	1⅛	1¼	1⅜	1½	1⅝
3/16	.117	.141	.164	.188	.211	.234	.258	.281	.305
¼	.156	.188	.219	.250	.281	.313	.344	.375	.406
5/16	.195	.234	.273	.313	.352	.391	.430	.469	.508
⅜	.234	.281	.328	.375	.422	.469	.516	.563	.609
7/16	.273	.328	.383	.438	.492	.547	.602	.656	.711
½	.313	.375	.438	.500	.563	.625	.688	.750	.813
9/16	.352	.422	.492	.563	.633	.703	.773	.844	.914
⅝	.391	.469	.547	.625	.703	.781	.859	.938	1.016
11/16	.430	.516	.602	.688	.773	.859	.945	1.031	1.117
¾	.469	.563	.656	.750	.844	.938	1.031	1.125	1.219
13/16	.508	.609	.711	.813	.914	1.016	1.117	1.219	1.320
⅞	.547	.656	.766	.875	.984	1.094	1.203	1.313	1.422
15/16	.586	.703	.820	.938	1.055	1.172	1.289	1.406	1.523
1	.625	.750	.875	1.000	1.125	1.250	1.375	1.500	1.625
1 1/16	.664	.797	.930	1.063	1.195	1.328	1.461	1.594	1.727
1⅛	.703	.844	.984	1.125	1.266	1.406	1.547	1.688	1.828
1 3/16	.742	.891	1.039	1.188	1.336	1.484	1.633	1.781	1.930
1¼	.781	.938	1.094	1.250	1.406	1.563	1.719	1.875	2.031
1 5/16	....	.984	1.148	1.313	1.477	1.641	1.805	1.969	2.133
1⅜	....	1.031	1.203	1.375	1.547	1.719	1.891	2.063	2.234
1 7/16	....	1.078	1.258	1.438	1.617	1.797	1.977	2.156	2.336
1½	....	1.125	1.313	1.500	1.688	1.875	2.063	2.250	2.438
1 9/16	....	1.172	1.367	1.563	1.758	1.953	2.148	2.344	2.539
1⅝	....	1.219	1.422	1.625	1.828	2.031	2.234	2.438	2.641
1 11/16	....	1.266	1.477	1.688	1.898	2.109	2.320	2.531	2.742
1¾	....	1.313	1.531	1.750	1.969	2.188	2.406	2.625	2.844
1 13/16	....	....	1.586	1.813	2.039	2.266	2.492	2.719	2.945
1⅞	....	....	1.641	1.875	2.109	2.344	2.578	2.813	3.047
1 15/16	....	....	1.695	1.938	2.180	2.422	2.664	2.906	3.148
2	....	....	1.750	2.000	2.250	2.500	2.750	3.000	3.250
2 1/16	....	....	1.805	2.063	2.320	2.578	2.836	3.094	3.352
2⅛	....	....	1.859	2.125	2.391	2.656	2.922	3.188	3.453
2 3/16	....	....	1.914	2.188	2.461	2.734	3.008	3.281	3.555
2¼	....	....	1.969	2.250	2.531	2.813	3.094	3.375	3.656
2 5/16	....	....	2.023	2.313	2.602	2.891	3.180	3.469	3.758
2⅜	....	....	2.078	2.375	2.672	2.969	3.266	3.563	3.859
2 7/16	....	....	2.133	2.438	2.742	3.047	3.352	3.656	3.961
2½	....	....	2.188	2.500	2.813	3.125	3.438	3.750	4.063
2⅝	....	....	2.297	2.625	2.953	3.281	3.609	3.938	4.266
2¾	....	....	2.406	2.750	3.094	3.438	3.781	4.125	4.469
2⅞	....	....	2.516	2.875	3.234	3.594	3.953	4.313	4.672
3	....	....	2.625	3.000	3.375	3.750	4.125	4.500	4.875

Table 2.4   Screw Threads

SCREW THREADS
American National Form
American Standard, B 1.1—1935.

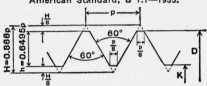

DIAMETER		AREA		Number of Threads per Inch	DIAMETER		AREA		Number of Threads per Inch
Total D In.	Net K In.	Total Dia., D Sq. In.	Net Dia., K Sq. In.		Total D In.	Net K In.	Total Dia., D Sq. In.	Net Dia., K Sq. In.	
1/4	.185	.049	.027	20	3	2.675	7.069	5.621	4
3/8	.294	.110	.068	16	3 1/4	2.925	8.296	6.720	4
1/2	.400	.196	.126	13	3 1/2	3.175	9.621	7.918	4
5/8	.507	.307	.202	11	3 3/4	3.425	11.045	9.214	4
3/4	.620	.442	.302	10	4	3.675	12.566	10.608	4
7/8	.731	.601	.419	9					
					4 1/4	3.798	14.186	11.330	2 7/8
1	.838	.785	.551	8	4 1/2	4.028	15.904	12.741	2 3/4
1 1/8	.939	.994	.693	7	4 3/4	4.255	17.721	14.221	2 5/8
1 1/4	1.064	1.227	.890	7					
1 3/8	1.158	1.485	1.054	6					
1 1/2	1.283	1.767	1.294	6	5	4.480	19.635	15.766	2 1/2
1 3/4	1.490	2.405	1.744	5	5 1/4	4.730	21.648	17.574	2 1/2
					5 1/2	4.953	23.758	19.268	2 3/8
2	1.711	3.142	2.300	4 1/2	5 3/4	5.203	25.967	21.262	2 3/8
2 1/4	1.961	3.976	3.021	4 1/2					
2 1/2	2.175	4.909	3.716	4	6	5.423	28.274	23.095	2 1/4
2 3/4	2.425	5.940	4.619	4					

Sizes over 4″ are old U. S. Standard; there is no American Standard.
Dimensions are maximum; specify "Free Fit—Class 2." For Bolts from 2½″ to 6″ diameter it is always necessary to bill the number of threads per inch.

e   Occasionally a problem may be encountered which combines a stress-strain problem with some other factor such as thermal expansion. The following problem of this type was taken from a professional engineer's license examination.

Problem A heavy steel strut 20 ft long between two walls undergoes a temperature rise of 40°F. If the walls each yield 0.01 in., what will be the unit stress in the strut?

If the member were free to expand, its increase in length would be $\Delta = 40 \times 0.0000067 \times 20 \times 12 = 0.064$ in. The actual expansion measured by the yielding of the walls is 0.02 in. The strain is therefore $0.064 - 0.02 = 0.044$. Therefore

$$f = \frac{E\Delta}{l} = \frac{30,000,000 \times 0.044}{12 \times 20} = 5,500 \text{ psi}$$

2.21   Nonhomogeneous members

a   Formula (2.3) may be written in the form

$$\delta = \frac{f}{E}$$

Therefore if two materials work together to resist the same type of stress in unison,

$$\delta = \frac{f_1}{E_1} = \frac{f_2}{E_2} \quad \text{or} \quad f_1 = \frac{E_1}{E_2} f_2$$

If we designate the ratio E_1/E_2 by n, the formula becomes $f_1 = nf_2$. In other words, if two materials having different moduli of elasticity are used together, they do not both work to the limit of their stress, but each carries stress in the proportion given by the above formula, up to the capacity of the weaker material. This principle is used in several common design problems, such as the design of flitch plate (or wood and steel) beams, and composite (or rolled-steel and concrete) beams, and will be referred to elsewhere.

Problem   What is the carrying capacity of a short wood post $11\frac{1}{2}$ in. square, with two steel side plates (one each side), each being $11 \times \frac{1}{2}$ in.?   Assume 1,000 psi on the wood with $E = 1,200,000$; 20,000 psi on the steel with $E = 29,000,000$.

From the above,

$$n = \frac{30,000,000}{1,200,000} = 25$$

The combination of stresses could be either

$$f_s = nf_w = 25 \times 1,000 = 25,000$$
$$\text{and} \qquad f_w = 1,000$$

or

$$f_w = \frac{f_s}{n} \ = \frac{20,000}{25} \qquad = 800$$
$$\text{and} \qquad f_s = 20,000$$

The controlling stresses therefore stay within the limits of the second combination and are 20,000 psi on steel and 800 psi on wood, and the capacity would be

$$20,000 \times 2 \times 11 \times \tfrac{1}{2} = 220,000$$
$$800 \times 11.5 \times 11.5 = \underline{105,800}$$
$$\text{Total capacity} = \overline{325,800}$$

2.30   DEFLECTION

a   Deflection may or may not be of importance in a structure.   If the structure carries a suspended plaster ceiling, that part of the load which is applied after the plaster has set may cause sufficient deflection to crack plaster.   Likewise, any beam carrying a brick wall may deflect enough to crack the brickwork.   Any floor which carries vibratory machinery, crowds of people, or small groups marching in unison (such as church floors or lodges) should be designed with deflection in mind.   Deflection and vibration go together, and even though the deflection is not enough to crack plaster, the vibration may be sufficient to affect the reputation of the building for safety—particularly in a church, a school, or a theater.   In a house, an apartment house, or an office building, the effect of vibration is not so important.   As a matter of actual safety, however, deflection does not indicate weakness.   A short beam may be overloaded to the verge of collapse without an apparent deflection, while, on the other hand, a long-span shallow beam may deflect far beyond the so-called allowable deflection and still be perfectly safe.

If deflection is to be considered, the computed deflection in inches should not exceed $\frac{1}{360}$ of the span, or span in feet/30.   With structural steel, using a fiber stress of 20,000 psi, it is not necessary to investigate for deflection unless the span of the beam in feet exceeds 1.6 times the depth of the beam in inches.   In wood, the ratio of span in feet to depth in inches is about 1.25, depending on the allowable fiber stress and the modulus of elasticity of the lumber.   With reinforced concrete, there are so many factors which influence the design, such as continuity, tension taken in the concrete, etc., that deflection is more or less uncertain; but reinforced concrete in general is less subject to deflection than steel or timber.

Although no allowance is made for the fact, we know that a poured-concrete floor slab bonds to a steel beam in such a way as to form a T beam.   Since the governing function of any given beam for deflection is the moment of inertia of the section, the effect of this T-beam action is to raise the neutral axis and thus to increase the moment of inertia and reduce the deflection accordingly.

Bar joists in general follow the same rules of deflection as steel beams except that the shallow-end construction (see Fig. 4.33) increases the deflection.   Load tests on identical joists with different types of top support—all loaded to the tabular load capacity of the joist as listed in Art. 4.13—gave the following results as compared with the computed deflection of a bare steel beam of uniform equal depth.

A joist system with $2\frac{1}{2}$-in. top slab deflected 35 percent of the computed deflection.

A joist system with $1\frac{1}{2}$-in. top slab deflected 47 percent of the computed deflection.

Table 2.5 Deflection Coefficients

$$f_s = 20{,}000, \; E = 30{,}000{,}000$$

Span, ft	Coefficient	Span, ft	Coefficient	Span, ft	Coefficient	Span, ft	Coefficient
1	.02	21	8.81	41	33.62	61	74.42
2	.08	22	9.68	42	35.28	62	76.88
3	.18	23	10.58	43	36.98	63	79.38
4	.32	24	11.52	44	38.72	64	81.92
5	.50	25	12.5	45	40.5	65	84.5
6	.72	26	13.52	46	42.32	66	87.12
7	.98	27	14.58	47	44.18	67	89.78
8	1.28	28	15.68	48	46.08	68	92.48
9	1.62	29	16.82	49	48.02	69	95.22
10	2.00	30	18.00	50	50.00	70	98.00
11	2.42	31	19.22	51	52.02	71	100.82
12	2.88	32	20.48	52	54.08	72	103.68
13	3.38	33	21.78	53	56.18	73	106.58
14	3.92	34	23.12	54	58.32	74	109.52
15	4.5	35	24.5	55	60.5	75	112.5
16	5.12	36	25.92	56	62.72	76	115.52
17	5.78	37	27.38	57	64.98	77	118.58
18	6.48	38	28.88	58	67.28	78	121.68
19	7.22	39	30.42	59	69.62	79	124.82
20	8.00	40	32.00	60	72.00	80	128.00

A joist system with metal deck tack welded to the joists deflected 110 percent of the computed deflection.

The results of the above tests indicate the effect of a properly bonded concrete slab in reducing deflection and the increase in deflection as a result of shallow ends.

b The deflection of a uniformly loaded rolled-steel beam stressed to 20,000 psi may be found by referring to Table 2.5, selecting the coefficient for the span, and dividing by the depth in inches. Thus, to determine the deflection of a 10-in. beam on a 16-ft span, with the fiber stress 20,000 psi,

$$\Delta = \frac{\text{coefficient}}{\text{depth}} = \frac{5.12}{10} = 0.512 \text{ in.}$$

If the fiber stress is not exactly the usual 20,000 psi, the deflection is corrected by the ratio of S required/S furnished. For instance, assume that a beam on a uniformly loaded 20-ft span requires $S = 38.8$. This would require a 14 WF 30 (depth 13.86 in.), which according to Art. 1.32 has an $S = 41.8$. The deflection is therefore

$$\Delta = \frac{S \text{ required}}{S \text{ furnished}} \times \frac{\text{coefficient}}{\text{depth}} =$$
$$\frac{38.8}{41.8} \times \frac{8.00}{13.86} = 0.536$$

c If the load is applied to the beam in any other manner than as a uniform load, a correction factor must be applied to obtain maximum deflection in accordance with Table 2.6.

Thus, to determine the deflection of a 10-in. steel beam on a 17-ft span with a centrally concentrated load, stressed to 17,500 psi,

$$\Delta = \frac{17.5}{20} \times 0.8 \times \frac{5.78}{10} = 0.405$$

Other examples are given in Art. 4.10(*e*, *f*, and *g*). If the load condition does not come under any of the cases for which the diagrams are listed, the method of approach is by means

Table 2.6 Deflection Factors for Types of Loading

Diagram (Fig. 3.13)	Load conditions	Deflection factor
1	Uniformly distributed	1.0
2	Load increasing uniformly to one end	.97
3	Load increasing uniformly to center	.96
7	Centrally located concentrated load	.8
12	Fixed at one end, freely supported at other, uniformly distributed	.42
13	Fixed at one end, freely supported at other, centrally located concentrated load	.48
15	Uniformly distributed load on fixed end beam	.3
16	Centrally concentrated load on fixed end beam	.4
18	Cantilever—load increasing uniformly to fixed end	1.92
19	Cantilever—uniformly loaded	2.4
22	Cantilever—concentrated load at free end	3.2

of the moment-area method discussed in Art. 2.31, which follows.

d The deflection of a wood beam or joist for a uniform load is

$$\Delta = \frac{15fL^2}{Ec}$$

Because the fiber stress and modulus of elasticity vary for different kinds of lumber, no simple deflection table like Table 2.5 can be set up. The various modifications given in Table 2.6 for different conditions of loading will modify the above formula for timber also.

e The tables of coefficients for beam deflections in Table 2.7 were published in *Engineering News-Record* by Robins Fleming and will prove quite helpful for determining the deflection of any point on a beam under a number of various loading conditions. The coefficient F is the multiplier to be used for PL^3 for concentrated loads and for WL^3 for uniform loads in the formulae of Fig. 3.13.

f The generally accepted methods of computing deflection in a reinforced-concrete beam or slab are based on a number of assumptions of variables, so that at best the result is an approximation probably far on the safe side. A simple, rather direct approach is based on the theory that, for a computed stress in the steel, the deflection is the same as for a steel beam with the same type of load and fixity, and of a depth equal to twice the distance from the neutral axis to the plane of the tensile steel. Since reinforced-concrete beams or slabs are usually continuous or semicontinuous, the factor for continuity taken from Table 2.6 must be applied—0.3 for a fully continuous uniformly loaded beam or 0.42 for a semicontinuous end condition. Thus

$$\Delta = \frac{CD}{2d\,(1-k)} \times \frac{A_s \text{ required}}{A_s \text{ furnished}}$$

where C is the deflection coefficient for the span taken from Table 2.5, D is the deflection factor from Table 2.6, and d, k, and A_s have the meaning usually applied to them in reinforced-concrete formulae.

For example, referring to the concrete slab designed in Art. 5.40b, compute the deflection of the slab noted. For a $10\frac{1}{2}$-ft slab, $C = 2.20$.

(The coefficient from Table 2.5 for 21, divided by 4.) $D = 0.3$ (from Table 2.6), A_s required $= 0.458$, A_s furnished $= 0.48$.

$$\Delta = \frac{2.20 \times 0.3}{2 \times 3 \times 0.625} \times \frac{0.458}{0.48} = 0.168$$

2.31 Moment-area method

a For irregular loading conditions or conditions for which the deflection cannot be readily computed by the methods described in Art. 2.30, there are several methods for determining deflections. One will be described here—the conjugate-beam, or moment-area, method. It takes the name from certain similarities between the method of calculation and the method of calculating a complex beam. Without explaining the mathematical derivation, the steps in the solution are:

1. Set down the beam diagram, compute the reactions and moments, and select the beam as described in Art. 4.10.

2. Lay out a moment diagram of the beam as described in Art. 3.12. This moment diagram becomes the equivalent of the beam-load diagram in an ordinary beam problem, and the areas of the moment diagram are the applied loads.

3. Divide the moment diagram into triangles, and other shapes of which the area, and center of gravity may be readily obtained. Compute the area of these various parts of the moment diagrams and compute the reactions, as described in Art. 3.10. These reactions are the product $EI\theta$, which gives the slope deflection θ at the support.

4. Locate the point of zero shear. This is the point of maximum deflection.

5. Compute the moment at the point of zero shear. This moment is the product $EI\Delta$, from which the deflection Δ may be computed.

The above method may be used to determine moment at any intermediate point. For simplicity in determining the area of any fraction of a parabola, refer to Table 1.18.

Problem Compute the deflection of a steel beam under the following load conditions, and locate the point of maximum deflection (see

Table 2.7   Coefficients for Beam Deflection

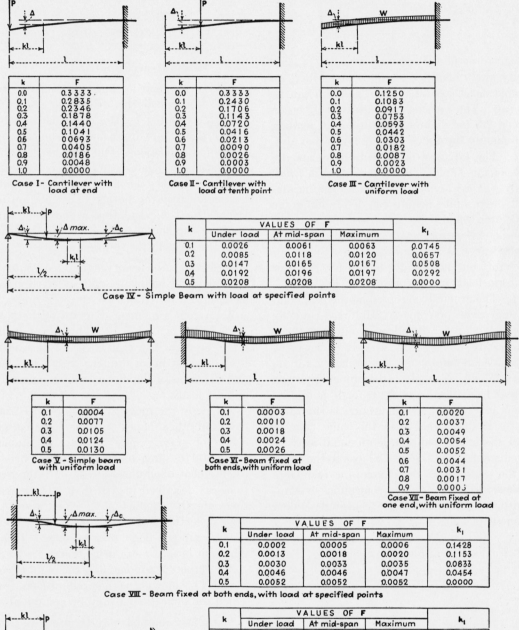

k	F
0.0	0.3333
0.1	0.2835
0.2	0.2346
0.3	0.1878
0.4	0.1440
0.5	0.1041
0.6	0.0693
0.7	0.0405
0.8	0.0186
0.9	0.0048
1.0	0.0000

Case I – Cantilever with load at end

k	F
0.0	0.3333
0.1	0.2430
0.2	0.1706
0.3	0.1143
0.4	0.0720
0.5	0.0416
0.6	0.0213
0.7	0.0090
0.8	0.0026
0.9	0.0003
1.0	0.0000

Case II – Cantilever with load at tenth point

k	F
0.0	0.1250
0.1	0.1083
0.2	0.0917
0.3	0.0753
0.4	0.0593
0.5	0.0442
0.6	0.0303
0.7	0.0182
0.8	0.0087
0.9	0.0023
1.0	0.0000

Case III – Cantilever with uniform load

k	VALUES OF F			k_1
	Under load	At mid-span	Maximum	
0.1	0.0026	0.0061	0.0063	0.0745
0.2	0.0085	0.0118	0.0120	0.0657
0.3	0.0147	0.0165	0.0167	0.0508
0.4	0.0192	0.0196	0.0197	0.0292
0.5	0.0208	0.0208	0.0208	0.0000

Case IV – Simple Beam with load at specified points

k	F
0.1	0.0004
0.2	0.0077
0.3	0.0105
0.4	0.0124
0.5	0.0130

Case V – Simple beam with uniform load

k	F
0.1	0.0003
0.2	0.0010
0.3	0.0018
0.4	0.0024
0.5	0.0026

Case VI – Beam fixed at both ends, with uniform load

k	F
0.1	0.0020
0.2	0.0037
0.3	0.0049
0.4	0.0054
0.5	0.0052
0.6	0.0044
0.7	0.0031
0.8	0.0017
0.9	0.0005

Case VII – Beam Fixed at one end, with uniform load

k	VALUES OF F			k_1
	Under load	At mid-span	Maximum	
0.1	0.0002	0.0005	0.0006	0.1428
0.2	0.0013	0.0018	0.0020	0.1153
0.3	0.0030	0.0033	0.0035	0.0833
0.4	0.0046	0.0046	0.0047	0.0454
0.5	0.0052	0.0052	0.0052	0.0000

Case VIII – Beam fixed at both ends, with load at specified points

k	VALUES OF F			k_1
	Under load	At mid-span	Maximum	
0.1	0.0018	0.0030	0.0036	0.1623
0.2	0.0054	0.0058	0.0067	0.1487
0.3	0.0084	0.0079	0.0089	0.1289
0.4	0.0097	0.0091	0.0097	0.0916
0.5	0.0091	0.0091	0.0093	0.0528
0.6	0.0069	0.0076	0.0076	0.0197
0.7	0.0040	0.0053	0.0053	0.0091
0.8	0.0016	0.0028	0.0028	0.0345
0.9	0.0002	0.0008	0.0008	0.0570

Case IX – Beam fixed at one end, with load at specified points

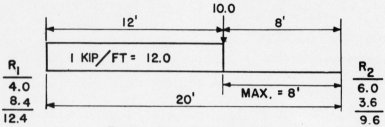

Fig. 2.5   Beam Load Diagram

Fig. 2.5). (See Art. 4.10 for method of computation of beam).

$$M = 8 \times 9.6 \quad = 76.8$$
$$S = 0.6 \times 76.8 = 46.08$$

Use 14 WF 34 ($S = 48.5$).

Divide Fig. 2.5 into three parts, two triangles and a parabola. The moment at 6 ft from R_1 is (Fig. 2.6)

$$12.4 \times 6 = 74.4$$
$$- (6 \times 3) = \underline{18.0}$$
$$56.4$$

The altitude of the triangle at this point is $76.8/2 = 38.4$. The altitude of the parabola therefore is $56.4 - 38.4 = 18.0$ (which would be the moment on a uniformly loaded beam carrying 1 kip per ft in a 12-ft span).

We may compute the areas and apply them as loads to the beam, and determine the reactions and point of zero shear. Referring to Table 1.18, let us compute the area at the mid-point of the beam. Starting from R_2,

Triangle $A_1 =$ 307.2

2/12 of 76.8 = 12.8 = small triangle,
     $12.8 \times 2/2 =$ 12.8

Small rectangle, $76.8 - 12.8 = 64 \times 2 = 128.0$

Parabola, $2/12 = 0.167$. From Table
     1.18, $0.05 \times 18 \times 12 =$ $\underline{10.8}$
                                    458.8

$R_2 = 452.8$, so the point of zero shear is just less than 10 ft from R_2.

    Height at 10 ft $= 64 + (0.55 \times 18) = 73.9$
$$458.8 - 452.8 = 6$$
$$\frac{6}{73.9} = 0.081$$

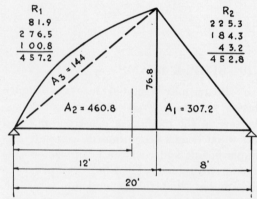

Fig. 2.6   Moment Diagram as Beam Load

Therefore the point of zero shear of the conjugate beam, which is point of maximum deflection of the real beam, is $10 - 0.08 = 9.92$ ft from R_2.

From this point of zero shear, the maximum moment may be computed

$$M = 452.8 \times 9.92 = 4{,}491.8$$
$$- \underline{1{,}550.9}$$
$$2{,}940.9$$

$- 307.2 \times 4.59$ $= 1{,}410.$

$-\dfrac{1.92}{12} \times 76.8 \times \dfrac{1.92}{2} \times \dfrac{1.92 \times 2}{3} =$ 15.1

$- 64.5 \times 1.92 \times 0.96$ $= 118.$

$- 10.8 \times 1.92 \times 1.375$ $= \underline{\quad 7.8}$
                                 $- 1{,}550.9$

Then $EI\Delta = 2{,}932.9$ in ft^3-kip units, and

$$\Delta = \frac{2{,}932{,}900 \times 1{,}728}{30{,}000{,}000 \times 339.2} = 0.5 \text{ in.}$$

(It is interesting to note that the computed deflection for a uniformly loaded beam for equal section modulus on this span is 0.545 in.)

3

Moments

3.10 SIMPLE BEAMS

a Beams may be divided into two primary classes, simple, and restrained or continuous. Because of the method of construction, steel and wood beams are ordinarily computed as simple beams and concrete beams as continuous or restrained. There are several conditions under which this general rule is varied. A cantilever beam is obviously restrained. Sometimes, too, steel beams are rigidly connected for the sake of wind bracing, but this is a special condition and not the rule. The 1946 AISC Code recognizes also semirigid framing, the suggested method of computation for which is given in Art. 4.16.

b If any structure is to be sustained in equilibrium, the sum of the moments about any point on it must be algebraically equal to zero. Therefore, if an imaginary section could be cut at any given point within the beam,

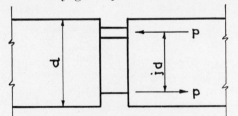

Fig. 3.1 Moment Couple Method

the sum of all external moments at either side of the section cut must be balanced by an internal moment or resisting moment within the beam. Although this principle is elementary mechanics, it may be well to recall it as the foundation for the solution of all beam problems. If we could concentrate all internal

tension at a point and all internal compression at a point, as is indicated in Fig. 3.1, the stress couple thus obtained would be a measure of the external moment at this point. This stress-couple idea is useful in some aspects of design, and there will be occasion to refer to this formula later on:

$$M = Pjd \quad \text{or} \quad P = \frac{M}{jd} \quad (3.1)$$

c Ordinary beam problems, however, involving steel or wood beams, are most readily solved by the use of the section-modulus formula, the fundamental beam formula,

$$M = f\frac{I}{c} \quad \text{or} \quad M = fS \quad \text{or} \quad S = \frac{M}{f} \quad (3.2)$$

d Practically all engineers have been taught the general method of beam design, as given in most mechanics or materials of construction textbooks. In general, these methods will be given, but they will be by-passed by various short cuts and simplifications.

e After the beam has been described, with a diagram to show load conditions if necessary, the first step is to obtain the reactions. The general method of finding reactions is to take moments about one end. The reaction at the left end for each load is the product of the load multiplied by its distance from the right end and divided by the total length. The total reaction is the sum of all reactions at that end, the balance of the load going to the opposite end. Most textbooks state the formula in this manner:

$$R_1 = \frac{P_1L_1 + P_2L_2 + P_3L_3 + \cdots P_nL_n}{L}$$

distances being taken from the right end. But each one can better be taken separately:

$$R_1 = \frac{P_1 L_1}{L} + \frac{P_2 L_2}{L} + \frac{P_3 L_3}{L} + \cdots \frac{P_n L_n}{L} \quad (3.3)$$

setting down the reactions from each load separately. The advantages of this method are (1) if any load is changed it is easier to change the reaction accordingly, and (2) frequently the relation of L_n/L will give an even fraction which can be solved by observation without the use of a slide rule. Obviously, for any symmetrically loaded beam the reactions are each half the total load of the beam.

f The general rule for obtaining the bending moment at any section of a simple beam may be stated as follows: Multiply one end reaction by the length from the end of the section. From the moment thus obtained, subtract the sum of the moments of the loads lying between the section and the chosen reaction, using as moment arms each length from the center of gravity of the load to the section cut. The general formula then becomes

$$M_a = R_1 a - P_1 a_1 - P_2 a_2 - P_3 a_3 - \cdots P_n a_n \quad (3.4)$$

where a is the distance from the reaction to the section cut, and a_1, a_2, etc., the distance from each load to the section cut.

g Ordinarily the only M in which we are interested is the moment at the dangerous or critical section. Without going into the proof of the axiom, it will be stated that the moment is maximum at the point on the beam where the shear is zero. The shear diagrams in Fig. 3.13 will permit solving the shear diagram of any such problem. It is not necessary to set down a shear diagram for each beam problem but it is necessary to have a mental picture of the diagram in order to locate this point of zero shear. The simple method of locating the point of zero shear is to subtract the various loads successively from the reaction until the result becomes zero. A little experience will show which reaction to select (see Art. 3.11).

h For the sake of simplicity in discussion, simple beam problems may be placed in one of five classifications.

Class I—Uniformly distributed load ($M = WL/8$).

Class II—Equal, concentrated loads equally spaced.

Class III—Simple triangular, trapezoidal, or cantilever load condition.

Class IV—Combination of any two or more of the preceding three classes.

Class V—Irregular or complex load conditions.

A glance at the beam will permit placing it in one of the above classifications. Classes I and II do not require any sketch and their calculation is quite simple. Classes III and V will require load diagrams; Class V may become quite complicated. Class IV may be simple or complicated, depending on the combinations used. Only the computation of the moment will be considered here. Beam selection will be left to other articles.

The beam diagrams and formulae given in Fig. 3.13 give shear and moment diagrams for various general conditions of loading. The formula for maximum moment is derived in all instances from the general formula in Art. 3.10*f*. The equivalent tabular load for each of the various load conditions is the ratio of load which, applied to a beam uniformly loaded on this span, would give the same maximum moment. For example, for Case 7 (Fig. 3.13), a centrally concentrated load, the equivalent tabular load is $2P$, or the effect of this type of loading causes the same moment as twice the same load if applied uniformly as in Case 1. Thus a load of 10,000 lb centrally concentrated on a 16-ft span would cause 40 ft-kips moment; but for a uniform load on a 16-ft span it would require 20,000 lb to cause 40 ft-kips moment.

i *Class II, equal concentrated loads, equally spaced,* is common for girders, or main supporting beams. The general formula may be written $M = CWL$, where C is

For one load,	.25
For two or three loads,	.167
For four or five loads,	.15
For six or seven loads,	.143
For eight or nine loads,	.139

j In Class III are grouped certain beam loadings which are encountered occasionally and which may best be solved by means of the formulae in Fig. 3.13. Cases 2 and 3 are found in hip and valley roof design. A beam with trapezoidal load, as indicated in Fig. 3.2, may be part of a roof construction, but it is more frequently the condition found in basement walls. It may be solved with an error

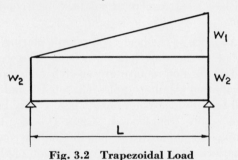

Fig. 3.2　Trapezoidal Load

of not over 3 percent by dividing it between uniform and triangular load, as shown in the sketch, and adding the results, or it may be solved accurately by the general method similar to the problem in Art. 3.10o.

Problem　A state license examination has this question: A vertical surface 40 ft high and 40 ft wide is exposed to a wind pressure of 30 psf. What is the total overturning moment? What is the total horizontal shear? This problem comes under Fig. 3.13, Case 19, cantilever beam, uniformly distributed load. The shear $V = W = wL$.

$$V = 40 \times 40 \times 30 = 48,000 \text{ lb maximum}$$
$$M_{max} = \frac{wL^2}{2} = \frac{48,000 \times 40}{2} = 960,000 \text{ ft-lb}$$

k　*Class IV, combined loadings.* Any two symmetrical systems of loadings may be combined, and this is frequently the simplest method of solution. For instance, a beam carries a uniform load of 1,000 lb per ft on 15 ft and a centrally concentrated load of 6,000 lb. What is the total moment? From Fig. 3.13, Case 1,

$$M = \frac{WL}{8} = \frac{15,000 \times 15}{8} = 28,125$$

From Fig. 3.13, Case 7,

$$M = \frac{PL}{4} = \frac{6,000 \times 15}{4} = 22,500$$

Total $M = 50,625$ ft-lb

A simpler method would be to double the concentrated load and treat it as uniform (because of the ratio of denominators of the above two formulae). Thus, $15,000 + 12,000 = 27,000$.

$$M = \frac{27,000 \times 15}{8} = 50,625 \text{ ft-lb}$$

(See Art. 4.10c).

Obviously a symmetrical loading cannot be combined with an unsymmetrical loading by adding moments, since the point of maximum bending does not occur at the same point. In this case, it is advisable to treat the problem as indicated in the next paragraph.

l　*Class V, irregular or complex loading conditions,* is a general method for moments. If the problem does not come within the limits of one of the above classes, it must fall into this class. A sketch is necessary. It is preferable to divide the problem into two distinct steps as follows:

1. Compute the reaction from each load at each end. This may often be done by observation, as in the beam sketched in Fig. 3.3. The load of 10,000 lb is at the $\frac{1}{4}$ point—therefore $\frac{1}{4} \times 10,000$ goes to the opposite end—

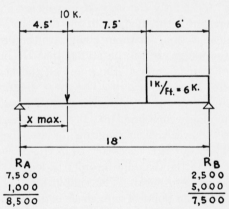

Fig. 3.3　Comp ex Loaded Beam

2,500. The balance of this load goes to the left end. The center of gravity of the 6,000-lb load is 3 ft out, or $\frac{1}{6}$ span; therefore $\frac{1}{6} \times 6,000 = 1,000$ goes to the left end, and 5,000 to the right end.

2. With the total end reactions known, subtracting from either end, the point where

the shear becomes zero is readily found—the critical section. For this purpose it is advisable to have a mental picture of the various shear diagrams, Fig. 3.13.

3. Compute M, the difference between all clockwise and counterclockwise moments to one side or the other of this critical section. The sides will be identical, so select the simpler problem of the two. In the problem above, $M = 8,500 \times 4.5 = 38,250$ ft-lb.

Problem This question is from a state license examination: The left half of a simple beam of 20 ft span is loaded with 2,000 lb per lin ft. Where is the point of maximum moment? What is its value? (See Fig. 3.4.)

The computation of end reactions, R_A and R_B and the computation of critical section are

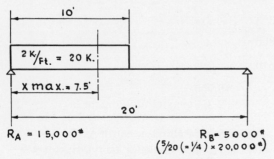

Fig. 3.4   Complex Loaded Beam

indicated. The method of computation of moment then becomes

$$M = \begin{array}{r} 15,000 \times 7.5 = 112,500 \\ - 15,000 \times 3.75 = -56,250 \\ \hline 56,250 \end{array}$$

m This brings out a little short cut in a problem of this kind, where there is no change in uniform load condition between the critical section and the end of the beam. Since the counterclockwise moment is exactly half the clockwise moment, the final computation might have been written

$$M = 15,000 \times \frac{7.5}{2} = 56,250$$

Note that this applies only when the reaction is entirely used up by uniform load.

n The problem shown in Fig. 3.5 is selected because it may clarify the location of point of zero shear. From R_A deduct the

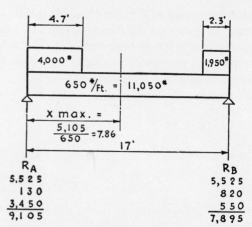

Fig. 3.5   Spandrel Beam Loading

4,000-lb load on the 4.7-ft length, leaving 5,105. This load must be used up in uniform load at 650 lb per ft, or $x = 5,105/650 = 7.86$.

$$\begin{array}{r} M = 9,105 \times 7.86 = 71,700 \\ - 4,000 \times 5.51 = 22,040 \\ - 5,105 \times 3.93 = 20,100 \\ \hline -42,140 \\ 29,560 \text{ maximum} \\ \text{moment} \end{array}$$

o Probably the most complicated of beams coming under this classification is one involving a trapezoidal load over part of the span, in combination with loads of other types. The point of zero shear must be found by means of a quadratic equation. The reactions are computed and set down in the usual manner,

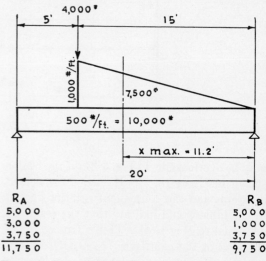

Fig. 3.6   Beam with Uniformly Increasing Load

as has been done in Fig. 3.6. From inspection it may be seen that the dangerous section lies between the 4,000-lb load and R_B. The triangular load increases from R_B so that at any point x ft from R_B, by similar triangles,

$$\frac{w_x}{1,000} = \frac{x}{15} \quad \text{or} \quad w_x = \frac{1,000x}{15}$$

The area of the triangle to the right of this would be

$$\frac{w_x x}{2} \quad \text{or from similar triangles} \quad \frac{1,000x^2}{30} = 33.3x^2$$

The area of the rectangle to the right would be $500x$. Therefore the shear crosses the zero line where $33.3x^2 + 500x = 9,750$.

$$x^2 + 15x = 293$$
$$x + 7.5 = \sqrt{349.25} = 18.7$$
$$x = 18.7 - 7.5 = 11.2$$

From this point the computation is simple.

$$M = 9,750 \times 11.2 = 109,200$$
$$- 500 \times 11.2 \times 5.6 = 31,360$$
$$- \frac{11.2}{15} \times 1,000 \times \frac{11.2}{2} \times \frac{11.2}{3} = 15,610$$
$$\frac{- 46,950}{62,250} \text{ maximum moment}$$

This method may be used for solving accurately any trapezoidal load beam as noted in Art. 3.10j.

p Attention should be called to several points with regard to cantilever beams which

simply fixed at a point as indicated in Fig. 3.13 but are supported by an uplift load, or a countermoment on a beam or a wall at the end against overturning. The reaction then becomes the sum of the downward load plus the uplift load.

Assume a cantilever beam as shown in Fig. 3.7. The load of 10 kips on a lever arm of 8 ft produces a cantilever moment of 80 ft-kips. The tendency to rotate is resisted by the connection to the beam at A; and to balance the overturning moment of 80 ft-kips it would require a load of 8 kips on the lever

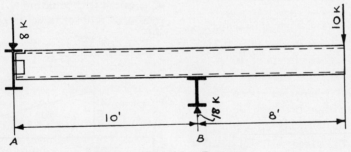

Fig. 3.7   Cantilever Beam

may be overlooked. In Fig. 3.13 for the beams shown in Cases 18, 19, 21, and 22, the load diagrams and the consequent reactions given in the table would indicate that the reactions are equal to P or to W. This is true so far as the load of the cantilever beam itself is concerned. However, cantilever beams are not

arm of 10 ft, thus putting a total reaction of 18 kips on beam B instead of merely the cantilever load. Perhaps a more direct approach to the problem of obtaining the reaction would be to take moments about A. Then

$$10R_B = 18 \times 10$$
$$R_B = 18$$

A problem involving a combined simple and cantilever loading may be rather confusing. Figure 3.8 indicates a problem of this type. It will be noted that there are two points of zero shear, one within the simple span, 8.375 ft from the end, where the moment is 28.0 ft-

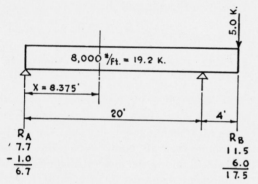

Fig. 3.8   Cantilever Beam—Fully Loaded

kips, and the cantilever moment, 24.0 ft-kips. In order to design the beam it is necessary to compute the moment at both points.

In connection with this beam, it is well to note that the simple beam or uplift end of the cantilever must be checked against the possibility of the simple span having full live and dead load, while the cantilever span supports dead load only. Let us assume in the preceding problem that the total load consists of 50 percent dead load and 50 percent live load. In this case the load condition and reactions are as indicated in Fig. 3.9. Although the cantilever moment is only half the original cantilever moment, R_A is increased so that the point of zero shear moves further out into the span, and the maximum moment becomes $7.34 \times 4.59 = 33.69$ ft-kips.

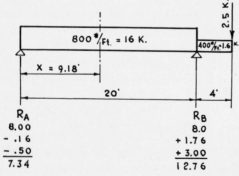

Fig. 3.9   Cantilever Beam—Partially Loaded

If the uplift arm is relatively short or if the load available to resist uplift is very low, it becomes necessary also to investigate the uplift with the cantilever fully loaded and the uplift span with the dead load only.

q Moving loads. Moving loads on two wheels, such as the load of a traveling crane on a crane girder or a road roller or a truck on a bridge, present a special problem in that the position of the load to produce maximum moment must be determined. The general statement for the position of loads on a simple span is as follows: The maximum bending moment in a simple beam with a moving load occurs when the heavier load is as far from one end of the beam as the center of gravity of all the moving loads is from the other end of the beam. Obviously, with a single moving load, this moment occurs when the load is at the center of the span.

If two wheels carry equal loads, such as on the end truck of a traveling crane, and the wheel base a, the distance between the wheels, is less than $0.586L$ (Fig. 3.10),

$$M_{max} = \frac{P(L - a/2)^2}{2L} \qquad (3.5)$$

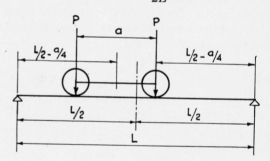

Fig. 3.10   Beam with Equal Moving Loads

When the wheel base exceeds $0.586L$, $M_{max} = PL/4$. M will occur twice on the span as the load moves along. The maximum shear V is at one end when the first wheel is about to leave the span.

Problem A 10-ton crane on a steel-beam runway having a 20-ft span has a wheel base of 11 ft and a wheel load of 25,000 lb. Figure maximum moment and shear.

$$M_{max} = \frac{25 (20 - 11/2)^2}{2 \times 20} = 131.4 \text{ ft-kip}$$

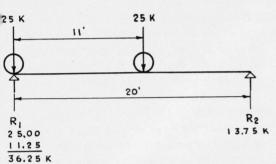

Fig. 3.11   Design of Beam with Equal Moving Loads

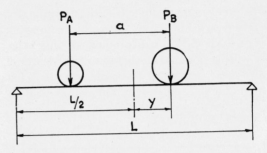

Fig. 3.12   Beam with Unequal Moving Loads

The maximum shear is the maximum reaction when the load is in the position indicated in Fig. 3.11, 36.25 kips.

If two unequal rolling loads are a fixed distance apart (Fig. 3.12), the maximum moment is under the heavier load in the position computed by the formula

$$y = \frac{P_A \, a}{2 \,(P_A + P_B)} \tag{3.6}$$

The maximum shear occurs as the heavier wheel is about to leave the span.

Problem   How shall a truck be placed on a span of 30 ft to produce the greatest bending moment? The loads are 5 tons on the front axle and 15 tons on the rear axle. The distance between the axles is 14 ft.

$$y = \frac{5 \times 14}{2 \times 20} = 1.75 \text{ ft}$$

The greatest moment occurs when the rear wheel is $15 - 1.75 = 13.25$ ft on the span, and the front is $30 - (13.25 + 14) = 2.75$ ft from the other end.

3.11   Shear and moment diagrams

Although usually shear and moment diagrams are not necessary for the solution of beams, the engineer should know their construction. The shear diagram provides the means of locating the point of maximum moment on a beam (see Art. 3.10), and although it is usually unnecessary to go to the trouble of drawing it, for irregularly loaded beams it is at least necessary to have a mental picture of the diagram. The shear diagram is also used in computation of stirrups in a concrete beam (see Art. 5.30).

The shear diagram represents graphically the actual vertical shear at all points along a beam, and the moment diagram represents the moment at all points along the beam. Figure 3.13 shows the general shape of shear and moment diagrams for the various types of uniformly loaded and concentrated load beams.

a   The shear diagram is drawn by laying out to scale—a vertical scale to represent load and a horizontal scale to represent length—a beam diagram showing all upward loads drawn as straight lines up (reactions) and downward loads downward, a straight drop for a concentrated load and a slant line downward for a uniform load. Reference to Fig. 3.13 will indicate the following facts about shear diagrams:

1. Concentrated loads are indicated by a straight drop downward.

2. Uniform loads are indicated by a sloping line downward.

3. Uniform loads that vary on several parts of a beam are indicated by sloping lines which change slope at points where the ratio of uniform load changes.

4. Uniformly increasing or decreasing loads are represented by curved lines.

5. Through sections where no loads either uniform or concentrated are applied, the line of the shear diagram is parallel with the base line.

6. A properly drawn shear diagram is a good check on the reactions of a beam.

b   The moment diagram is useful for solving several problems in structural design and is referred to under the following headings:

1. SIMPLE BEAM—UNIFORMLY DISTRIBUTED LOAD

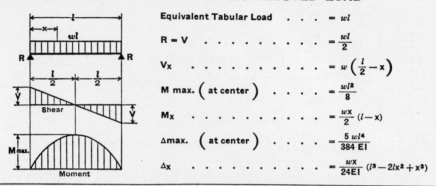

Equivalent Tabular Load . . .	$= wl$
R = V	$= \dfrac{wl}{2}$
V_x	$= w\left(\dfrac{l}{2} - x\right)$
M max. (at center)	$= \dfrac{wl^2}{8}$
M_x	$= \dfrac{wx}{2}(l - x)$
Δmax. (at center)	$= \dfrac{5\,wl^4}{384\,EI}$
Δ_x	$= \dfrac{wx}{24EI}(l^3 - 2lx^2 + x^3)$

2. SIMPLE BEAM—LOAD INCREASING UNIFORMLY TO ONE END

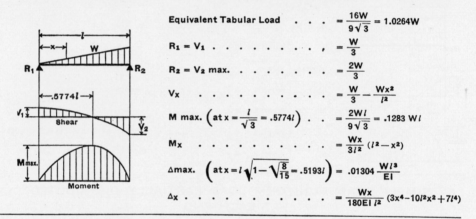

Equivalent Tabular Load . . .	$= \dfrac{16W}{9\sqrt{3}} = 1.0264W$
$R_1 = V_1$ . . . . ,	$= \dfrac{W}{3}$
$R_2 = V_2$ max.	$= \dfrac{2W}{3}$
V_x	$= \dfrac{W}{3} - \dfrac{Wx^2}{l^2}$
M max. $\left(\text{at } x = \dfrac{l}{\sqrt{3}} = .5774l\right)$ . . .	$= \dfrac{2Wl}{9\sqrt{3}} = .1283\,Wl$
M_x	$= \dfrac{Wx}{3l^2}(l^2 - x^2)$
Δmax. $\left(\text{at } x = l\sqrt{1 - \sqrt{\dfrac{8}{15}}} = .5193l\right)$	$= .01304\,\dfrac{Wl^3}{EI}$
Δ_x	$= \dfrac{Wx}{180EI\,l^2}(3x^4 - 10l^2x^2 + 7l^4)$

3. SIMPLE BEAM—LOAD INCREASING UNIFORMLY TO CENTER

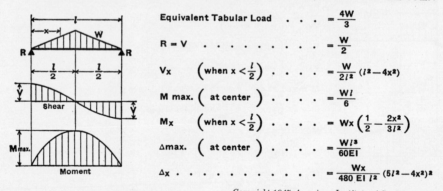

Equivalent Tabular Load . . .	$= \dfrac{4W}{3}$
R = V	$= \dfrac{W}{2}$
V_x $\left(\text{when } x < \dfrac{l}{2}\right)$	$= \dfrac{W}{2l^2}(l^2 - 4x^2)$
M max. (at center)	$= \dfrac{Wl}{6}$
M_x $\left(\text{when } x < \dfrac{l}{2}\right)$	$= Wx\left(\dfrac{1}{2} - \dfrac{2x^2}{3l^2}\right)$
Δmax. (at center)	$= \dfrac{Wl^3}{60EI}$
Δ_x	$= \dfrac{Wx}{480\,EI\,l^2}(5l^2 - 4x^2)^2$

Fig. 3.13   Beam Diagrams and Formulae

Art. 2.31—Computation of deflection by the use of moment-area method.

Art. 3.21—Finding contraflexure points, and positive moment in continuous beams.

Art. 4.20—Determination of length of cover plates on a plate girder.

c The moment diagrams for problems involving concentrated loads only are simple to draw. It is only necessary to compute the moment at points of load, lay them out to scale above the base line, and connect the points with straight lines.

4. SIMPLE BEAM—UNIFORM LOAD PARTIALLY DISTRIBUTED

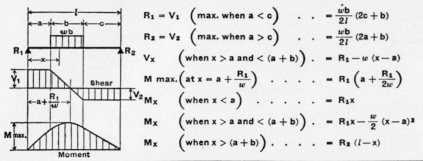

$$R_1 = V_1 \left(\text{max. when } a < c \right) \quad \cdots \quad = \frac{wb}{2l}(2c+b)$$

$$R_2 = V_2 \left(\text{max. when } a > c \right) \quad \cdots \quad = \frac{wb}{2l}(2a+b)$$

$$V_x \left(\text{when } x > a \text{ and } < (a+b) \right) . = R_1 - w(x-a)$$

$$M \text{ max.} \left(\text{at } x = a + \frac{R_1}{w} \right) \cdots = R_1 \left(a + \frac{R_1}{2w} \right)$$

$$M_x \left(\text{when } x < a \right) \cdots = R_1 x$$

$$M_x \left(\text{when } x > a \text{ and } < (a+b) \right) . = R_1 x - \frac{w}{2}(x-a)^2$$

$$M_x \left(\text{when } x > (a+b) \right) \cdots = R_2(l-x)$$

5. SIMPLE BEAM—UNIFORM LOAD PARTIALLY DISTRIBUTED AT ONE END

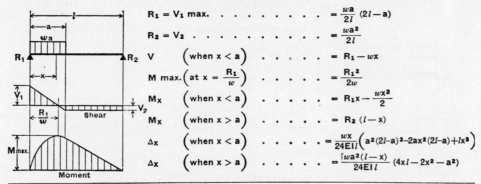

$$R_1 = V_1 \text{ max.} \cdots = \frac{wa}{2l}(2l-a)$$

$$R_2 = V_2 \cdots = \frac{wa^2}{2l}$$

$$V \left(\text{when } x < a \right) \cdots = R_1 - wx$$

$$M \text{ max.} \left(\text{at } x = \frac{R_1}{w} \right) \cdots = \frac{R_1^2}{2w}$$

$$M_x \left(\text{when } x < a \right) \cdots = R_1 x - \frac{wx^2}{2}$$

$$M_x \left(\text{when } x > a \right) \cdots = R_2(l-x)$$

$$\Delta_x \left(\text{when } x < a \right) \cdots = \frac{wx}{24EIl}\left(a^2(2l-a)^2 - 2ax^2(2l-a) + lx^3 \right)$$

$$\Delta_x \left(\text{when } x > a \right) \cdots = \frac{[wa^2(l-x)]}{24EIl}(4xl - 2x^2 - a^2)$$

6. SIMPLE BEAM—UNIFORM LOAD PARTIALLY DISTRIBUTED AT EACH END

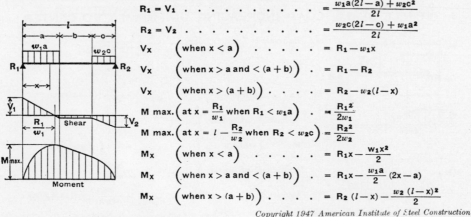

$$R_1 = V_1 \cdots = \frac{w_1 a(2l-a) + w_2 c^2}{2l}$$

$$R_2 = V_2 \cdots = \frac{w_2 c(2l-c) + w_1 a^2}{2l}$$

$$V_x \left(\text{when } x < a \right) \cdots = R_1 - w_1 x$$

$$V_x \left(\text{when } x > a \text{ and } < (a+b) \right) . = R_1 - R_2$$

$$V_x \left(\text{when } x > (a+b) \right) \cdots = R_2 - w_2(l-x)$$

$$M \text{ max.} \left(\text{at } x = \frac{R_1}{w_1} \text{ when } R_1 < w_1 a \right) . = \frac{R_1^2}{2w_1}$$

$$M \text{ max.} \left(\text{at } x = l - \frac{R_2}{w_2} \text{ when } R_2 < w_2 c \right) = \frac{R_2^2}{2w_2}$$

$$M_x \left(\text{when } x < a \right) \cdots = R_1 x - \frac{w_1 x^2}{2}$$

$$M_x \left(\text{when } x > a \text{ and } < (a+b) \right) . = R_1 x - \frac{w_1 a}{2}(2x-a)$$

$$M_x \left(\text{when } x > (a+b) \right) \cdots = R_2(l-x) - \frac{w_2(l-x)^2}{2}$$

Fig. 3.13　Beam Diagrams and Formulae (Continued)

Moment diagrams involving uniform loads, even through part of the span, require the construction of parabolas (see Table 1.18). For a beam carrying a uniform load throughout its full length plus one or more concentrated loads, the simplest method is to construct the two separate moment diagrams, one above the line, the other beneath the line. If the use of the moment diagram requires a level base line, reconstruct the combined diagram above the base line by adding the length of ordinate below the base line to each ordinate on top of the parabola. Then construct a smooth curve through the various points. If

7. SIMPLE BEAM—CONCENTRATED LOAD AT CENTER

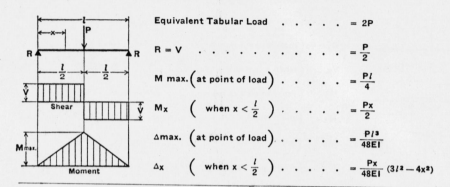

Equivalent Tabular Load . . . . . . $= 2P$

$R = V$ . . . . $= \dfrac{P}{2}$

M max. $\left(\text{at point of load}\right)$ . . . . . $= \dfrac{Pl}{4}$

M_x $\left(\text{when } x < \dfrac{l}{2}\right)$ . . . . . $= \dfrac{Px}{2}$

Δmax. $\left(\text{at point of load}\right)$ . . . . . $= \dfrac{Pl^3}{48EI}$

Δ_x $\left(\text{when } x < \dfrac{l}{2}\right)$ . . . . . $= \dfrac{Px}{48EI}(3l^2 - 4x^2)$

8. SIMPLE BEAM—CONCENTRATED LOAD AT ANY POINT

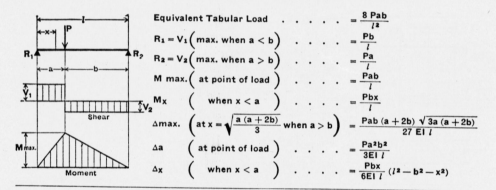

Equivalent Tabular Load . . . . . . $= \dfrac{8\,Pab}{l^2}$

$R_1 = V_1\left(\text{max. when } a < b\right)$ . . . . $= \dfrac{Pb}{l}$

$R_2 = V_2\left(\text{max. when } a > b\right)$ . . . . $= \dfrac{Pa}{l}$

M max. $\left(\text{at point of load}\right)$ . . . . $= \dfrac{Pab}{l}$

M_x $\left(\text{when } x < a\right)$ . . . . $= \dfrac{Pbx}{l}$

Δmax. $\left(\text{at } x = \sqrt{\dfrac{a(a+2b)}{3}} \text{ when } a > b\right)$ $= \dfrac{Pab(a+2b)\sqrt{3a(a+2b)}}{27\,EI\,l}$

Δa $\left(\text{at point of load}\right)$ . . . . $= \dfrac{Pa^2b^2}{3EI\,l}$

Δ_x $\left(\text{when } x < a\right)$ . . . . $= \dfrac{Pbx}{6EI\,l}(l^2 - b^2 - x^2)$

9. SIMPLE BEAM—TWO EQUAL CONCENTRATED LOADS SYMMETRICALLY PLACED

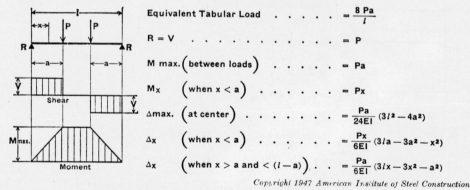

Equivalent Tabular Load . . . . . . $= \dfrac{8\,Pa}{l}$

$R = V$ . . . . $= P$

M max. $\left(\text{between loads}\right)$ . . . . . $= Pa$

M_x $\left(\text{when } x < a\right)$ . . . . . . $= Px$

Δmax. $\left(\text{at center}\right)$ . . . . $= \dfrac{Pa}{24EI}(3l^2 - 4a^2)$

Δ_x $\left(\text{when } x < a\right)$ . . . . . . $= \dfrac{Px}{6EI}(3la - 3a^2 - x^2)$

Δ_x $\left(\text{when } x > a \text{ and } < (l-a)\right)$ . . . $= \dfrac{Pa}{6EI}(3lx - 3x^2 - a^2)$

Fig. 3.13   Beam Diagrams and Formulae (Continued)

the beam carries a uniform load through one section only, compute the moment at the beginning and the end of the load, then draw a base line through these two points and construct a parabola on the new base line, the height of the parabola to be determined by the moment at the center of the uniform-load area. Properly drawn, the parabola at its ends should be tangent to the straight lines (see Fig. 3.13, Case 4).

The construction and use of moment diagrams for continuous beams is discussed in Art. 3.21 on the Hardy Cross method of moment distribution.

10.　SIMPLE BEAM—TWO EQUAL CONCENTRATED LOADS UNSYMMETRICALLY PLACED

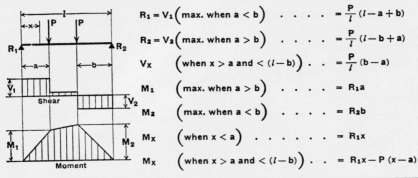

$R_1 = V_1 \left(\text{max. when } a < b \right)$ . . . . . $= \dfrac{P}{l}(l - a + b)$

$R_2 = V_2 \left(\text{max. when } a > b \right)$ . . . . . $= \dfrac{P}{l}(l - b + a)$

$V_x \quad \left(\text{when } x > a \text{ and } < (l - b) \right)$ . . $= \dfrac{P}{l}(b - a)$

$M_1 \quad \left(\text{max. when } a > b \right)$ . . . . . $= R_1 a$

$M_2 \quad \left(\text{max. when } a < b \right)$ . . . . . $= R_2 b$

$M_x \quad \left(\text{when } x < a \right)$ . . . . . . $= R_1 x$

$M_x \quad \left(\text{when } x > a \text{ and } < (l - b) \right)$ . . $= R_1 x - P(x - a)$

11.　SIMPLE BEAM—TWO UNEQUAL CONCENTRATED LOADS UNSYMMETRICALLY PLACED

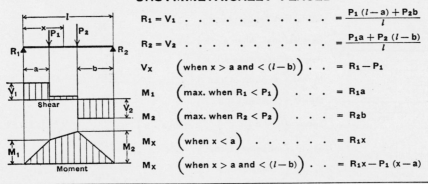

$R_1 = V_1$ . . . . $= \dfrac{P_1(l - a) + P_2 b}{l}$

$R_2 = V_2$ . . . . $= \dfrac{P_1 a + P_2(l - b)}{l}$

$V_x \quad \left(\text{when } x > a \text{ and } < (l - b) \right)$ . . $= R_1 - P_1$

$M_1 \quad \left(\text{max. when } R_1 < P_1 \right)$ . . . $= R_1 a$

$M_2 \quad \left(\text{max. when } R_2 < P_2 \right)$ . . . $= R_2 b$

$M_x \quad \left(\text{when } x < a \right)$ . . . . . $= R_1 x$

$M_x \quad \left(\text{when } x > a \text{ and } < (l - b) \right)$ . . $= R_1 x - P_1(x - a)$

12.　BEAM FIXED AT ONE END, SUPPORTED AT OTHER— UNIFORMLY DISTRIBUTED LOAD

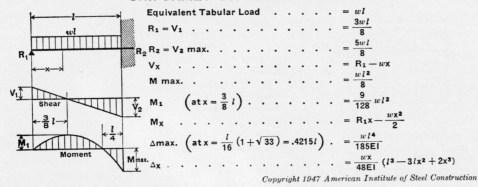

Equivalent Tabular Load . . . . . $= wl$

$R_1 = V_1$ . . . . $= \dfrac{3wl}{8}$

$R_2 = V_2$ max. . . . . $= \dfrac{5wl}{8}$

V_x . . . . $= R_1 - wx$

M max. . . . . $= \dfrac{wl^2}{8}$

$M_1 \quad \left(\text{at } x = \dfrac{3}{8} l \right)$ . . . . $= \dfrac{9}{128} wl^2$

M_x . . . . $= R_1 x - \dfrac{wx^2}{2}$

Δ max. $\left(\text{at } x = \dfrac{l}{16}(1 + \sqrt{33}) = .4215 l \right)$. $= \dfrac{wl^4}{185 EI}$

Δ_x . . . . $= \dfrac{wx}{48 EI}(l^3 - 3lx^2 + 2x^3)$

Fig. 3.13　Beam Diagrams and Formulae (Continued)

3.20 MOMENTS—CONTINUOUS BEAMS

a Continuous beams, that is, beams over three or more supports, are statically indeterminate structures and are not subject to analysis by simple beam methods. The continuous-beam diagrams in Fig. 3.13 give the moment and the shear resulting from (1) a uniformly distributed load on equal spans, with beams of constant moment of inertia, and (2) concentrated loads under several different conditions on equal spans, with beams of constant moment of inertia. For steel

13. BEAM FIXED AT ONE END, SUPPORTED AT OTHER— CONCENTRATED LOAD AT CENTER

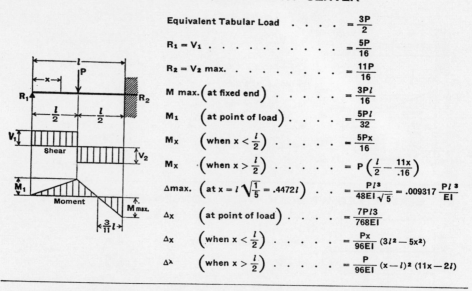

Equivalent Tabular Load $\ldots \ldots = \dfrac{3P}{2}$

$R_1 = V_1 \ldots \ldots \ldots \ldots = \dfrac{5P}{16}$

$R_2 = V_2$ max. $\ldots \ldots \ldots = \dfrac{11P}{16}$

M max. $\left(\text{at fixed end}\right) \ldots \ldots = \dfrac{3Pl}{16}$

$M_1 \quad \left(\text{at point of load}\right) \ldots \ldots = \dfrac{5Pl}{32}$

$M_x \quad \left(\text{when } x < \dfrac{l}{2}\right) \ldots \ldots = \dfrac{5Px}{16}$

$M_x \quad \left(\text{when } x > \dfrac{l}{2}\right) \ldots \ldots = P\left(\dfrac{l}{2} - \dfrac{11x}{.16}\right)$

Δmax. $\left(\text{at } x = l\sqrt{\dfrac{1}{5}} = .4472l\right) \ldots = \dfrac{Pl^3}{48EI\sqrt{5}} = .009317\,\dfrac{Pl^3}{EI}$

$\Delta_x \quad \left(\text{at point of load}\right) \ldots \ldots = \dfrac{7Pl^3}{768EI}$

$\Delta_x \quad \left(\text{when } x < \dfrac{l}{2}\right) \ldots \ldots = \dfrac{Px}{96EI}(3l^2 - 5x^2)$

$\Delta_x \quad \left(\text{when } x > \dfrac{l}{2}\right) \ldots \ldots = \dfrac{P}{96EI}(x-l)^2(11x - 2l)$

14. BEAM FIXED AT ONE END, SUPPORTED AT OTHER— CONCENTRATED LOAD AT ANY POINT

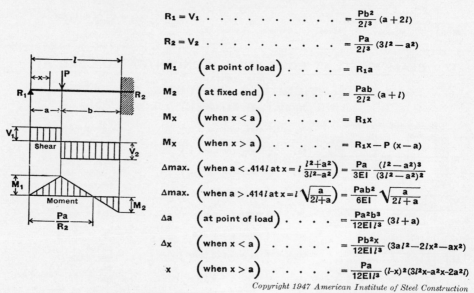

$R_1 = V_1 \ldots \ldots \ldots \ldots = \dfrac{Pb^2}{2l^3}(a + 2l)$

$R_2 = V_2 \ldots \ldots \ldots \ldots = \dfrac{Pa}{2l^3}(3l^2 - a^2)$

$M_1 \quad \left(\text{at point of load}\right) \ldots \ldots = R_1 a$

$M_2 \quad \left(\text{at fixed end}\right) \ldots \ldots = \dfrac{Pab}{2l^2}(a + l)$

$M_x \quad \left(\text{when } x < a\right) \ldots \ldots = R_1 x$

$M_x \quad \left(\text{when } x > a\right) \ldots \ldots = R_1 x - P(x - a)$

Δmax. $\left(\text{when } a < .414l \text{ at } x = l\dfrac{l^2 + a^2}{3l^2 - a^2}\right) = \dfrac{Pa}{3EI}\dfrac{(l^2 - a^2)^3}{(3l^2 - a^2)^2}$

Δmax. $\left(\text{when } a > .414l \text{ at } x = l\sqrt{\dfrac{a}{2l + a}}\right) = \dfrac{Pab^2}{6EI}\sqrt{\dfrac{a}{2l + a}}$

$\Delta a \quad \left(\text{at point of load}\right) \ldots \ldots = \dfrac{Pa^2b^3}{12EI\,l^3}(3l + a)$

$\Delta_x \quad \left(\text{when } x < a\right) \ldots \ldots = \dfrac{Pb^2x}{12EI\,l^3}(3al^2 - 2lx^2 - ax^2)$

$x \quad \left(\text{when } x > a\right) \ldots \ldots = \dfrac{Pa}{12EI\,l^3}(l-x)^2(3l^2x - a^2x - 2a^2l)$

Fig. 3.13 Beam Diagrams and Formulae (Continued)

beams which are naturally of a constant moment of inertia, these tables are quite satisfactory, but until welding comes more generally into use, this condition will be the exception rather than the rule in steel construction. For concrete beams or for built-up steel beams in which the moment of inertia may be varied by adding or omitting cover plates, these charts do not give the maximum results to be designed for. The maximum negative moment at any support results when the two adjacent members are fully loaded and all other panels have dead load only. The maximum positive moment results when the beam

15. BEAM FIXED AT BOTH ENDS—UNIFORMLY DISTRIBUTED LOADS

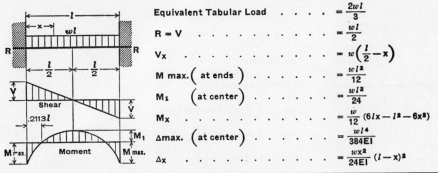

Equivalent Tabular Load . . . . $= \dfrac{2wl}{3}$

$R = V$ . . . . $= \dfrac{wl}{2}$

V_x . . . . $= w\left(\dfrac{l}{2} - x\right)$

M max. (at ends) . . . . . . $= \dfrac{wl^2}{12}$

M_1 (at center) . . . . . . $= \dfrac{wl^2}{24}$

M_x . . . . $= \dfrac{w}{12}(6lx - l^2 - 6x^2)$

Δmax. (at center) . . . . . $= \dfrac{wl^4}{384EI}$

Δ_x . . . . $= \dfrac{wx^2}{24EI}(l - x)^2$

16. BEAM FIXED AT BOTH ENDS—CONCENTRATED LOAD AT CENTER

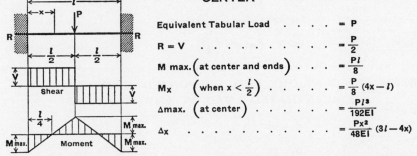

Equivalent Tabular Load . . . . $= P$

$R = V$ . . . . $= \dfrac{P}{2}$

M max. (at center and ends) . . . . $= \dfrac{Pl}{8}$

M_x $\left(\text{when } x < \dfrac{l}{2}\right)$ . . . . . $= \dfrac{P}{8}(4x - l)$

Δmax. (at center) . . . . . . $= \dfrac{Pl^3}{192EI}$

Δ_x . . . . $= \dfrac{Px^2}{48EI}(3l - 4x)$

17. BEAM FIXED AT BOTH ENDS—CONCENTRATED LOAD AT ANY POINT

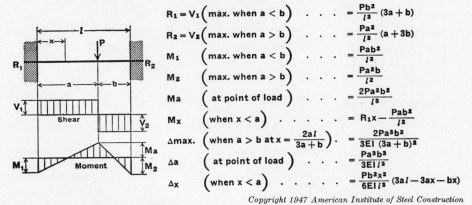

$R_1 = V_1$ (max. when $a < b$) . . . $= \dfrac{Pb^2}{l^3}(3a + b)$

$R_2 = V_2$ (max. when $a > b$) . . . $= \dfrac{Pa^2}{l^3}(a + 3b)$

M_1 (max. when $a < b$) . . . $= \dfrac{Pab^2}{l^2}$

M_2 (max. when $a > b$) . . . $= \dfrac{Pa^2b}{l^2}$

M_a (at point of load) . . . . $= \dfrac{2Pa^2b^2}{l^3}$

M_x (when $x < a$) . . . . . $= R_1x - \dfrac{Pab^2}{l^2}$

Δmax. $\left(\text{when } a > b \text{ at } x = \dfrac{2al}{3a + b}\right)$. $= \dfrac{2Pa^3b^2}{3EI(3a + b)^2}$

Δ_a (at point of load) . . . . $= \dfrac{Pa^3b^3}{3EIl^3}$

Δ_x (when $x < a$) . . . . . $= \dfrac{Pb^2x^2}{6EIl^3}(3al - 3ax - bx)$

Fig. 3.13 Beam Diagrams and Formulae (Continued)

or slab in question is loaded, the spans on either side of the span in question carry dead load only, and the balance of the spans are alternately loaded and unloaded. Obviously the dead load is always applied to all spans.

The charts (Fig. 3.13) are useful in indicating the general type of moment resulting; or, since under normal conditions the maximum moment is the negative moment, the charts give an approximation of the maximum moment, from which the size of beam may be determined.

Occasionally a problem is encountered which may be solved by the use of the coefficients

18. CANTILEVER BEAM—LOAD INCREASING UNIFORMLY TO FIXED END

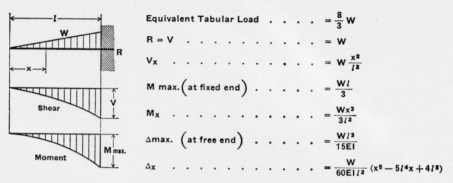

Equivalent Tabular Load . . . . $= \dfrac{8}{3} W$

$R = V$ . . . . $= W$

V_x . . . . $= W \dfrac{x^2}{l^2}$

M max. $\left(\text{at fixed end}\right)$ . . . . . $= \dfrac{Wl}{3}$

M_x . . . . $= \dfrac{Wx^3}{3l^2}$

Δmax. $\left(\text{at free end}\right)$ . . . . . $= \dfrac{Wl^3}{15EI}$

Δ_x . . . . $= \dfrac{W}{60EIl^2}\,(x^5 - 5l^4x + 4l^5)$

---

19. CANTILEVER BEAM—UNIFORMLY DISTRIBUTED LOAD

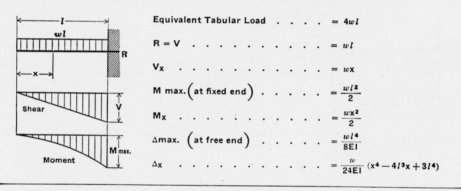

Equivalent Tabular Load . . . . $= 4wl$

$R = V$ . . . . $= wl$

V_x . . . . $= wx$

M max. $\left(\text{at fixed end}\right)$ . . . . . $= \dfrac{wl^2}{2}$

M_x . . . . $= \dfrac{wx^2}{2}$

Δmax. $\left(\text{at free end}\right)$ . . . . . $= \dfrac{wl^4}{8EI}$

Δ_x . . . . $= \dfrac{w}{24EI}\,(x^4 - 4l^3x + 3l^4)$

---

20. BEAM FIXED AT ONE END, FREE BUT GUIDED AT OTHER—UNIFORMLY DISTRIBUTED LOAD

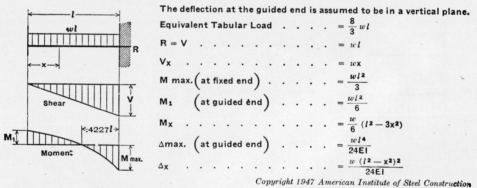

The deflection at the guided end is assumed to be in a vertical plane.

Equivalent Tabular Load . . . . $= \dfrac{8}{3} wl$

$R = V$ . . . . $= wl$

V_x . . . . $= wx$

M max. $\left(\text{at fixed end}\right)$ . . . . . $= \dfrac{wl^2}{3}$

M_1 $\left(\text{at guided end}\right)$ . . . . $= \dfrac{wl^2}{6}$

M_x . . . . $= \dfrac{w}{6}\,(l^2 - 3x^2)$

Δmax. $\left(\text{at guided end}\right)$ . . . . $= \dfrac{wl^4}{24EI}$

Δ_x . . . . $= \dfrac{w\,(l^2 - x^2)^2}{24EI}$

Fig. 3.13   Beam Diagrams and Formulae (Continued)

found in Fig. 3.13. Below is a typical problem of this type.

Problem   A floor is made up of 2-in. boards (actually $1\frac{5}{8}$ in. thick) 20 ft long and is supported on joists 4 ft apart. With a fiber stress of 1,600 psi, what is the maximum total load per square foot which may be put on the floor?

This indicates five equal spans. Reference to the continuous beam diagrams in Fig. 3.13 for five spans indicates that the maximum moment is at the first support from the end, and amounts to $(304/2,888)wL^2$, or $0.105WL$.

21. CANTILEVER BEAM—CONCENTRATED LOAD AT ANY POINT

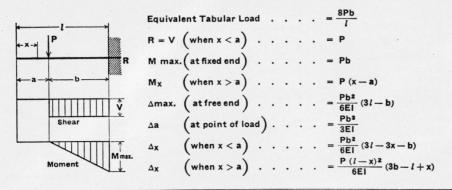

Equivalent Tabular Load . . . . $= \dfrac{8Pb}{l}$

$R = V$ $\left(\text{when } x < a\right)$ . . . . . $= P$

M max. $\left(\text{at fixed end}\right)$ . . . . . $= Pb$

M_x $\left(\text{when } x > a\right)$ . . . . . $= P(x - a)$

Δmax. $\left(\text{at free end}\right)$ . . . . $= \dfrac{Pb^2}{6EI}(3l - b)$

Δa $\left(\text{at point of load}\right)$ . . . . $= \dfrac{Pb^3}{3EI}$

Δx $\left(\text{when } x < a\right)$ . . . . . $= \dfrac{Pb^2}{6EI}(3l - 3x - b)$

Δx $\left(\text{when } x > a\right)$ . . . . $= \dfrac{P(l - x)^2}{6EI}(3b - l + x)$

22. CANTILEVER BEAM—CONCENTRATED LOAD AT FREE END

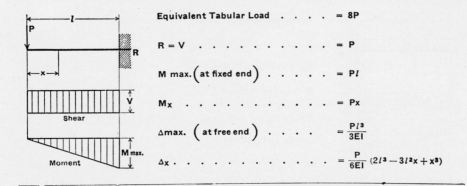

Equivalent Tabular Load . . . . $= 8P$

$R = V$ . . . . $= P$

M max. $\left(\text{at fixed end}\right)$ . . . . . $= Pl$

M_x . . . . $= Px$

Δmax. $\left(\text{at free end}\right)$ . . . . $= \dfrac{Pl^3}{3EI}$

Δx . . . . $= \dfrac{P}{6EI}(2l^3 - 3l^2 x + x^3)$

23. BEAM FIXED AT ONE END, FREE BUT GUIDED AT OTHER—CONCENTRATED LOAD AT GUIDED END

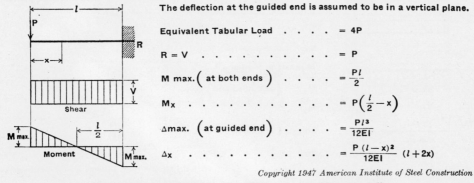

The deflection at the guided end is assumed to be in a vertical plane.

Equivalent Tabular Load . . . . $= 4P$

$R = V$ . . . . $= P$

M max. $\left(\text{at both ends}\right)$ . . . . $= \dfrac{Pl}{2}$

M_x . . . . $= P\left(\dfrac{l}{2} - x\right)$

Δmax. $\left(\text{at guided end}\right)$ . . . . $= \dfrac{Pl^3}{12EI}$

Δx . . . . $= \dfrac{P(l - x)^2}{12EI}(l + 2x)$

Copyright 1947 American Institute of Steel Construction

Fig. 3.13   Beam Diagrams and Formulae (Continued)

The section modulus per foot width is $\frac{1}{6}bd^2$, or

$$S = \frac{12 \times 1.625^2}{6} = 5.28 \text{ cu in.}$$

We will assume a trial load of 100 psf on the floor.

$W = 100 \times 4 = 400$ lb
$M = 0.105 \times 400 \times 4 \times 12 = 2016$ in.-lb

$$f = \frac{2,016}{5.28} = 382 \text{ psi}$$

Therefore if 100 psf causes a stress of 382 psi,

24. BEAM OVERHANGING ONE SUPPORT—UNIFORMLY DISTRIBUTED LOAD

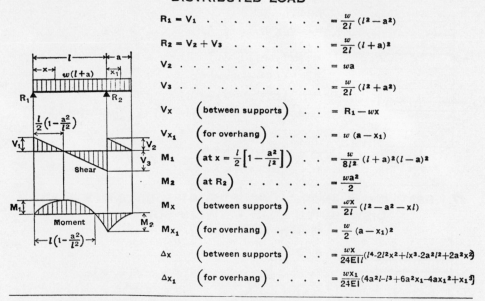

$$R_1 = V_1 \quad \ldots \ldots \ldots \ldots = \frac{w}{2l}(l^2 - a^2)$$

$$R_2 = V_2 + V_3 \quad \ldots \ldots \ldots = \frac{w}{2l}(l + a)^2$$

$$V_2 \quad \ldots \ldots \ldots \ldots \ldots \ldots = wa$$

$$V_3 \quad \ldots \ldots \ldots \ldots \ldots \ldots = \frac{w}{2l}(l^2 + a^2)$$

$$V_x \quad \text{(between supports)} \quad \ldots = R_1 - wx$$

$$V_{x_1} \quad \text{(for overhang)} \quad \ldots \ldots = w(a - x_1)$$

$$M_1 \quad \left(\text{at } x = \frac{l}{2}\left[1 - \frac{a^2}{l^2}\right]\right) \ldots = \frac{w}{8l^2}(l + a)^2(l - a)^2$$

$$M_2 \quad \left(\text{at } R_2\right) \quad \ldots \ldots \ldots = \frac{wa^2}{2}$$

$$M_x \quad \text{(between supports)} \quad \ldots = \frac{wx}{2l}(l^2 - a^2 - xl)$$

$$M_{x_1} \quad \text{(for overhang)} \quad \ldots \ldots = \frac{w}{2}(a - x_1)^2$$

$$\Delta_x \quad \text{(between supports)} \quad \ldots = \frac{wx}{24EIl}(l^4 - 2l^2x^2 + lx^3 - 2a^2l^2 + 2a^2x^2)$$

$$\Delta_{x_1} \quad \text{(for overhang)} \quad \ldots \ldots = \frac{wx_1}{24EI}(4a^2l - l^3 + 6a^2x_1 - 4ax_1^2 + x_1^3)$$

25. BEAM OVERHANGING ONE SUPPORT—UNIFORMLY DISTRIBUTED LOAD ON OVERHANG

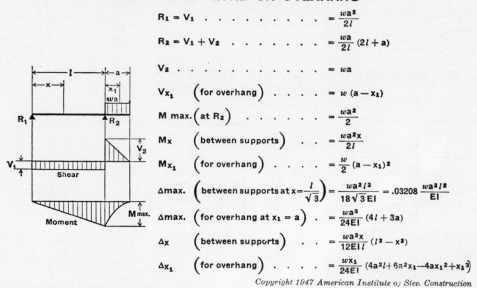

$$R_1 = V_1 \quad \ldots \ldots \ldots \ldots = \frac{wa^2}{2l}$$

$$R_2 = V_1 + V_2 \quad \ldots \ldots \ldots = \frac{wa}{2l}(2l + a)$$

$$V_2 \quad \ldots \ldots \ldots \ldots \ldots \ldots = wa$$

$$V_{x_1} \quad \text{(for overhang)} \quad \ldots \ldots = w(a - x_1)$$

$$M \text{ max.} \left(\text{at } R_2\right) \quad \ldots \ldots \ldots = \frac{wa^2}{2}$$

$$M_x \quad \text{(between supports)} \quad \ldots = \frac{wa^2x}{2l}$$

$$M_{x_1} \quad \text{(for overhang)} \quad \ldots \ldots = \frac{w}{2}(a - x_1)^2$$

$$\Delta \text{max.} \left(\text{between supports at } x = \frac{l}{\sqrt{3}}\right) = \frac{wa^2l^2}{18\sqrt{3}EI} = .03208\frac{wa^2l^2}{EI}$$

$$\Delta \text{max.} \quad \text{(for overhang at } x_1 = a) \quad \ldots = \frac{wa^3}{24EI}(4l + 3a)$$

$$\Delta_x \quad \text{(between supports)} \quad \ldots = \frac{wa^2x}{12EIl}(l^2 - x^2)$$

$$\Delta_{x_1} \quad \text{(for overhang)} \quad \ldots \ldots = \frac{wx_1}{24EI}(4a^2l + 6a^2x_1 - 4ax_1^2 + x_1^3)$$

Fig. 3.13　Beam Diagrams and Formulae (Continued)

the allowable load per square foot for 1,600 psi stress will be

$$\frac{1,600}{382} \times 100 = 419 \text{ psf}$$

b　Most continuous-beam problems do not give any assurance of constant load, so that instead of using the charts for an exact solution, some other method must be used. For spans which vary by not over 20 percent, with approximately equal uniform loads, it is ac-

26. BEAM OVERHANGING ONE SUPPORT—CONCENTRATED LOAD AT END OF OVERHANG

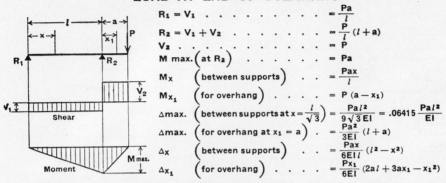

$R_1 = V_1$ . . . . $= \dfrac{Pa}{l}$

$R_2 = V_1 + V_2$ . . . . $= \dfrac{P}{l}(l+a)$

V_2 . . . . $= P$

M max. $\left(\text{at } R_2\right)$ . . . . . . $= Pa$

M_x $\left(\text{between supports}\right)$ . . $= \dfrac{Pax}{l}$

M_{x_1} $\left(\text{for overhang}\right)$ . . . . $= P(a-x_1)$

Δmax. $\left(\text{between supports at } x=\dfrac{l}{\sqrt 3}\right) = \dfrac{Pal^2}{9\sqrt 3\,EI} = .06415\dfrac{Pal^2}{EI}$

Δmax. $\left(\text{for overhang at } x_1 = a\right)$. $= \dfrac{Pa^2}{3EI}(l+a)$

Δ_x $\left(\text{between supports}\right)$ . . $= \dfrac{Pax}{6EIl}(l^2-x^2)$

Δ_{x_1} $\left(\text{for overhang}\right)$ . . . . $= \dfrac{Px_1}{6EI}(2al+3ax_1-x_1^2)$

27. BEAM OVERHANGING ONE SUPPORT—UNIFORMLY DISTRIBUTED LOAD BETWEEN SUPPORTS

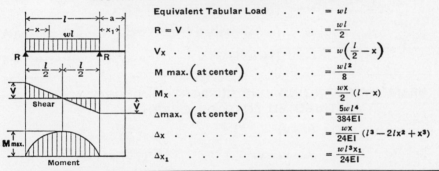

Equivalent Tabular Load . . . . $= wl$

$R = V$ . . . . $= \dfrac{wl}{2}$

V_x . . . . $= w\left(\dfrac{l}{2}-x\right)$

M max. $\left(\text{at center}\right)$ . . . . . $= \dfrac{wl^2}{8}$

M_x . . . . $= \dfrac{wx}{2}(l-x)$

Δmax. $\left(\text{at center}\right)$ . . . . . $= \dfrac{5wl^4}{384EI}$

Δ_x . . . . $= \dfrac{wx}{24EI}(l^3-2lx^2+x^3)$

Δ_{x_1} . . . . $= \dfrac{wl^3x_1}{24EI}$

28. BEAM OVERHANGING ONE SUPPORT—CONCENTRATED LOAD AT ANY POINT BETWEEN SUPPORTS

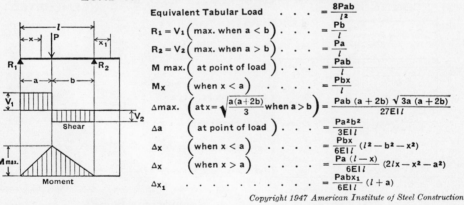

Equivalent Tabular Load . . . . $= \dfrac{8Pab}{l^2}$

$R_1 = V_1\left(\text{max. when } a<b\right)$ . . . $= \dfrac{Pb}{l}$

$R_2 = V_2\left(\text{max. when } a>b\right)$ . . . $= \dfrac{Pa}{l}$

M max. $\left(\text{at point of load}\right)$ . . . $= \dfrac{Pab}{l}$

M_x $\left(\text{when } x<a\right)$ . . . . $= \dfrac{Pbx}{l}$

Δmax. $\left(\text{at } x=\sqrt{\dfrac{a(a+2b)}{3}}\text{ when } a>b\right) = \dfrac{Pab(a+2b)\sqrt{3a(a+2b)}}{27EIl}$

Δa $\left(\text{at point of load}\right)$ . . . $= \dfrac{Pa^2b^2}{3EIl}$

Δ_x $\left(\text{when } x<a\right)$ . . . . $= \dfrac{Pbx}{6EIl}(l^2-b^2-x^2)$

Δ_x $\left(\text{when } x>a\right)$ . . . . $= \dfrac{Pa(l-x)}{6EIl}(2lx-x^2-a^2)$

Δ_{x_1} . . . . $= \dfrac{Pabx_1}{6EIl}(l+a)$

Fig. 3.13   Beam Diagrams and Formulae (Continued)

curate enough to use the ordinary moment coefficients as follows:

1. Beams and slabs of one span, positive moment near center (simple beam):

$$M = \frac{wL^2}{8}$$

2. Beams and slabs continuous for two spans only, positive moment near center (semi-continuous):

$$M = \frac{wL^2}{14}$$

29   CONTINUOUS BEAM—TWO EQUAL SPANS—UNIFORM LOAD ON ONE SPAN

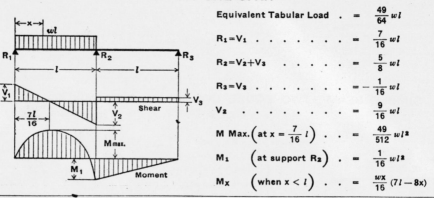

Equivalent Tabular Load . $= \dfrac{49}{64} wl$

$R_1 = V_1 \ldots \ldots \ldots = \dfrac{7}{16} wl$

$R_2 = V_2 + V_3 \ldots \ldots = \dfrac{5}{8} wl$

$R_3 = V_3 \ldots \ldots \ldots = -\dfrac{1}{16} wl$

$V_2 \ldots \ldots \ldots \ldots = \dfrac{9}{16} wl$

M Max. $\left(\text{at } x = \dfrac{7}{16} l\right) \ldots = \dfrac{49}{512} wl^2$

$M_1 \quad \left(\text{at support } R_2\right) . = \dfrac{1}{16} wl^2$

$M_x \quad \left(\text{when } x < l\right) \ldots = \dfrac{wx}{16}(7l - 8x)$

30.   CONTINUOUS BEAM—TWO EQUAL SPANS—CONCENTRATED LOAD AT CENTER OF ONE SPAN

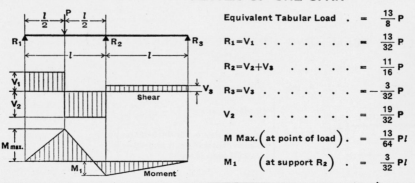

Equivalent Tabular Load . $= \dfrac{13}{8} P$

$R_1 = V_1 \ldots \ldots \ldots = \dfrac{13}{32} P$

$R_2 = V_2 + V_3 \ldots \ldots = \dfrac{11}{16} P$

$R_3 = V_3 \ldots \ldots \ldots = -\dfrac{3}{32} P$

$V_2 \ldots \ldots \ldots \ldots = \dfrac{19}{32} P$

M Max. $\left(\text{at point of load}\right) . = \dfrac{13}{64} Pl$

$M_1 \quad \left(\text{at support } R_2\right) . = \dfrac{3}{32} Pl$

31.   CONTINUOUS BEAM—TWO EQUAL SPANS—CONCENTRATED LOAD AT ANY POINT

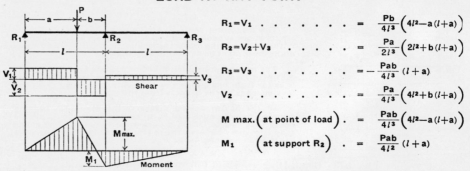

$R_1 = V_1 \ldots \ldots \ldots = \dfrac{Pb}{4l^3}\left(4l^2 - a(l+a)\right)$

$R_2 = V_2 + V_3 \ldots \ldots = \dfrac{Pa}{2l^3}\left(2l^2 + b(l+a)\right)$

$R_3 = V_3 \ldots \ldots \ldots = -\dfrac{Pab}{4l^3}(l+a)$

$V_2 \ldots \ldots \ldots \ldots = \dfrac{Pa}{4l^3}\left(4l^2 + b(l+a)\right)$

M max. $\left(\text{at point of load}\right) . = \dfrac{Pab}{4l^3}\left(4l^2 - a(l+a)\right)$

$M_1 \quad \left(\text{at support } R_2\right) . = \dfrac{Pab}{4l^2}(l+a)$

Fig. 3.13   Beam Diagrams and Formulae (Continued)

Negative moment over interior support:

$$M = \frac{wL^2}{9}$$

3. Beams and slabs continuous for more than two spans (fully continuous), positive moment near center of interior spans:

$$M = \frac{wL^2}{16}$$

Negative moment at first interior support:

$$M = \frac{wL^2}{10}$$

32. SIMPLE BEAM—ONE CONCENTRATED MOVING LOAD

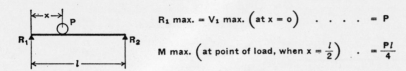

R_1 max. $= V_1$ max. $\left(\text{at } x = 0\right)$ . . . . $= P$

M max. $\left(\text{at point of load, when } x = \dfrac{l}{2}\right)$. $= \dfrac{Pl}{4}$

33. SIMPLE BEAM—TWO EQUAL CONCENTRATED MOVING LOADS

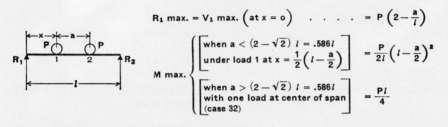

R_1 max. $= V_1$ max. $\left(\text{at } x = 0\right)$ . . . . $= P\left(2 - \dfrac{a}{l}\right)$

M max. $\begin{cases} \left[\begin{array}{l}\text{when } a < (2 - \sqrt{2})\, l = .586l \\ \text{under load 1 at } x = \frac{1}{2}\left(l - \frac{a}{2}\right)\end{array}\right] = \dfrac{P}{2l}\left(l - \dfrac{a}{2}\right)^2 \\[4ex] \left[\begin{array}{l}\text{when } a > (2 - \sqrt{2})\, l = .586l \\ \text{with one load at center of span} \\ \text{(case 32)}\end{array}\right] = \dfrac{Pl}{4} \end{cases}$

34. SIMPLE BEAM—TWO UNEQUAL CONCENTRATED MOVING LOADS

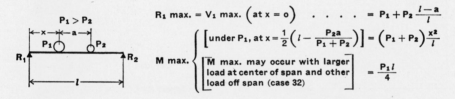

R_1 max. $= V_1$ max. $\left(\text{at } x = 0\right)$ . . . . $= P_1 + P_2\dfrac{l - a}{l}$

M max. $\begin{cases} \left[\text{under } P_1, \text{ at } x = \frac{1}{2}\left(l - \frac{P_2 a}{P_1 + P_2}\right)\right] = \left(P_1 + P_2\right)\dfrac{x^2}{l} \\[3ex] \left[\begin{array}{l}\text{M max. may occur with larger} \\ \text{load at center of span and other} \\ \text{load off span (case 32)}\end{array}\right] = \dfrac{P_1 l}{4} \end{cases}$

GENERAL RULES FOR SIMPLE BEAMS CARRYING MOVING CONCENTRATED LOADS

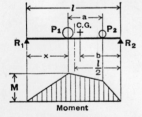

The maximum shear due to moving concentrated loads occurs at one support when one of the loads is at that support. With several moving loads, the location that will produce maximum shear must be determined by trial.

The maximum bending moment produced by moving concentrated loads occurs under one of the loads when that load is as far from one support as the center of gravity of all the moving loads on the beam is from the other support.

In the accompanying diagram, the maximum bending moment occurs under load P_1 when $x = b$. It should also be noted that this condition occurs when the center line of the span is midway between the center of gravity of loads and the nearest concentrated load.

Fig. 3.13   Beam Diagrams and Formulae (Continued)

Negative moment at other interior supports:

$$M = \frac{wL^2}{12}$$

Negative moment at end supports for cases 1, 2, and 3:

$$M = \text{not less than } \frac{wL^2}{24}$$

c The most modern practice in concrete recommends a complete analysis of the beams, or even an analysis combining beams and columns. The method of approach to such problems is to determine by one of several methods the statically indeterminate moments at the supports or at the joints, and apply these in-

CONTINUOUS BEAM DIAGRAMS

EQUAL SPANS, SIMILARLY LOADED, CONSTANT MOMENT OF INERTIA SUPPORTS AT SAME LEVEL

UNIFORMLY DISTRIBUTED LOAD

Reaction and shear coefficients of wl Moment coefficients of wl^2

w = Load per unit length

2 SPANS   **4 SPANS**

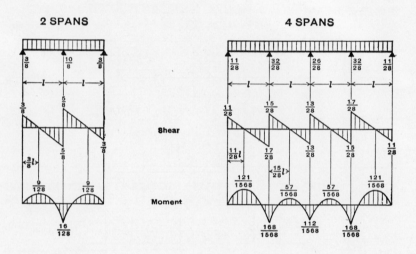

3 SPANS   **5 SPANS**

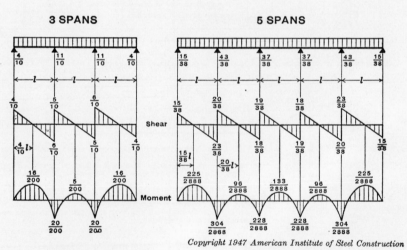

Fig. 3.13   Beam Diagrams and Formulae (Continued)

determinate moments to the ordinary static-moment diagrams. When the moments have been determined, the reactions, points of contraflexure, and other necessary information may be obtained. In simple beams the necessary information is dependent only on load, span, and conditions of loading. From this information a moment is obtainable from which, for any given material and fiber stress the design may be made. In continuous beams or rigid frames, however, the stiffness factor K, which is the ratio I/L of each member

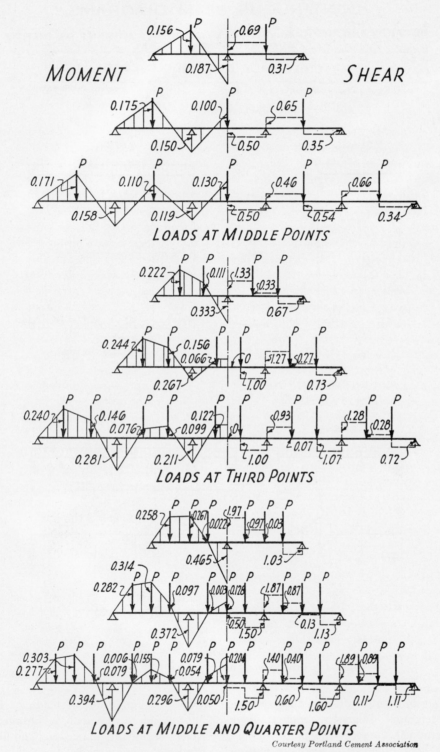

Fig. 3.13   Beam Diagrams and Formulae (Continued)

Courtesy Portland Cement Association

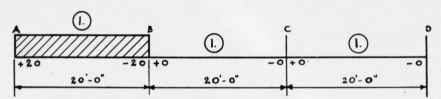

Fig. 3.14   First Step in Moment-Distribution Problem

respectively, controls the distribution of the indeterminate moments and enters into each of the various methods of solution. Since I/L is a factor for each individual member, it becomes a ratio between the various members; therefore it makes no difference if L is taken in feet and I in inches, or vice versa. The main idea is to keep the mathematics in the simplest possible terms. In any case, the units must be kept the same for the stiffness factors of all members in a series.

Until a few years ago the common method of approach to the problem of continuous-beam moments was the rather cumbersome three-moment theorem. This has been replaced in most offices by the Hardy Cross method of moment distribution—a close approximation devised by Prof. Hardy Cross, given in Art. 3.21. No other method of solution for continuous beams is given because no other method is so usable in actual design.

d   The shear at the end of a continuous beam is determined by the sum of the shear in the beam simply supported, with a correction plus or minus due to the difference between the end moments. This correction is found by $\dfrac{(-M_1) - (-M_2)}{L}$, the correction being added to the end with the greater negative moment and subtracted from the end with the lesser negative moment. Since the negative moments may vary depending on adjacent spans, it is advisable in computing shears to add the full correction but to subtract only $\frac{2}{3}$ of the full correction. This correction is not usually large for interior bays but may be an appreciable amount in an end bay (see Fig. 3.13).

3.21   Method of moment distribution

a   The Hardy Cross method of moment distribution starts by assuming each span as

a fixed beam, similar to Case 15, 16, or 17 of the beam diagrams in Fig. 3.13. However, since the moment must be the same on both sides of a support—that is, since the slope of both beams must be tangent to the same line over a support—the moment on both sides of the support must be the same. The Hardy Cross method is a means of adjusting the assumed moments to an approximately correct result—correct within all necessary limits.

Fixed end moments, frequently designated as "fem," for all normal conditions are given in the series of charts in Fig. 3.24.

For any combination of load conditions, add the fixed end moments. Thus for a trapezoidal load, add Case 5 and Case 12 of Fig. 3.24.

To eliminate some cumbersome calculation, coefficients of influence are given in Table 3.1 for Case 15, and in Tables 3.2 and 3.3 for Cases 14 and 11.

b   The various steps in the design are as follows, referring to Fig. 3.14 as typical:

1. Compute for each span a stiffness factor $K = I/L$. Since this is a ratio only, I may be taken as 1 for each if the beam is of the same section over all supports. In Fig. 3.14 all spans are alike and the beam is continuous, so $K = 1$ for all spans. Put this figure in a circle over each span.

2. Compute the fixed end moment in each span from Fig. 3.24. To distinguish between positive and negative moment, ordinarily bending upward is considered negative, downward positive. It will simplify this problem, however, if the convention is forgotten until the corrected moment has been obtained, and bending in a clockwise direction about a joint is considered positive, counterclockwise negative. The computed moments are set down under the ends of the beam as has been done in Fig. 3.14.

3. If the slope on each side of the support

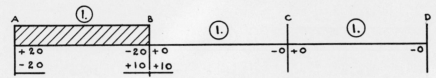

Fig. 3.15   First Distribution in Moment-Distribution Problem

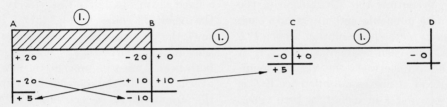

Fig. 3.16   First Carry-over in Moment-Distribution Problem

is to be tangent to the same line, the algebraic sum of the moments about a joint must equal zero. At point B there is an unbalanced moment of -20. At A there is an unbalanced moment of $+20$. Since end A is freely supported, the moment on both sides of the joint must equal zero.

The moments may be balanced in turn by adding and subtracting in proportion to the stiffness ratio K till each joint comes to an algebraic total of zero. At the free end A, since the adjacent span has no stiffness, the full moment must be distributed on one side. Set down the balancing moment and draw a line under it as in Fig. 3.15.

4. This process of balancing, however, sets up a "carry-over" moment in the opposite end of the same beam span, equal to one-half the balancing moment and of the same sign. (This carry-over factor is one-half only when the beam span is of uniform section throughout. For instance, concrete beams bracketed at the columns have a different carry-over factor. See Art. 3.21h.) Set down the carry-over moment as in Fig. 3.16.

This carry-over moment again unbalances the joints, and they must again be balanced, carried over, balanced again, carried over again, etc., until sufficient accuracy is reached, as in Fig. 3.17.

5. The final M is obtained by adding all moments algebraically (original, balancing, and carry-over moments), and these will balance both sides of any joint.

6. The procedure for application of positive moment and obtaining shears is shown in Arts. 3.21e and 3.21f.

c With a free end like A or D in the preceding problem, the computation can be greatly simplified by multiplying K for the end span by $\frac{3}{4}$, balancing the end moment once, and avoiding the end span in any further calculations. If K is not the same in all spans, the percentage of stiffness is put down each side of the joint as in Fig. 3.18 where this shortcut method has been applied to the problem of the last paragraph. The figure 0.43 at B represents 0.75/1.75, and 0.57 is 1/1.75. This calculation has been carried to a finer conclusion than in the earlier paragraph, and is probably more accurate.

d A typical problem from actual design calculations is shown in Figs. 3.19 and 3.20. In determination of K, I has been assumed at 10 throughout, so that in span BC, $K = 10/15 = 0.667$. In the two end spans, the multiplier 0.75 has been used as described in the preceding paragraph.

e In accordance with the statement made in Art. 3.20c, the actual moments throughout, including maximum positive moments, are found by computing the simple moment and plotting it, then applying the indeterminate moments to the static-moment diagrams.

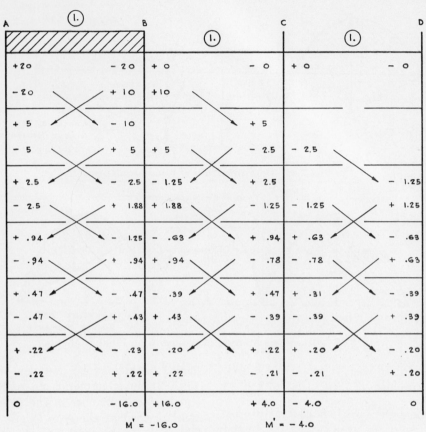

Fig. 3.17   Complete Moment-Distribution Problem

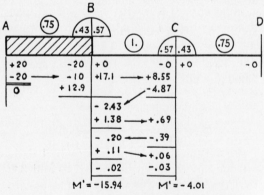

Fig. 3.18   Short Cut in Moment-Distribution
Problem

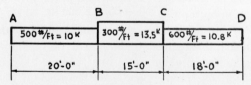

Fig. 3.19   Complex Moment-Distribution
Problem

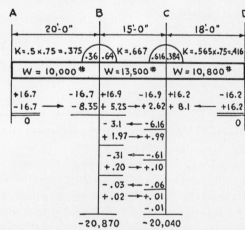

Fig. 3.20   Solution of Moment-Distribution
Problem

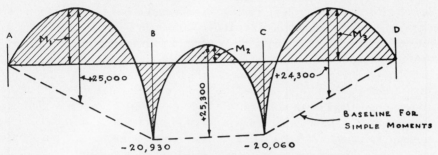

Fig. 3.21   Determination of Final Moments

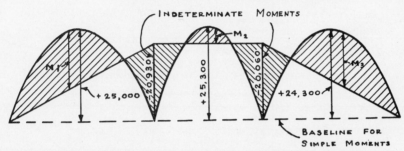

Fig. 3.22   Alternative Method of Determining Final Moments

To compute the positive moments of each span in the problem of Figs. 3.19 and 3.20:

$$M_1 = \frac{10,000 \times 20}{8} = 25,000$$

$$M_2 = \frac{13,500 \times 15}{8} = 25,300$$

$$M_3 = \frac{10,800 \times 18}{8} = 24,300$$

Laying the moments out graphically permits obtaining the maximum positive and negative moments. For a close approximation of the actual positive moments,

$$M_1 = 25,000 - \frac{20,870}{2} = 14,565$$

$$M_2 = 25,300 - \frac{20,870 + 20,040}{2} = 4,845$$

$$M_3 = 24,300 - \frac{20,040}{2} = 14,280$$

Instead of constructing the moment diagrams as shown in Fig. 3.21, they may be constructed on a straight base line as shown in Fig. 3.22, and the indeterminate moments laid off above the line to obtain actual moments.

f Having obtained the maximum moments, the next step is to compute reactions. The simplest method is to compute the reactions as a simple beam, which for a uniformly loaded beam may be done by observation. Then apply a correction to each reaction, equal to the difference in end moments on a span, divided by the span length. This correction is added to the reaction where the actual negative end moment is the greater, and subtracted from the reaction where the actual negative end moment is the lesser. Applying this method to the problem in Art. 3.21*e*, the reactions for the first span are 5,000 lb. The correction is

$$\frac{20,870}{20} = 1,044 \text{ lb}$$

$$R_a = 5,000 - 1,044 = 3,956 \text{ lb}$$
$$R_b = 5,000 + 1,044 = 6,044 \text{ lb}$$

For the second span, the normal reactions are 6,750 at each end, and the corrections

$$\frac{830}{15} = 55$$

$$R_b = 6,750 + 55 = 6,805 \text{ lb}$$
$$R_c = 6,750 - 55 = 6,695 \text{ lb}$$

For the third span, the normal reactions are 5,400. The correction is

$$\frac{20,040}{18} = 1,113$$

$$R_c = 5,400 + 1,113 = 6,513 \text{ lb}$$
$$R_d = 5,400 - 1,113 = 4,287 \text{ lb}$$

g *The indirect Hardy Cross method.* There are certain problems which cannot be solved directly, but which require an indirect approach: certain moments are assumed, the structure is balanced using these moments, and correction from the resulting shears is obtained. We approach the method by putting forth two axioms: (1) for equal deflections the moment varies as I/L^2 or as K/L, and (2) the horizontal thrust varies as I/L^3 or as K/L^2.

Problem Assume a crane column subject to a horizontal thrust, with unequal section

above and below the load point. Treating the column as a beam, the method is indicated in Fig. 3.23. Assume in span AB a moment of 100, the sign being the same at both ends of the span. In order to satisfy axiom 1, the moment in the span BC would be $\frac{3}{4} \times 100 = 75$; but observation indicates that the bending would be of the opposite sign. If we balance the center joint and carry over, we arrive at the final moments indicated. The shear in each span is obtained by dividing the sum of the two end moments by the span.

$$V_{AB} = \frac{95 + 90}{10} = 18.5$$

Table 3.1   Value of Coefficient C_1 for Single Concentrated Load on Beam

Case 15 of Fig. 3.24; fem $= C_1WL$

C_1	+.00	.01	.02	.03	.04	.05	.06	.07	.08	.09
.0		.010	.019	.028	.037	.045	.053	.061	.068	.075
.1	.081	.087	.093	.098	.104	.108	.113	.117	.121	.125
.2	.128	.131	.134	.136	.139	.141	.142	.144	.145	.146
.3	.147	.148	.148	.148	.148	.148	.147	.147	.146	.145
.4	.144	.143	.141	.140	.138	.136	.134	.132	.130	.127
.5	.125	.122	.120	.117	.114	.111	.108	.105	.102	.099
.6	.096	.093	.090	.086	.083	.080	.076	.073	.070	.066
.7	.063	.060	.056	.053	.050	.047	.044	.041	.038	.035
.8	.032	.029	.027	.024	.022	.019	.017	.015	.013	.011
.9	.009	.007	.006	.005	.003	.002	.002	.001	.000	.000

(Application: For load at .26L from near end, .74L from far end, $C_1 = .142$ at near end and .050 at far end.) For uniformly spaced equal loads the following may be used:

         For 1 load: fem $= .125WL$ For 2 loads: fem $= .111WL$

         For 3 loads: fem $= .104WL$ For 4 loads: fem $= .10 \ WL$

$$\text{For } n \text{ loads:} \quad \text{fem} = \frac{n+2}{12(n+1)} WL$$

Table 3.2   Value of Coefficient C_2 for Partial Uniform Load on Beam for Loaded End

Case 14 of Fig. 3.24; fem $= C_2WL$

C_2	+ .00	.01	.02	.03	.04	.05	.06	.07	.08	.09
.0		.005	.010	.014	.019	.023	.028	.032	.036	.040
.1	.044	.047	.051	.054	.058	.061	.064	.067	.070	.073
.2	.075	.078	.080	.083	.085	.087	.089	.091	.093	.095
.3	.097	.098	.100	.101	.103	.104	.105	.106	.107	.108
.4	.109	.110	.111	.112	.112	.113	.113	.114	.114	.114
.5	.115	.115	.115	.115	.115	.115	.115	.115	.115	.114
.6	.114	.114	.113	.113	.112	.112	.111	.111	.110	.110
.7	.109	.108	.108	.107	.106	.105	.105	.104	.103	.102
.8	.101	.100	.100	.099	.098	.097	.096	.095	.094	.093
.9	.092	.091	.090	.089	.089	.088	.087	.086	.085	.084

The coefficient at the loaded end of the beam is given by the formula: $C_2 = \dfrac{a(6 - 8a + 3a^2)}{12}$

Table 3.3   Value of Coefficient C_3 for Partial Uniform Load
on Beam for Unloaded End

Case 14 of Fig. 3.24; fem $= C_3WL$

C_3	+.00	.01	.02	.03	.04	.05	.06	.07	.08	.09
.0		.000	.000	.000	.001	.001	.001	.002	.002	.003
.1	.003	.004	.004	.005	.006	.007	.008	.008	.009	.010
.2	.011	.011	.013	.015	.016	.017	.018	.019	.021	.022
.3	.023	.025	.026	.027	.029	.030	.032	.033	.034	.036
.4	.037	.039	.040	.042	.043	.045	.046	.048	.049	.051
.5	.052	.054	.055	.056	.058	.059	.061	.062	.063	.065
.6	.066	.067	.069	.070	.071	.072	.073	.074	.076	.077
.7	.078	.079	.079	.080	.081	.082	.083	.084	.084	.085
.8	.085	.086	.086	.087	.087	.087	.088	.088	.088	.088
.9	.088	.088	.087	.087	.087	.086	.086	.085	.085	.084

The coefficient at the unloaded end of the beam is given by the formula: $C_3 = \dfrac{a^2\,(4 - 3a)}{12}$

$$V_{BC} = \frac{90 + 82.5}{20} = 8.6$$

This gives a total shear of 27.1, corresponding to the assumed moment of 100. But the actual shear is 60, so the moments corresponding to this shear would be $60/27.1$ of the computed M in Fig. 3.23; or using the ordinary moment conventions, $M_A = -213$, $M_B = 199$, $M_C = -183$.

h *Continuity in beams and columns with variable moment of inertia.* The preceding discussion of the Hardy Cross method has been based on the assumption that the members have a constant moment of inertia. If members have a variable moment of inertia, as is the case with concrete beams with haunched ends, or with gusset-braced steel beams, the stiffness coefficient K, the carry-over factor C, and the fixed-end moment will vary depending on a number of factors.

For prismatic members $K = 4EI/L$, but since $4E$ is constant in any structure, K varies as I/L, and this is the stiffness factor we have previously used in this section. In Figs. 3.25 and 3.26 the stiffness factor K is selected from the charts and divided by 4. Thus when the relation of minimum d to maximum d equals 1, as in the beams considered previously, $K = 4I/4L$. For any other combination of a with minimum d over maximum d, the value of K may be selected from charts No. 1 of Figs. 3.25 and 3.26 and the K we use is $K/4$. The carry-over factor C may be similarly selected, directly from charts No. 2 of Figs. 3.25 and 3.26.

Charts No. 3 of Figs. 3.25 and 3.26, giving uniform load fem coefficient, may be readily understood when it is noted that for the minimum to maximum depth ratio of 1, the factor is 0.083, or $\frac{1}{12}WL$. In other words, the fem coefficient for uniformly loaded beams of variable moment of inertia is not $\frac{1}{12}WL$, but fWL, the factor f being selected from Table 3 on each chart. For a concentrated load, the coefficient f corresponds to C in charts No. 4 of Figs. 3.25 and 3.26. Note that the end of the beam is designated by the reading at the top and the bottom of the chart.

It is also well to note that these charts are laid out for either a ratio minimum d to maximum d or a factor b, which represents the ratio minimum I to maximum I. The former would probably be used for concrete beams, the latter for steel beams.

i The conditions for which the engineer must design are not normally constant load conditions as described in this section. The maximum positive and negative moments and the maximum reactions result from the following combinations of live load (dead load always being present).

1. When alternate spans are loaded, there

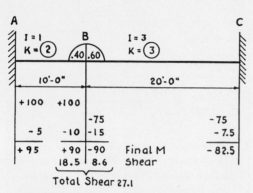

Fig. 3.23   Indirect Hardy-Cross Method

is maximum positive moment in the loaded spans and maximum negative moment in the unloaded spans.

2. When two adjacent spans are loaded, with alternate spans beyond them unloaded, there is maximum negative moment, maximum shears, and maximum reactions at the support between the two loaded spans.

Therefore, to design for all maximum conditions over each interior support, two designs must be made—for load condition 1 and for load condition 2 (see Art. 5.41e).

j The American Concrete Institute Code recommends that the moment of inertia to be used for stiffness computation should be based on the gross section of the T beam, allowing for the effect of the flange, but with no allowance for the reinforcement. The curves given in Fig. 3.27 give a method of computation o

Fig. 3.24   Determination of Fixed End Moments

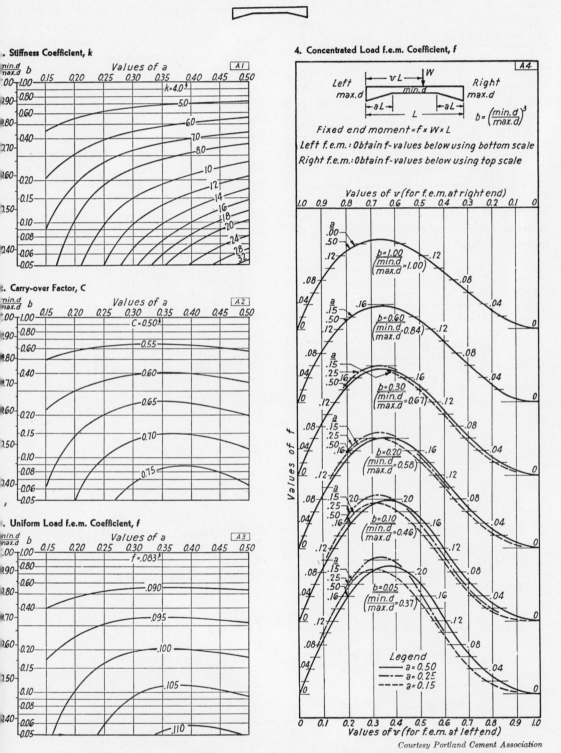

Fig. 3.25　Factors for Moment Distribution—Symmetrical Members with Straight Haunches

Courtesy Portland Cement Association

1. Stiffness Coefficient, k

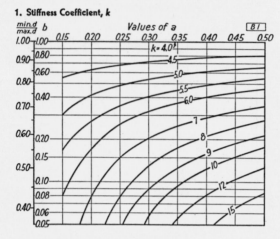

2. Carry-over Factor, C

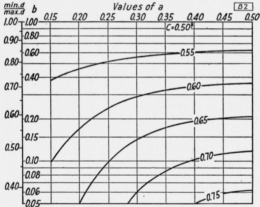

3. Uniform Load f.e.m. Coefficient, f

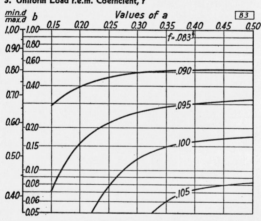

4. Concentrated Load f.e.m. Coefficient, f

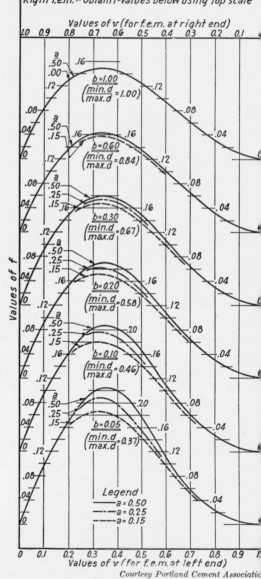

Fixed end moment = $f \times W \times L$

Left f.e.m.:- Obtain f-values below using bottom scale

Right f.e.m.:- Obtain f-values below using top scale

$$b = \left(\frac{min.d}{max.d}\right)^3$$

Fig. 3.26   Factors for Moment Distribution—Symmetrical Members with Parabolic Haunches

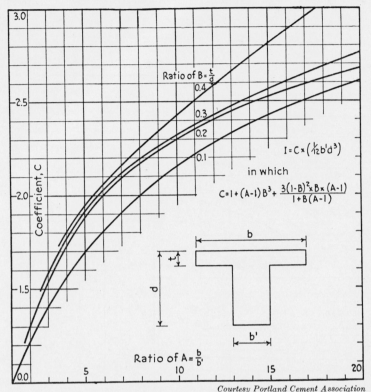

Fig. 3.27 Moment of Inertia for T-Beams

the I of the gross section for various conditions. This curve is from the publications of the Portland Cement Association.

3.22 Gable-end rigid frame

a The entire subject of rigid frames is too large and important to cover with any degree of thoroughness in such a work as this. However, the gable-end rigid frame in Fig. 3.28 is by far the most commonly used frame in building construction, and it may be solved using formulae given with the figure.

Other loading conditions, such as three, five, or seven equivalent loads, develop moments which lie between the limits of uniform and equivalent central concentrated loads. By equivalent load is meant the resultant load from the same uniform load per running foot of frame. For example, a 40-ft frame with 1 kip per ft uniform load has a total uniform load of 40 kips. The equivalent central concentrated load is 20 kips, the equivalent load applied at the three quarter-points is 10 kips, and so on.

Rigid frames of this type must be designed for the following factors:

1. Size of main members
2. Moment at the eave for design of joint
3. Moment at the peak for design of joint
4. Horizontal thrust at base

There are certain relationships between moments and horizontal thrusts for frames under vertical loads, and an understanding of these relationships will assist greatly in eliminating error in design. These relationships are sketched in Fig. 3.28. A basic axiom for these relationships is that vertical load on a frame induces a horizontal thrust at the base of the frame, or a tendency to spread; and the moment at any point in the frame is the ordinary vertical load moment derived by the methods of Arts. 3.10 and 3.11, corrected by the negative moment resulting from the horizontal thrust.

Reference to Fig. 3.28, Case I, will illustrate this axiom. The triangle on the base line AB is the moment diagram for a cantilever mo-

RIDGE AND RECTANGULAR FRAMES
(RECTANGULAR WHEN Q = 0)

General Formulas :

$$K = \frac{I_2 h}{I_1 m} \qquad Q = \frac{f}{h}$$

$$N = 4(K + 3 + 3Q + Q^2)$$

* In formulas for M_x, "x" is always measured from point B.

Plus sign (+) denotes moments which cause tension on the inside of the frame when the vertical loads act downward and the horizontal loads, applied to the left side of the frame, act toward the right. The direction of the reactions, and the signs of all terms in the moment formulas, are shown correctly for this condition. When the direction of the loads (but not their position) is reversed the direction of the reactions may, and the signs for all moments will, be reversed.

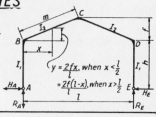

$$y = \frac{2fx}{l}, \text{ when } x < \frac{l}{2}$$
$$= \frac{2f(l-x)}{l}, \text{ when } x > \frac{l}{2}$$

CASE I - UNIFORMLY DISTRIBUTED VERTICAL LOAD ENTIRE SPAN

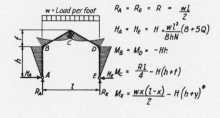

$$R_A = R_E = R = \frac{wl}{2}$$

$$H_A = H_E = H = \frac{wl^2}{8hN}(8 + 5Q)$$

$$M_B = M_D = -Hh$$

$$M_C = \frac{Rl}{4} - H(h+f)$$

$$M_x = \frac{wx(l-x)}{2} - H(h+y)^*$$

CASE IA - UNIFORMLY DISTRIBUTED VERTICAL LOAD HALF SPAN (LEFT)

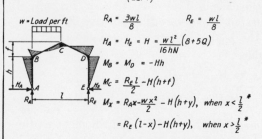

$$R_A = \frac{3wl}{8} \qquad R_E = \frac{wl}{8}$$

$$H_A = H_E = H = \frac{wl^2}{16hN}(8 + 5Q)$$

$$M_B = M_D = -Hh$$

$$M_C = \frac{R_E l}{2} - H(h+f)$$

$$M_x = R_A x - \frac{wx^2}{2} - H(h+y), \text{ when } x < \frac{l}{2}^*$$

$$= R_E(l-x) - H(h+y), \text{ when } x > \frac{l}{2}^*$$

CASE II - ONE CONCENTRATED ROOF LOAD AT ANY POSITION

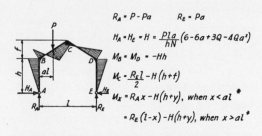

$$R_A = P - Pa \qquad R_E = Pa$$

$$H_A = H_E = H = \frac{Pla}{hN}(6 - 6a + 3Q - 4Qa^2)$$

$$M_B = M_D = -Hh$$

$$M_C = \frac{R_E l}{2} - H(h+f)$$

$$M_x = R_A x - H(h+y), \text{ when } x < al^*$$

$$= R_E(l-x) - H(h+y), \text{ when } x > al^*$$

CASE III - BRACKET LOAD ON ONE COLUMN (LEFT COLUMN)

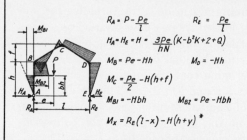

$$R_A = P - \frac{Pe}{l} \qquad R_E = \frac{Pe}{l}$$

$$H_A = H_E = H = \frac{3Pe}{hN}(K - b^2 K + 2 + Q)$$

$$M_B = Pe - Hh \qquad M_D = -Hh$$

$$M_C = \frac{Pe}{2} - H(h+f)$$

$$M_{B1} = -Hbh \qquad M_{B2} = Pe - Hbh$$

$$M_x = R_E(l-x) - H(h+y)^*$$

CASE IVA - UNIFORM HORIZONTAL LOAD INCLINED (ROOF) PORTION ONLY

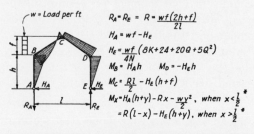

$$R_A = R_E = R = \frac{wf(2h+f)}{2l}$$

$$H_A = wf - H_E$$

$$H_E = \frac{wf}{4N}(8K + 24 + 20Q + 5Q^2)$$

$$M_B = H_A h \qquad M_D = -H_E h$$

$$M_C = \frac{Rl}{2} - H_E(h+f)$$

$$M_x = H_A(h+y) - Rx - \frac{wy^2}{2}, \text{ when } x < \frac{l}{2}^*$$

$$= R(l-x) - H_E(h+y), \text{ when } x > \frac{l}{2}^*$$

CASE IVB - UNIFORM HORIZONTAL LOAD VERTICAL (COLUMN) PORTION ONLY

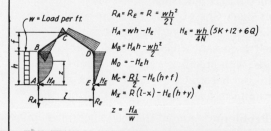

$$R_A = R_E = R = \frac{wh^2}{2l}$$

$$H_A = wh - H_E \qquad H_E = \frac{wh}{4N}(5K + 12 + 6Q)$$

$$M_B = H_A h - \frac{wh^2}{2}$$

$$M_D = -H_E h$$

$$M_C = \frac{Rl}{2} - H_E(h+f)$$

$$M_x = R(l-x) - H_E(h+y)^*$$

$$z = \frac{H_A}{w}$$

CASE V - UNIFORM HORIZONTAL LOAD ON BOTH INCLINED AND VERTICAL SURFACES

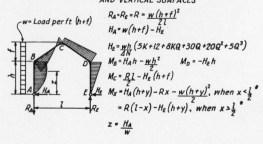

$$R_A = R_E = R = \frac{w(h+f)^2}{2l}$$

$$H_A = w(h+f) - H_E$$

$$H_E = \frac{wh}{4N}(5K + 12 + 8KQ + 30Q + 20Q^2 + 5Q^3)$$

$$M_B = H_A h - \frac{wh^2}{2} \qquad M_D = -H_E h$$

$$M_C = \frac{Rl}{2} - H_E(h+f)$$

$$M_x = H_A(h+y) - Rx - \frac{w(h+y)^2}{2}, \text{ when } x < \frac{l}{2}^*$$

$$= R(l-x) - H_E(h+y), \text{ when } x > \frac{l}{2}^*$$

$$z = \frac{H_A}{w}$$

CASE VI - ONE HORIZONTAL CONCENTRATED LOAD AT ANY POSITION ON COLUMN (b ≤ 1.0)

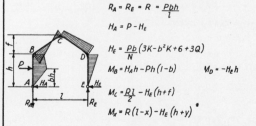

$$R_A = R_E = R = \frac{Pbh}{l}$$

$$H_A = P - H_E$$

$$H_E = \frac{Pb}{N}(3K - b^2 K + 6 + 3Q)$$

$$M_B = H_A h - Ph(1-b) \qquad M_D = -H_E h$$

$$M_C = \frac{Rl}{2} - H_E(h+f)$$

$$M_x = R(l-x) - H_E(h+y)^*$$

Fig. 3.28 Gable-End Rigid Frames

ment about B due to a horizontal thrust H applied at the base A. This cantilever moment at B is carried around the corner and applied as a negative moment at the end of a parabola. From B to C to D the moment diagram is a parabola derived as in Fig. 3.13, Case 1, corrected by a negative moment equal to the product of thrust H times the total height to the point in question. The moment at the eave is always negative for this type of load, but it may be either positive or negative at the peak. Stating these moments in formulae,

$$M_B (= M_D) = -Hh$$

$$M_C = +M - H(h+f) = +M - M_B\left(1 + \frac{f}{h}\right)$$

where M is the simple beam moment at the peak.

b Although a gable-end rigid frame is seldom uniformly loaded, the formulae for uniformly loaded frames may be used as a basis of calculation, and corrections applied to these results for the load condition applicable. It will be found that the moment at the eave is greater for uniform load than for any other type of equivalent roof load, while the moment at the peak is greater for equivalent central concentrated load.

c The American Institute of Steel Construction has published an excellent pamphlet on "Single Span Rigid Frames in Steel," from which the method of design for roof loads applied as a series of equivalent concentrated loads, with modifications, is as follows. Compute the horizontal thrust H_E from Fig. 3.29 for uniform load, using Chart I. Modify H_E:

For three loads at quarter points, each equal to $\frac{1}{4}wL$, $\qquad H_3 = 0.94 H_E$

For five loads at one-sixth points, each equal to $\frac{1}{6}wL$, $\qquad H_5 = 0.975 H_E$

Beyond five loads, the result so closely approaches that for a uniform load that H_E may be used without correction. The above figures will vary slightly for different pitch, ratio of height to span, and other factors, but the result is accurate within 2 percent. If the designer prefers greater accuracy, the sum of the horizontal thrusts obtained from Chart II of Fig. 3.29 may be used.

d Because of the allowable increase in the unit stresses for wind loads, it is frequently unnecessary to make any revision in the design for wind. However, it is advisable to check the design on the basis of moments obtained from Fig. 3.30.

e Solution of the various formulae in Figs. 3.29 and 3.30 requires either an assumption of size of column and beam from which I_B/I_C may be solved or an assumption of the relationship. The controlling moment for size of beam and column is the negative moment at the eave. A rough approximation from which this ratio may be determined is an assumption of $M_B = M_D = \frac{1}{16}Wl^2$, or one-half the uniform load moment on a simply supported beam on the total span. With this moment and the direct load on the column, a beam and column may be selected from which the relationships may be assumed, and the final size usually computed after one trial calculation.

Problem Assume the load conditions indicated in Fig. 3.31, using wide-flange steel sections and no increase in depth of section at the knee (from AISC pamphlet referred to above).

$$Q = \frac{15}{20} = 0.75$$

Assume $I_2/I_1 = 1.0$.

$$K = \frac{1}{1} \times \frac{20}{52.2} = 0.38$$

From Chart I, Fig. 3.29,

$$C_1 = 0.059$$
$$H_E = 0.059 \times 1.0 \times \frac{100^2}{20} = 29.5$$

From Chart V, Fig. 3.30,

$$C_6 = 0.525$$
$$H_E = 0.525 \times 0.6 \times 20 \quad = \underline{6.3}$$
$$\text{Total } H_E = 35.8 \text{ kips}$$

RIDGE & RECTANGULAR FRAMES
(Rectangular when Q = 0)
MOMENT COEFFICIENTS - HINGED COLUMN BASES

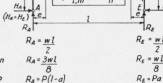

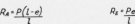

$H_E = C_1 w l^2/h$ for uniform vertical load on full span
    $(H_E = C_1 w l^2/2h$ when half-span only is loaded)
$H_E = C_2 C_1 P l/h$ for concentrated load P on span, distant al from _either_ end.
    $(H_E = 2C_2 C_1 P l/h$ for equal concentrated loads P, distant al from _both_ ends)
$H_E = C_3 P e/h$ for concentrated load P on _either_ bracket of length e.
    $(H_E = 2C_3 P e/h$ for equal concentrated loads P on _both_ brackets)

For uniform load full span	$R_A = \dfrac{wl}{2}$	$R_E = \dfrac{wl}{2}$
For uniform load left half span	$R_A = \dfrac{3wl}{8}$	$R_E = \dfrac{wl}{8}$
For concentrated roof load P	$R_A = P(l-a)$	$R_E = Pa$
For concentrated bracket load P	$R_A = \dfrac{P(l-e)}{l}$	$R_E = \dfrac{Pe}{l}$

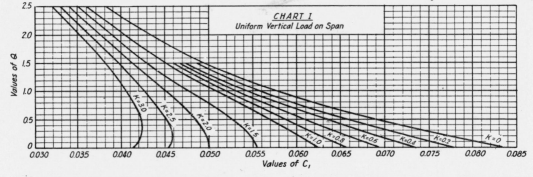

CHART I
Uniform Vertical Load on Span

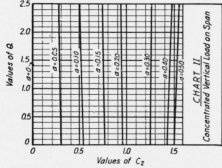

CHART II
Concentrated Vertical Load on Span

Illustrative Problem : (Chart II)

Given : $P = 20^k$; $l = 80'$; $al = 20'(a = 0.25)$; $h = 18$; $f = 10'$; $m = 41.23'$

From Chart I (using $K_1 = 0.44$ and $Q = 0.56$) $C_1 = 0.062$

From Chart II (using $a = 0.25$) $C_2 = 1.12$

Then $H_E = H_A = 0.062 \times 1.12 \times 20 \times \dfrac{80}{18} = 6.17^k$

Note: When a second 20^k load is symmetrically placed on other side of ξ $H_E = H_A = 12.34^k$

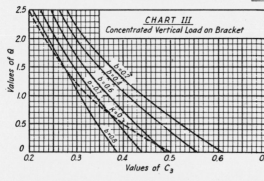

CHART III
Concentrated Vertical Load on Bracket

Illustrative Problem : (Chart III)

Given : $P = 20^K$; $l = 80'$; $e = 2'$; $h = 18'$; $bh = 14'(b = 0.78)$ $h = 10'$; $m = 41.23'$

Entering Chart III (using $b = 0.78$ and $Q = 0.56$)

    $C_3 = 0.355$, when $K_1 = 3.0$

    $C_3 = 0.385$, when $K_1 = 0$

    $C_3 = 0.38$, when $K_1 = 0.44$ (by interpolation)

Then $H_E = H_A = 0.38 \times 20 \times \dfrac{2}{18} = 0.84^k$

Note: When both brackets have 20^K loads $H_E = H_A = 1.68^K$

Note : Solid lines (Chart III) plotted for K = 3.0 (varying values of b)
Dotted line (Chart III) plotted for K = 0.0 (all values of b)

Fig. 3.29   Moment Coefficients—Gable-End Rigid Frames, Vertical Loads

RIDGE & RECTANGULAR FRAMES
(Rectangular when $Q=0$)

MOMENT COEFFICIENTS - HINGED COLUMN BASES

$H_E = C_4 wh$, for uniform load against roof.
$H_E = C_5 wh$, for uniform load against vertical side.
$H_E = C_6 wh$, for uniform load against total height.
$H_E = Pb(C_7 - b^2 C_8)$, for concentrated load P on one vertical side $(b \leqslant 1.0)$.
   $(H_E = P$, for concentrated load P on both vertical sides at same elevation.

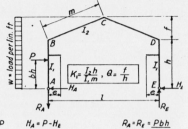

For concentrated horizontal load P	$H_A = P - H_E$	$R_A = R_E = \dfrac{Pbh}{l}$
For uniform load against roof	$H_A = wf - H_E$	$R_A = R_E = \dfrac{wf(2h+f)}{2l}$
For uniform load against vertical side	$H_A = wh - H_E$	$R_A = R_E = \dfrac{wh^2}{2l}$
For uniform load against total height	$H_A = w(h+f) - H_E$	$R_A = R_E = \dfrac{w(h+f)^2}{2l}$

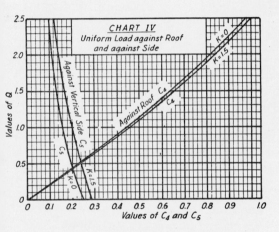

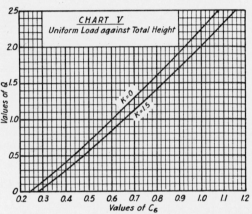

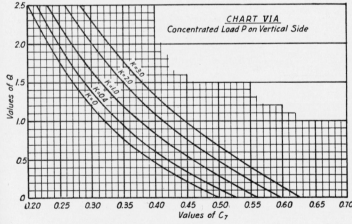

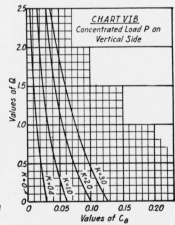

Fig. 3.30   Moment Coefficients—Gable-End Rigid Frames, Horizontal Loads

For the girder the moment at D' (Fig. 3.32) with wind is

$$He \quad 35.8 \times 20.38 = -730$$
$$eccentric \quad 1.0 \times \frac{1.25^2}{2} = - \quad 1$$
$$Re \quad 53.67 \times 1.25 = + \quad \underline{67}$$
$$- 664 \text{ ft-kips}$$

and without wind it is

$$He \quad 29.5 \times 20.38 = -601$$
$$ecce \quad 1.0 \times \frac{1.25^2}{2} = - \quad 1$$
$$Re \quad 50 \quad \times 1.25 = + \quad \underline{63}$$
$$- 539 \text{ ft-kips}$$

The critical condition is without wind, since stress with wind may be increased $33\frac{1}{3}$ percent.

The axial force at D' is

$$P = 29.5 \cos \alpha + 50 \sin \alpha = 42.6 \text{ kips}$$

Try 30 WF 124.

The bracing is assumed to be 15 ft o.c.

$$\frac{l}{r} = \frac{15 \times 12}{2.16} = 83.3$$
$$f_a = 13.64 \text{ ksi}$$
$$\frac{ld}{bt} = \frac{15 \times 12 \times 30.16}{10.52 \times 0.93} = 555$$
$$f_b = 20.00 \text{ ksi}$$
$$\%_{od} + \%_{oe} = \frac{42.6}{36.45 \times 13.64} + \frac{539 \times 12}{354.6 \times 20}$$
$$= 0.086 + 0.912 = 0.998$$

which is satisfactory.

The moment at the peak is

$$\frac{1.0 \times 100^2}{8} = +1,250$$
$$29.5 \times 35 = -1,032$$
$$+ \quad 218 \text{ ft-kips}$$

which is satisfactory.

For the column the moment at D'' (Fig. 3.32) is

$$29.5 \times 18.70 = 552 \text{ ft-kips}$$

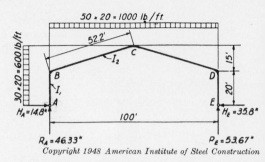

Fig. 3.31   Load Conditions for Rigid-Frame Problem

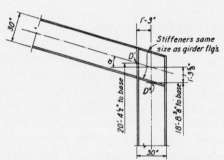

Fig. 3.32   Detail at Knee of Rigid Frame

The axial force at $D'' = 50$ kips. Try 30 WF 124. The column is assumed braced at mid-height

$$\frac{l}{r} = \frac{10 \times 12}{2.16} = 55.6$$
$$f_a = 15.50 \text{ ksi}$$
$$\frac{ld}{bt} = \frac{10 \times 12 \times 30.16}{10.52 \times 0.93} = 370$$
$$f_b = 20.00 \text{ ksi}$$
$$\frac{50}{36.45 \times 15.50} + \frac{552 \times 12}{354.6 \times 20} = 0.088 + 0.934$$
$$= 1.022$$

A 2.2 percent overstress would generally be permitted.

The web shear at D' is

$$50 \times \cos \alpha - 29.5 \sin \alpha = 39.4 \text{ kips}$$
$$\text{Unit shear} = \frac{39,400}{30.16 \times 0.585} = 2,240 \text{ psi}$$

The calculated weight of the frame (exclusive of base details) = 18,540 lb.

4

Steel in Bending

4.10 STEEL BEAMS

a It is well to repeat here two fundamental statements. First, the strength of a structural member is dependent upon two factors, the material used, and its shape and size. Second, with the moment induced in a beam by any system of loading known, there are two methods of computing the internal resisting moment in the beam, the moment-couple method, indicated in Fig. 3.1, and the section-modulus method. Because steel beams are homogeneous and because the section modulus is easily tabulated for standard beam sections, this method is generally used.

To select a steel beam, it is therefore necessary to compute the moment as described in Art. 3.10. Reduce this moment to inch-pound units, and divide by the allowable fiber stress to obtain the section modulus. Then from Table 4.1 or Tables 1.5 to 1.10 select the beam which will furnish the required section modulus and otherwise satisfy the required conditions.

The various handbooks have tables of maximum bending moment in foot-pounds and allowable uniform load in kips on different spans, but the simplest and best way is to use the section-modulus method for all types of beam loading.

Usually the two governing factors in the selection of a steel beam are section modulus required and economy of weight. Occasionally shallower depth, deflection, lateral deflection, shear, or buckling of the web will control, but these will be discussed in later paragraphs.

If the section modulus required is greater than that obtainable in the wide-flange sections listed in Table 1.5, it is necessary to use either a cover-plated beam as treated in Art. 4.22 or, for still greater strength, a plate girder as treated in Art. 4.20.

b Until the Gray Mill was used, about 1908, the only sections available for I beams were the American Standard beams, listed as such in the handbooks and in Table 1.7. Now both United States Steel Corp. and Bethlehem Steel Co. are rolling a uniform list of wide-flange sections and light beams. The wide-flange sections require a slight increase over base cost, usually about 5 percent, but the better range of sections available, the economy of weight of about 10 percent for equal section modulus, the more uniform strength due to the method of rolling, and the wider flange for the same strength beam—have caused the wide-flange sections largely to displace the old American Standard beam sections. The best designation for wide-flange beams is WF, instead of B as used by Bethlehem or CB as used by United States Steel. Thus we would note 10 WF 21 (or 10 **WF** 21) instead of 10 B 21 or 10 CB 21. For light-weight beams the designation is B, as 10 B 15, for either United States Steel or Bethlehem sections.

If American Standard beams are used it is best policy to use the lightest section in each group listed—3 I 5.7, 4 I 7.7, etc., including both 12 I 31.8 and 12 I 40.8, 15 I 42.9, 15 I 42.9, 15 I 60.8, etc. (Note that American Standard beams are always indicated as I.)

The reason for selecting the lightest beam only is that if others are called for, a long delay may be encountered while waiting for a rolling.

American Standard channels are frequently used for a special purpose where one flat side is desirable, or occasionally for other purposes, as will be noted later. They are not ordinarily used as floor beams, however, because of their narrow flange, lower efficiency in bending for a given depth, and the difficulty in supporting concrete forms from a channel.

Angles are not economical as beams, although they are used as lintels and will be discussed under that heading. T's are not economical and are only used in making up such things as stair landings, marquees, etc. Z bars are now practically off the market. Do not use car or ship sections; they are hard to get and are not economical.

c The general formula for moment is $M = fS$, or $S = M/f$ [Formula (3.2)]. In steel-beam problems M is ordinarily figured in foot-pounds or foot-kips and S in inch units. M as computed from Art. 3.10 must, therefore, be reduced to inches before finding the section modulus.

The AISC Code, which is the generally accepted design code for steel, uses a stress in bending of 20,000 psi. If we use M in foot-kips, with a 20,000-psi fiber stress, the basic formula for a uniform-load moment of 1 ft-kip becomes $S = \dfrac{12 \times 1,000M}{20,000}$, or $S = 0.6M$. Expressing it as a statement rather than a formula, the section modulus is six-tenths of the moment in foot-kips.

This simplification combined with the formulae for moments given in Fig. 3.13 will greatly simplify the computation of steel beams. For instance, for a uniformly distributed load on a simple beam (Case 1),

$$M = \frac{wL^2}{8} = \frac{WL}{8} \qquad (4.1)$$

$$S = 0.6M = \frac{0.6WL}{8} = \frac{WL}{13.33} = 0.075WL \qquad (4.2)$$

Thus we may go directly from the combination of total load and length to section modulus.

Similarly, combining the formula for Case 7, centrally concentrated load,

$$S = \frac{PL}{6.67} = 0.15PL \qquad (4.3)$$

For the beams listed in Art. 3.10, Class II, $S = C(WL/6.67)$ using C as given in the paragraph noted.

Referring to the problem in Art. 3.10*k*,

$$S = 0.6 \times 50.625 = 30.4$$

From Table 4.1, select 12 WF 27. This could have been arrived at directly from the problem set up in Art. 3.10*k*.

$$15,000 + 12,000 = 27,000$$
$$S = \frac{27.0 \times 15}{13.33} = 30.4$$

d A fairly common type of problem encountered in practice is the determination of permissible load on a beam—the capacity of an existing structure. This may be approached directly by use of the formula $S = 0.075WL$, writing in S and L and solving for W. It is preferable to compute the section modulus required to carry a load of 100 psf, and by prorating the actual against required section modulus, determine the load.

Problem Floor beams in a building are spaced 7 ft 6 in. apart on a 19-ft span. The beams are 18 WF 50. What total floor load per square foot will the beams carry?

$$W = 7.5 \times 19 \times 100 = 14,250$$
$$S = 0.075 \times 14.25 \times 19 = 20.3$$
$$\text{Allowable } W = \frac{89.0}{20.3} \times 100 = 438 \text{ psf}$$

e *Deflection of a steel beam.* Occasionally the selection of a beam is modified by deflection. Sometimes the depth available is reduced by architectural limitations, or with light loads on a long span, the economical beam would deflect beyond the allowable limit. The allowable deflection is ordinarily taken at 1/360 of the span, or

$$\Delta = \frac{L}{30} = \text{deflection in inches}$$

Deflection beyond this limit may crack plastered ceilings, and beams deflected beyond this point will give appreciable vibration under moving load.

The deflection of a steel beam on a simple span carrying a uniformly distributed load throughout its entire length may be obtained by dividing the coefficient from Table 2.5 for the required span by the depth of the beam in inches, and multiplying by the ratio S required/S furnished.

Problem Select a beam and compute the deflection in a steel beam carrying 1,500 lb per running foot on a span of 20 ft—no limitations as to depth.

$$W = 1.5 \times 20 = 30 \text{ kips}$$

From Formula (4.2)

$$S = 0.075 \times 30 \times 20 = 45$$

From Art. 4.11 select 14 WF 34 ($S = 48.5$). From Table 2.5

$$\Delta = \frac{45}{48.5} \times \frac{8}{14} = 0.53 \text{ in.}$$

f In Table 2.6 the "relative deflection" is given for different types of loading. This means the ratio of deflection of a beam loaded in accordance with the diagrams in Fig. 3.13 to the deflection under equal fiber stress of a simple supported uniformly loaded beam. In other words, for a regularly loaded beam in any of these classifications, compute the deflection as described above and multiply by the relative deflection.

Problem Compute the beam required and the deflection in a simple steel beam on a 20-ft span carrying a centrally concentrated load of 25 kips and properly supported laterally.

From Formula (4.3)

$$S = 0.15 \times 25 \times 20 = 75$$

From Art. 4.11 select 18 WF 50 ($S = 89.0$). From Tables 2.5 and 2.6

$$\Delta = 0.8 \times \frac{75}{89.0} \times \frac{8}{18} = 0.3 \text{ in.}$$

g In order to bring the beam within the deflection limits, it is not necessary to use a deeper beam. A reduction of the fiber stress by increasing S proportionately will accomplish the same thing. All these deflection tables are based on fiber stress of 20,000 psi, and in accordance with Hooke's law, the deflection is directly proportional to the fiber stress.

Problem Let us assume a uniformly distributed load of 1,500 lb per ft on 20 ft

$$W = 30,000$$

At 20,000 psi fiber stress,

$$S = 0.075 \times 30 \times 20 = 45$$

From Table 4.1 we may use 14 WF 34, 12 WF 36, 10 WF 45, or 8 WF 58. The allowable deflection would be $\frac{20}{30}$, or 0.667 in. The actual deflection for each of the above beams, allowing for actual fiber stress and using the subscript for the beam size, would be

$$\Delta_{14} = \frac{45}{48.5} \times \frac{8}{14} = 0.53 \text{ in.}$$

$$\Delta_{12} = \frac{45}{45.9} \times \frac{8}{12.24} = 0.64 \text{ in.}$$

$$\Delta_{10} = \frac{45}{49.1} \times \frac{8}{10.12} = 0.724 \text{ in.}$$

$$\Delta_{8} = \frac{45}{52} \times \frac{8}{8.75} = 0.791 \text{ in.}$$

It will be seen that the 8- and 10-in. beams are beyond the deflection limit. In order to use beams of these two depths, the section modulus will have to be increased approximately thus,

$$S_{10} = \frac{0.724}{0.667} \times 49.1 = 53.3$$

Use 10 WF 49.

$$S_{8} = \frac{0.791}{0.667} \times 52 = 61.7$$

The latter value is beyond the S furnished by the heaviest 8 WF rolled, therefore 8 in. cannot be used.

It will be found that for any of the loads ordinarily encountered, uniformly distributed or concentrated on simple beams, stressed to 20,000 psi, the deflection limit will not be exceeded until L in feet is greater than $1.67d$ in inches. Therefore, a glance at the beam length and depth will tell whether it is necessary to check deflection. Thus on a span of 15 ft 6 in., using a 10-in. beam, $L = 1.55d$, and it is unnecessary to check for deflection.

h *Lateral deflection of beams.* The top flange of a simple beam is a compression member, and if the full unit fiber stress is to be

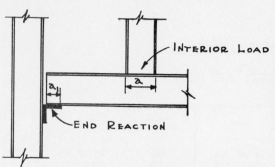

Fig. 4.1   Web Shear and Buckling

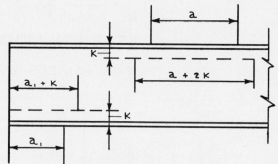

**Fig. 4.2   Distribution for Web Shear and
Buckling**

utilized, the top flange must be braced against lateral deflection.

The AISC specification has this clause: "Compression on extreme fibers of rolled sections, plate girders and built-up members,

With $\dfrac{ld}{bt}$ not in excess of 600, 20,000

With $\dfrac{ld}{bt}$ in excess of 600, $\dfrac{12,000,000}{\dfrac{ld}{bt}}$

In a cantilever beam, l shall be taken as twice the length of the compression flange of a beam not fully stayed at its outer end."

The steel-beam tables (1.5 to 1.8) have three columns with the heading Laterally unsupported beams. The first of these three columns is headed d/bt and may be used in the above formula. The second column, L_u, is the maximum unsupported length in feet for which a member may be used without reduction of stress, where ld/bt is not in excess of 600. The third column, U, is a coefficient to be used for selection of a beam when ld/bt is in excess of 600, or where the unbraced length is greater than L_u in the table. This is a simplified method of approach proposed by Samuel Reubene (*Engineering News-Record*, Apr. 6, 1950). U is the product of the section modulus required for a beam at 20,000-psi fiber stress multiplied by the unbraced length in feet.

An example of the computation of such a laterally unbraced beam is as follows: Suppose the concentrated loads on a beam with laterally unsupported length of 40 ft produce

a moment of 260 ft-kips; select the proper beam. From Formula (4.2)

$$S = 0.6 \times 260 = 156$$
$$U = 156 \times 40 = 6,240$$

From Table 1.5 any of the following beams may be used:

18 WF 114, $U = 6,965$ ⎫ (Vertical deflection
21 WF 112, $U = 6,674$ ⎬ might eliminate
　　　　　　　　　　　　⎭ these two beams.)

24 WF 120, $U = 6,924$
30 WF 132, $U = 6,615$

i Web shear and buckling. The AISC Code allows a shear value of 13,000 psi on the gross section of the webs of rolled beams and plate girders. The shear value of each beam is given as V in Tables 1.5 to 1.8. This shear value is the maximum allowable shear as read from a shear diagram at either end of the beam.

Under certain conditions of loading, a beam which is safe in bending or in shear will not have sufficient strength if a portion of the web is considered as a column.

The AISC Code requires that rolled beams shall be so proportioned that the compression stress at the web toe of the fillets, resulting from concentrated loads and computed by the following formulae, shall not exceed 24,000 psi. For interior loads

$$f = \frac{P}{t(a + 2k)} \qquad (4.4)$$

For end reaction

$$f = \frac{R}{t(a_1 + k)} \qquad (4.5)$$

The value of k is listed in Tables 1.5 to 1.8.

Table 4.1   Section Moduli for Shapes Used as Beams

SECTION MODULUS TABLE

FOR SHAPES USED AS BEAMS

Section Modulus	Shape	Section Modulus	Shape	Section Modulus	Shape
1105.1	36 WF 300	220.9	24 WF 94	98.2	18 WF 55
1031.2	36 WF 280	220.1	18 WF 114	97.5	12 WF 72
951.1	36 WF 260	216.0	14 WF 136	94.1	16 WF 58
892.5	36 WF 245	202.2	18 WF 105	92.2	14 WF 61
		202.0	14 WF 127		
835.5	36 WF 230	197.6	21 WF 96	89.0	18 WF 50
811.1	33 WF 240	197.6	24 I 100	88.4	18 I 54.7
				88.0	12 WF 65
740.6	33 WF 220	196.3	24 WF 84	86.1	10 WF 77
		189.4	14 WF 119		
669.6	33 WF 200	185.8	24 I 90	80.7	16 WF 50
		184.4	18 WF 96	80.1	10 WF 72
663.6	36 WF 194	182.5	12 WF 133	78.1	12 WF 58
649.9	30 WF 210	176.3	14 WF 111	77.8	14 WF 53
				74.5	18 ⌞ 58
621.2	36 WF 182	175.4	24 WF 76	73.7	10 WF 66
586.1	30 WF 190	173.9	24 I 79.9		
		168.0	21 WF 82	72.4	16 WF 45
579.1	36 WF 170	166.1	16 WF 96	70.7	12 WF 53
		163.6	14 WF 103	70.2	14 WF 48
541.0	36 WF 160	163.4	12 WF 120	69.1	18 ⌞ 51.9
528.2	30 WF 172	160.0	20 I 95	67.1	10 WF 60
		156.1	18 WF 85	64.7	12 WF 50
502.9	36 WF 150	151.3	16 WF 88		
492.8	27 WF 177			64.4	16 WF 40
486.4	33 WF 152	150.7	21 WF 73	64.2	15 I 50
		150.6	14 WF 95	63.7	18 ⌞ 45.8
446.8	33 WF 141	150.2	20 I 85	62.7	14 WF 43
444.5	27 WF 160	144.5	12 WF 106	61.0	18 ⌞ 42.7
413.5	24 WF 160	141.7	18 WF 77	60.4	10 WF 54
				60.4	8 WF 67
404.8	33 WF 130	139.9	21 WF 68	58.9	15 I 42.9
402.9	27 WF 145	138.1	14 WF 87	58.2	12 WF 45
379.7	30 WF 132	134.7	12 WF 99		
372.5	24 WF 145	130.9	14 WF 84	56.3	16 WF 36
		128.2	18 WF 70	54.6	14 WF 38
354.6	30 WF 124	127.8	16 WF 78	54.6	10 WF 49
330.7	24 WF 130			53.6	15 ⌞ 50
		126.4	21 WF 62	52.0	8 WF 58
327.9	30 WF 116	126.3	20 I 75	51.9	12 WF 40
317.2	21 WF 142	126.3	10 WF 112	50.3	12 I 50
		125.0	12 WF 92	49.1	10 WF 45
299.2	30 WF 108	121.1	14 WF 78		
299.2	27 WF 114	117.0	18 WF 64	48.5	14 WF 34
299.1	24 WF 120	116.9	20 I 65.4	46.2	15 ⌞ 40
284.1	21 WF 127	115.9	16 WF 71	45.9	12 WF 36
274.4	24 WF 110	115.7	12 WF 85	44.8	12 I 40.8
		112.4	10 WF 100	43.2	8 WF 48
266.3	27 WF 102	112.3	14 WF 74	42.2	10 WF 39
263.2	12 WF 190				
250.9	24 I 120	107.8	18 WF 60	41.8	14 WF 30
249.6	21 WF 112	107.1	12 WF 79	41.7	15 ⌞ 33.9
		104.2	16 WF 64	39.4	12 WF 31
248.9	24 WF 100	103.0	14 WF 68	37.8	12 I 35
		101.9	18 I 70	36.0	12 I 31.8
242.8	27 WF 94	99.7	10 WF 89	35.5	8 WF 40
234.3	24 I 105.9			35.0	10 WF 33
222.2	12 WF 161				

Table 4.1   Section Moduli for Shapes Used as Beams (*Continued*)

SECTION MODULUS TABLE
FOR SHAPES USED AS BEAMS

Section Modulus	Shape	Source	Section Modulus	Shape	Source	Section Modulus	Shape	Source
34.1	12 WF 27	2	14.8	12 B 14	2	7.8	10 Jr 9	7
31.1	8 WF 35	2	14.2	8 I 18.4	1	7.8	8 B 10	2
30.8	10 WF 29	2	14.1	8 WF 17	2	7.7	7 ⊔ 14.75	1
29.2	10 I 35	1	14.0	8 M 17	6	7.3	6 I 12.5	1
28.9	8 M 34.3	3	13.8	10 B 15	2	7.2	6 B 12	2
27.4	8 WF 31	2	13.5	9 ⊔ 20	1	6.9	7 ⊔ 12.25	1
26.9	12 ⊔ 30	1	13.4	10 ⊔ 15.3	1			
			13.4	6 WF 20	2	6.5	10 Jr ⊔ 8.4	7
26.4	10 WF 25	2	12.9	6 M 20	3	6.0	7 ⊔ 9.8	1
						6.0	5 I 14.75	1
25.3	12 B 22	2	12.0	12 Jr 11.8	7	5.8	6 ⊔ 13	1
24.4	10 I 25.4	1	12.0	7 I 20	1	5.4	4 WF 13	5
24.3	8 WF 28	2	11.8	8 B 15	2	5.2	4 M 13	4
23.9	12 ⊔ 25	1	11.3	9 ⊔ 15	1	5.1	6 B 8.5	2
			10.9	8 ⊔ 18.75	1	5.0	6 ⊔ 10.5	1
21.5	10 WF 21	2				4.8	5 I 10	1
21.4	12 B 19	2	10.5	10 B 11.5	2			
21.4	12 ⊔ 20.7	1	10.5	9 ⊔ 13.4	1	4.7	8 Jr 6.5	7
21.0	8 M 24	6	10.4	7 I 15.3	1	4.4	10 Jr ⊔ 6.5	7
20.8	8 WF 24	2	10.1	6 WF 15.5	2	4.3	6 ⊔ 8.2	1
20.6	10 ⊔ 30	1	10.1	6 B 16	2	4.2	4 WF 10	5
			9.9	8 B 13	2			
18.8	10 B 19	2	9.9	5 WF 18.5	2	3.5	7 Jr 5.5	7
18.1	10 ⊔ 25	1	9.5	5 M 18.9	2	3.5	5 ⊔ 9	1
						3.3	4 I 9.5	1
17.5	12 B 16.5	2	9.3	12 Jr ⊔ 10.6	7	3.0	5 ⊔ 6.7	1
17.0	8 WF 20	2	9.0	8 ⊔ 13.75	1	3.0	4 I 7.7	1
16.8	6 WF 25	2	8.7	6 I 17.25	1			
16.2	10 B 17	2	8.5	5 WF 16	2	2.4	6 Jr 4.4	7
16.0	8 I 23	1	8.1	8 ⊔ 11.5	1	2.3	4 ⊔ 7.25	1
15.7	10 ⊔ 20	1				1.9	4 ⊔ 5.4	1
15.7	6 M 25	3				1.9	3 I 7.5	1
15.2	8 M 20	6				1.7	3 I 5.7	1
						1.4	3 ⊔ 6	1
						1.2	3 ⊔ 5	1
						1.1	3 ⊔ 4.1	1

Index to Source Numbers.
1. All Structural Mills.
2. Carnegie-Illinois, Bethlehem.
3. Carnegie-Illinois, Inland.
4. Carnegie-Illinois.
5. Bethlehem.
6. Phoenix.
7. Jones and Laughlin.

NOTE: On this page, if the bold-face shape at the head of the group is one which because of its "source" is not available for the particular job, examine the adjacent upper groups for a lighter shape that is available.

Web shear or buckling of the web will control the selection of the beam infrequently; in general, when:

The beam is short but very heavily loaded.

A heavy load occurs very close to one end of the beam.

A column is carried on a beam or on a grillage.

A heavily loaded beam bears over the top of another beam and is placed at right angles to it.

Under any of these conditions, the beam selected should be investigated for web shear and for buckling before being chosen. Certain applications of this statement may be given later.

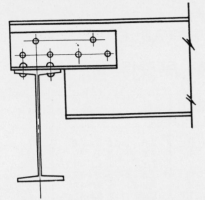

Fig. 4.3   Reduced Depth—End of Beam

4.11   Design of steel details

While it is obvious that the design of steel details is as important as the design of the member itself, these details are ordinarily selected by the steel company detailer from standards set up by the American Institute of Steel Construction. Thus, while it is the duty of the designer to check the shop drawings (see Art. 11.16), it is not necessary to repeat all the detail information given in the AISC Manual relative to all of the standard types of connections. Table 4.2, taken from the Manual, is the series most commonly used for beam-to-beam connections.

4.12   Special steel details

a   Reduced end depth of beam. This problem is frequently encountered in detailing beams. It is shown in Fig. 4.3. The solution involves a problem in moment, shear, properties of complex sections, and riveting. Assume a 16 WF 36 bearing on an 18 WF 55,

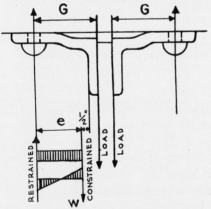

Fig. 44.   Angle Legs in Bending

carrying a reaction of 20,000 lb, and with half the web of the 16-in. beam cut away. From the table for shearing value of beams (Table 1.5), the shear on a 16 WF 36 is 62 kips for the full web, or 31 kips for the half web. The reaction of 20 kips must be developed in the rivets on either side of the cut. The beam has a web thickness of 0.299 in., and from the table for ¾-in. rivets

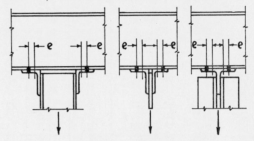

Fig. 4.5   Hangers

in double shear on enclosed bearing (Table 9.1), each rivet is good for 9.0 kips. This would require the use of three rivets. These can be located in staggered rows as shown in Fig. 4.3 and would require a 6-in. upstanding leg to take them.

The moment required at the cut would be 20.0 × 4 in. = 80.0 in.-kips. This would require a section modulus of $\frac{80}{20} = 4.0$. From observation, the least angle which could be used to furnish a 6-in. leg would give a beam of greater section than an 8 WF 17, which has an S of 14.1. Therefore it is not neces-

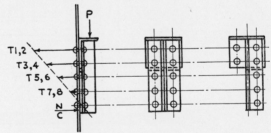

Fig. 4.6   Bracket with Stiffeners

sary to compute the S of the section, which is made up of 2 Ls, $6 \times 3\frac{1}{2} \times \frac{3}{8}$ and half of a 16 WF 36. However, in some problems it might be necessary to compute the section modulus of a compound section as described in Art. 1.31.

b   Angle legs in bending—fixed ends. When an angle forms part of a wind-bracing bracket,

Table 4.2 Standard Beam Connections

RIVETS ¾″   HOLES $13/16$″

STANDARD BEAM CONNECTIONS

"B" SERIES

B   ALLOWABLE LOADS IN KIPS

		Rivets in Outstanding Legs		Rivets in Web Legs		Maximum Value	
		No.	Shear	Bearing	Shear	Section	R
B 10	$2'5\frac{1}{2}''$ $2\text{L}^s\ 4 \times 3\frac{1}{2} \times \frac{7}{16}$	20	132.5	300 t t=thickness of web	132.5	36 WF (all weights)	132.5
B 9	$2'2\frac{1}{2}''$ $2\text{L}^s\ 4 \times 3\frac{1}{2} \times \frac{7}{16}$	18	119.3	270 t	119.3	33 WF (all weights)	119.3
B 8	$1'11\frac{1}{2}''$ $2\text{L}^s\ 4 \times 3\frac{1}{2} \times \frac{7}{16}$	16	106.0	240 t	106.0	30 WF (all weights)	106.0
B 7	$1'8\frac{1}{2}''$ $2\text{L}^s\ 4 \times 3\frac{1}{2} \times \frac{7}{16}$	14	92.8	210 t	92.8	27 WF (all weights)	92.8
B 6	$1'5\frac{1}{2}''$ $2\text{L}^s\ 4 \times 3\frac{1}{2} \times \frac{7}{16}$	12	79.5	180 t	79.5	24 WF 160 to 84 76 24 I (all weights)	79.5 79.2† 79.5

†The values tabulated for these connections have been reduced to those permitted by web bearing.

Table 4.2   Standard Beam Connections (Continued)

HOLES 1³⁄₁₆″   RIVETS ¾″

STANDARD BEAM CONNECTIONS

"B" SERIES

ALLOWABLE LOADS IN KIPS   B

	Rivets in Out-standing Legs		Rivets in Web Legs		Maximum Value			
	No.	Shear	Bearing	Shear	Section	R	Section	R
B 5 1′2½″ 2⌐ 4×3½×⁷⁄₁₆	10	66.3	150 t t=thickness of web	66.3	21Wᶠ142 to 73 68 62	66.3 64.5† 60.0†	20I (all weights)	66.3
B 4 1′1½″ 2⌐ 4×3½×⅜	8	53.0	120 t	53.0	18Wᶠ114 to 77 70 64 60 55 50 16Wᶠ 96 to 64 58 50 45 40 36	53.0 52.6† 48.4† 49.9† 46.8† 43.0† 53.0 48.8† 45.6† 41.5† 36.8† 35.9†	18I (all weights) 15 I 50	53.0 53.0 42.9 → 49.2†
B 3 8½″ 2⌐ 4×3½×⅜	6	39.8	90 t	39.8	14 Wᶠ 38 34 30 · 12 Wᶠ 36 31 27	28.2† 25.8† 24.3† 27.5† 23.8† 21.6†	12 I 50 and 40.8 35 31.8	39.8 38.5† 31.5†
B 2 5½″ 2⌐ 6×4×⅜	4	26.5	120 t	53.0	10Wᶠ(all wts.) 8 Wᶠ 20 17	26.5 26.2† 23.9†	10I(35 and 25.4) 8I(23.0 & 18.4)	26.5 26.5
B 1 3″ 2⌐ 6×4×⅜	2	13.3	60 t	26.5	7I(20 and 15.3) 6I(17.25 and 12.5)	13.3 13.3	5 I 14.75 10	13.3 12.6

†The values tabulated for these connections have been reduced to those permitted by web bearing or web shear, whichever governs.

a hanger, or another similar member where the faces are held at right angles but are caused to bend as indicated in Fig. 4.4, the angle leg or T leg is computed as a cantilever with the load applied on half the lever arm e. Figures 4.5, 4.6, and 4.7 show practical applications of this condition.

For a direct hanger load on two angles or one T, the total load per inch of length of angle or T for a fiber stress of 20,000 psi is $P = 13.33 \, t^2/e$. The allowable loads in kips per inch on two angles or a structural T according to this formula are given in Table 4.3.

Where the pull is one-sided as in an angle wind-bracing detail similar to Fig. 4.7, but with cap and seat angles, the allowable load

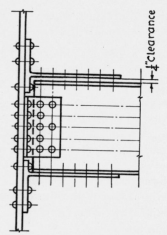

Fig. 4.7   Wind Bracing Connection

Table 4.3   Angle and Structural T Connections for Hangers and Brackets

Allowable loads in kips per inch on two angles or structural T

Arm e, in.	Thickness, t, in inches, of angle or flange of T							
	$\frac{5}{16}$	$\frac{3}{8}$	$\frac{7}{16}$	$\frac{1}{2}$	$\frac{9}{16}$	$\frac{5}{8}$	$\frac{11}{16}$	$\frac{3}{4}$
$\frac{1}{2}$	2.60	3.56	5.12	6.68	8.40	10.44	12.58	15.00
$\frac{3}{4}$	1.74	2.50	3.42	4.44	5.60	6.96	8.38	9.96
1	1.30	1.88	2.56	3.33	4.20	5.20	6.30	7.50
$1\frac{1}{4}$	1.04	1.50	2.06	2.67	3.36	4.16	5.04	6.00
$1\frac{1}{2}$	.88	1.26	1.70	2.22	2.80	3.48	4.20	5.00
$1\frac{3}{4}$	.74	1.08	1.46	1.90	2.40	2.98	3.60	4.28
2	.66	.94	1.28	1.66	2.10	2.60	3.16	3.74
$2\frac{1}{4}$	.58	.84	1.14	1.48	1.88	2.32	2.80	3.33
$2\frac{1}{2}$	.52	.76	1.02	1.33	1.68	2.08	2.52	3.00
$2\frac{3}{4}$	.48	.68	.94	1.22	1.54	1.90	2.30	2.72
3	.44	.62	.86	1.12	1.40	1.74	2.10	2.50
$3\frac{1}{4}$	.40	.58	.78	1.02	1.30	1.60	1.94	2.30

Arm e, in.	Thickness, t, in inches, of angle or flange of T							
	$\frac{13}{16}$	$\frac{7}{8}$	$\frac{15}{16}$	1	$1\frac{1}{16}$	$1\frac{1}{8}$	$1\frac{3}{16}$	$1\frac{1}{4}$
$\frac{1}{2}$	17.56	20.40	23.40	26.60	30.20	33.60	37.60	41.60
$\frac{3}{4}$	11.70	13.60	15.60	17.78	20.20	22.40	25.00	27.60
1	8.80	10.20	11.70	13.33	15.10	16.80	18.80	20.80
$1\frac{1}{4}$	7.04	8.16	9.36	10.67	12.00	13.46	15.00	16.60
$1\frac{1}{2}$	5.86	6.80	7.80	8.88	10.00	11.20	12.50	13.80
$1\frac{3}{4}$	5.04	5.84	6.68	7.62	8.60	9.64	10.70	11.90
2	4.40	5.10	5.86	6.68	7.52	8.40	9.36	10.38
$2\frac{1}{4}$	3.92	4.54	5.20	5.92	6.70	7.46	8.36	9.22
$2\frac{1}{2}$	3.52	4.08	4.68	5.33	6.04	6.72	7.50	8.30
$2\frac{3}{4}$	3.20	3.72	4.26	4.86	5.48	6.12	6.80	7.54
3	2.94	3.40	3.92	4.44	5.02	5.60	6.26	6.92
$3\frac{1}{4}$	2.72	3.14	3.60	4.10	4.62	5.16	5.76	6.38

For single unrestrained angles use one-quarter of the loads tabulated above.

duces to half as much, since only one side resisting the tension; hence $P = 6.67t^2/e$.

Problem A problem in the design of a ind bracing connection will indicate the use Table 4.3.

Assume a wind-bracing connection designed take wind moments in either direction of 50 ft-kips, allowing normal working stresses be increased by 33 percent for wind stresses. ssuming that wind rather than live and dead ads governs the beam selection, the allow- ble working stress on the beam is $20,000 \times 33 = 26,667$ psi. The S required for the eam would be

$$S = \frac{250 \times 12}{26.667} = 113.6$$

se 21 WF 62.

Under all conditions the moment will be ransferred into the column by means of a noment couple through the top and bottom ivets—compression on one group, tension on he other. The direct stress resulting from mo- nent is

$$\frac{\text{Moment in foot-kips}}{\text{Depth of beam in feet}} = \frac{250}{1.75} = 142.5 \text{ kips}$$

See Art. 3.10b.) Using $\frac{7}{8}$-in. rivets in single hear, this would require

$$\frac{142.9}{9.02 \times 1.33} = 11.9 = 12 \text{ rivets}$$

The same number would be required from the T to the column flange.

Because of the way in which the T is ap- plied, it may be assumed that if failure oc- curred by tearing the T from the face of the column, all 12 rivets would fail simultane- ously. Therefore we may consider the load of 8 rivets to be concentrated along the line just above the top flange of the beam or just below the bottom flange. The stress on this line is therefore $8/12 \times 142.9 = 95.3$ kips. For any such wind stress it is safe to assume that the column at this point is a 14-in. column, so the stress per inch width is $95.3/14 = 6.8$ kips. The center gage line on the T is $5\frac{1}{2}$ in., and assuming $\frac{1}{2}$-in. web and $\frac{1}{2}$-in. fillets, the

e distance is $\dfrac{5\frac{1}{2} - 1\frac{1}{2}}{2} = 2$ in. Since Table 4.3 is based on 20,000-psi fiber stress and we are permitted a $33\frac{1}{3}$ percent increase, we may use

the table by dividing 6.8 by 1.33, or use 5.1. This, however, would be for two sides, while the load we used is from one side only. We must therefore use $5.1 \times 2 = 10.2$. With $e = 2$, $t = 1\frac{1}{4}$ in.

Only the 30 WF 210, 33 WF 220 and 240, 36 WF 194, and all heavier sections will fur- nish this thickness of flange together with enough web length to make the connection. Of these the 36 WF 194 is the lightest. The flange width of 12 in., however, or 6 in. for half flange, is less than should be used, so it is desirable to go to one of the larger sections. If we allow an edge distance at the end of the flange of the T of $1\frac{1}{2}$ in. and five spaces at $2\frac{5}{8}$ in. plus $\frac{1}{8}$ in. for splitting the T, we have $14\frac{3}{4}$ in. By splitting a 36 WF 230, we can get two connections from one length of beam without any waste of material. This seems to be the lightest practicable section and is there- fore most economical.

c *Stair strings,* or stringers, constitute a special design problem frequently encountered —not so much in the design of the details as in the fact that a wide variety of standard channels, junior channels, steel plates, and pressed-steel channels are used as stair strings. Table 4.4 is a table of standard stair strings.

d It is frequently necessary with a canti- lever beam to use a system of framing which permits the beam to occupy the same space vertically as the member which supports it, so as to avoid the greater depth required by the framing shown in Fig. 3.7. Since this re- quirement is encountered so frequently in connection with the design of stair-supporting members, it has come to be known as a "stair cantilever" detail. It consists of converting the moment into a moment couple taken through top and bottom plates, at the same time taking the shear through a standard end connection.

Let us assume the condition indicated in Fig. 3.8. From the computations, the simple beam carries a moment of 33.69 ft-kips, and $S = 0.6 \times 33.69 = 20.2$. The cantilever mo- ment is 24.0 ft-kips, and $S = 0.6 \times 24 = 14.4$. For stair cantilevers, although it is not neces- sary to use the same beam for the simple beam and the cantilever, it is advisable to use

Table 4.4 Stair Loads, Strings, and Risers

Total allowable uniform loads in kips and deflections in inches for stair strings

Section properties

Property	6.5	8.4	10.6	15.3	20.7	6.53	8.5	10.63	7.84	10.2	8.03	9.33
Depth	10	10	12	10	12	10	10	10	12	12	10	12
Weight	6.5	8.4	10.6	15.3	20.7	6.53	8.5	10.63	7.84	10.2	8.03	9.33
Web	.15	.17	.19	.24	.28	3/16	1/4	5/16	3/16	1/4	3/16	3/16
Area	1.91	2.47	3.12	4.47	6.03	1.88	2.5	3.13	2.25	3.0	2.3	2.68
I	22.1	32.3	55.8	66.9	128.1	15.6	20.8	26.0	27.0	36.0	25.9	41.9
S	4.4	6.5	9.3	13.4	21.4	3.12	4.16	5.2	4.5	6.0	5.2	7.0

Loads and deflections

Span, ft.	6.5 Load	6.5 Defl.	8.4 Load	8.4 Defl.	10.6 Load	10.6 Defl.	15.3 Load	15.3 Defl.	20.7 Load	20.7 Defl.	6.53 Load	6.53 Defl.	8.5 Load	8.5 Defl.	10.63 Load	10.63 Defl.	7.84 Load	7.84 Defl.	10.2 Load	10.2 Defl.	8.03 Load	8.03 Defl.	9.33 Load	9.33 Defl.
3	19.7	.019	28.7	.019	41.3	.016	59.4	.019	89.5	.016	13.9	.019	18.5	.019	23.2	.019	20.0	.016	27.6	.016	23.2	.019	31.1	.016
4	14.7	.033	21.5	.033	31.0	.028	44.6	.033	71.2	.028	10.4	.033	13.9	.033	17.4	.033	15.0	.028	20.0	.028	17.4	.033	23.3	.028
5	11.8	.052	17.2	.052	24.8	.043	35.7	.052	56.9	.043	8.3	.052	11.1	.052	13.9	.052	12.0	.043	16.0	.043	13.9	.052	18.6	.043
6	9.8	.074	14.3	.074	20.7	.062	29.8	.074	47.4	.062	6.9	.074	9.3	.074	11.6	.074	10.0	.062	13.3	.062	11.6	.074	15.5	.062
7	8.4	.101	12.3	.101	17.7	.084	25.4	.101	40.7	.084	5.9	.101	7.9	.101	9.9	.101	8.6	.084	11.5	.084	9.9	.101	13.3	.084
8	7.4	.132	10.7	.132	15.5	.110	22.3	.132	35.6	.110	5.2	.132	6.9	.132	8.7	.132	7.5	.110	10.0	.110	8.7	.132	11.7	.110
9	6.6	.168	9.6	.168	13.8	.140	19.8	.168	31.7	.140	4.6	.168	6.2	.168	7.7	.168	6.7	.140	8.9	.140	7.7	.168	10.4	.140
10	5.9	.207	8.6	.207	12.4	.172	17.9	.207	28.4	.172	4.2	.207	5.6	.207	6.9	.207	6.0	.172	8.0	.172	6.9	.207	9.3	.172
11	5.4	.250	7.8	.250	11.3	.209	16.2	.250	25.9	.209	3.8	.250	5.0	.250	6.3	.250	5.5	.209	7.4	.209	6.3	.250	8.5	.209
12	4.9	.298	7.2	.298	10.3	.248	14.9	.298	23.8	.248	3.5	.298	4.6	.298	5.8	.298	5.0	.248	6.7	.248	5.8	.298	7.8	.248
13	4.5	.350	6.6	.350	9.5	.291	13.7	.350	21.9	.291	3.2	.350	4.3	.350	5.3	.350	4.6	.291	6.2	.291	5.3	.350	7.2	.291
14	4.2	.406	6.1	.406	8.9	.338	12.8	.406	20.3	.338	3.0	.406	4.0	.406	5.0	.406	4.3	.338	5.7	.338	5.0	.406	6.7	.338
15	3.9	.466	5.7	.466	8.3	.388	11.9	.466	19.0	.388	2.8	.466	3.7	.466	4.6	.466	4.0	.388	5.3	.388	4.6	.466	6.2	.388
16	3.7	.530	5.4	.530	7.7	.441	11.1	.530	17.8	.441	2.6	.530	3.5	.530	4.3	.530	3.8	.441	5.1	.441	4.3	.530	5.8	.441
17	3.5	.598	5.1	.598	7.3	.498	10.4	.598	16.8	.498	2.4	.598	3.3	.598	4.1	.598	3.5	.498	4.7	.498	4.1	.598	5.5	.498
18	3.3	.670	4.8	.670	6.9	.559	9.9	.670	15.8	.559	2.3	.670	3.1	.670	3.9	.670	3.3	.559	4.4	.559	3.9	.670	5.2	.559
19	3.1	.747	4.5	.747	6.5	.622	9.3	.747	15.0	.622	2.2	.747	2.9	.747	3.7	.747	3.2	.622	4.3	.622	3.7	.747	4.9	.622
20	2.9	.828	4.3	.828	6.2	.690	8.9	.828	14.2	.690	2.1	.828	2.8	.828	3.5	.828	3.0	.690	4.0	.690	3.5	.828	4.7	.690

Dimensions, in.

	6.5	8.4	10.6	15.3	20.7	8.03	9.33
T	9.228	8.934	10.664	8.125	9.875	9.25	11.25
M	.261	.38	.418	.633	.723	3/16	3/16
N	.14	.18	.20	.24	.28	3/8	3/8
K	.386	.63	.668	.938	1.06	3/16	3/16
R	.125	.25	.25	.34	.38	3/16	3/16
Y	.19	.29	.27	.64	.70	.26	.23

From the Architectural Metal Handbook, copyright 1947 by the National Association of Ornamental Metal Manufacturers. See also notes and additional data at top of facing page.

Table 4.4 Stair Loads, Strings, and Risers (Continued)

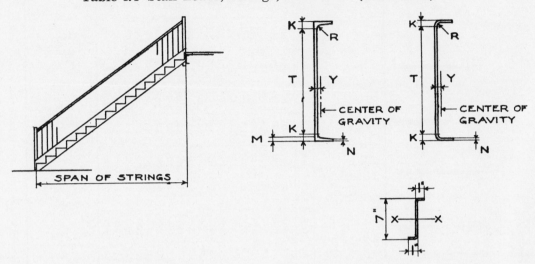

The span in feet given in the table opposite is the horizontal distance between supports.

Allowable loads and deflections shown in table are based on fiber stress of 20,000 psi. For stress of 18,000 psi, deduct 10 percent.

Deflections for loads less than shown in table are directly proportional to the load.

Loads are applicable for sections braced against lateral deflection. Stair strings with treads or with treads and risers are considered laterally braced.

Loads shown in italics will cause deflections exceeding $\frac{1}{360}$ of the span.

Total allowable uniform loads in kips and deflections in inches for 7-in. risers

USS Gage	10		12		14	
I	7.02		5.48		3.88	
S	2.0		1.57		1.11	
Span, ft.	Load	Defl.	Load	Defl.	Load	Defl.
3.5	7.6	.04	6.0	.04	4.2	.04
4.0	6.7	.05	5.3	.05	3.7	.05
5.0	5.3	.07	4.2	.07	3.0	.07
6.0	4.4	.11	3.5	.11	2.5	.11
7.0	3.8	.15	3.0	.15	2.1	.15
8.0	3.3	.19	2.6	.19	1.9	.19

beam of the same depth; so from Table 4.1 we shall select for the simple beam 10 WF 21 and for the cantilever 10 B 17. Thus from the moment couple

$$P = \frac{24 \times 12}{10} = 28.8 \text{ kips}$$

This requires a net area of $28.8/20 = 1.44$ sq in. in the plate or, allowing for two $\frac{3}{4}$-in. rivets in the width of a 5-in. plate, $t = 1.44/(5 - 1.75) = 0.44$. Use $\frac{1}{2} \times$ 5-in.

The flange thickness of a 10 B 17 (Table 1.6) is 0.329 and of a 10 WF 21, 0.340. From Table 9.1, single shear at 6.63 will control the rivet value, and the number of rivets is $28.8/6.63 = 4.4$. Use six $\frac{3}{4}$-in. rivets. Figure 4.8 shows a detail using beams of equal depth, and Fig. 4.9, the same detail with a supporting beam of greater depth.

4.13 Beam-bearing plates

When a beam is supported by a masonry wall or pier, it is essential that the beam reaction be distributed over an area sufficient to keep the average pressure on the masonry within the allowable limits. Steel bearing plates are generally used for this pressure distribution.

The following method of design is recommended,

where R = reaction of beam in kips

$A = B \times C$ = area of plate in square inches

t = thickness of plate in inches

f = bearing pressure on masonry in kips per square inch

k = distance from outer face of beam flange to web toe of fillet in inches

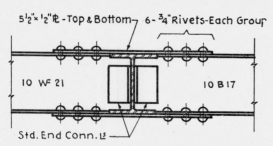

Fig. 4.8   Stair Cantilever, Beams of Equal Depth

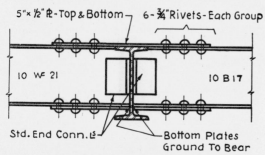

Fig. 4.9   Stair Cantilever, Beams of Unequal Depth

1. Determine the required area $A = R/f$. When f is not given in the building code or specification, a bearing value may be obtained from Art. 1.22 or Art. 8.20.

2. Determine C and solve for B. The length of bearing C is usually governed by the available wall thickness or some other structural consideration.

3. Determine n and solve for t^2 by substituting in the formula $t^2 = 0.15fn^2$.

Problem   An 18 WF 50 beam has a span of 16 ft and supports a uniform load of 69 kips including its own weight. One end of the beam rests on a masonry wall with an allowable bearing pressure of 0.250 ksi. The length of bearing C is limited to 10 in. Design the bearing plate.

$$R = \frac{69}{2} = 34.5 \text{ kips}$$

$$A = \frac{34.5}{0.250} = 138 \text{ sq in.}$$

$$B = \frac{138}{10} = 13.8 \text{ in.}; \quad \text{use 14 in.}$$

$$n = \frac{14}{2} - 1\tfrac{1}{16} = 5\tfrac{15}{16}; \quad \text{say 6 in.}$$

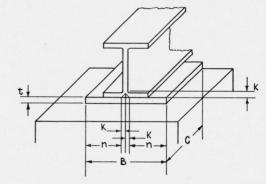

Fig. 4.10   Beam-Bearing Plate

$$f = \frac{34.5}{14 \times 10} = 0.246 \text{ ksi}$$

$$t^2 = 0.15 \times 0.246 \times 6 \times 6 = 1.33 \text{ in.}^2$$

$$t = 1.15 \text{ in.}; \quad \text{use } 1\tfrac{1}{4} \text{ in.}$$

Use 10 in. $\times$ $1\tfrac{1}{4}$ in. $\times$ 1 ft 2 in. bearing plate.

Steel bearing plates may be materially reduced in size and weight by setting them upon strong masonry, locally built into the wall or pier to distribute the load over the weaker masonry. For this purpose, template of bluestone or other hard stone, or rich concrete masonry may be used. In designing such masonry the overhang of any course beyond the course above should not exceed $\tfrac{3}{4}$ of the thickness of the course, and the stronger masonry should be carried down far enough to obtain an adequate base area on the weaker masonry.

Steel beams supported by masonry should always be properly anchored to the wall.

Some specifications call for "standard bearing plates under all beams." The steel handbooks do not list any such members, but for ordinary brick bearing, if no other bearing stress is given, 200 psi may be used. With wide-flange beams, the area furnished by the flange itself is frequently enough to provide sufficient bearing area, particularly on concrete walls. However, in the interest of economy of labor, it is well to have some kind of bearing plate bedded by the mason at the proper level before the beam is set. Frequently $\tfrac{1}{4}$-in.-thick leveling plates the width of the beam flange are used for this purpose.

.14 Unsymmetrical bending in purlins

a Any beam the main axis of which is not
orizontal—as found most frequently in roof
urlins on a sloping roof—must be analyzed
or the effect of this unsymmetrical bending.
ome textbooks and handbooks discuss this
ubject at length, working out "S polygons"
nd otherwise complicating a simple problem.
he simplest approach is to make a vector
nalysis of the applied loads, apply the two
omponents parallel to the two axes of the
eam, and compute the unit stresses obtained
y dividing the vector moment by the section
nodulus in each direction.

Inasmuch as the component parallel with
he slope of the roof is usually greater than
an be carried on the full span, it is common
ractice to divide the span by putting in one
r more rows of sag rods in the length of the
pan. The rods serve as a support the weak
vay of the beam, carrying the thrust load up
o the peak of the roof and balancing it against
corresponding load from the other side of
he roof. This is an important reason why the
vector analysis of loads is a simpler method
of approach to the problem than the S-polygon
method.

Problem Select a purlin for a span of 21 ft
ind a uniform load of 420 lb per running foot,
he roof to have $\frac{1}{5}$ pitch (see Fig. 4.11).

The pitch of a roof is stated in terms of a
atio of center height to total span, so $\frac{1}{5}$ pitch
means a slope of 1 on $2\frac{1}{2}$. The total load on
one beam is

$$W = 21 \times 420 = 8,820$$

From the triangle relationship,

$$1^2 + 2.5^2 = 7.25$$
$$\sqrt{7.25} = 2.7$$

Therefore,

$$W_p = \frac{1}{2.7} \times 8,820 = 3,267$$

$$W_n = \frac{2.5}{2.7} \times 8,820 = 8,167$$

Using the normal load only and disregarding
deflection,

$$S = \frac{8.167 \times 21}{13.33} = 12.86$$

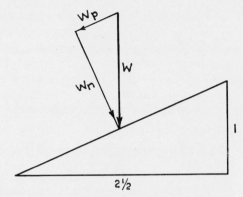

Fig. 4.11 Load Distribution on Sloping Beam

Try 8 WF 17.

$$M_n = \frac{8,167 \times 21 \times 12}{8} = 257,300 \text{ in.-lb}$$

$$M_p = \frac{3,267 \times 21 \times 12}{8} = 102,900 \text{ in.-lb}$$

$$f_n = \frac{257,300}{14.1} = 18,250$$

$$f_p = \frac{102,900}{2.6} = \frac{39,580}{57,830}$$

Although f_p could be reduced greatly by using
sag rods, it is obvious that the 8 WF 17 will
not do. Try 10 WF 21.

$$f_n = \frac{257,300}{21.5} = 11,970$$

$$f_p = \frac{102,900}{3.4} = \frac{30,260}{42,230}$$

This is still too high without sag rods.

The effect of introducing sag rods is to make
the beam a continuous beam so far as W_p
is concerned, and thus introduce different
coefficients (see Art. 3.20a) and divide the
fiber stress by the square of the number of
parts.

The combined effect for introducing sag
rods is as follows:

For a single row of sag rods, the divisor
is 4.

For two rows of sag rods, the divisor is
$1.25 \times 9 = 11.25$.

For three rows of sag rods, the divisor is
$1.25 \times 16 = 20$.

If a single row of sag rods is used with a
10 WF 21, the calculation becomes,

$$f_n = 11,970$$

$$f_p = \frac{30,260}{4} = \frac{7,565}{19,535} \text{ psi}$$

Thus, using one row of sag rods, the 10 WF 21 may be used.

b The area of sag rods required must be computed also. The rods are ordinarily run from beam to beam, 3 in. below the top of the beam and staggered laterally 3 in. The load for which they are designed is the cumulative W or thrust from the eave to the peak.

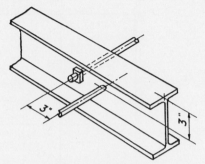

Fig. 4.12 Use of Tie Rods or Sag Rods in Purlin

Problem Assume that the purlin designed above is used on a roof which is 10 beam spaces wide. Thus there will be 5 beams either side of the peak purlin. The eave purlin will be assumed to carry half the purlin load.

From the preceding problem $W = 3,267$ for full span or 1,633 for half span as carried by a row of sag rods. Then

$$P = 4.5 \times 1,633 = 7,350$$

$$A = \frac{7,350}{20,000} = 0.368 \text{ sq in. net}$$

From Table 2.4 a $\frac{7}{8}$-in. round rod would be required just below the peak. Since the rod is run in short lengths from beam to beam, the size may be decreased as the load drops off. A tabulation of the loads and sizes is as follows:

$\frac{3}{4}$-in. rod is good for $0.302 \times 20,000 = 6,040$, or $3.7 \times 1,633$. Therefore it may be used in the second bay, which carries $3\frac{1}{2}$ bays.

$\frac{5}{8}$-in. rod is good for $0.202 \times 20,000 = 4,040$, or $2.5 \times 1,633$. Thus it may be used below the upper two bays.

Rods of less than $\frac{5}{8}$-in. diameter should not be used. Therefore, it will be necessary to use $\frac{7}{8}$-in. sag rods for one beam space each side of the peak, then $\frac{3}{4}$-in. sag rods for the second beam, and $\frac{5}{8}$-in. from this beam down to the eaves.

The final design is indicated in Fig. 4.13.

4.15 Semirigid framing

The latest AISC Code recognizes semirigid framing as a legitimate saving in girders which

frame to columns. In the members which ar affected (probably 15 to 20 percent of the stee members) a saving of 10 to 20 percent may b made, or $1\frac{1}{2}$ to 4 percent of the total steel o the job, at no extra cost in details.

The method of computation given here i taken from "Progress Report No. 1 on Riv eted Semi-Rigid Beam to Column Buildin; Connections," issued by the American Insti tute of Steel Construction. The propose method of design may be summarized in th following rules of procedure:

1. Design the beam for maximum bendin; moment, assuming simple supports (no re straint). (See the methods of Arts. 3.10 anc 4.10.)

2. Calculate the stiffness constants for the next lighter beam size and the less stiff, or minimum, ΣK_c of the two supporting columns and then compute the ratio $K_B/\Sigma K_c$. [$K_B = I/L$ for the beam, and $\Sigma K_c = \Sigma (I/L)$ for the column.]

3. Select the type of semirigid connection to be used (see Fig. 4.14) and obtain from the appropriate table (4.5, 4.6, 4.7, or 4.8) the dependable percentage of rigidity for this next lighter beam size on the required span.

4. Choose the curves appropriate for the required types of loading and enter Fig. 4.15, 4.16, or 4.17, with the computed $K_B/\Sigma K_c$ and move vertically upward to an intersection with the dependable percentage of rigidity obtained from the tables. Interpolate between the plotted curves when necessary. Move horizontally to the left and read the redesign

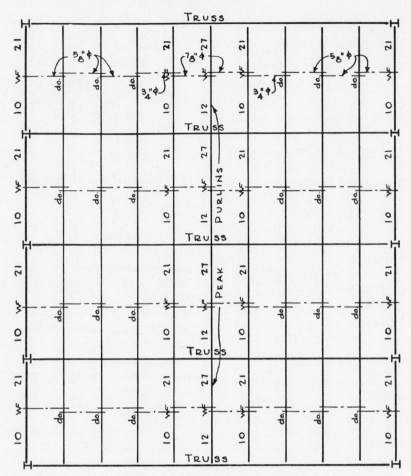

Fig. 4.13   Plan of Pitched Roof

coefficient F from the vertical scale. For interior spans in frames having nearly equal bay widths, the dotted curves may be used; otherwise use the solid-line percentage curves. If the bending is produced by a combination of uniform loading and concentrated loads, a weighted F coefficient may be derived from the F values obtained individually from Fig. 4.15 and 4.16; or as located at mid-span, regardless of its actual location, for the purpose of obtaining its F coefficient.

5. Multiply the required section modulus previously calculated for the simple span design by the redesign coefficient, and select the lightest beam which will provide a section modulus equal to the product of this multiplication.

6. When a particular beam is repeated un-

der identical loading conditions a number of times in a frame, and the size determined by step 5 is less than that assumed in step 2, a further economy may sometimes be effected by repeating the procedure until K_B in step 2 exactly agrees with the beam size actually used.

7. When the bending moment in a beam is produced by a combination of two or more types of loading, an adjusted redesign coefficient may be obtained by weighting the coefficients for each type of loading (read from the curves) in proportion to the contribution of each type of load to the total moment.

Assume, for example, that a total moment is 40 percent due to uniform loading and 60 percent due to a concentrated load. Also assume that, for uniform loading $F = 0.81$,

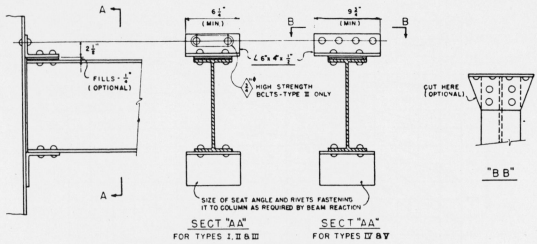

FILLS - ¼" (OPTIONAL)

6 ¼" (MIN.)

9 ¾" (MIN.)

2 ½"

∟ 6"x 4"x ½"

¾"⌀ HIGH STRENGTH BOLTS - TYPE II ONLY

CUT HERE (OPTIONAL)

SIZE OF SEAT ANGLE AND RIVETS FASTENING IT TO COLUMN AS REQUIRED BY BEAM REACTION

SECT "AA"   SECT "AA"
FOR TYPES I, II & III   FOR TYPES IV & V

"B B"

¾ φ rivets for Type I and IV connections
¾ φ bolts as noted, and ¾ φ rivets, for Type II connections
⅞ φ rivets for Type III and V connections

Fig. 4.14   Semirigid Connections

and for the concentrated load $F = 0.86$. For the combined loading,

$$F = (0.4 \times 0.81) + (0.6 \times 0.86) = 0.84$$

Example A *Given:* Uniformly loaded beams, framing between columns spaced 26 ft on centers. Total load on each beam, 30 kips (45 percent live, 55 percent dead). Story heights, 10 ft. Columns, 12 WF 53 at the sixth floor, and 12 WF 79 at the fourth floor. Beams will frame to column flanges.

Required: Size of beams, at the sixth and fourth floors, semirigidly framed to columns.

$$M_s = \frac{30 \times 26}{8} = 97.5 \text{ kip-ft} = 1,170 \text{ kip-in.}$$

$$\text{Required } S = \frac{1,170}{20} = 58.5$$

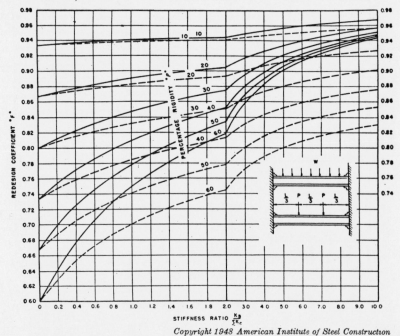

Fig. 4.15   Redesign Coefficient Curves, Uniform and Third-Point Loading

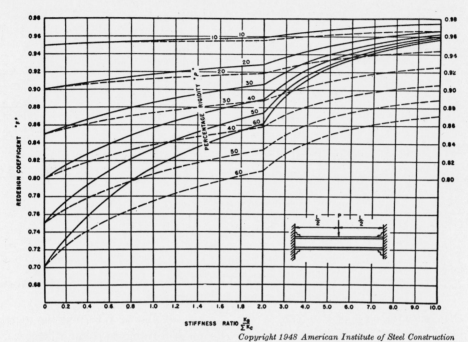

Fig. 4.16　Redesign Coefficient Curves, Single Concentrated Load at Mid-Span

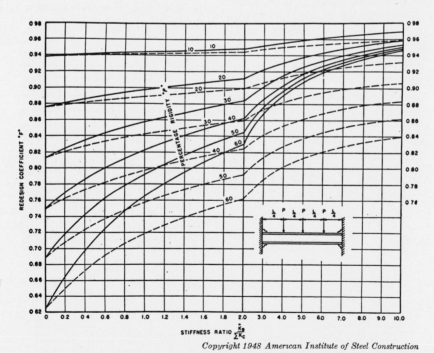

Fig. 4.17　Redesign Coefficient Curves, Quarter-Point Loading

Table 4.5   Percentage of Rigidity—Two $\frac{3}{4}$-in. Rivets or Bolts

BEAM	SPAN IN FEET											
	8	10	12	14	16	18	20	22	24	26	28	30
10 WF 21	37	39	40	42	35	27	20	14	9	4	—	—
	37	39	40	42	43	44	45	46	46	47	47	47
25	29	32	34	35	25	16	7	—	—	—	—	—
	29	32	34	35	36	37	38	39	40	40	41	42
29	27	29	30	29	18	8	—	—	—	—	—	—
	27	29	30	31	32	33	34	34	35	36	36	36
12 WF 27	29	31	32	32	22	10	—	—	—	—	—	—
	29	31	32	33	34	35	36	37	38	38	38	39
31	25	27	29	27	16	5	—	—	—	—	—	—
	25	27	29	30	31	32	33	34	34	35	35	35
36	22	24	25	22	10	—	—	—	—	—	—	—
	22	24	25	27	27	28	29	30	30	30	31	31
40	20	22	23	17	4	—	—	—	—	—	—	—
	20	22	23	24	25	26	27	27	28	28	28	29
45	18	20	21	14	—	—	—	—	—	—	—	—
	18	20	21	22	23	23	24	24	25	25	26	26
50	17	18	19	10	—	—	—	—	—	—	—	—
	17	18	19	20	21	22	22	23	23	24	24	24
14 WF 30	27	29	31	26	15	4	—	—	—	—	—	—
	27	29	31	32	33	34	35	36	37	37	38	38
34	24	26	28	20	7	—	—	—	—	—	—	—
	24	26	28	29	30	31	32	32	33	33	34	34
38	21	23	25	16	1	—	—	—	—	—	—	—
	21	23	25	26	27	28	29	30	31	31	31	31
43	20	21	22	11	—	—	—	—	—	—	—	—
	20	21	22	23	24	25	26	26	27	27	28	28
48	18	19	20	7	—	—	—	—	—	—	—	—
	18	19	20	21	22	23	24	24	25	25	25	25
53	15	17	19	4	—	—	—	—	—	—	—	—
	15	17	19	20	21	21	22	22	23	23	23	23

Upper Lines Give p-Values for Type I.
Lower Lines Give p-Values for Type II.

The required simple beam is **16 WF 40** ($S = 64.4$) or 14 WF 43 ($S = 62.7$).

Since the simple beam requirements would almost be satisfied with the next lighter section, the redesign computations will be made at once using the second lighter section.

At the sixth floor, Type II semirigid connections will be specified. From Table 4.5, $p = 33$ percent for a 14 WF 34 beam on a 26-ft span.

$$K_B = \frac{339.2}{26 \times 12} = 1.09$$

$$\Sigma K_c = \frac{2 \times 426.2}{10 \times 12} = 7.10$$

$$\frac{K_B}{\Sigma K_c} = \frac{1.09}{7.10} = 0.153$$

Interpolating between the solid-line curves for $p = 30$ percent and $p = 40$ percent in Fig. 4.15, a redesign coefficient $F = 0.79$ is obtained. (Note that the maximum effect of frame action in this problem, as indicated by the relationship $K_B/\Sigma K_c$, is so small that there is little difference between F values derived

Table 4.6   Percentage of Rigidity—Two $\frac{7}{8}$-in. Rivets

BEAM	SPAN IN FEET											
	8	10	12	14	16	18	20	22	24	26	28	30
10 WF 21	44	46	48	49	51	52	51	46	42	38	35	33
25	38	40	42	43	45	46	40	35	30	25	21	17
29	34	36	38	39	40	39	32	26	20	15	10	6
12 WF 27	34	36	38	39	40	41	41	35	29	24	19	15
31	30	32	34	35	36	37	36	29	23	17	12	7
36	27	29	30	32	33	34	29	21	14	7	1	—
40	24	26	27	29	30	31	22	14	7	—	—	—
45	23	24	25	26	27	28	18	9	—	—	—	—
50	21	22	23	24	25	24	14	5	—	—	—	—
14 WF 30	30	32	34	36	38	39	40	33	27	22	17	12
34	27	29	31	32	34	35	34	27	20	14	8	3
38	24	26	28	30	31	32	29	22	14	7	1	—
43	22	24	26	27	28	29	23	14	6	—	—	—
48	19	21	23	24	25	26	19	10	1	—	—	—
53	19	20	21	22	23	24	15	6	—	—	—	—

by the solid and dotted curves; hence the more conservative solid-line value may be taken for both interior and end bays.)

Required redesign $S = 58.5 \times 0.79 = 46.2$

Use 14 WF 34 ($S = 48.5$). The saving in weight is 15 percent and the saving in depth is 2 in.

At the fourth floor, Type V semirigid connections may be used. A 14 WF 30 beam will be tried. From Table 4.8, $p = 56$ percent for a 14 WF 30 beam on a 26-ft span.

$$K_B = \frac{289.6}{26 \times 12} = 0.93$$

$$\Sigma K_c = \frac{2 \times 663.0}{10 \times 12} = 11.05$$

$$\frac{K_B}{\Sigma K_c} = \frac{0.93}{11.05} = 0.084$$

Interpolating between $p = 50$ percent and $p = 60$ percent in Fig. 4.15, an F value of 0.64 is obtained.

Required redesign $S = 58.5 \times 0.64 = 37.4$

Use 14 WF 30 ($S = 41.8$). The saving in weight is 25 percent.

Example B. *Required:* To design a line of girder beams, each spanning 24 ft and supporting 31-kip concentrated loads at their third points. Story height = 10 ft. Exterior beams frame to flange of 12 WF 65 wall col-

Table 4.7 Percentage of Rigidity—Four $\frac{3}{4}$-in. Rivets

BEAM	SPAN IN FEET												
	10	12	14	16	18	20	22	24	26	28	30	32	34
14 WF 30	36	39	41	43	44	46	47	48	49	50	51	52	50
34	32	35	37	39	40	42	43	44	45	46	47	45	42
38	30	32	34	36	37	39	40	41	42	43	42	38	35
43	27	29	31	33	34	35	36	37	38	39	35	30	26
48	25	27	28	30	31	32	33	34	35	35	30	25	20
53	23	25	26	28	29	30	31	32	33	31	26	21	16
16 WF 36	31	34	36	38	39	41	42	44	45	46	42	39	36
40	28	31	33	35	36	38	39	40	41	40	35	30	26
45	26	28	30	32	33	35	36	37	38	35	30	25	21
50	24	26	28	30	31	32	33	34	35	30	25	20	16
58	21	23	24	26	27	29	30	31	29	23	17	12	7
64	19	21	23	24	25	27	28	29	25	18	12	6	1
71	17	19	20	22	23	24	25	26	22	15	8	1	—
78	16	18	19	20	21	22	23	24	19	11	4	—	—
18 WF 50	23	25	27	29	31	32	33	34	34	35	33	28	24
55	22	24	25	27	28	29	30	31	32	33	29	24	20
60	20	22	24	25	26	27	28	29	30	31	25	20	15
64	19	21	22	24	25	26	27	28	28	27	21	16	11
70	17	19	21	22	23	24	25	26	26	24	18	12	7
77	16	18	19	20	21	22	23	24	24	21	15	9	4
85	15	17	18	19	20	21	21	22	22	18	11	5	—
21 WF 62	20	22	23	25	26	27	28	28	29	29	24	19	14
68	18	20	22	23	24	25	26	26	27	27	21	16	12
73	17	19	20	21	22	23	24	25	26	24	18	12	7

Table 4.8 Percentage of Rigidity—Four $\frac{7}{8}$-in. Rivets

BEAM	SPAN IN FEET												
	10	12	14	16	18	20	22	24	26	28	30	32	34
14 WF 30	41	44	47	49	51	52	54	55	56	57	58	59	60
34	38	41	43	45	47	49	50	51	52	53	53	54	54
38	35	38	40	42	44	45	46	47	48	49	50	51	51
43	32	34	36	38	40	41	42	43	44	45	46	47	48
48	29	32	35	36	37	38	39	40	41	42	43	44	44
53	27	29	31	33	34	36	37	38	38	39	40	41	41
16 WF 36	35	38	41	43	45	47	48	49	50	51	52	53	53
40	32	35	37	40	42	43	44	45	46	47	48	49	49
45	30	32	34	36	38	40	41	42	43	44	44	45	45
50	27	30	32	34	35	37	38	39	40	40	41	41	42
58	24	26	28	30	31	33	34	35	36	36	37	38	39
64	22	24	26	28	29	30	31	32	33	34	34	35	35
71	21	23	24	26	27	28	29	30	31	32	32	33	33
78	19	21	22	24	25	26	27	28	28	29	30	31	31
18 WF 50	27	30	32	34	35	36	37	38	39	40	40	41	41
55	25	28	30	32	33	34	35	36	36	37	38	39	39
60	24	26	28	29	30	31	32	33	34	35	35	36	36
64	22	24	26	28	29	30	30	31	32	33	33	34	34
70	21	23	24	26	27	28	29	30	30	31	31	32	32
77	19	21	22	24	25	26	26	27	28	28	29	29	30
85	17	19	21	22	23	24	24	25	26	27	27	28	28
21 WF 62	22	24	26	28	29	30	31	32	33	34	34	35	35
68	20	22	24	26	27	28	29	30	30	31	31	32	32
73	19	21	23	24	25	26	27	28	29	30	30	31	31

umns. Interior columns are 12 WF 79, with webs normal to webs of girder beams.

$$M_s = 31 \times 8 = 248 \text{ kip-ft} = 2{,}976 \text{ kip-in.}$$

$$\text{Required } S = \frac{2{,}976}{20} = 148.8$$

The required simple beam is 21 WF 73 ($S = 150.7$).

Type V semirigid connections will be specified. From Table 4.8, $p = 30$ percent for a 21 WF 68 beam on a 24-ft span.

$$K_B = \frac{1{,}478.3}{24 \times 12} = 5.15$$

$$\text{The lesser } \Sigma K_c = \frac{2 \times 216.4}{10 \times 12} \text{ (minor axis of 12 WF 79)} = 3.61$$

$$\frac{K_B}{\Sigma K_c} = \frac{5.13}{3.61} = 1.43$$

From Fig. 4.15 $F = 0.86$ for end bays (from solid lines) and $F = 0.84$ for interior bays (from dotted lines). For end bays,

$$\text{Required redesign } S = 148.8 \times 0.86 = 128.0$$

Use 21 WF 68 ($S = 139.9$). For interior bays,

$$\text{Required redesign } S = 148.8 \times 0.84 = 125.0$$

Use 21 WF 62 ($S = 126.4$). (Actually, for a 21 WF 62 beam, $p = 32$ percent, $K_B = 4.64$, and $K_B/\Sigma K_c = 1.28$; $F = 0.83$ instead of 0.84; and required redesign $S = 123.5$.) The saving in weight is 7 percent in end bays and 15 percent in interior bays.

Example C *Required:* To design a semirigidly connected beam to carry a uniform load of 1.7 kips per linear foot, and a concentrated load of 22 kips located 7 ft from one end, when the center-to-center distance of supporting columns is 20 ft. Columns just below the beam are 12 WF 71 and story height is 12 ft; columns immediately above the beam are 12 WF 65 and this story height is 10 ft. Beam will frame to webs of supporting columns.

M_s occurs at point of concentrated load.

$$M_s \text{ due to concentrated load} = \frac{22 \times 13 \times 7}{20} = 100.1 \text{ kip-ft}$$

$$M_s \text{ due to uniform load} = (1.7 \times 10 \times 7) - (1.7 \times 7 \times 3.5) = \underline{77.3} \text{ kip-ft}$$

$$\text{Total } M_s = 177.4 \text{ kip-ft} = 2{,}129 \text{ kip-in.}$$

$$\text{Required } S = \frac{2{,}129}{20} = 106.5$$

The required simple beam is 18 WF 60 ($S = 107.8$).

If Type IV semirigid connections are specified, $p = 29$ percent for an 18 WF 55 beam on a 20-ft span. For an 18 WF 55,

$$K_B = \frac{889.9}{20 \times 12} = 3.70$$

$$\Sigma K_c = \frac{174.6}{10 \times 12} + \frac{195.3}{12 \times 12} = 2.81$$

$$\frac{K_B}{\Sigma K_c} = \frac{3.70}{2.81} = 1.32$$

Moment due to uniform loading $= 100.1/177.4 = 0.57$ of total moment. From Fig. 4.15, $F = 0.86$ for uniform loading. Moment due to concentrated load $= 0.43$ of total moment.

Although the concentrated load is not at mid-span, the F value obtained from Fig. 4.16 ($F = 0.90$) will err on the "safe" side. A weighted F value, for the combination of uniform and concentrated loading, may be computed as,

$$F = 0.57 \times 0.86 + 0.43 \times 0.90 = 0.88$$

$$\text{Required redesign } S = 106.5 \times 0.88 = 93.7$$

Use 18 WF 55 ($S = 98.2$). A saving of $8\frac{1}{3}$ percent $= 100$ lb of plain material.

If Type V semirigid connections had been specified, p would equal 36 percent for an 18 WF 50 beam on a 20-ft span, instead of 29 percent for the 18 WF 55 beam; K_B/K_c would have been 1.18 instead of 1.32; the weighted F value would have been 0.86; and the required redesign S would have been 91.6. Thus it will be seen that a $12\frac{1}{2}$ percent increase in the rigidity of the connections, resulting from the use of $\frac{7}{8}$-in.-diameter instead of $\frac{3}{4}$-in.-diameter tension rivets, would produce but a $2\frac{1}{2}$ percent decrease in the required section

modulus, which would be insufficient to permit the use of this next lighter beam. Had the lighter beam proved to be adequate using the larger rivets, the added saving in main material would have been 100 lb. Such a saving would probably not have warranted changing to $\frac{7}{8}$-in. tension rivets here if the balance of the fabrication was based on using $\frac{3}{4}$-in. rivets.

4.16 Lintels

a Lintels are ordinarily steel members used in masonry walls to carry the masonry over an opening. The type of lintel used depends on (1) the span, (2) the wall thickness, (3) the type of masonry, and (4) the type of window or door over which the lintel is used. The simplest type of lintel is a loose angle lintel, used in a brick wall when the span is not too great. The flat leg of the angle, not over $3\frac{1}{2}$ in. wide, provides a seat for one course of brick, and the upstanding leg provides the strength. The smallest angle used is usually $3 \times 3 \times \frac{1}{4}$ in. and the maximum span as governed by deflection is limited in feet to about $1\frac{2}{3}$ times the depth in inches. Thus a 3×3-in. angle under light load should span not over 5 ft. Other angles often used for lintels are 4×3 in. and $5 \times 3\frac{1}{2}$ in., with the longer leg vertical. It is seldom that section modulus controls the design of a lintel unless there is a concentrated load applied immediately over the lintel.

The masonry load ordinarily figured on a simple short lintel is the weight of a triangle of masonry of a height equal to the span, plus any concentrations which come immediately over the opening. Certainly a very safe assumption is a rectangle of height equal to the

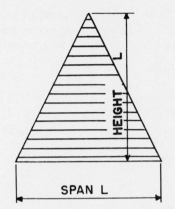

Fig. 4.18   Masonry Load to be Carried on a Short Lintel

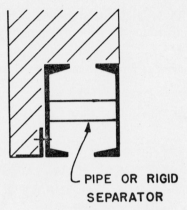

Fig. 4.19   Built-up Lintel

span. A good simple rule for bearing for angle lintels is 1 in. of bearing at each end for each foot of clear span, but not less than 4 in. at each end.

Problem   Assume a 12-in. brick wall on a clear span of 4 ft 6 in. with no load except the wall itself. On the basis of a triangle of masonry carried, with sides equal to the span,

$$W = \frac{4.5 \times 120 \times 4.5}{2} = 1,215$$

$$S = 0.6 \left(\frac{1.215 \times 4.5}{6} \right) = 0.55$$

It is advisable to use three angles to carry the three brick thickness of walls. Using the minimum angle specified above, $3 \times 3 \times \frac{1}{4}$ in., the section modulus furnished is 1.74, and our final lintel is three angles, $3 \times 3 \times \frac{1}{4}$ in., 5 ft 4 in. long. This allows for 5 in. of bearing at each end.

b   If span or section modulus requirements are beyond the limitations of $5 \times 3\frac{1}{2} \times \frac{3}{8}$-in. angles, it is ordinarily better to use a fabricated lintel—the simplest lintel to use being built up of two channels with separators between them and an angle riveted to the outer channel to carry the face brick, as shown in Fig. 4.19.

c   It has been mentioned that the type of window to some extent controls the lintel. This is an architectural rather than a structural provision, but it is well to call attention

to it. Figure 4.20 shows a very common condition—the outer angle is set about $\frac{3}{4}$ in. lower than the inner angles so as to form a weather break and a point for calking the frame.

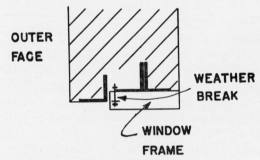

Fig. 4.20   Angle Lintel—Showing Weather Break

d   Where factory-type steel sash is used, it is necessary to provide a surface against which the sash section can finish and a means of fastening the steel sash in place. Since factory-type sash units are usually longer than the economical span for loose angle lintels, and in fact are frequently continuous under an eave purlin, provision must usually be made to fabricate the lintel accordingly. The catalogs of the various steel-sash companies suggest methods of providing for the various details to support the sash, but two of the most common details are shown in Fig. 4.21.

e   In buildings using corrugated steel or asbestos-cement siding, the lintel and girt are combined, and $2 \times 2 \times \frac{1}{4}$-in. or greater angles

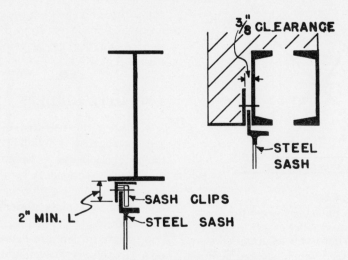

Fig. 4.21   Lintel Types for Steel Sash

are used at the sides and sills of all steel sash windows. The details generally used for this condition are indicated in Art. 10.41.

4.17   Torsion in lintels and spandrels

a   For reasons of practicability, lintels or spandrel beams are frequently placed in a wall in such a manner that they are subject to torsion as well as to direct load stress, and in some instances horizontal wall cracks develop at or above the top flange of the spandrel as a result of such torsion. This condition

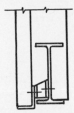

Fig. 4.22   Spandrel Subject to Torsion

is indicated in Fig. 4.22. In this construction, the only concentric load is a light-weight concrete masonry backup wall, frequently without the benefit of slab or joist bearing on the wall. The 4-in. face brick, which is usually heavier than the 8-in. backup, applies an eccentric load on an approximate 6-in. lever arm that, particularly in a long beam, causes the beam to roll at the center of the span, the

bottom flange deflecting inward and the upper flange outward.

The detail shown in Fig. 4.23 will usually aggravate the tendency to crack. The method of attachment of the shelf angle by means of clip angles spaced 2 to 3 ft will permit the roll of the shelf angle with relation to the web of the beam itself, a condition which is prevented by the method of attachment shown in Fig. 4.22. It should be noted that metal wall ties do not make a rigid wall, and the face brick can apply load independently of the backup.

b   Inasmuch as an accurate computation of stresses is involved and factors to be used for built-up sections are not readily obtainable, it is preferable to design against the occurrence of such a condition. If beams can be framed into the spandrel or attached to the top flange, this tendency to roll can usually be eliminated. A poured-concrete slab resting on the top flange or the ends of bar joists tack-welded to the beam will accomplish the

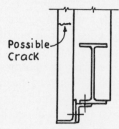

Fig. 4.23   Spandrel Subject to Torsion

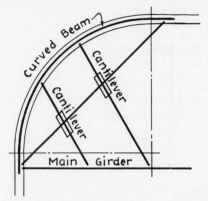

Fig. 4.24　Plan Showing Curved Beam

same purpose. Where this is impossible, a section should be used which is capable of resisting lateral as well as vertical stresses. Some engineers make a practice of tying the facing to the top flange so that the moment produced by eccentricity is restricted by a moment couple, and building up the top and bottom flanges to take the horizontal stresses produced by this moment couple. The section shown in Fig. 4.19 will resist such stresses,

curvature, and carrying the support points by means of cantilevers from the main construction, using the cantilever detail shown in Figs. 4.8 or 4.9.

4.20 PLATE GIRDERS

a　When the required section modulus is greater than that available in rolled wide-flange sections or economical cover-plated wide-flange sections, it becomes necessary to build up a plate-girder section. The various parts of a plate girder are indicated in Fig. 4.25.

b　Plate girders are figured by two methods, (1) the section-modulus method, based on the computation of the section modulus to resist a given moment, and (2) the flange-area method, by which sufficient area is provided in tension and compression to resist the moment couple, as indicated in Art. 3.10. Both methods are recognized as good engineering. The AISC Code suggests the section-modulus method based on the strength of the gross

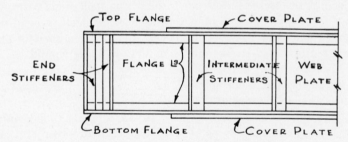

Fig. 4.25　Parts of a Plate Girder

particularly if rigid separators are used. If the beam required is too long to permit the use of standard channels, the proper resistance may sometimes be developed by using a flatwise channel on the top flange and building up the bottom flange by rigidly connecting the shelf angle and putting a continuous angle at the inner edge of the bottom flange with the leg turned out and up.

c　Another type of spandrel which is subject to torsion is a curved beam, as indicated in Fig. 4.24. This is usually carried by breaking the curve up into short lengths so that the beam between supports has only a small

section. Many cities require the section-modulus method based on the strength of net section. New York City recognizes either the section-modulus method using the net section or the flange-area method. A safe procedure is to design by the flange-area method and check by the section-modulus method—both designs based on net section.

The AISC Code contains several other requirements relative to plate girders, as follows:

Sec. 26(*b*)　Plate girder webs shall have a thickness of not less than 1/170 of the unsupported distance between flanges.

Sec. 26(*c*)　The thickness of outstanding parts

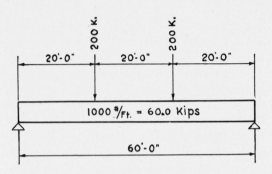

Fig. 4.26　Load Diagram for Plate-Girder Problem

$$W = 120 \times 2 = 240 \text{ kips}$$

$$S = \frac{240 \times 120}{13.33} = 2,160$$

of flanges shall conform to the requirements of Sec. 18(c)—that is, the ratio of projecting width of plates or angles to thickness shall be not greater than sixteen. The width shall be taken from the free edge to the first row of rivets or welds.

The total cross sectional area of cover plates of riveted plate girders shall not exceed 70 percent of the total flange area.

Sec. 26(d)　Rivets and welds, connecting flange to web, or cover plates to flange, shall be proportioned to resist the maximum horizontal shear at the plane in question resulting from the bending forces on the girder. Additionally, rivets and welds connecting flange to web shall be proportioned to transmit any loads applied directly to the flange.

c　The flange area method requires the following steps in design:

1. With the required moment on the girder known, assume an approximate over-all depth of girder. This should be between $\frac{1}{12}$ and $\frac{1}{21}$ of the span and may be set by allowable clearances determined by architectural considerations. Since plate girders are beams, their depths may be determined also by deflection limitations, as set forth in Art. 4.10g. If neither of the above factors governs, the depth may be selected between a minimum of $d = \sqrt{S/1.25}$, which approximates a girder having 70 percent of its flange in area of plates, and $d = \sqrt{S/0.4}$, which approximates the minimum practical flange plates with four angles.

For example, select the over-all depth to use for a plate girder carrying 2 kips per ft on a span of 120 ft.

Minimum $d = \sqrt{\dfrac{2,160}{1.25}}$ = approximately 42 in.

Maximum $d = \sqrt{\dfrac{2,160}{0.4}}$ = approximately 73.5 in.

For deflection, minimum $d = \dfrac{120}{1.61} = 74.5$ in.

On this basis, the approximate depth of girder to assume would be 74.5 in.

Again, assume the girder shown in Fig. 4.26.

$$M = 230 \times 30 = 6,900$$
$$- 30 \times 15 = - 450$$
$$- 200 \times 10 = - 2,000$$
$$\underline{ -2,450}$$
$$S = 0.6 \times 4,450 = 2,670$$

Minimum $d = \sqrt{\dfrac{2,670}{1.25}}$ = approximately 46.5 in.

Maximum $d = \sqrt{\dfrac{2,670}{0.4}}$ = approximately 81.7 in.

For deflection, approximate $d = \dfrac{60}{1.61} = 37.3$

On this basis, start with an assumed depth of about 48 in.

2. Assume the distance between centers of gravity of flanges *jd* to be 0.9 of the out-to-out of cover plates.

3. Assume a trial web plate of a depth to the nearest inch of approximately *jd*, and compute the required thickness to take the shear, from the formula

$$t = \frac{V}{13d}$$

where V is the shear in kips.

4. Calculate the required flange area

$$A = \frac{Md}{f(jd)^2}$$

where M is given in inch-pounds. This formula is developed from Formula (3.1).

5. Deduct $\frac{1}{6}$ of the gross area of the web and find the required net area of flange angle and cover plates.

6. From Table 4.16 select the flange angles and cover plates to furnish the net area determined by step 5.

7. Determine the true value jd of the designed section, the distance back-to-back of angles, less the figure $2y$ for the flange section selected from Table 4.16. Where this figure is preceded in the tables by a plus sign, $2y$ should be added to the depth back-to-back of angles instead of subtracted.

8. On the basis of the true values as determined, recalculate the required flange area as described in step 4 above. If this area does not agree with the selected flange area, repeat steps 5–8 until results are satisfactory.

Table 4.16 values may be extended in a straight-line ratio or interpolated. In each column, there are four cross lines. The upper cross line indicates that, for a plate thickness below this line, the plate area is less than 50 percent of the flange. The lower cross line indicates that, for plate thicknesses below this line, the plate area is over 65 percent of the flange. These tables are based on net section, but may be adjusted for gross section.

d The section-modulus method starts with the determination of moment by the method of Art. 3.10 and of required section modulus by the method of Art. 4.10. By definition, $S = I/c$. With S determined and d assumed, c may be taken as $d/2$. Then $I = Sc$.

The web is computed as described in the flange-area method in step 3. The moment of inertia of the component parts may be computed as follows:

Web from Table 4.9.

Cover plates from Table 4.10, 4.11, or 4.12. (Moment of inertia of plates about their flatwise gravity axis may be disregarded.)

Angles and rivet holes from Tables 4.10, 4.11, and 4.12.

Having computed the moment of inertia of the net section, determine the actual depth and section modulus, and correct as required.

The moment of inertia for sections or depths not included in Tables 4.10 and 4.11 may be arrived at by several simple applications of rules pertaining to moment of inertia. Since the moment of inertia of angles, for instance, is the sum of I_0, which may be disregarded; and Ad^2, the moment of inertia for any thickness not given, may be interpolated for the same depth (or for any variation of depth d); the moment will vary roughly as the square of the depth. The actual variation is as the square of the depth between neutral axes, but the difference is so slight as to be negligible.

e As an example of plate-girder design by the flange-area method, let us design the plate-girder section for the girder shown in Fig. 4.26. The first step is discussed in detail in Art. 4.20 *c*. For a 48-in. total depth, approximate web $= 0.9 \times 48 = 43.2$. Assume 44 in. depth; $t = 230/(13 \times 44) = 0.4$. In order to develop $\frac{7}{8}$-in. rivets in double shear, we would require $\frac{9}{16}$ in. thickness (see Table 9.1). Therefore the web area is $\frac{9}{16} \times 44 = 24.75$.

Flange area $A = \dfrac{4,450 \times 12 \times 48}{20 \times 43.2^2} = 68.67$ sq in.

$$-24.75/6 = -4.12$$

Required net area of flange angle and cover plates $= 68.67 - 4.12 = 64.55$

Try two $8 \times 8 \times 1$-in. angles with $20 \times 2\frac{1}{4}$ Covers, $A = 64.5$ (Table 4.16).

$$d = 44.5 \qquad jd = 44.5 - 0.54 = 43.96$$
$$+ \ \underline{\ 4.5\ }$$
$$49.0$$

Check flange area $A = \dfrac{4,450 \times 12 \times 49}{20 \times 43.96^2} = 67.7$

Less $\frac{1}{6}$ web $\qquad\qquad \underline{-4.1}$

$$63.6$$

Therefore the section selected is sufficient. Check this section by the section-modulus method. From Table 4.9,

$$I \text{ of web} = 3,993$$

From Table 4.11, for four angles $8 \times 8 \times 1$ in. with 44-in. web plates,

$$I = \left(\frac{44}{42}\right)^2 \times 21,740 = 23,860$$

From Table 4.12 for two flange plates 18 in. net by $2\frac{1}{4}$ in. at $44.5 + 2.25 = 46.75$ depth,

$$I = 40.5 \times 1,092.5 = 44,246$$
$$3,993 + 23,860 + 44,246 = 72,099$$

For the flange holes, angle at 43.5-in. depth,

$$I = -2 \times 946 = -1,892$$

For the web holes at 35.5-in. average depth,

$$I = -2 \times 2.56 \times 630 = -3,226$$
$$\text{Total of holes} = -5,118$$
$$\text{Net } I = 66,981$$

$$S = \frac{66,981}{24.5} = 2,734 \text{ furnished (2,670 required)}$$

Therefore the girder is satisfactory.

f The AISC Code, Sec. 26(*e*), requires bearing stiffeners on the webs of plate girders at unframed ends and at points of concentrated loads. If h/t is equal to or greater than 70, intermediate stiffeners are required at all points where v exceeds $64,000,000/(h/t)^2$, in which $h =$ clear depth between flanges in inches, $t =$ web thickness in inches, and $v =$ greatest unit shear in the panel in pounds per square inch. The clear distance between intermediate stiffeners, if required, shall not exceed 84 in., or $S = 11,000t/\sqrt{v}$.

Referring to the girders in Fig. 4.26 and paragraph *e* above,

$$h = 44.5 - 16 = 28.5$$
$$t = 0.5625$$
$$h/t = 50.7$$
$$\frac{64,000,000}{50.7^2} = 24,930$$
$$v = \frac{230,000}{44 \times .5625} = 9,295$$

Therefore intermediate stiffeners are not required.

g Tables 4.17 and 4.19 give the properties of flange sections used in the construction of a patented "WP girder" (patent rights held by Weiskopf and Pickworth, New York). This girder may frequently be used to advantage because of the economy of fabrication. It uses as flange sections split-beam T sections, sometimes with cover plates, and double webs. The properties given in these tables may be used in conjunction with those in Table 4.12 to develop the moment of inertia, or the flange area.

Let us design a WP girder as an alternate for the girder designed in paragraph *e* above.

We need two web plates and will assume $42 \times \frac{3}{8}$-in. plates. Then the gross web is $42 \times 0.75 = 31.5$ sq in. On the basis of flange area computed in paragraph *e*,

$$A = 68.67$$
$$\tfrac{1}{6} \text{ of } 31.5 = 5.25$$
$$\text{Required net area of flange} = 63.42$$

Try 30 WF 210 half beam, $6 \times \frac{3}{4}$-in. filler plates, $8 \times 6 \times \frac{3}{4}$-in. angles, and $15 \times 1\frac{1}{4}$-in. cover.

$$A = 65.9$$

The total depth is

$$\text{Web plate} = 42$$
$$2 \times 2\tfrac{11}{16} = 5.375$$
$$\text{2 cover plates} = 2.5$$
$$\text{Total overall depth} = 49.875$$
$$jd = 47.375 - 4.8 = 42.575$$

$$\text{Flange area } A = \frac{4,450 \times 12 \times 49.875}{20 \times (42.575)^2} = 73.47$$
$$- 5.25$$
$$\text{Required net} = 68.22$$

Therefore increase the cover plate to $15 \times 1\frac{1}{2}$ in.

h *Length of cover plates.* For practical purposes and for economy, any cover plate over $\frac{7}{8}$ in. thick is usually made up of two or more plates, and the plates may be stopped off at varying lengths as required by moment considerations. The AISC requires that cover plates shall be equal in thickness or shall diminish in thickness from the flange angles outward. No plate shall be thicker than the flange angles. Cover plates shall not extend more than 16t (of the thinnest plate) beyond the outer row of rivets connecting to the flange angle. The total cross-sectional area of cover

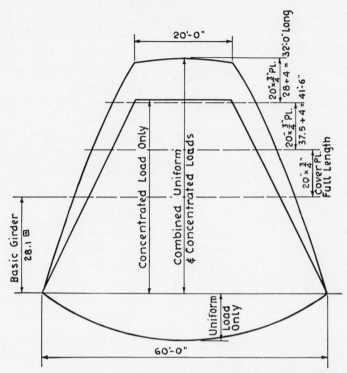

Fig. 4.27   Determination of Length of Cover Plates

plates shall not exceed 70 percent of total flange area.

Problem   What will be the length of cover plates required for the plate girder designed in Art. 4.20*e*? The general method of approach is to lay out the moment diagram, then pro-rate the flange area on the basis of height of the maximum ordinate, starting from the basic girder at the base line—that is, the flange area included in the web and angles.

This graphical method of approach is indicated in Fig. 4.27. The net flange area furnished is made up of

$$\frac{1}{6} \text{ of web} = \ \ 4.12$$
$$2 \text{ angles } 8 \times 8 \times 1 \text{ in., net} = 24.0$$
$$\text{Basic girder} = 28.12$$
$$\text{Cover plate, net} = 40.5$$
$$28.12 + 40.5 = 68.62$$

We will use three plates $\frac{3}{4}$ in. thick for the $2\frac{1}{4}$ in. thickness of cover plates. The basic girder represents $28.12/68.6 = 41$ percent of the flange. The remaining 59 percent is divided equally between the three cover plates. Lines are drawn parallel with the base to

show the percentage intercepts of the maximum ordinate, and the intersections of these lines with the moment diagram represent the length of cover plate required. The innermost cover plate is full length. On each of the others, we shall allow 2 ft at each end to develop the plate. The length of cover plates may be scaled from the diagram in Fig. 4.27.

4.21   Cover-plated beams

When the required section modulus for a given depth is greater than that available in any rolled section of that depth, it is frequently the practice to take a section of slightly lesser depth and rivet or weld top and bottom cover plates on the section. This method does not, of course, increase the shear area or buckling area, so care should be taken to check against overstress in these. It is not necessary to run cover plates full length of the beam, but they may be stopped off as for plate girders.

Problem   Find the section modulus of a 36 WF 300 with top and bottom cover plates, $20 \times \frac{3}{4}$ in., welded on.

Table 4.9   Moment of Inertia of Vertical Plate

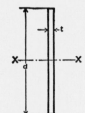

MOMENT OF INERTIA

OF ONE PLATE ABOUT AXIS X-X

To obtain the moment of inertia for any thickness of plate not listed below, multiply the value for a plate one inch thick by the desired thickness.

Depth d Inches	Thickness t, Inches							
	$\frac{3}{8}$	$\frac{7}{16}$	$\frac{1}{2}$	$\frac{9}{16}$	$\frac{5}{8}$	$\frac{3}{4}$	$\frac{7}{8}$	1
10	31.3	36.5	41.7	46.9	52.1	62.5	72.9	83.3
11	41.6	48.5	55.5	62.4	69.3	83.2	97.1	110.9
12	54.0	63.0	72.0	81.0	90.0	108.0	126.0	144.0
13	68.7	80.1	91.5	103.0	114.4	137.3	160.2	183.1
14	85.8	100.0	114.3	128.6	142.9	171.5	200.1	228.7
15	105.5	123.0	140.6	158.2	175.8	210.9	246.1	281.3
16	128.0	149.3	170.7	192.0	213.3	256.0	298.7	341.3
17	153.5	179.1	204.7	230.3	255.9	307.1	358.2	409.4
18	182.3	212.6	243.0	273.4	303.8	364.5	425.3	486.0
19	214.3	250.1	285.8	321.5	357.2	428.7	500.1	571.6
20	250.0	291.7	333.3	375.0	416.7	500.0	583.3	666.7
21	289.4	337.6	385.9	434.1	482.3	578.8	675.3	771.8
22	332.8	388.2	443.7	499.1	554.6	665.5	776.4	887.3
23	380.2	443.6	507.0	570.3	633.7	760.4	887.2	1013.9
24	432.0	504.0	576.0	648.0	720.0	864.0	1008.0	1152.0
25	488.3	569.7	651.0	732.4	813.8	976.6	1139.3	1302.1
26	549.3	640.8	732.3	823.9	915.4	1098.5	1281.6	1464.7
27	615.1	717.6	820.1	922.6	1025.2	1230.2	1435.2	1640.3
28	686.0	800.3	914.7	1029.0	1143.3	1372.0	1600.7	1829.3
29	762.2	889.2	1016.2	1143.2	1270.3	1524.3	1778.4	2032.4
30	843.8	984.4	1125.0	1265.6	1406.3	1687.5	1968.8	2250.0
31	931.0	1086.1	1241.3	1396.5	1551.6	1861.9	2172.3	2482.6
32	1024.0	1194.7	1365.3	1536.0	1706.7	2048.0	2389.3	2730.7
33	1123.0	1310.2	1497.4	1684.5	1871.7	2246.1	2620.4	2994.8
34	1228.3	1433.0	1637.7	1842.4	2047.1	2456.5	2865.9	3275.3
35	1339.8	1563.2	1786.5	2009.8	2233.1	2679.7	3126.3	3572.9
36	1458.0	1701.0	1944.0	2187.0	2430.0	2916.0	3402.0	3888.0
37	1582.9	1846.7	2110.5	2374.4	2638.2	3165.8	3693.4	4221.1
38	1714.8	2000.5	2286.3	2572.1	2857.9	3429.5	4001.1	4572.7
39	1853.7	2162.7	2471.6	2780.6	3089.5	3707.4	4325.3	4943.3
40	2000.0	2333.3	2666.7	3000.0	3333.3	4000.0	4666.7	5333.3
41	2153.8	2512.7	2871.7	3230.7	3589.6	4307.6	5025.5	5743.4
42	2315.3	2701.1	3087.0	3472.9	3858.8	4630.5	5402.3	6174.0
43	2484.6	2898.7	3312.8	3726.9	4141.0	4969.2	5797.4	6625.6
44	2662.0	3105.7	3549.3	3993.0	4436.7	5324.0	6211.3	7098.7
45	2847.7	3322.3	3796.9	4271.5	4746.1	5695.3	6644.5	7593.8
46	3041.8	3548.7	4055.7	4562.6	5069.6	6083.5	7097.4	8111.3
47	3244.5	3785.2	4326.0	4866.7	5407.4	6488.9	7570.4	8651.9
48	3456.0	4032.0	4608.0	5184.0	5760.0	6912.0	8064.0	9216.0
49	3676.5	4289.3	4902.0	5514.8	6127.6	7353.1	8578.6	9804.1
50	3906.3	4557.3	5208.3	5859.4	6510.4	7812.5	9114.6	10417
51	4145.3	4836.2	5527.1	6218.0	6908.9	8290.7	9672.5	11054
52	4394.0	5126.3	5858.7	6591.0	7323.3	8788.0	10253	11717
53	4652.4	5427.8	6203.2	6978.6	7754.0	9304.8	10856	12406
54	4920.8	5740.9	6561.0	7381.1	8201.3	9841.5	11482	13122

Copyright 1947 American Institute of Steel Construction

Table 4.9   Moment of Inertia of Vertical Plate (*Continued*)

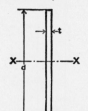

MOMENT OF INERTIA

OF ONE PLATE ABOUT AXIS X-X

To obtain the moment of inertia for any thickness of plate not listed below, multiply the value for a plate one inch thick by the desired thickness.

Depth d Inches	Thickness t, Inches							
	3/8	7/16	1/2	9/16	5/8	3/4	7/8	1
55	5199.2	6065.8	6932.3	7798.8	8665.4	10398	12132	13865
56	5488.0	6402.7	7317.3	8232.0	9146.7	10976	12805	14635
57	5787.3	6751.8	7716.4	8680.9	9645.5	11575	13504	15433
58	6097.3	7113.5	8129.7	9145.9	10162	12195	14227	16259
59	6418.1	7487.8	8557.5	9627.1	10697	12836	14976	17115
60	6750.0	7875.0	9000.0	10125	11250	13500	15750	18000
61	7093.2	8275.3	9457.5	10640	11822	14186	16551	18915
62	7447.8	8689.0	9930.3	11172	12413	14896	17378	19861
63	7814.0	9116.3	10419	11721	13023	15628	18232	20837
64	8192.0	9557.3	10923	12288	13653	16384	19115	21845
65	8582.0	10012	11443	12873	14303	17164	20025	22885
66	8984.3	10482	11979	13476	14974	17969	20963	23958
67	9398.8	10965	12532	14098	15665	18798	21931	25064
68	9826.0	11464	13101	14739	16377	19652	22927	26203
69	10266	11977	13688	15399	17110	20532	23954	27376
70	10719	12505	14292	16078	17865	21438	25010	28583
72	11664	13608	15552	17496	19440	23328	27216	31104
74	12663	14774	16884	18995	21105	25327	29548	33769
76	13718	16004	18291	20577	22863	27436	32009	36581
78	14830	17301	19773	22245	24716	29660	34603	39546
80	16000	18667	21333	24000	26667	32000	37333	42667
82	17230	20102	22974	25845	28717	34461	40204	45947
84	18522	21609	24696	27783	30870	37044	43218	49392
86	19877	23190	26502	29815	33128	39754	46379	53005
88	21296	24845	28395	31944	35493	42592	49691	56789
90	22781	26578	30375	34172	37969	45563	53156	60750
92	24334	28390	32445	36501	40557	48668	56779	64891
94	25956	30282	34608	38934	43260	51912	60563	69215
96	27648	32256	36864	41472	46080	55296	64512	73728
98	29412	34314	39216	44118	49020	58825	68629	78433
100	31250	36458	41667	46875	52083	62500	72917	83333
102	33163	38690	44217	49744	55271	66326	77380	88434
104	35152	41011	46869	52728	58587	70304	82021	93739
106	37219	43422	49626	55829	62032	74439	86845	99251
108	39366	45927	52488	59049	65610	78732	91854	104976
110	41594	48526	55458	62391	69323	83188	97052	110917
112	43904	51221	58539	65856	73173	87808	102443	117077
114	46298	54015	61731	69447	77164	92597	108029	123462
116	48778	56908	65037	73167	81297	97556	113815	130075
118	51345	59902	68460	77017	85575	102690	119804	136919
120	54000	63000	72000	81000	90000	108000	126000	144000
122	56745	66203	75660	85118	94575	113491	132406	151321
124	59582	69512	79443	89373	99303	119164	139025	158885
126	62512	72930	83349	93768	104186	125024	145861	166698
128	65536	76459	87381	98304	109227	131072	152917	174763

Table 4.10   Moment of Inertia of Two Flange Plates (1-in. width)

Depth d, in.	$\frac{3}{8}$ in.	$\frac{1}{2}$ in.	$\frac{5}{8}$ in.	$\frac{3}{4}$ in.	$\frac{7}{8}$ in.	1 in.	$1\frac{1}{4}$ in.	$1\frac{1}{2}$ in.	$1\frac{3}{4}$ in.	2 in.
$36\frac{1}{2}$	255	342	431	520	611	703	891	1,084	1,281	1,484
$42\frac{1}{2}$	345	462	581	702	823	946	1,197	1,453	1,714	1,982
$48\frac{1}{2}$	448	600	754	910	1,067	1,225	1,547	1,876	2,210	2,552
$54\frac{1}{2}$	565	756	950	1,145	1,342	1,540	1,943	2,353	2,769	3,194
$60\frac{1}{2}$	695	926	1,168	1,407	1,648	1,891	2,383	2,884	3,392	3,908

Table 4.11   Moment of Inertia of Four Flange Angles

Depth d, in.	$6 \times 4 \times$				$6 \times 6 \times$			
	$\frac{1}{2}$ in.	$\frac{5}{8}$ in.	$\frac{3}{4}$ in.	$\frac{7}{8}$ in.	$\frac{1}{2}$ in.	$\frac{5}{8}$ in.	$\frac{3}{4}$ in.	$\frac{7}{8}$ in.
$36\frac{1}{2}$	5,690	6,980	8,220	9,410	6,400	7,860	9,270	10,630
$42\frac{1}{2}$	7,820	9,610	11,330	12,970	8,890	10,930	12,910	14,820
$48\frac{1}{2}$	10,310	12,670	14,940	17,120	11,800	14,520	17,160	19,710
$54\frac{1}{2}$	13,130	16,150	19,050	21,830	15,120	18,620	22,010	25,300
$60\frac{1}{2}$	16,290	20,040	23,660	27,130	18,850	23,230	27,480	31,590

Depth d, in.	$8 \times 6 \times$					$8 \times 8 \times$				
	$\frac{1}{2}$ in.	$\frac{5}{8}$ in.	$\frac{3}{4}$ in.	$\frac{7}{8}$ in.	1 in.	$\frac{1}{2}$ in.	$\frac{5}{8}$ in.	$\frac{3}{4}$ in.	$\frac{7}{8}$ in.	1 in.
$36\frac{1}{2}$	7,690	9,470	11,200	12,850	14,480	8,190	10,100	11,950	13,750	15,490
$42\frac{1}{2}$	10,650	13,120	15,540	17,850	20,130	11,460	14,140	16,750	19,280	21,740
$48\frac{1}{2}$	14,100	17,380	20,590	23,680	26,720	15,280	18,880	22,370	25,770	29,080
$54\frac{1}{2}$	18,030	22,240	26,360	30,330	34,230	19,660	24,300	28,810	33,210	37,500
$60\frac{1}{2}$	22,450	27,710	32,850	37,810	42,690	24,600	30,420	36,080	41,600	46,990

$$I_1 \text{ (36 WF)} = 20,290.2$$
$$I_2 \text{ (cover plate about axis)} = 2 \times \frac{20 \times 0.75^3}{12} = 1.4$$
$$A_2 x_2^2 = 2 \times 15 \times 18.74^2 = \underline{10,533.0}$$
$$\text{Total } I = 30,824.6$$
$$c = 18.36 + 0.75 = 19.11$$
$$S = \frac{30,824.6}{19.11} = 1,614$$

Problem In a second type of problem frequently encountered, architectural limitations prevent the use of a depth greater than 30 in. for a single beam carrying a total uniform load of 300 kips on a span of 36 ft. Design a cover-plated beam to carry this load.

$$S \text{ required} = \frac{300 \times 36}{13.33} = 810$$

From the definition, $S = I/c$; therefore $I = Sc$.
  Required $I = 15 \times 810 = 12,150$
  I of 27 WF 145 = 5,414.3

Center to center distance of flanges = 26.88 − 0.975 = 25.9 in.
  Area of hole for $\frac{7}{8}$-in. rivets = 0.975 sq in.
  I of two pairs of holes (from Table 4.12) = $2 \times 0.975 \times 335 = 653.3$
  Net I of 27 WF = 5,414.3 − 653.3 = 4,761
  Net I required in plates = 12,150 − 4,761 = 7,389

For 30-in.-deep beam, $\frac{30 - 26.88}{2} = 1.56$ in.

Use $1\frac{9}{16}$ in. thick plates.

Table 4.12   Moment of Inertia of Unit Areas about an Axis

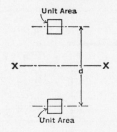

MOMENT OF INERTIA
OF
A PAIR OF UNIT AREAS
ABOUT AXIS X-X

d	.0	.1	.2	.3	.4	.5	.6	.7	.8	.9
10	50	51	52	53	54	55	56	57	58	59
11	61	62	63	64	65	66	67	68	70	71
12	72	73	74	76	77	78	79	81	82	83
13	85	86	87	88	90	91	92	94	95	97
14	98	99	101	102	104	105	107	108	110	111
15	113	114	116	117	119	120	122	123	125	126
16	128	130	131	133	134	136	138	139	141	143
17	145	146	148	150	151	153	155	157	158	160
18	162	164	166	167	169	171	173	175	177	179
19	181	182	184	186	188	190	192	194	196	198
20	200	202	204	206	208	210	212	214	216	218
21	221	223	225	227	229	231	233	235	238	240
22	242	244	246	249	251	253	255	258	260	262
23	265	267	269	271	274	276	278	281	283	286
24	288	290	293	295	298	300	303	305	308	310
25	313	315	318	320	323	325	328	330	333	335
26	338	341	343	346	348	351	354	356	359	362
27	365	367	370	373	375	378	381	384	386	389
28	392	395	398	400	403	406	409	412	415	418
29	421	423	426	429	432	435	438	441	444	447
30	450	453	456	459	462	465	468	471	474	477
31	481	484	487	490	493	496	499	502	506	509
32	512	515	518	522	525	528	531	535	538	541
33	545	548	551	554	558	561	564	568	571	575
34	578	581	585	588	592	595	598	602	606	609
35	613	616	620	623	627	630	634	637	641	644
36	648	652	655	659	662	666	670	673	677	681
37	685	688	692	696	699	703	707	711	714	718
38	722	726	730	733	737	741	745	749	753	757
39	761	764	768	772	776	780	784	788	792	796
40	800	804	808	812	816	820	824	828	832	836
41	841	845	849	853	857	861	865	869	874	878
42	882	886	890	895	899	903	907	912	916	920
43	925	929	933	937	942	946	950	955	959	964
44	968	972	977	981	986	990	995	999	1004	1008
45	1013	1017	1022	1026	1031	1035	1040	1044	1049	1053
46	1058	1063	1067	1072	1076	1081	1086	1090	1095	1100
47	1105	1109	1114	1119	1123	1128	1133	1138	1142	1147
48	1152	1157	1162	1166	1171	1176	1181	1186	1191	1196
49	1201	1205	1210	1215	1220	1225	1230	1235	1240	1245

Table 4.12　Moment of Inertia of Unit Areas about an Axis (*Continued*)

MOMENT OF INERTIA
OF
A PAIR OF UNIT AREAS
ABOUT AXIS X-X

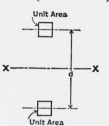

d	.0	.1	.2	.3	.4	.5	.6	.7	.8	.9
50	1250	1255	1260	1265	1270	1275	1280	1285	1290	1295
51	1301	1306	1311	1316	1321	1326	1331	1336	1342	1347
52	1352	1357	1362	1368	1373	1378	1383	1389	1394	1399
53	1405	1410	1415	1420	1426	1431	1436	1442	1447	1453
54	1458	1463	1469	1474	1480	1485	1491	1496	1502	1507
55	1513	1518	1524	1529	1535	1540	1546	1551	1557	1562
56	1568	1574	1579	1585	1590	1596	1602	1607	1613	1619
57	1625	1630	1636	1642	1647	1653	1659	1665	1670	1676
58	1682	1688	1694	1699	1705	1711	1717	1723	1729	1735
59	1741	1746	1752	1758	1764	1770	1776	1782	1788	1794
60	1800	1806	1812	1818	1824	1830	1836	1842	1848	1854
61	1861	1867	1873	1879	1885	1891	1897	1903	1910	1916
62	1922	1928	1934	1941	1947	1953	1959	1966	1972	1978
63	1985	1991	1997	2003	2010	2016	2022	2029	2035	2042
64	2048	2054	2061	2067	2074	2080	2087	2093	2100	2106
65	2113	2119	2126	2132	2139	2145	2152	2158	2165	2171
66	2178	2185	2191	2198	2204	2211	2218	2224	2231	2238
67	2245	2251	2258	2265	2271	2278	2285	2292	2298	2305
68	2312	2319	2326	2332	2339	2346	2353	2360	2367	2374
69	2381	2387	2394	2401	2408	2415	2422	2429	2436	2443
70	2450	2457	2464	2471	2478	2485	2492	2499	2506	2513
71	2521	2528	2535	2542	2549	2556	2563	2570	2578	2585
72	2592	2599	2606	2614	2621	2628	2635	2643	2650	2657
73	2665	2672	2679	2686	2694	2701	2708	2716	2723	2731
74	2738	2745	2753	2760	2768	2775	2783	2790	2798	2805
75	2813	2820	2828	2835	2843	2850	2858	2865	2873	2880
76	2888	2896	2903	2911	2918	2926	2934	2941	2949	2957
77	2965	2972	2980	2988	2995	3003	3011	3019	3026	3034
78	3042	3050	3058	3065	3073	3081	3089	3097	3105	3113
79	3121	3128	3136	3144	3152	3160	3168	3176	3184	3192
80	3200	3208	3216	3224	3232	3240	3248	3256	3264	3272
81	3281	3289	3297	3305	3313	3321	3329	3337	3346	3354
82	3362	3370	3378	3387	3395	3403	3411	3420	3428	3436
83	3445	3453	3461	3469	3478	3486	3494	3503	3511	3520
84	3528	3536	3545	3553	3562	3570	3579	3587	3596	3604
85	3613	3621	3630	3638	3647	3655	3664	3672	3681	3689
86	3698	3707	3715	3724	3732	3741	3750	3758	3767	3776
87	3785	3793	3802	3811	3819	3828	3837	3846	3854	3863
88	3872	3881	3890	3898	3907	3916	3925	3934	3943	3952
89	3961	3969	3978	3987	3996	4005	4014	4023	4032	4041

Table 4.13   Net Area of Girder Flange Angles

GIRDER FLANGE ANGLES

TWO ANGLES—NET AREA

2 Holes Out   4 Holes Out   6 Holes Out

Size	Thickness (In.)	RIVETS (2 Holes Out)				RIVETS (4 Holes Out)				RIVETS (6 Holes Out)			
		3/4"	7/8"	1"	1⅛"	3/4"	7/8"	1"	1⅛"	3/4"	7/8"	1"	1⅛"
6 x 4	7/8	14.43	14.21	13.99	13.77	12.90	12.46	12.02	11.58	11.37			
	3/4	12.57	12.38	12.19	12.00	11.25	10.88	10.50	10.13	9.94			
	5/8	10.63	10.47	10.31	10.16	9.53	9.22	8.91	8.60	8.44			
	9/16	9.64	9.49	9.35	9.21	8.65	8.37	8.09	7.81	7.67			
	1/2	8.62	8.50	8.37	8.25	7.75	7.50	7.25	7.00	6.88			
	7/16	7.59	7.48	7.38	7.27	6.83	6.61	6.39	6.17	6.06			
	3/8	6.56	6.47	6.38	6.28	5.91	5.72	5.53	5.34	5.25			
5 x 5	7/8	14.43	14.21	13.99	13.77	12.90	12.46	12.02	11.58				
	3/4	12.57	12.38	12.19	12.00	11.25	10.88	10.50	10.13				
	5/8	10.63	10.47	10.31	10.16	9.53	9.22	8.91	8.59				
	1/2	8.62	8.50	8.37	8.25	7.75	7.50	7.25	7.00				
	7/16	7.59	7.48	7.38	7.27	6.83	6.61	6.39	6.17				
	3/8	6.56	6.47	6.38	6.28	5.91	5.72	5.53	5.34				
6x3½	1/2	8.12	8.00	7.87	......	7.25	7.00	......	......	6.38			
	3/8	6.18	6.09	6.00	......	5.53	5.34	......	......	4.87			
	5/16	5.19	5.11	5.04	......	4.65	4.49	......	......	4.10			
5x3½	3/4	10.31	10.12	9.93	......	8.99	8.62	......	......				
	5/8	8.75	8.59	8.43	......	7.65	7.34	......	......				
	1/2	7.12	7.00	6.87	......	6.25	6.00	......	......				
	7/16	6.29	6.18	6.08	......	5.53	5.31	......	......				
	3/8	5.44	5.35	5.26	......	4.79	4.60	......	......				
	5/16	4.57	4.49	4.42	......	4.03	3.87	......	......				
5 x 3	1/2	6.62	6.50	......	......	5.75	5.50	......	......				
	3/8	5.06	4.97	......	......	4.41	4.22	......	......				
	5/16	4.25	4.17	......	......	3.71	3.55	......	......				
4 x 4	3/4	9.57	9.38	9.19	9.00	8.26	7.88	......	......				
	5/8	8.13	7.97	7.81	7.66	7.03	6.72	......	......				
	1/2	6.62	6.50	6.37	6.25	5.75	5.50	......	......				
	7/16	5.85	5.74	5.64	5.53	5.09	4.87	......	......				
	3/8	5.06	4.97	4.88	4.78	4.41	4.22	......	......				
	5/16	4.25	4.17	4.10	4.02	3.71	3.55	......	......				
4x3½	5/8	7.51	7.35	7.19	......	6.42	6.10	......	......				
	1/2	6.12	6.00	5.87	......	5.25	5.00	......	......				
	7/16	5.41	5.30	5.20	......	4.65	4.43	......	......				
	3/8	4.68	4.59	4.50	......	4.03	3.84	......	......				
	5/16	3.95	3.87	3.80	......	3.41	3.25	......	......				
4 x 3	5/8	6.87	6.71	......	......	5.77	5.46	......	......				
	1/2	5.62	5.50	......	......	4.75	4.50	......	......				
	7/16	4.97	4.86	......	......	4.21	3.99	......	......				
	3/8	4.30	4.21	......	......	3.65	3.46	......	......				
	5/16	3.63	3.55	......	......	3.09	2.93	......	......				
	1/4	2.94	2.88	......	......	2.50	2.38	......	......				

Table 4.13 Net Area of Girder Flange Angles (*Continued*)

GIRDER FLANGE ANGLES

Size	Thickness In.	2 Holes Out RIVETS 3/4"	7/8"	1"	1 1/8"	4 Holes Out RIVETS 3/4"	7/8"	1"	1 1/8"	6 Holes Out RIVETS 3/4"	7/8"	1"	1 1/8"
9 x 4	1	22.25	22.00	21.75	21.50	20.50	20.00	19.50	19.00	18.75	18.00	17.25	16.50
	7/8	19.69	19.47	19.25	19.03	18.16	17.72	17.28	16.84	16.63	15.97	15.31	14.66
	3/4	17.07	16.88	16.69	16.50	15.75	15.38	15.00	14.63	14.44	13.88	13.32	12.76
	5/8	14.37	14.21	14.05	13.90	13.27	12.96	12.65	12.33	12.18	11.71	11.24	10.77
	9/16	13.02	12.88	12.73	12.59	12.03	11.75	11.47	11.19	11.05	10.62	10.20	9.78
	1/2	11.62	11.50	11.37	11.25	10.75	10.50	10.25	10.00	9.88	9.50	9.12	8.75
8 x 8	1 1/8	31.49	31.21	30.93	30.65	29.52	28.96	28.40	27.83	27.55	26.71	25.86	25.02
	1	28.25	28.00	27.75	27.50	26.50	26.00	25.50	25.00	24.75	24.00	23.25	22.50
	7/8	24.93	24.71	24.49	24.27	23.40	22.96	22.52	22.08	21.86	21.21	20.56	19.90
	3/4	21.57	21.38	21.19	21.00	20.25	19.88	19.50	19.13	18.94	18.38	17.82	17.25
	5/8	18.13	17.97	17.81	17.66	17.03	16.72	16.41	16.09	15.94	15.47	15.00	14.53
	9/16	16.38	16.23	16.09	15.95	15.39	15.11	14.83	14.55	14.41	13.99	13.57	13.15
	1/2	14.62	14.50	14.37	14.25	13.75	13.50	13.25	13.00	12.87	12.50	12.13	11.75
8 x 6	1	24.25	24.00	23.75	23.50	22.50	22.00	21.50	21.00	20.75	20.00	19.25	18.50
	7/8	21.43	21.21	20.99	20.77	19.90	19.46	19.02	18.58	18.36	17.71	17.06	16.40
	3/4	18.57	18.38	18.19	18.00	17.25	16.88	16.50	16.13	15.94	15.38	14.82	14.25
	5/8	15.63	15.47	15.31	15.16	14.53	14.22	13.91	13.59	13.44	12.97	12.50	12.03
	9/16	14.14	13.99	13.85	13.71	13.15	12.87	12.59	12.31	12.17	11.75	11.32	10.90
	1/2	12.62	12.50	12.37	12.25	11.75	11.50	11.25	11.00	10.87	10.50	10.13	9.75
	7/16	11.09	10.98	10.88	10.77	10.33	10.11	9.89	9.67	9.56	9.24	8.91	8.58
8 x 4	1	20.25	20.00	19.75	19.50	18.50	18.00	17.50	17.00	16.75	16.00	15.25	14.50
	7/8	17.93	17.71	17.49	17.27	16.40	15.96	15.52	15.08	14.86	14.21	13.56	12.90
	3/4	15.57	15.38	15.19	15.00	14.25	13.88	13.50	13.13	12.94	12.38	11.82	11.25
	5/8	13.13	12.97	12.81	12.66	12.03	11.72	11.41	11.10	10.94	10.47	10.00	9.53
	9/16	11.88	11.73	11.59	11.45	10.89	10.61	10.33	10.05	9.90	9.50	9.09	8.64
	1/2	10.62	10.50	10.37	10.25	9.75	9.50	9.25	9.00	8.87	8.50	8.13	7.75
	7/16	9.35	9.24	9.14	9.03	8.59	8.37	8.15	7.93	7.83	7.50	7.18	6.84
7 x 4	7/8	16.19	15.97	15.75	15.53	14.66	14.22	13.78	13.34	13.13	12.47	....	....
	3/4	14.07	13.88	13.69	13.50	12.75	12.38	12.00	11.63	11.44	10.88	....	....
	5/8	11.89	11.73	11.57	11.42	10.79	10.48	10.15	9.84	9.70	9.23	....	....
	9/16	10.76	10.61	10.47	10.33	9.77	9.49	9.21	8.93	8.78	8.38	....	....
	1/2	9.62	9.50	9.37	9.25	8.75	8.50	8.25	8.00	7.87	7.50	....	....
	7/16	8.47	8.36	8.26	8.15	7.71	7.49	7.27	7.05	6.95	6.62	....	....
	3/8	7.32	7.23	7.14	7.04	6.67	6.48	6.27	6.08	6.01	5.73	....	....
6 x 6	1	20.25	20.00	19.75	19.50	18.50	18.00	17.50	17.00	16.75	16.00	....	....
	7/8	17.93	17.71	17.49	17.27	16.40	15.96	15.52	15.08	14.87	14.21	....	....
	3/4	15.57	15.38	15.19	15.00	14.25	13.88	13.50	13.13	12.94	12.38	....	....
	5/8	13.13	12.97	12.81	12.66	12.03	11.72	11.41	11.09	10.94	10.47	....	....
	9/16	11.88	11.73	11.59	11.45	10.89	10.61	10.33	10.05	9.91	9.49	....	....
	1/2	10.62	10.50	10.37	10.25	9.75	9.50	9.25	9.00	8.87	8.50	....	....
	7/16	9.35	9.24	9.14	9.03	8.59	8.37	8.15	7.93	7.82	7.50	....	....
	3/8	8.06	7.97	7.88	7.78	7.41	7.22	7.03	6.84	6.75	6.47	....	....

Table 4.14   Area of One Cover Plate

AREA OF ONE COVER PLATE

GROSS AREA

Plate Width, Inches	Plate Thickness, Inches														
	$\frac{1}{4}$	$\frac{5}{16}$	$\frac{3}{8}$	$\frac{7}{16}$	$\frac{1}{2}$	$\frac{9}{16}$	$\frac{5}{8}$	$\frac{11}{16}$	$\frac{3}{4}$	$\frac{13}{16}$	$\frac{7}{8}$	$\frac{15}{16}$	1	$1\frac{1}{8}$	$1\frac{1}{4}$
24	6.0	7.5	9.0	10.5	12.0	13.5	15.0	16.5	18.0	19.5	21.0	22.5	24.0	27.0	30.0
22	5.5	6.9	8.2	9.6	11.0	12.4	13.7	15.1	16.5	17.9	19.2	20.6	22.0	24.8	27.5
20	5.0	6.2	7.5	8.7	10.0	11.2	12.5	13.7	15.0	16.2	17.5	18.7	20.0	22.5	25.0
18	4.5	5.6	6.7	7.9	9.0	10.1	11.2	12.4	13.5	14.6	15.8	16.9	18.0	20.3	22.5
16	4.0	5.0	6.0	7.0	8.0	9.0	10.0	11.0	12.0	13.0	14.0	15.0	16.0	18.0	20.0
14	3.5	4.4	5.2	6.1	7.0	7.9	8.7	9.6	10.5	11.4	12.2	13.1	14.0	15.7	17.5
12	3.0	3.7	4.5	5.2	6.0	6.7	7.5	8.2	9.0	9.7	10.5	11.2	12.0	13.5	15.0
10	2.5	3.1	3.7	4.4	5.0	5.6	6.2	6.9	7.5	8.1	8.7	9.4	10.0	11.2	12.5
8	2.0	2.5	3.0	3.5	4.0	4.5	5.0	5.5	6.0	6.5	7.0	7.5	8.0	9.0	10.0

NET AREA
TWO RIVET HOLES DEDUCTED

Rivet Diam. In.	Plate Width In.	Plate Thickness, Inches														
		$\frac{1}{4}$	$\frac{5}{16}$	$\frac{3}{8}$	$\frac{7}{16}$	$\frac{1}{2}$	$\frac{9}{16}$	$\frac{5}{8}$	$\frac{11}{16}$	$\frac{3}{4}$	$\frac{13}{16}$	$\frac{7}{8}$	$\frac{15}{16}$	1	$1\frac{1}{8}$	$1\frac{1}{4}$
$\frac{3}{4}$	16	3.6	4.5	5.3	6.2	7.1	8.0	8.9	9.8	10.7	11.6	12.5	13.4	14.2	16.0	17.8
	14	3.1	3.8	4.6	5.4	6.1	6.9	7.7	8.4	9.2	10.0	10.7	11.5	12.2	13.8	15.3
	12	2.6	3.2	3.8	4.5	5.1	5.8	6.4	7.0	7.7	8.3	9.0	9.6	10.2	11.5	12.8
	10	2.1	2.6	3.1	3.6	4.1	4.6	5.2	5.7	6.2	6.7	7.2	7.7	8.2	9.3	10.3
	8	1.6	2.0	2.3	2.7	3.1	3.5	3.9	4.3	4.7	5.1	5.5	5.9	6.2	7.0	7.8
$\frac{7}{8}$	18	4.0	5.0	6.0	7.0	8.0	9.0	10.0	11.0	12.0	13.0	14.0	15.0	16.0	18.0	20.0
	16	3.5	4.4	5.2	6.1	7.0	7.9	8.7	9.6	10.5	11.4	12.2	13.1	14.0	15.7	17.5
	14	3.0	3.7	4.5	5.2	6.0	6.7	7.5	8.2	9.0	9.7	10.5	11.2	12.0	13.5	15.0
	12	2.5	3.1	3.7	4.4	5.0	5.6	6.2	6.9	7.5	8.1	8.7	9.4	10.0	1.2	12.5
	10	2.0	2.5	3.0	3.5	4.0	4.5	5.0	5.5	6.0	6.5	7.0	7.5	8.0	.0	10.0
	8	1.5	1.9	2.2	2.6	3.0	3.4	3.7	4.1	4.5	4.9	5.2	5.6	6.0	6.7	7.5
1	22	4.9	6.2	7.4	8.6	9.9	11.1	12.3	13.6	14.8	16.0	17.3	18.5	19.7	22.2	24.7
	20	4.4	5.5	6.7	7.8	8.9	10.0	11.1	12.2	13.3	14.4	15.5	16.6	17.7	20.0	22.2
	18	3.9	4.9	5.9	6.9	7.9	8.9	9.8	10.8	11.8	12.8	13.8	14.8	15.7	17.7	19.7
	16	3.4	4.3	5.2	6.0	6.9	7.7	8.6	9.5	10.3	11.2	12.0	12.9	13.7	15.5	17.2
	14	2.9	3.7	4.4	5.1	5.9	6.6	7.3	8.1	8.8	9.5	10.3	11.0	11.7	13.2	14.7
	12	2.4	3.0	3.7	4.3	4.9	5.5	6.1	6.7	7.3	7.9	8.5	9.1	9.7	11.0	12.2
$1\frac{1}{8}$	24	5.4	6.7	8.1	9.4	10.7	12.1	13.4	14.8	16.1	17.5	18.8	20.2	21.5	24.2	26.9
	22	4.9	6.1	7.3	8.5	9.7	11.0	12.2	13.4	14.6	15.8	17.1	18.3	19.5	21.9	24.4
	20	4.4	5.5	6.6	7.7	8.7	9.8	10.9	12.0	13.1	14.2	15.3	16.4	17.5	19.7	21.9
	18	3.9	4.8	5.8	6.8	7.7	8.7	9.7	10.7	11.6	12.6	13.6	14.5	15.5	17.4	19.4
	16	3.4	4.2	5.1	5.9	6.7	7.6	8.4	9.3	10.1	11.0	11.8	12.7	13.5	15.2	16.9
	14	2.9	3.6	4.3	5.0	5.7	6.5	7.2	7.9	8.6	9.3	10.1	10.8	11.5	12.9	14.4
$1\frac{1}{4}$	24	5.3	6.6	8.0	9.3	10.6	12.0	13.3	14.6	15.9	17.3	18.6	19.9	21.2	23.9	26.6
	22	4.8	6.0	7.2	8.4	9.6	10.8	12.0	13.2	14.4	15.6	16.8	18.0	19.2	21.7	24.1
	20	4.3	5.4	6.5	7.5	8.6	9.7	10.8	11.9	12.9	14.0	15.1	16.2	17.2	19.4	21.6
	18	3.8	4.8	5.7	6.7	7.6	8.6	9.5	10.5	11.4	12.4	13.3	14.3	15.2	17.2	19.1
	16	3.3	4.1	5.0	5.8	6.6	7.5	8.3	9.1	9.9	10.8	11.6	12.4	13.2	14.9	16.6

Diameter of Hole is assumed $\frac{1}{8}$ in. larger than Nominal Diameter of Rivet.

Table 4.15   Gross Area of Girder Flange Angles

GIRDER FLANGE ANGLES

Size	Thickness	TWO ANGLES GROSS AREA	FOUR ANGLES			
			I-4 Ls	2y	I-4 Ls	2x
	In.	In.²	In.⁴	In.	In.⁴	In.
6 x 4	7/8	15.96	111	4.2	39	2.2
	3/4	13.88	98	4.2	35	2.2
	5/8	11.72	84	4.1	30	2.1
	9/16	10.62	77	4.0	28	2.0
	1/2	9.50	70	4.0	25	2.0
	7/16	8.36	62	3.9	22	1.9
	3/8	7.22	54	3.9	20	1.9
5 x 5	7/8	15.96	71	3.1		
	3/4	13.88	63	3.0		
	5/8	11.72	54	3.0		
	1/2	9.50	45	2.9		
	7/16	8.36	40	2.8		
	3/8	7.22	35	2.8		
6 x 3½	1/2	9.00	66	4.2	17	1.7
	3/8	6.84	52	4.1	13	1.6
	5/16	5.74	44	4.0	11	1.5
5 x 3½	3/4	11.62	56	3.5	22	2.0
	5/8	9.84	48	3.4	19	1.9
	1/2	8.00	40	3.3	16	1.8
	7/16	7.06	36	3.3	14	1.8
	3/8	6.10	31	3.2	13	1.7
	5/16	5.12	26	3.2	11	1.7
5 x 3	1/2	7.50	38	3.5	10	1.5
	3/8	5.72	30	3.4	8	1.4
	5/16	4.80	25	3.4	7	1.4
4 x 4	3/4	10.88	31	2.5		
	5/8	9.22	27	2.5		
	1/2	7.50	22	2.4		
	7/16	6.62	20	2.3		
	3/8	5.72	18	2.3		
	5/16	4.80	15	2.2		
4 x 3½	5/8	8.60	26	2.6	18	2.1
	1/2	7.00	21	2.5	15	2.0
	7/16	6.18	19	2.5	14	2.0
	3/8	5.34	17	2.4	12	1.9
	5/16	4.50	14	2.4	10	1.9
4 x 3	5/8	7.96	24	2.7	12	1.7
	1/2	6.50	20	2.7	10	1.7
	7/16	5.74	18	2.6	9	1.6
	3/8	4.96	16	2.6	8	1.6
	5/16	4.18	14	2.5	7	1.5
	1/4	3.38	11	2.5	6	1.5

Table 4.15   Gross Area of Girder Flange Angles (*Continued*)

GIRDER FLANGE ANGLES

Size	Thickness	TWO ANGLE GROSS AREA	FOUR ANGLES			
			I-4 Ls	2y	I-4 Ls	2x
	In.	In.²	In.⁴	In.	In.⁴	In.
9 x 4	1	24.00	388	7.0	48	2.0
	$7/8$	21.22	347	6.9	43	1.9
	$3/4$	18.38	304	6.8	38	1.8
	$5/8$	15.46	260	6.7	33	1.7
	$9/16$	14.00	236	6.7	30	1.7
	$1/2$	12.50	213	6.6	28	1.6
8 x 8	$1 1/8$	33.46	392	4.8		
	1	30.00	356	4.7		
	$7/8$	26.46	318	4.6		
	$3/4$	22.88	279	4.6		
	$5/8$	19.22	238	4.5		
	$9/16$	17.36	216	4.4		
	$1/2$	15.50	195	4.4		
8 x 6	1	26.00	323	5.3	155	3.3
	$7/8$	22.96	289	5.2	140	3.2
	$3/4$	19.88	254	5.1	123	3.1
	$5/8$	16.72	216	5.0	105	3.0
	$9/16$	15.12	197	5.0	96	3.0
	$1/2$	13.50	177	4.9	87	2.9
	$7/16$	11.86	157	4.9	77	2.9
8 x 4	1	22.00	278	6.1	46	2.1
	$7/8$	19.46	249	6.0	42	2.0
	$3/4$	16.88	219	5.9	38	1.9
	$5/8$	14.22	187	5.8	32	1.8
	$9/16$	12.86	171	5.8	30	1.8
	$1/2$	11.50	154	5.7	27	1.7
	$7/16$	10.12	136	5.7	24	1.7
7 x 4	$7/8$	17.72	172	5.1	41	2.1
	$3/4$	15.38	151	5.0	36	2.0
	$5/8$	12.96	130	4.9	31	1.9
	$9/16$	11.74	118	4.9	29	1.9
	$1/2$	10.50	107	4.8	26	1.8
	$7/16$	9.24	95	4.8	23	1.8
	$3/8$	7.96	82	4.7	20	1.7
6 x 6	1	22.00	142	3.7		
	$7/8$	19.46	128	3.6		
	$3/4$	16.88	113	3.6		
	$5/8$	14.22	97	3.5		
	$9/16$	12.86	88	3.4		
	$1/2$	11.50	80	3.4		
	$7/16$	10.12	71	3.3		
	$3/8$	8.72	62	3.3		

Copyright 1947 American Institute of Steel Construction

Table 4.16 Properties of Plate-Girder Flanges

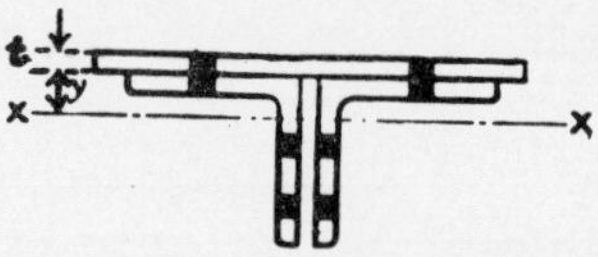

Angles 6 × 6 in., cover plates 14 in. wide, $\frac{7}{8}$-in. rivets

Cover plate thickness	Thickness of angles																%
	$\frac{3}{8}$		$\frac{7}{16}$		$\frac{1}{2}$		$\frac{9}{16}$		$\frac{5}{8}$		$\frac{3}{4}$		$\frac{7}{8}$		1		
	A	$2y$	A	$2y$	A	$2y$	A	$2y$	A	$2y$	A	$2y$	A	$2y$	A	$2y$	
0	7.22	3.28	8.37	3.32	9.50	3.36	10.61	3.42	11.72	3.46	13.88	3.56	15.96	3.64	18.00	3.72	
$\frac{5}{8}$	14.72	1.32															
$\frac{3}{4}$	16.22	1.08	17.37	1.24													
$\frac{7}{8}$	17.72	0.85	18.87	1.02	20.00	1.17	21.11	1.32									
1	19.22	0.64	20.37	0.82	21.50	0.96	22.61	1.12	23.72	1.24							
$1\frac{1}{8}$	20.72	0.44	21.87	0.62	23.00	0.77	24.11	0.92	25.22	1.04							
$1\frac{1}{4}$			23.27	0.42	24.50	0.58	25.61	0.72	26.72	0.86	28.88	1.11					
$1\frac{3}{8}$			24.87	0.24	26.00	0.39	27.11	0.54	28.22	0.68	30.38	0.93	32.46	1.14			
$1\frac{1}{2}$					27.50	0.22	28.61	0.36	29.72	0.50	31.88	0.75	33.96	0.97			50
$1\frac{5}{8}$							30.11	0.20	31.22	0.32	33.38	0.58	35.46	0.80	37.50	1.00	
$1\frac{3}{4}$							31.61	0.03	32.72	0.16	34.88	0.42	36.96	0.64	39.00	0.84	
$1\frac{7}{8}$									34.22	0.00	36.38	0.25	38.46	0.48	40.50	0.68	45
2											37.88	0.09	39.96	0.32	42.00	0.52	
																	40
																	35

Angles 6 × 6 in., cover plates 16 in. wide, $\frac{7}{8}$-in. rivets

Cover plate thickness	$\frac{3}{8}$ A	$\frac{3}{8}$ $2y$	$\frac{7}{16}$ A	$\frac{7}{16}$ $2y$	$\frac{1}{2}$ A	$\frac{1}{2}$ $2y$	$\frac{9}{16}$ A	$\frac{9}{16}$ $2y$	$\frac{5}{8}$ A	$\frac{5}{8}$ $2y$	$\frac{3}{4}$ A	$\frac{3}{4}$ $2y$	$\frac{7}{8}$ A	$\frac{7}{8}$ $2y$	1 A	1 $2y$	%
0	7.22	3.28	8.37	3.32	9.50	3.36	10.61	3.42	11.72	3.46	13.88	3.56	15.96	3.64	18.00	3.72	
$\frac{5}{8}$	15.97	1.20	17.12	1.36													
$\frac{3}{4}$	17.72	0.94	18.87	1.12	20.00	1.26	21.11	1.40									
$\frac{7}{8}$	19.47	0.72	20.62	0.89	21.75	1.03	22.86	1.18	23.97	1.30							
1	21.22	0.52	22.37	0.68	23.50	0.82	24.61	0.98	25.72	1.10	27.88	1.34					
$1\frac{1}{8}$			24.12	0.48	25.25	0.62	26.36	0.78	27.47	0.90	29.63	1.14					
$1\frac{1}{4}$					27.00	0.43	28.11	0.58	29.22	0.70	31.38	0.94	33.46	1.16			
$1\frac{3}{8}$					28.75	0.25	29.86	0.39	30.97	0.51	33.13	0.76	35.21	0.97	37.25	1.16	50
$1\frac{1}{2}$							31.61	0.22	32.72	0.34	34.88	0.58	36.96	0.80	39.00	1.00	
$1\frac{5}{8}$									34.47	0.18	36.63	0.40	38.71	0.63	40.75	0.82	45
$1\frac{3}{4}$											38.38	0.24	40.46	0 46	42.50	0.66	
$1\frac{7}{8}$											40.13	0.08	42.21	0.30	44.25	0.49	
2											41.88	+0.08	43.96	0.14	46.00	0.34	40
																	35

Dimensions in inches and square inches. Values of A are net areas of one flange only and are based on deduction of three holes from each angle and two from each cover plate—all $\frac{1}{8}$ in. larger than the nominal diameter of the rivet.

Heavy rules indicate relationship of gross area of angles to total gross area of flange, expressed in last column as percentage.

Courtesy Bethlehem Steel Co.

Table 4.16   Properties of Plate-Girder Flanges (*Continued*)

Angles 8 × 6 in. (long leg vertical), cover plates 14 in. wide, $\frac{7}{8}$-in. rivets

Cover plate thickness	Thickness of angles													%
	$\frac{7}{16}$		$\frac{1}{2}$		$\frac{9}{16}$		$\frac{5}{8}$		$\frac{3}{4}$		$\frac{7}{8}$		1		
	A	2y	A	2y	A	2y	A	2y	A	2y	A	2y	A	2y	
0	9.24	4.90	10.50	4.94	11.75	5.00	12.97	5.04	15.38	5.12	17.71	5.22	20.00	5.30	
$\frac{7}{8}$	19.74	1.97													
1	21.24	1.71	22.50	1.92											
$1\frac{1}{8}$	22.74	1.46	24.00	1.68	25.25	1.88									
$1\frac{1}{4}$	24.24	1.23	25.50	1.45	26.75	1.64	27.97	1.82							
$1\frac{3}{8}$	25.74	1.01	27.00	1.23	28.25	1.42	29.47	1.60	31.88	1.92					
$1\frac{1}{2}$	27.24	0.81	28.50	1.02	29.75	1.22	30.97	1.40	33.38	1.72					
$1\frac{5}{8}$	28.74	0.62	30.00	0.82	31.25	1.02	32.47	1.20	34.88	1.52	37.21	1.82			
$1\frac{3}{4}$			31.50	0.62	32.75	0.82	33.97	1.00	36.38	1.32	38.71	1.62			50
$1\frac{7}{8}$					34.25	0.63	35.47	0.82	37.88	1.14	40.21	1.44	42.50	1.70	
2					35.75	0.45	36.97	0.64	39.38	0.96	41.71	1.26	44.00	1.52	
$2\frac{1}{8}$							38.47	0.46	40.88	0.78	43.21	1.08	45.50	1.34	
$2\frac{1}{4}$							39.97	0.28	42.38	0.60	44.71	0.90	47.00	1.17	45
$2\frac{3}{8}$									43.88	0.42	46.21	0.72	48.50	0.99	
$2\frac{1}{2}$									45.38	0.26	47.71	0.56	50.00	0.82	40
															35

Angles 8 × 6 in. (long leg vertical), cover plates 16 in. wide, $\frac{7}{8}$-in. rivets

Cover plate thickness	$\frac{7}{16}$ A	2y	$\frac{1}{2}$ A	2y	$\frac{9}{16}$ A	2y	$\frac{5}{8}$ A	2y	$\frac{3}{4}$ A	2y	$\frac{7}{8}$ A	2y	1 A	2y	%
0	9.24	4.90	10.50	4.94	11.74	5.00	12.97	5.04	15.38	5.12	17.71	5.22	20.00	5.30	
$\frac{7}{8}$	21.48	1.77	22.75	1.98											
1	23.24	1.52	24.50	1.72	25.74	1.92	26.97	2.08							
$1\frac{1}{8}$	24.98	1.28	26.25	1.48	27.50	1.68	28.72	1.84							
$1\frac{1}{4}$	26.74	1.04	28.00	1.24	29.24	1.44	30.47	1.62	32.88	1.93					
$1\frac{3}{8}$	28.48	0.82	29.75	1.02	31.00	1.22	32.22	1.39	34.63	1.71	36.96	2.00			
$1\frac{1}{2}$			31.50	0.82	32.74	1.02	33.97	1.18	36.38	1.50	38.71	1.78			
$1\frac{5}{8}$			33.25	0.62	34.50	0.82	35.72	0.98	38.13	1.30	40.46	1.58	42.75	1.84	50
$1\frac{3}{4}$					36.24	0.62	37.47	0.78	39.88	1.10	42.21	1.40	44.50	1.64	
$1\frac{7}{8}$							39.22	0.59	41.63	0.91	43.96	1.20	46.25	1.45	45
2							40.97	0.42	43.38	0.73	45.71	1.01	48.00	1.27	
$2\frac{1}{8}$									45.13	0.55	47.46	0.84	49.75	1.09	
$2\frac{1}{4}$									46.88	0.37	49.21	0.66	51.50	0.91	
$2\frac{3}{8}$											50.96	0.48	53.25	0.74	40
$2\frac{1}{2}$											52.71	0.32	55.00	0.58	
															35

Dimensions in inches and square inches. Values of *A* are net areas of one flange only and are based on deduction of three holes from each angle and two from each cover plate—all $\frac{1}{8}$ in. larger than the nominal diameter of the rivet.

Heavy rules indicate relationship of gross area of angles to total gross area of flange, expressed in last column as percentage.

Courtesy Bethlehem Steel Co.

Table 4.16 Properties of Plate-Girder Flanges (*Continued*)

Angles 8 × 6 in. (short leg vertical), cover plates 18 in. wide, $\frac{7}{8}$-in. rivets

Cover plate thickness	Thickness of angles														%
	$\frac{7}{16}$		$\frac{1}{2}$		$\frac{9}{16}$		$\frac{5}{8}$		$\frac{3}{4}$		$\frac{7}{8}$		1		
	A	2y	A	2y	A	2y	A	2y*	A	2y*	A	2y*	A	2y*	
0	10.11	2.90	11.50	2.94	12.87	3.00	14.22	3.04	16.88	3.12	19.46	3.22	22.00	3.30	
$\frac{7}{8}$	24.11	0.74	25.50	0.88	26.87	1.02	28.22	1.14							
1	26.11	0.54	27.50	0.68	28.87	0.82	30.22	0.94							
$1\frac{1}{8}$	28.11	0.36	29.50	0.50	30.87	0.64	32.22	0.76	34.88	0.98					
$1\frac{1}{4}$	30.11	0.18	31.50	0.32	32.87	0.46	34.22	0.58	36.88	0.80	39.46	1.00			
$1\frac{3}{8}$			33.50	0.14	34.87	0.28	36.22	0.40	38.88	0.62	41.46	0.84			5
$1\frac{1}{2}$					36.87	0.12	38.22	0.24	40.88	0.46	43.46	0.66	46.00	0.86	
$1\frac{5}{8}$							40.22	0.08	42.88	0.30	45.46	0.50	48.00	0.70	
$1\frac{3}{4}$							42.22	+0.09	44.88	0.14	47.46	0.34	50.00	0.54	4
$1\frac{7}{8}$									46.88	+0.02	49.46	0.18	52.00	0.38	
2									48.88	+0.18	51.46	0.04	54.00	0.22	
$2\frac{1}{8}$											53.46	+0.12	56.00	0.07	4
$2\frac{1}{4}$											55.46	+0.28	58.00	+0.08	
$2\frac{3}{8}$											57.46	+0.42	60.00	+0.23	
$2\frac{1}{2}$													62.00	+0.37	3

Dimensions in inches and square inches. Values of *A* are net areas of one flange only and are based on deduction of three holes from each angle and two from each cover plate—all $\frac{1}{8}$ in. larger than the nominal diameter of the rivet.

Heavy rules indicate relationship of gross area of angles to total gross area of flange, expressed in last column as percentage.

*Values marked + must be added to back-to-back of angles to obtain center-to-center of flanges.

Courtesy Bethlehem Steel Co.

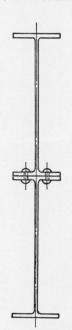

Fig. 4.28 Compound Steel Beam

Unit *I* on depth of 26.88 + 1.56 = 28.44 is 404

Net width of plate required $= \dfrac{7,389}{1.56 \times 404} =$ 11.7 in.

Gross width (allowing for two $\frac{7}{8}$-in. rivets) $= 11.7 + 2 = 13.7$ in. Use $14 \times 1\frac{9}{16}$-in. plate

The inner plate should be $\frac{13}{16} \times 14$ in., and the outer plate should be $\frac{3}{4} \times 14$ in.

The length may be determined as for the cover plates of plate girders, except that it is not necessary to run any cover plates full length.

4.22 Compound steel beams

a Occasionally it may prove simpler to use a compound steel beam—or, as it is sometimes called, a "tandem beam"—than to use a plate girder or cover-plated beam. This type of beam is formed by riveting or welding one beam on top of the other instead of placing

146

Table 4.16   Properties of Plate-Girder Flanges (*Continued*)

Angles 8 × 8 in., cover plates 18 in. wide, $\frac{7}{8}$-in. rivets

Cover plate thickness	Thickness of angles													%
	$\frac{1}{2}$		$\frac{9}{16}$		$\frac{5}{8}$		$\frac{3}{4}$		$\frac{7}{8}$		1		$1\frac{1}{8}$		
	A	2y	A	2y	A	2y	A	2y	A	2y	A	2y	A	2y	
0	12.50	4.38	13.99	4.42	15.47	4.46	18.38	4.56	21.21	4.64	24.00	4.74	26.71	4.82	
$\frac{7}{8}$	26.50	1.72													
1	28.50	1.48	29.99	1.66											
$1\frac{1}{8}$	30.50	1.26	31.99	1.44	33.47	1.59									
$1\frac{1}{4}$	32.50	1.04	33.99	1.22	35.47	1.38	38.38	1.68							
$1\frac{3}{8}$	34.50	0.84	35.99	1.02	37.47	1.18	40.38	1.48							
$1\frac{1}{2}$	36.50	0.64	37.99	0.82	39.47	0.98	42.38	1.28	45.21	1.54					
$1\frac{5}{8}$	38.50	0.46	39.99	0.63	41.47	0.80	44.38	1.09	47.21	1.35	50.00	1.60			
$1\frac{3}{4}$			41.99	0.44	43.47	0.60	46.38	0.90	49.21	1.17	52.00	1.41			50
$1\frac{7}{8}$					45.47	0.42	48.38	0.72	51.21	0.97	54.00	1.23	56.71	1.45	
2					47.47	0.24	50.38	0.55	53.21	0.81	56.00	1.06	58.71	1.28	
$2\frac{1}{8}$							52.38	0.38	55.21	0.64	58.00	0.90	60.71	1.12	
$2\frac{1}{4}$							54.38	0.21	57.21	0.47	60.00	0.72	62.71	0.95	45
$2\frac{3}{8}$							56.38	0.04	59.21	0.30	62.00	0.56	64.71	0.78	
$2\frac{1}{2}$									61.21	0.14	64.00	0.40	66.71	0.62	40
															35

Angles 8 × 8 in., cover plates 20 in. wide, $\frac{7}{8}$-in. rivets

Cover plate thickness	$\frac{1}{2}$		$\frac{9}{16}$		$\frac{5}{8}$		$\frac{3}{4}$		$\frac{7}{8}$		1		$1\frac{1}{8}$		%
	A	2y	A	2y	A	2y	A	2y	A	2y	A	2y	A	2y	
0	12.50	4.38	13.99	4.42	15.47	4.46	18.38	4.56	21.21	4.64	24.00	4.74	26.71	4.82	
$\frac{7}{8}$	28.25	1.60	29.74	1.77											
1	30.50	1.35	31.99	1.52	33.47	1.68									
$1\frac{1}{8}$	32.75	1.12	34.24	1.29	35.72	1.45	38.63	1.74							
$1\frac{1}{4}$	35.00	0.90	36.49	1.07	37.97	1.23	40.88	1.53							
$1\frac{3}{8}$	37.25	0.70	38.74	0.86	40.22	1.02	43.13	1.32	45.96	1.58					
$1\frac{1}{2}$	39.50	0.50	40.99	0.66	42.47	0.82	45.38	1.12	48.21	1.38	51.00	1.62			
$1\frac{5}{8}$			43.24	0.48	44.72	0.64	47.63	0.93	50.46	1.18	53.25	1.42	55.96	1.64	50
$1\frac{3}{4}$					46.97	0.46	49.88	0.75	52.71	1.00	55.50	1.24	58.21	1.46	
$1\frac{7}{8}$							52.13	0.57	54.96	0.82	57.75	1.06	60.46	1.28	
2							54.38	0.39	57.21	0.64	60.00	0.88	62.71	1.10	45
$2\frac{1}{8}$							56.63	0.22	59.46	0.48	62.25	0.72	64.96	0.93	
$2\frac{1}{4}$									61.71	0.30	64.50	0.54	67.21	0.76	
$2\frac{3}{8}$									63.96	0.14	66.75	0.38	69.46	0.60	
$2\frac{1}{2}$									66.21	+ 0.02	69.00	0.22	71.71	0.44	40
															35

Dimensions in inches and square inches. Values of A are net areas of one flange only and are based on deduction of three holes from each angle and two from each cover plate—all $\frac{1}{8}$ in. larger than the nominal diameter of the rivet.

Heavy rules indicate relationship of gross area of angles to total gross area of flange, expressed in last column as percentage.

*Values marked + must be added to back-to-back of angles to obtain center-to-center of flanges.

Courtesy Bethlehem Steel Co.

Table 4.17   Properties of Split-Beam T's, WP Girders

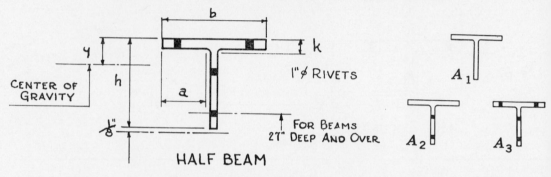

HALF BEAM

Using 1-in. rivets

Half beam	b	Thickness Flange	Thickness Web	h	k	$2k$	y	A_1	A_2	A_3	I_o / 2 Ts	$2y$
36 WF 300	$16\frac{5}{8}$	$1\frac{11}{16}$	$\frac{15}{16}$	$18\frac{1}{4}$	$2\frac{11}{16}$	$5\frac{3}{8}$	4.1	44.0	41.8	38.1	2,390	8.2
280	$16\frac{5}{8}$	$1\frac{9}{16}$	$\frac{7}{8}$	$18\frac{1}{4}$	$2\frac{9}{16}$	$5\frac{1}{8}$	4.1	41.0	39.1	35.5	2,240	8.2
260	$16\frac{1}{2}$	$1\frac{7}{16}$	$\frac{7}{8}$	18	$2\frac{7}{16}$	$4\frac{7}{8}$	4.0	38.2	36.3	33.0	2,080	8.1
33 WF 240	$15\frac{7}{8}$	$1\frac{3}{8}$	$\frac{7}{8}$	$16\frac{5}{8}$	$2\frac{3}{8}$	$4\frac{3}{4}$	3.7	35.2	33.3	30.1	1,610	7.4
220	$15\frac{3}{4}$	$1\frac{1}{4}$	$\frac{13}{16}$	$16\frac{1}{2}$	$2\frac{1}{4}$	$4\frac{1}{2}$	3.7	32.3	30.5	27.6	1,480	7.4
30 WF 210	$15\frac{1}{8}$	$1\frac{5}{16}$	$\frac{13}{16}$	$15\frac{1}{16}$	$2\frac{1}{4}$	$4\frac{1}{2}$	3.3	30.8	29.0	26.1	1,140	6.6
190	15	$1\frac{3}{16}$	$\frac{3}{4}$	$14\frac{15}{16}$	$2\frac{1}{8}$	$4\frac{1}{4}$	3.2	27.9	26.3	23.6	1,030	6.5
27 WF 177	$14\frac{1}{8}$	$1\frac{3}{16}$	$\frac{3}{4}$	$13\frac{1}{2}$	$2\frac{1}{16}$	$4\frac{1}{8}$	2.9	26.0	24.3	21.6	770	5.9
24 WF 160	$14\frac{1}{8}$	$1\frac{1}{8}$	$\frac{11}{16}$	$12\frac{1}{4}$	$1\frac{13}{16}$	$3\frac{5}{8}$	2.5	23.4	22.7	20.1	540	5.0
21 WF 142	$13\frac{1}{8}$	$1\frac{1}{8}$	$\frac{11}{16}$	$10\frac{5}{8}$	$1\frac{3}{4}$	$3\frac{1}{2}$	2.1	20.8	20.1	17.6	330	4.3
18 WF 114	$11\frac{7}{8}$	1	$\frac{5}{8}$	$9\frac{1}{4}$	$1\frac{9}{16}$	$3\frac{1}{8}$	1.8	16.7	16.0	13.8	200	3.7
36 WF 194	$12\frac{1}{8}$	$1\frac{1}{4}$	$\frac{13}{16}$	$18\frac{1}{8}$	$2\frac{1}{16}$	$4\frac{1}{8}$	4.8	28.5	26.7	23.9	1,770	9.6
182	$12\frac{1}{8}$	$1\frac{3}{16}$	$\frac{3}{4}$	$18\frac{1}{16}$	2	4	4.7	26.7	25.0	22.4	1,650	9.5
170	12	$1\frac{1}{8}$	$\frac{11}{16}$	$17\frac{15}{16}$	$1\frac{7}{8}$	$3\frac{3}{4}$	4.7	24.9	23.4	20.9	1,540	9.5
160	12	1	$\frac{11}{16}$	$17\frac{7}{8}$	$1\frac{13}{16}$	$3\frac{5}{8}$	4.7	23.5	22.0	19.7	1,450	9.5
33 WF 152	$11\frac{5}{8}$	$1\frac{1}{16}$	$\frac{5}{8}$	$16\frac{5}{8}$	$1\frac{13}{16}$	$3\frac{5}{8}$	4.2	22.3	20.8	18.5	1,160	8.5
141	$11\frac{1}{2}$	$\frac{15}{16}$	$\frac{5}{8}$	$16\frac{1}{2}$	$1\frac{11}{16}$	$3\frac{3}{8}$	4.2	20.7	19.3	17.2	1,080	8.5
30 WF 132	$10\frac{1}{2}$	1	$\frac{5}{8}$	15	$1\frac{11}{16}$	$3\frac{3}{8}$	3.9	19.3	17.9	15.7	820	7.8
124	$10\frac{1}{2}$	$\frac{15}{16}$	$\frac{5}{8}$	$14\frac{15}{16}$	$1\frac{5}{8}$	$3\frac{1}{4}$	3.9	18.1	16.8	14.7	770	7.7
27 WF 114	$10\frac{1}{8}$	$\frac{15}{16}$	$\frac{9}{16}$	$13\frac{1}{2}$	$1\frac{9}{16}$	$3\frac{1}{8}$	3.4	16.7	15.4	13.3	570	6.8
21 WF 96	9	$\frac{15}{16}$	$\frac{9}{16}$	$10\frac{7}{16}$	$1\frac{9}{16}$	$3\frac{1}{8}$	2.5	14.0	13.4	11.3	260	5.0
24 I 120	$8\frac{1}{16}$		$\frac{13}{16}$	$11\frac{7}{8}$	$1\frac{7}{8}$	$3\frac{3}{8}$	3.5	17.5	16.6		470	7.0
105.9	$7\frac{7}{8}$		$\frac{5}{8}$	$11\frac{7}{8}$	$1\frac{7}{8}$	$3\frac{3}{4}$	3.2	15.4	14.7		410	6.4

A_1 is the gross area of split beam tee, A_2 allows for holes in web, and A_3 allows for holes in web and flange. Dimensions are in inches or square inches.

them side by side. Although the beams used are usually of the same size, the use of existing material may dictate the use of different-sized beams. Two beams joined thus will furnish from 20 to 30 percent more strength than if used side by side, as well as providing a much greater stiffness (Fig. 4.28).

b In the design of a compound beam, compute the moment and shear, and lay out a shear diagram. Compute the required section modulus, and select the beams to make up this required section modulus, estimating the strength of the combined section from the assumption made in paragraph *a*. Check the section modulus of the assumed section. Since the only holes taken out are at or near the neutral axis, it is perfectly sound to base the analysis on gross section. If the original assumption was high or low, revise the assumed beams and recheck.

Table 4.18   Properties of Split-Column T's, WP Girders

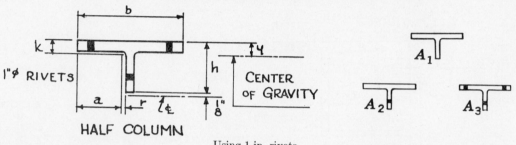

Using 1-in. rivets

Half column 14 WF	b	Thickness		h	k	$2k$	y	A_1	A_2	A_3	I_o 2 Ts	$2y$
		Flange	Web									
426	$16\frac{3}{4}$	$3\frac{1}{16}$	$1\frac{7}{8}$	$9\frac{1}{4}$	$3\frac{5}{8}$	$7\frac{1}{4}$	2.4	62.4	60.3	53.5	550	4.7
398	$16\frac{5}{8}$	$2\frac{13}{16}$	$1\frac{13}{16}$	9	$3\frac{7}{16}$	$6\frac{7}{8}$	2.3	58.3	56.3	49.9	500	4.5
370	$16\frac{1}{2}$	$2\frac{11}{16}$	$1\frac{11}{16}$	$8\frac{7}{8}$	$3\frac{1}{4}$	$6\frac{1}{2}$	2.2	54.2	52.3	46.3	440	4.3
342	$16\frac{3}{8}$	$2\frac{7}{16}$	$1\frac{9}{16}$	$8\frac{5}{8}$	$3\frac{1}{16}$	$6\frac{3}{8}$	2.0	50.1	48.4	42.8	390	4.0
314	$16\frac{1}{4}$	$2\frac{5}{16}$	$1\frac{7}{16}$	$8\frac{1}{2}$	$2\frac{7}{8}$	$5\frac{3}{4}$	1.9	46.0	44.4	39.2	340	3.8
287	$16\frac{1}{8}$	$2\frac{1}{16}$	$1\frac{5}{16}$	$8\frac{1}{4}$	$2\frac{11}{16}$	$5\frac{3}{8}$	1.8	42.0	40.6	35.8	300	3.6
264	16	$1\frac{15}{16}$	$1\frac{1}{4}$	$8\frac{1}{8}$	$2\frac{9}{16}$	$5\frac{1}{8}$	1.7	38.7	37.3	32.9	270	3.4
246	16	$1\frac{13}{16}$	$1\frac{1}{8}$	8	$2\frac{7}{16}$	$4\frac{7}{8}$	1.7	36.0	34.7	30.7	240	3.3
237	$15\frac{7}{8}$	$1\frac{3}{4}$	$1\frac{1}{8}$	$7\frac{15}{16}$	$2\frac{3}{8}$	$4\frac{3}{4}$	1.6	34.7	33.5	29.5	230	3.2
228	$15\frac{7}{8}$	$1\frac{11}{16}$	$1\frac{1}{16}$	$7\frac{7}{8}$	$2\frac{5}{16}$	$4\frac{5}{8}$	1.6	33.4	32.2	28.4	220	3.1
219	$15\frac{7}{8}$	$1\frac{5}{8}$	1	$7\frac{13}{16}$	$2\frac{1}{4}$	$4\frac{1}{2}$	1.6	32.0	30.9	27.3	200	3.1
211	$15\frac{3}{4}$	$1\frac{9}{16}$	1	$7\frac{3}{4}$	$2\frac{3}{16}$	$4\frac{3}{8}$	1.5	30.9	29.8	26.3	190	3.0
202	$15\frac{3}{4}$	$1\frac{1}{2}$	$\frac{15}{16}$	$7\frac{11}{16}$	$2\frac{1}{8}$	$4\frac{1}{4}$	1.5	29.6	28.5	25.1	180	2.9
193	$15\frac{3}{4}$	$1\frac{7}{16}$	$\frac{7}{8}$	$7\frac{5}{8}$	$2\frac{1}{16}$	$4\frac{1}{8}$	1.5	28.2	27.2	24.0	170	2.8
184	$15\frac{5}{8}$	$1\frac{3}{8}$	$\frac{7}{8}$	$7\frac{9}{16}$	2	4	1.4	26.9	26.0	22.9	160	2.8
176	$15\frac{5}{8}$	$1\frac{5}{16}$	$\frac{13}{16}$	$7\frac{1}{2}$	$1\frac{15}{16}$	$3\frac{7}{8}$	1.4	25.8	24.8	21.9	150	2.8
167	$15\frac{5}{8}$	$1\frac{1}{4}$	$\frac{13}{16}$	$7\frac{7}{16}$	$1\frac{7}{8}$	$3\frac{3}{4}$	1.4	24.4	23.6	20.8	143	2.7
158	$15\frac{1}{2}$	$1\frac{3}{16}$	$\frac{3}{4}$	$7\frac{3}{8}$	$1\frac{13}{16}$	$3\frac{5}{8}$	1.3	23.1	22.3	19.6	134	2.6
150	$15\frac{1}{2}$	$1\frac{1}{8}$	$\frac{11}{16}$	$7\frac{5}{16}$	$1\frac{3}{4}$	$3\frac{1}{2}$	1.3	21.9	21.2	18.6	126	2.6
142	$15\frac{1}{2}$	$1\frac{1}{16}$	$\frac{11}{16}$	$7\frac{1}{4}$	$1\frac{11}{16}$	$3\frac{3}{8}$	1.3	20.8	20.1	17.7	118	2.5
136	$14\frac{3}{4}$	$1\frac{1}{16}$	$\frac{11}{16}$	$7\frac{1}{4}$	$1\frac{11}{16}$	$3\frac{3}{8}$	1.3	19.9	19.2	16.8	114	2.5
127	$14\frac{3}{4}$	1	$\frac{5}{8}$	$7\frac{3}{16}$	$1\frac{5}{8}$	$3\frac{1}{4}$	1.2	18.6	17.9	15.7	105	2.5
119	$14\frac{5}{8}$	$\frac{15}{16}$	$\frac{9}{16}$	$7\frac{7}{8}$	$1\frac{9}{16}$	$3\frac{1}{8}$	1.2	17.4	16.8	14.7	95	2.4
111	$14\frac{5}{8}$	$\frac{7}{8}$	$\frac{9}{16}$	$7\frac{1}{16}$	$1\frac{1}{2}$	3	1.2	16.3	15.6	13.7	88	2.3
103	$14\frac{5}{8}$	$\frac{13}{16}$	$\frac{1}{2}$	7	$1\frac{7}{16}$	$2\frac{7}{8}$	1.1	15.1	14.5	12.7	81	2.3
95	$14\frac{1}{2}$	$\frac{3}{4}$	$\frac{1}{2}$	$6\frac{15}{16}$	$1\frac{3}{8}$	$2\frac{3}{4}$	1.1	13.9	13.4	11.7	74	2.2
87	$14\frac{1}{2}$	$\frac{11}{16}$	$\frac{7}{16}$	$6\frac{7}{8}$	$1\frac{5}{16}$	$2\frac{5}{8}$	1.1	12.7	12.3	10.7	66	2.1

A_1 is the gross area of split beam tee, A_2 allows for holes in web, and A_3 allows for holes in web and flange. Dimensions are in inches or square inches.

c It is necessary to get the longitudinal or horizontal shear per lineal inch along the two contact flanges to compute the riveting required. The longitudinal shear is found from the formula

$$v_h = \frac{V M_s}{I} \qquad (4.6)$$

where V is the vertical shear at the section and M_s the static moment of the section. This static moment is found by a tabulation of the parts as shown in the following problem. Theoretically, the horizontal shear increases directly as the vertical shear increases, and the total horizontal shear in any section is the average shear per inch from Formula (4.6), multiplied by the length in inches. This total

Table 4.19 Properties of Plate Girder Flanges, WP Girders

Using 1-in. rivets

Half beam	L $\frac{3}{4} \times$	Angles			Cover plates											
			w	t	$2\frac{1}{2}$	$2\frac{1}{4}$	2	$1\frac{3}{4}$	$1\frac{1}{2}$	$1\frac{1}{4}$	1	$\frac{7}{8}$	$\frac{3}{4}$	A_1	A_2	A_3
36WF300	8	$8 \times 8 \times 1\frac{1}{8}$	24	A	131.2	125.8	120.3	114.9	109.4	104.0	98.6	95.8	93.1	76.8	48.3	38.0
				y	2.0	2.2	2.3	2.5	2.7	2.9	3.1	3.2	3.3	4.1	3.7	4.1
36WF300	8	$8 \times 8 \times 1\frac{1}{8}$	20	A	121.2	116.8	112.3	107.9	103.4	99.0	94.6	92.3	90.1	76.8	48.3	38.0
				y	2.2	2.4	2.6	2.8	2.9	3.1	3.3	3.4	3.5	4.1	3.7	4.1
36WF300	8	$8 \times 8 \times \frac{7}{8}$	20	A	115.2	110.8	106.4	101.9	97.5	93.0	88.6	86.4	84.3	70.9	48.3	38.0
				y	2.0	2.2	2.4	2.6	2.8	3.0	3.1	3.2	3.3	4.0	3.7	4.1
36WF300	7	$8 \times 6 \times \frac{7}{8}$	24	A	120.3	114.9	109.4	104.0	98.6	93.1	87.7	84.9	82.2	65.9	46.9	38.0
				y	1.8	2.0	2.1	2.3	2.5	2.7	3.0	3.2	3.3	4.1	3.7	4.1
36WF300	7	$8 \times 6 \times \frac{7}{8}$	20	A	110.3	105.8	101.4	96.9	92.5	88.1	83.7	81.4	79.2	65.9	46.9	38.0
				y	2.1	2.3	2.4	2.6	2.8	3.0	3.2	3.3	3.4	4.1	3.7	4.1
36WF300	7	$8 \times 6 \times \frac{7}{8}$	18	A	105.3	101.4	97.4	93.4	89.5	85.6	81.7	79.7	77.8	65.9	46.9	38.0
				y	2.2	2.4	2.5	2.6	2.8	3.0	3.2	3.3	3.4	4.1	3.7	4.1
33WF240	6	$8 \times 6 \times \frac{7}{8}$	16	A	90.8	87.4	84.0	80.5	77.1	73.6	70.2	68.4	66.7	56.5	37.4	30.1
				y	2.0	2.2	2.3	2.5	2.7	2.9	3.0	3.1	3.2	3.8	3.3	3.7
30WF210	6	$8 \times 6 \times \frac{3}{4}$	15	A	81.8	78.6	75.4	72.2	69.0	65.9	62.7	61.1	59.5	49.9	33.4	26.1
				y	1.7	1.9	2.0	2.2	2.4	2.6	2.7	2.8	2.9	3.5	2.9	3.3
27WF177	5	$8 \times 6 \times \frac{3}{4}$	14	A	73.3	70.3	67.5	64.6	61.6	58.7	55.7	54.3	52.8	44.0	27.5	21.6
				y	1.5	1.7	1.8	2.0	2.2	2.4	2.5	2.6	2.7	3.3	2.6	2.9
36WF194	4	$7 \times 4 \times \frac{7}{8}$	12	A	66.4	63.9	61.5	59.0	56.6	54.2	51.8	50.5	49.3	42.0	28.2	23.9
				y	2.4	2.6	2.7	2.9	3.1	3.3	3.5	3.6	3.7	4.4	4.2	4.8
30WF132	4	$7 \times 4 \times \frac{3}{4}$	10	A	51.4	49.5	47.5	45.5	43.6	41.7	39.8	38.9	37.9	32.0	20.0	15.7
				y	1.8	2.0	2.1	2.3	2.5	2.7	2.8	2.9	3.0	3.7	3.3	3.9

A_1 is the gross area of split beam tee, A_2 allows for holes in web, and A_3 allows for holes in web and flange. Dimensions are in inches or square inches.

horizontal shear divided by the value of a rivet in single shear gives the number of rivets required to develop the horizontal shear and the consequent spacing of rivets. The beam is usually divided into sections and the riveting computed for each section.

Problem (See load diagram, Fig. 4.29.) Using 20,000 psi, S required (see Art. 4.10c) =

$0.45 \times 70 \times 36 = 1,134$. Try two 36 WF 150. The properties of the section are

$$A = 2 \times 44.16 = 88.32$$
$$I = 9,012 \times 2 = 18,024$$
$$88.32 \times 17.92^2 = \underline{28,360}$$
$$46,384$$
$$S = \frac{I}{c} = \frac{46,384}{35.84} = 1,294$$

The static moment is calculated in the following table:

Section	Area A	y	Static $M = Ay$
Web	$35.84 \times 0.625 = 22.4$	17.92	401.4
Top flange	$\dfrac{44.16 - 22.4}{2} = 10.88$	35.37	384.8
Bottom flange	$\dfrac{21.76}{2} = 10.88$	0.47	5.11
Total	44.16		791.31

The horizontal shear properties are calculated as follows:

$$\text{Shear } a \text{ to } b = \frac{35k \times 791.31 \times 72}{46{,}384} = \frac{43.0k}{6.63} = 6\tfrac{1}{2} \quad \text{(use 8 rivets minimum)}$$

$$\text{Shear } b \text{ to } c = \frac{105 \times 791.31 \times 72}{46{,}384} = \frac{129.0k}{6.63} = 19\tfrac{1}{2} \quad \text{(use 20 rivets)}$$

$$\text{Shear } c \text{ to } d = \frac{175 \times 791.31 \times 72}{46{,}384} = \frac{215k}{6.63} = 32\tfrac{1}{2} \quad \text{(use 34 rivets)}$$

.23 Crane-runway girders

a One of the problems encountered in the esign of steel-mill buildings is the design of rane runways. It involves not only the deign of the crane girder, but also the column nd bracing. Shop superintendents frequently ondemn a crane for its excessive power conumption or high maintenance costs when the ault lies chiefly with the design of the crane unways. The stiffness of the whole structure is of the utmost importance. Lack of stiffness rings about bumpy movement of the crane, hrowing rails out of alignment and causing xcessive strains on the crane and its supporting structure and excessive wear on moving arts.

The design of the column is a problem in ccentricity and is given in Art. 7.10. A crane unway in a mill building also depends for its tiffness and rigidity largely on the bottom hord bracing of the roof trusses. Some suggestions on this bracing are given in Art. 10.40, Mill Buildings.

b In addition to those portions of the AISC Code which apply to any steel girder, he following sections also apply to the design of crane-runway girders—

[From Sec. 10(*c*)] The live load stresses shall be ncreased to allow for 25% impact stress. (This llowance ordinarily is made in the wheel loads given by the crane manufacturer.)

[From Sec. 10(*d*)] The lateral forces on crane runways to provide for the effect of crane trolleys shall if not otherwise specified, be 20% of the moving load of the crane, applied to the top of the rail, one half on each side of the runway, and considered as acting in either direction normal to the runway rail.

Wheel loads and wheel spacing are given in the catalogs of the various manufacturers. No table of standards which provides for general use can be given.

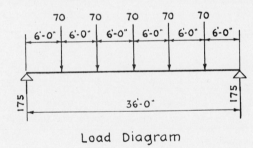

Load Diagram

Shear Diagram

Fig. 4.29 Problem Diagrams—Compound Steel Beams

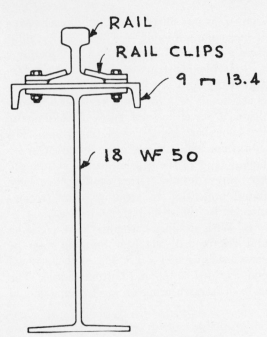

Fig. 4.30   Typical Crane Girder

$$M = 14.67 \frac{(25 - 3.5)^2}{50} = 135.5 \text{ ft-kips}$$

At 20,000 psi, $S = 0.6 \times 135.5 = 81.5$. Try 18 WF 50.

Laterally unsupported length =

$$\frac{L}{2} - \frac{a}{4} = 12.5 - 1.75 = 10.75$$

From Table 1.5, this is within the safe limit of unsupported span. From paragraph *c* the required S of top flange would be

$$0.05 \times 81.5 = 4.08$$

Required lateral S furnished by one flange = $\frac{9.9}{2} = 4.95$. Therefore, no additional stiffening of the top flange is necessary.

4.30 STEEL JOISTS

a   Bar joists, or open-web steel joists, are light-weight trusses, either welded or expanded, and adaptable for the support of

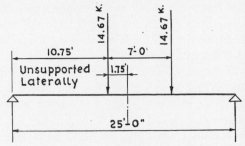

Fig. 4.31   Position of Crane for Maximum Moment

c   With the wheel load and wheel base of the crane carriage known, the design of the crane girder is a problem in moving-load moment, as described in Art. 3.10*g*. Because the crane beam must be considered laterally unsupported from the point of load to the column, it is necessary to check the beam on the basis of lateral deflection, as described in Art. 3.10*h*.

In order to provide for the transverse load from the crane, it is frequently desirable to lay a channel flatwise on the top flange of the crane girder, as shown in Fig. 4.30.

As quoted above in paragraph *b*, the crane runway provides for a lateral thrust of 20 percent of the moving load. Since this is about half the total load of the crane, it is 10 percent of the wheel load. This is applied to the top flange of the crane runway, so it must be resisted either by half the section modulus the weak way of the beams, or else by flatwise members applied to the top flanges.

Problem   Design the crane-runway girder for a 10-ton crane on a 50-ft crane bridge span—the runway-girder span to be 25 ft. The wheel base is 7 ft and the wheel load is 14,670 lb (see Fig. 4.31).

light loads up to a span of 30 ft. They have a level top chord with a constant depth of $2\frac{1}{2}$ in. at the end, which is designed to bear on masonry or a steel beam. The center section between the end bearings comes in standard depths varying by 2-in. increments from 8 to 16 in. Bar joists are designed to carry either 2 or $2\frac{1}{2}$-in. concrete slab, or precast plank or metal-deck roofs. They are spaced from 12 to 21 in. for floor loads and a greater distance for roofs. The top chord must be braced against lateral deflection, either by means of the poured-concrete slab or by some other method, and for better distribution of the loads, steel bridging ties the joists at intervals of not over 7 ft. Although there are

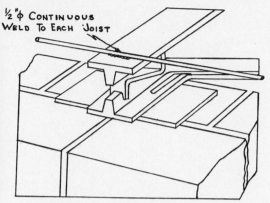

½"∅ CONTINUOUS
WELD TO EACH JOIST

Fig. 4.32   Bar Joist Bearing on Wall

a number of bar joists on the market, they are all designed in accordance with certain standards of top and bottom chord areas, web members, etc., so that for any joists the designation provides the same standard properties as for structural steel. Steel joists are designated as SJ-81, SJ-82, SJ-102, etc., the figure 8 or 10 indicating the depth and the final figure the chord members and web members. Thus SJ-82 and SJ-102 have the same chord section, but SJ-82 is 8 in. deep and SJ-102 is 10 in. deep.

Comparable with the bar joists in capacity but having a solid web are the Jones and Laughlin junior beams. They have a very narrow flange and a thin web, and are not to be confused with the so-called light beams rolled by U.S. Steel and Bethlehem.

b Bar-joist construction has received a bad name in some places because it has been improperly used. If its proper limitations are recognized and proper details are used in its design, it provides good, low-priced construc-

Bearing extends at least to ℄ of beam

Tack Weld to each beam

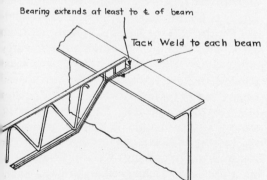

Fig. 4.33   Bar Joist Bearing on Steel Beam

tion. It is not suited to tall buildings because it lacks the stiffening effect of heavier, more rigidly connected construction. Neither is it a desirable construction for heavy concentrated or vibratory floor loads. Because the construction is built more or less to form a drum, it is well in some types of buildings to use acoustical treatment of the rooms. The vibration, which is probably the greatest inherent fault of the system, can be minimized by proper details. Other details have been found preferable to some of those recommended by the steel-joist catalogs.

c With welding becoming more common and economical, the best bridging may be cross bridging of $1 \times 1 \times \frac{1}{8}$ in. with flattened ends, welded to top and bottom chords. The ends of joists bearing on steel beams should

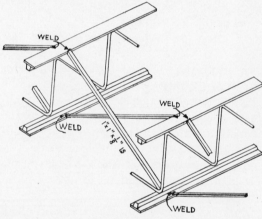

WELD

WELD

WELD

1"×1"×⅛"

WELD

Fig. 4.34   Typical Welded Bridging for Bar Joists

be tack welded rather than clipped to the beam. For wall-bearing ends, the most satisfactory wall anchor is a continuous ½-in. rod laid on top of the joists and tack welded to each joist. Where bracing beams are used parallel to a line of joists to stiffen columns, they should not be used in place of a bar joist, but should be dropped at least ½ in. lower than the plane of the top chord to avoid cracking the slab. Where joist spans change directions, the joist parallel with the supporting beam should be properly anchored to the beam, and a 3-ft wide strip of wire mesh should be laid near the top of the slab, centered on the beam line. It is also good practice to lay a strip of metal lath over any

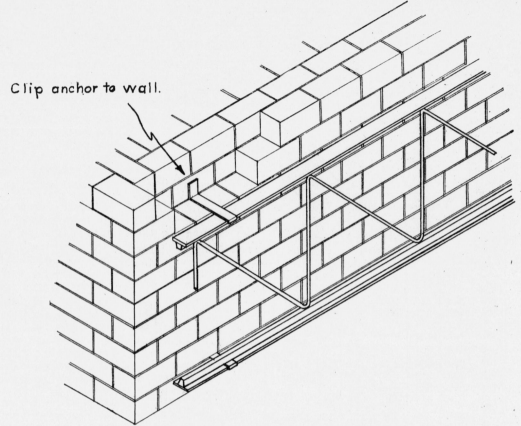

Clip anchor to wall.

Fig. 4.35   Anchorage of Bar Joist Parallel with Wall

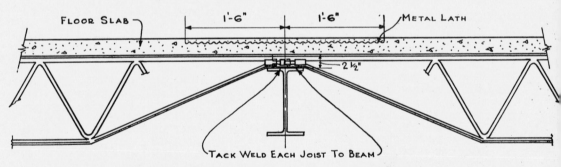

FLOOR SLAB   1'-6"   1'-6"   METAL LATH

2½"

TACK WELD EACH JOIST TO BEAM

Fig. 4.36   Bar-Joist Construction at Steel Beam

beam carrying joists the span of which is over 15 times the joist depth.

If a wood floor is to be laid on steel joists, the most satisfactory construction is to bed the sleepers in the concrete topping at right angles to the direction of the joists, with at least ½ in. of concrete between. Wood-top nailer joists and wood nailers wired to the top flange of ordinary joists almost invariably result in squeaky floors.

d   The joist tables published by the various manufacturers give allowable loads on spacings varying by 1-in. increments, implying that any desired spacing can be used. This is true with metal deck and tongue-and-groove concrete or gypsum plank, up to a maximum roof spacing of 30 in., but for poured concrete it is well to use spacings which will assure a lap of the floor lath and ceiling lath at a joist. If a span is picked at random, the lap point

Table 4.20 Steel Joists

Loads in pounds per square foot

Span	Joist	12 in. o.c.	13½ in. o.c.	15¾ in. o.c.	18¾ in. o.c.	23½ in. o.c.	30 in. o.c.	Span	Joist	12 in. o.c.	13½ in. o.c.	15¾ in. o.c.	18¾ in. o.c.	23½ in. o.c.	30 in. o.c.
6 ft	81	530	474	406	342	272	213	15 ft	103	243	216	185	155	124	97
7 ft	81	402	357	306	257	205	160		104	293	261	223	188	150	117
8 ft	81	308	274	235	197	157	123		123	272	243	207	174	139	109
	82	475	423	362	304	243	190		124	307	273	234	196	156	123
9 ft	81	242	216	185	155	124	97		125	333	297	254	213	170	133
	82	422	376	322	269	215	169		126	360	320	274	230	184	144
10 ft	81	197	176	150	126	101	79		145	387	344	295	247	197	155
	82	350	312	267	225	179	140		146	413	367	315	265	211	165
	102	380	338	290	243	194	152		147	454	404	346	290	232	181
	103	390	347	297	249	199	156	16 ft	81	77	68	59	49	39	31
	104	440	392	336	282	225	176		82	137	121	104	87	69	55
11 ft	81	162	145	123	103	83	65		102	164	146	125	105	84	66
	82	289	257	221	185	148	116		103	213	189	162	136	108	85
	102	346	308	263	222	176	138		104	260	231	198	166	133	104
	103	355	316	270	227	181	142		123	240	214	183	154	122	96
	104	400	357	305	256	204	160		124	287	255	219	184	147	115
12 ft	81	137	132	104	87	69	55		125	312	278	238	200	159	125
	82	243	234	186	156	124	98		126	337	300	257	216	172	135
	102	292	280	222	186	149	117		145	363	323	276	232	185	145
	103	325	312	248	208	166	130		146	387	345	295	248	198	155
	104	367	353	280	235	187	147		147	425	378	324	272	217	170
	123	367	353	280	235	187	147		166	400	356	305	256	204	160
	124	384	369	293	245	196	153		167	450	401	343	288	230	180
	125	417	371	317	267	213	167	17 ft	102	145	129	110	93	74	58
	126	450	400	343	288	230	180		103	189	168	144	121	97	76
13 ft	81	116	103	88	74	59	46		104	230	204	176	147	117	92
	82	207	184	157	133	105	83		123	212	189	162	136	108	85
	102	248	206	190	159	127	99		124	265	236	202	170	130	106
	103	300	248	229	192	153	120		125	294	262	224	188	150	118
	104	338	280	258	217	173	135		126	318	282	242	204	162	127
	123	338	280	258	217	173	135		145	342	303	260	318	174	137
	124	354	315	269	227	181	142		146	365	325	278	233	187	146
	125	384	342	293	246	196	154		147	400	356	305	256	204	160
	126	415	370	317	266	212	166		166	376	335	287	241	192	151
14 ft	81	100	89	76	64	51	40		167	424	377	323	272	216	170
	82	178	159	136	114	91	71	18 ft	102	129	115	99	87	66	52
	102	214	191	164	137	109	86		103	169	150	129	108	86	68
	103	278	248	212	178	142	111		104	205	183	157	132	105	83
	104	314	280	240	202	160	126		123	189	169	144	121	97	76
	123	313	278	239	201	159	125		124	236	210	181	152	121	95
	124	328	292	250	211	167	131		125	278	247	211	177	142	111
	125	357	318	272	229	183	143		126	300	267	229	192	153	120
	126	386	343	293	247	196	154		145	321	285	244	206	164	129
	145	414	369	315	265	211	166		146	344	306	263	221	176	138
	146	413	394	337	284	226	177		147	378	336	288	242	193	151
	147	486	432	370	311	248	194		166	356	316	271	228	182	143
15 ft	81	87	78	67	56	45	35		167	400	356	305	256	204	160
	82	155	138	118	99	79	62	19 ft	102	116	103	88	75	59	47
	102	187	167	143	120	96	75		103	151	135	116	97	77	61
									104	184	165	141	118	95	74
									123	170	151	130	108	87	68
									124	212	190	162	137	108	85

Table 4.20   Steel Joists (*Continued*)

Loads in pounds per square foot

Span	Joist	12 in. o.c.	13½ in. o.c.	15¾ in. o.c.	18¾ in. o.c.	23½ in. o.c.	30 in. o.c.
19 ft	125	263	234	200	168	134	105
	126	284	253	217	182	145	114
	145	288	256	220	185	148	115
	146	326	290	249	209	166	131
	147	358	318	273	229	183	143
	166	337	300	257	216	172	135
	167	379	337	289	246	194	152
20 ft	102	105	93	80	67	54	42
	103	137	121	104	87	69	55
	104	167	148	127	106	85	67
	123	153	136	117	98	78	61
	124	192	170	146	123	98	77
	125	237	211	181	158	121	95
	126	270	240	206	173	138	108
	145	260	231	198	166	133	104
	146	310	276	236	199	158	124
	147	340	303	259	218	174	136
	166	320	285	244	205	163	128
	167	360	320	274	231	184	144
21 ft	123	139	123	106	89	71	56
	124	174	155	132	111	89	70
	125	215	191	164	138	109	86
	126	257	228	196	164	131	103
	145	236	209	180	151	120	94
	146	295	263	225	189	151	118
	147	324	287	247	208	165	129
	166	305	271	233	195	156	122
	167	343	305	361	220	175	137
22 ft	123	127	113	96	81	64	51
	124	158	141	121	101	81	63
	125	196	174	149	125	100	78
	126	241	215	184	154	123	97
	145	215	192	164	138	110	86
	146	282	251	215	180	144	111
	147	309	275	236	198	157	123
	166	291	259	222	186	149	116
	167	327	291	249	209	167	131
23 ft	123	116	103	88	74	59	46
	124	145	129	111	93	74	58
	125	179	159	135	114	92	72
	126	221	196	168	141	112	88
	145	197	175	149	126	100	79
	146	258	229	197	165	132	103

Span	Joist	12 in. o.c.	13½ in. o.c.	15¾ in. o.c.	18¾ in. o.c.	23½ in. o.c.	30 in. o.c.
23 ft	147	296	263	226	189	151	118
	166	278	247	212	178	141	111
	167	313	278	239	201	160	125
24 ft	123	106	94	81	68	54	42
	124	133	118	101	85	68	53
	125	164	146	126	105	84	66
	126	202	180	154	130	103	81
	145	180	161	137	115	92	72
	146	237	211	181	152	121	95
	147	283	251	215	181	143	113
	166	267	237	203	170	136	107
	167	300	267	229	192	153	120
25 ft	145	166	147	127	106	85	66
	146	218	194	166	139	111	87
	147	262	233	200	168	134	105
	166	247	220	189	158	126	99
	167	288	256	219	184	147	115
26 ft	145	154	137	117	98	78	61
	146	202	180	154	130	102	81
	147	243	216	185	155	124	97
	166	229	203	175	147	117	92
	167	277	246	211	177	142	111
27 ft	145	143	127	109	91	73	57
	146	187	166	142	120	96	75
	147	225	200	172	144	114	90
	166	212	189	162	136	108	85
	167	257	228	196	164	131	103
28 ft	145	133	118	101	85	67	53
	146	174	155	133	111	89	70
	147	209	186	159	139	107	84
	166	197	175	150	126	101	79
	167	239	213	182	153	122	96
29 ft	166	184	164	140	118	94	74
	167	223	198	170	143	113	84
30 ft	166	172	153	131	110	88	64
	167	208	185	159	133	166	83
31 ft	166	161	143	123	103	82	64
	167	195	173	148	125	100	78
32 ft	166	151	135	115	102	77	60
	167	183	163	139	124	94	73

will come between joists more often than over joists, and there will almost surely be trouble when concrete is being poured. Assuming an 8-ft-long sheet of lath, with about 2- to 2½-in. lap, the following spaces will work out satisfactorily: 13½, 15¾, 18¾, and 23½ in. It is always well to double joists under partitions parallel with the joists, and to allow for the added effect of cross partitions within the middle third of a joist. Although the salesmen for metal deck frequently advocate the spacing of bar joists up to 4 or 4½ ft, based

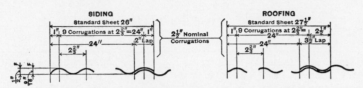

Fig. 4.37   Standard Corrugated Steel Sheets

on the safe spans for their material, this is not good practice, and the spacing should not be extended beyond $18\frac{3}{4}$ in. for floors, $23\frac{1}{2}$ in. for poured roofs, and 30 in. for metal-deck roofs. This limitation of 30 in. is the practical limitation on the efficiency of bridging between joists, and should never be exceeded for standard joists, that is, joists not over 16 in. in depth.

Several of the joist companies manufacture a long-span open-web joist for depths and spans much greater than those listed by the Steel Joist Institute. The depths range from 18 to 32 in., and spans from 25 to 64 ft. While these joists serve a satisfactory purpose, greater economy can be obtained by using rolled-steel beams spaced farther apart, and filling in with regular bar joists at right angles.

4.40 CORRUGATED SIDING AND ROOFING

a   Because of certain properties of strength obtained through corrugating the sheets, corrugated siding and roofing is a popular low-priced covering used primarily for industrial buildings. The commonest material used is

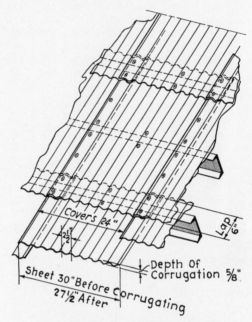

Fig. 4.38   Corrugated Steel Roofing

corrugated steel, either black, galvanized, or coated with asphalt and asbestos, but corrugated aluminum and asbestos-cement are also used. If the roof pitch is held to a minimum of 1 on $2\frac{1}{2}$, or 1 on 3 if the edges are

Table 4.21   Corrugated-Sheet-Steel Construction

Gage, U.S. standard	Thickness, in.	Weight, flat sheets, psf		Max. span between supports	
		Galvanized	Black	Roofing	Siding
12	.107	4.53	4.38	5'9''	5'10''
14	.077	3.28	3.13	5'9''	5'10''
16	.061	2.66	2.50	5'9''	5'10''
18	.049	2.16	2.00	5'9''	5'10''
20	.037	1.66	1.50	5'9''	5'10''
21	.034	1.53	1.38	5'9''	5'10''
22	.031	1.41	1.25	4'9''	5'10''
23	.028	1.28	1.13	4'9''	5'10''
24	.025	1.16	1.00	3'9''	4'10''
25	.021	1.03	.88	3'9''	4'10''
26	.018	.91	.75	2'9''	3'10''
28	.015	.78	.63	2'9''	3'10''

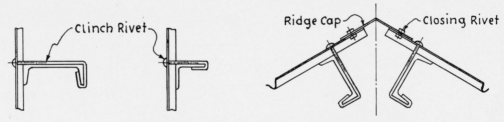

Fig. 4.39   Standard Connection by Clinch Rivets

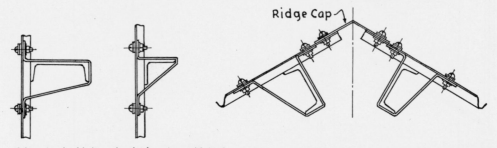

¼-in. galvanized bolts, galvanized washers with lead or asphalt-saturated felt washers underneath 18-ga galvanized metal straps, 1 in. wide

Fig. 4.40   Standard Connection by Straps and Bolts

cemented, no applied roofing is required over the corrugated material. The corrugations in aluminum and asbestos-cement have not yet been standardized, but Figs. 4.37 and 4.38 and Table 4.21 give the standards adopted for corrugated steel sheets.

Standard sheets are of all single-foot lengths from 4 to 12 ft. The minimum end lap for roofing with a pitch of less than 1 on 3 is 8 in., and for roofing with a pitch of over 1 on 3 it is 6 in. The minimum end lap for siding is 4 in.

b Because failure of corrugated roofing is usually caused by deflection, or sometimes—regardless of how carefully it may be maintained—by rusting around the bolt or rivet connections, the allowable fiber stress is usually limited to 12,000 psf. A standard roofing sheet 27½ in. wide covering 24 in. clear, as shown in Fig. 4.37, allows a length of span in inches (for standard sheets with a total load of 35 lb) of

$$l = 274\sqrt{t}$$

The maximum span for this loading would be

For 12 gage, 89.5 in.—7 ft 5½ in.
For 14 gage, 76.2 in.—6 ft 4 in.
For 16 gage, 67.5 in.—5 ft 7½ in.

For 18 gage, 60.5 in.—5 ft ½ in.
For 20 gage, 52.5 in.—4 ft 4½ in.
For 22 gage, 48.2 in.—4 ft 0 in.

In climates where snow load need not be considered but only uplift due to wind pressure, the formula may be reduced to

$$l = 363\sqrt{t}$$

and the maximum spans would be

For 16 gage, 89.5 in.—7 ft 5½ in.
For 18 gage, 80 in.   —6 ft 8 in.
For 20 gage, 69.6 in.—5 ft 9½ in.
For 22 gage, 64   in.—5 ft 0 in.

It is inadvisable to use less than 22-gage sheets for roofing. For siding, with a 15-psf wind load, the spacing of girts may be

$$l = 420\sqrt{t}$$

and the maximum spans would be

For 20 gage, 80.5 in.—6 ft 8½ in.
For 22 gage, 74 in.   —6 ft 2 in.
For 24 gage, 66.4 in.—5 ft 6 in.

c Details for the fastening of corrugated steel are standardized also. The method of fastening to girts and purlins shown in Fig. 4.39 may be used, although where the struc-

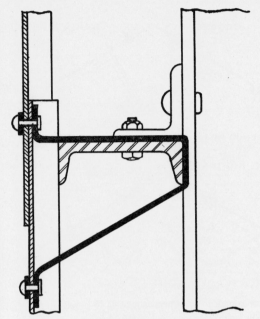

Fig. 4.41　Strap Fastening to Girts

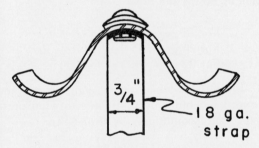

Fig. 4.42　Strap Fastener for Roofing

Fig. 4.43　Fastening of Corrugated Steel
to Wood Portion

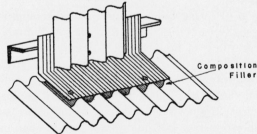

Fig. 4.44　Ridge Roll

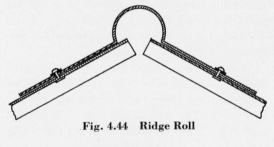

Fig. 4.45　Flashing from Monitor Siding
to Roofing

ture is subject to high winds, the details shown in Figs. 4.40 and 4.41 are preferable. Other details are shown in Art. 10.41, Girts.

4.50 METAL DECK, SUBWAY GRATING

a　Metal deck is a type of formed sheet steel manufactured by a number of companies for use as a flat roof deck (see Fig. 4.46). It is used in conjunction with tar and gravel or other standard membrane-type roofing, and sometimes carries a layer of insulation on which the roofing is laid. It may be attached to the steel beams by means of strap anchors or clips, or it may be tack welded to the beams. If this latter method is used, the specifications should require that all welds shall be field painted, since the heat of the weld burns off the asphaltic paint with which the deck is usually covered, and unless it is retouched, the deck will rust out at this point. It is probably inadvisable to use a metal deck

Table 4.22   Standard Subway Gratings

U = Safe uniform load, psf
C = Safe concentrated load, lb per ft of width
D = Deflection, in., based on fiber stress of 16,000 psi

Loads to right of heavy lines cause excessive deflection.

Bearing bar, in. (all types)	Reticulated Crimp bar, in.	Reticulated Weight, psf	Rectangular Cross bar, in.	Rectangular Weight, psf	Load and deflection	Span, ft 2	2½	3	3½	4	4½	5	5½	6
¾ × ⅛	¾ × ⅛	6.5	⅝ × ⅛	4.2	U	330	222	143						
					D	.085	.134	.192						
					C	330	265	215						
					D	.068	.108	.154						
¾ × 3/16	¾ × ⅛	8.0	⅝ × ⅛	5.9	U	500	320	217						
					D	.085	.134	.192						
					C	500	400	325						
					D	.068	.108	.154						
1 × ⅛	¾ × ⅛	7.5	¾ × ⅛	5.5	U	600	384	267	188	150				
					D	.064	.099	.143	.195	.256				
					C	600	480	400	330	300				
					D	.051	.080	.115	.156	.205				
1¼ × ⅛	¾ × ⅛	8.5	¾ × ⅛	6.9	U	950	600	420	303	232	184	146	120	
					D	.051	.081	.115	.157	.205	.259	.321	.389	
					C	950	750	630	530	465	415	365	330	
					D	.041	.064	.092	.125	.163	.207	.256	.310	
1¼ × 3/16	¾ × ⅛	10.5	¾ × ⅛	9.4	U	1,425	900	633	457	350	278	220	182	
					D	.051	.081	.115	.157	.205	.259	.321	.389	
					C	1,425	1,125	950	800	700	625	550	500	
					D	.041	.064	.092	.125	.163	.207	.256	.310	
1½ × ⅛	¾ × ⅛	9.5	1 × ⅛	8.1	U	1,365	880	610	445	340	266	220	182	150
					D	.043	.067	.094	.131	.166	.216	.267	.324	.385
					C	1,365	1,100	915	785	680	600	550	500	450
					D	.034	.053	.077	.104	.137	.173	.214	.259	.308
1½ × 3/16	¾ × ⅛	12.0	1 × ⅛	11.6	U	2,050	1,320	917	672	512	400	330	272	225
					D	.043	.067	.094	.131	.166	.216	.267	.324	.385
					C	2,050	1,650	1,375	1,175	1,025	900	825	750	675
					D	.034	.053	.077	104	.137	.173	.214	.259	.308
1¾ × 3/16	¾ × ⅛	13.5	1 × ⅛	13.3	U	2,800	1,780	1,230	915	700	544	440	364	308
					D	.038	.057	.082	.112	.147	.185	.229	.276	.330
					C	2,800	2,225	1,860	1,600	1,400	1,225	1,100	1,000	925
					D	.029	.046	.066	.090	.117	.148	.183	.221	.264
2 × 3/16	1 × ⅛	16.0	1 × ⅛	15.1	U	3,650	2,340	1,618	1,200	912	723	580	482	400
					D	.032	.050	.072	.099	.128	.163	.201	.243	.289
					C	3,650	2,925	2,425	2,100	1,825	1,625	1,450	1,325	1,200
					D	.026	.040	.057	.078	.102	.129	.160	.193	.230
2¼ × 3/16	1 × ⅛	17.5	1 × ⅛	16.8	U	4,650	2,960	2,065	1,515	1,150	912	.740	608	516
					D	.027	.044	.064	.087	.113	.148	.177	.214	.255
					C	4.650	3,700	3,100	2,650	2,300	2,050	1,850	1,675	1,550
					D	.023	.035	.051	.070	.091	.115	.142	.172	.204

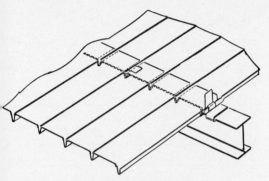

Fig. 4.46   Metal Deck

of less than 20 gage regardless of what the strength tables of the manufacturer may indicate. Moreover, because of the springiness and the consequent psychological effect, it is not advisable to go to the full span permitted by the manufacturer's tables. These metal decks have not been standardized, so no tables of strength are included here. Each manufacturer has his own tables from which the design may be selected.

b Subway grating is a type of flooring material used for factory mezzanine floors and platforms. Because of its open construction, it is frowned upon by state labor departments except for the above-named uses. Moreover, it is too costly to compete with standard reinforced-concrete slabs except for such special uses.

Subway grating is made in two general types —rectangular, and reticulated or crimped, as shown in plan in Fig. 4.47. The safe loads for standard types manufactured by the different manufacturers in accordance with the U.S. Government Federal Specification of Jan. 30, 1936, are listed in Table 4.22.

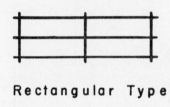

Rectangular Type

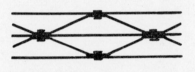

Reticulated Type

Fig. 4.47   Subway Grating

5

Reinforced Concrete in Bending

5.10 REINFORCED CONCRETE

a Steel can be used to resist a given tensile stress much more economically than an equal compressive stress. A bar of any shape will offer equal resistance, per square inch, to tension, whereas for compression the steel must be made into special shapes to provide sufficient lateral rigidity. Even then, the strength in compression is less than the strength in tension. Concrete, on the other hand, can only be used in tension to a very limited extent, but its compressive strength is comparatively high. In strength per dollar, the two materials are working advantageously when compression is taken by concrete and tension by steel, as is done in reinforced-concrete beams. In compression members of appreciable length, such as columns, a combination of the two materials is also quite advantageous. The two materials bond satisfactorily, so that they work in unison—that is, their coefficient of thermal expansion is almost identical.

b It is well for the designer to know the economical limits of reinforced-concrete construction. It is naturally a heavier-dead-load material than structural steel and is much more economical when the live loads are heavy as in warehouses. For light floor loads the advantage is with structural steel. For high buildings the area of concrete columns in the lower stories becomes so great that they occupy too much rentable area to be economical.

This limitation sometimes governs the choice of design even though live loads are heavy. To cut down the size of concrete columns in high buildings, it is common to put in a structural-steel core for the lower stories, but this practice is not economical.

Another objection sometimes offered to the use of reinforced concrete for factory buildings is that it is not so easy to make alterations or hang such equipment as trolley beams —in short, that the material is not so adaptable as steel. On the other hand, reinforced concrete is fireproof, while a steel skeleton must be encased to achieve the same result.

c The strength of reinforced concrete was formerly rated on the basis of the mix, as 1:2:4 or $1:1\frac{1}{2}:3$ or 1:1:2, indicating proportions respectively of cement, sand, and coarse aggregate (gravel or crushed stone). In 1918, however, the water-cement ratio law was put forth as the basis of determination of strength of concrete mixtures. The fundamental law may be stated as follows: For plastic mixtures, using sound and clean aggregates, the strength and other desirable properties of concrete under given job conditions are governed by the net quantity of mixing water used per sack of cement.

The water-cement ratio law was first established with respect to compressive strength. Subsequent studies, however, have shown that it applies equally well to flexural and tensile strength, to the resistance of concrete to wear, and to the bond between concrete and steel.

Still more recently, investigations have established that the properties of watertightness and resistance to weathering are controlled in the same way by the proportion of water to cement.

This principle may be more readily understood if the cement and water are thought of as forming a paste, which, on hardening, binds the aggregate particles together. The strength of this paste is determined by the proportions of cement and water. Increasing the water content dilutes the paste and reduces the strength. Similarly, the watertightness of the concrete is determined by the watertightness of the paste—a thin, watery paste, on hardening, will not form the dense, impermeable binding medium essential to watertight concrete.

It should be noted that in the statement of the water-cement ratio law above, its application is limited to plastic mixtures and to given job conditions.

As a result of the change in thinking brought about by the discovery and use of the water-cement ratio law, the old method of designating strength of concrete on the basis of mix has given place to stating allowable stresses as a proportion of the 28-day compression-test strength. Tables commonly recognize 2,000-, 2,500-, and 3,000-psi strength, and some codes recognize 3,750-psi concrete.

Since the cost of 3,000-psi concrete, particularly since the advent of transit-mixed concrete, is so little more than that of 2,000-psi concrete, it has become the practice of many engineers to base their designs on 3,000-psi concrete, and to specify accordingly. This is not only because of the greater strength for a given dead load but also because of the greater durability of the resultant structure. In this book, therefore, where tables are dependent on the strength of concrete, they are based on 3,000-psi concrete unless otherwise noted.

d There are available in some textbooks and handbooks series of tables of load capacities of beams and slabs for simple, semicontinuous, and continuous spans. These tables should be used cautiously, because there are so many varying factors in reinforced-concrete

design that members must be designed rather than selected as they are in structural-steel design. As many tables as it is advisable to use in general work are included here.

5.11 Reinforced-concrete design

a The tables and formulae given here are to be used for all reinforced-concrete design, whether beams, slabs, footings, retaining walls, or other structures. Other special formulae and tables are given in specific articles pertaining to special aspects of design, such as T beams, doubly reinforced beams, and so on.

b Formulae for rectangular-beam and slab design

$$k = \sqrt{2pn + (pn)^2} - pn = \cfrac{1}{1 + \cfrac{f_s}{nf_c}}$$

$$j = 1 - \frac{k}{3}$$

$$p = \frac{A_s}{bd} = \cfrac{\frac{1}{2}}{\cfrac{f_s}{f_c}\left(\cfrac{f_s}{nf_c} + 1\right)} = \frac{f_c k}{2f_s}$$

$$R = \tfrac{1}{2}f_c kj \quad \text{or} \quad pf_s j$$

$$M = \tfrac{1}{2}f_c kjbd^2 = Rbd^2 \quad \text{or} \quad bd^2 = \frac{2M}{f_c kj} = \frac{M}{R}$$

$$M = pf_s jbd^2 \quad \text{or} \quad bd^2 = \frac{M}{pf_s j}$$

$$A_s = \frac{M}{f_s jd} \quad \text{or} \quad f_s = \frac{M}{A_s jd}$$

$$f_c = \frac{2f_s p}{k} \quad \text{or} \quad \frac{f_s k}{n(1 - k)} \quad \text{or} \quad \frac{2M}{kjbd^2}$$

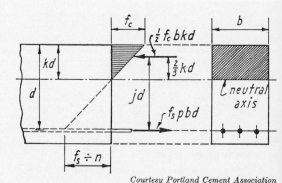

Courtesy Portland Cement Association

Fig. 5.1 Formulae for Rectangular Beam and Slab Design

Table 5.1   Reinforced Rectangular Concrete-Beam Constants

n	f_c'	f_c	$f_s = 16,000$ psi				$f_s = 18,000$ psi				$f_s = 20,000$ psi			
			R	k	j	p	R	k	j	p	R	k	j	p
15	2,000	650	108	.379	.874	.0077	101	.351	.883	.0063	95	.328	.891	.0053
		750	133	.413	.862	.0097	126	.385	.872	.0080	119	.360	.880	.0068
		800	147	.429	.857	.0107	137	.400	.867	.0089	131	.375	.875	.0075
		900	175	.458	.847	.0129	165	.429	.857	.0107	157	.403	.866	.0091
12	2,500	800	131	.375	.875	.0094	123	.348	.884	.0077	116	.324	.892	.0065
		950	170	.416	.861	.0124	161	.388	.871	.0102	152	.363	.879	.0086
		1,000	184	.429	.857	.0134	173	.400	.867	.0111	164	.375	.875	.0094
		1,125	218	.458	.847	.0161	207	.429	.857	.0134	196	.403	.866	.0113
10	3,000	975	161	.379	.874	.0115	151	.351	.883	.0095	142	.328	.891	.0080
		1,125	200	.413	.862	.0145	189	.385	.872	.0120	178	.360	.880	.0101
		1,200	221	.429	.857	.0161	208	.400	.867	.0133	197	.375	.875	.0113
		1,350	262	.458	.847	.0193	248	.429	.857	.0161	236	.403	.866	.0136

Table 5.2   Sectional Area of Various Numbers of Bars
Square inches

Bar no.	3	4	5	6	7	8	9	10	11
Size, in.	$\frac{3}{8}\phi$	$\frac{1}{2}\phi$	$\frac{5}{8}\phi$	$\frac{3}{4}\phi$	$\frac{7}{8}\phi$	1ϕ	$1\square$	$1\frac{1}{8}\square$	$1\frac{1}{4}\square$
Weight per ft, lb	0.376	0.668	1.043	1.502	2.044	2.670	3.400	4.303	5.313
Perimeter, in.	1.18	1.57	1.96	2.36	2.75	3.14	3.54	3.99	4.43
1 bar	0.11	0.20	0.31	0.44	0.60	0.79	1.00	1.27	1.56
2 bars	0.22	0.40	0.62	0.88	1.20	1.58	2.00	2.54	3.12
3 bars	0.33	0.60	0.93	1.32	1.80	2.37	3.00	3.81	4.68
4 bars	0.44	0.80	1.24	1.76	2.40	3.16	4.00	5.08	6.24
5 bars	0.55	1.00	1.55	2.20	3.00	3.95	5.00	6.35	7.80
6 bars	0.66	1.20	1.86	2.64	3.60	4.74	6.00	7.62	9.36
7 bars	0.77	1.40	2.17	3.08	4.20	5.53	7.00	8.89	10.92
8 bars	0.88	1.60	2.48	3.52	4.80	6.32	8.00	10.16	12.48
9 bars	0.99	1.80	2.79	3.96	5.40	7.11	9.00	11.43	14.04
10 bars	1.10	2.00	3.10	4.40	6.00	7.90	10.00	12.70	15.60
11 bars	1.21	2.20	3.41	4.84	6.60	8.69	11.00	13.97	17.16
12 bars	1.32	2.40	3.72	5.28	7.20	9.48	12.00	15.24	18.72
13 bars	1.43	2.60	4.03	5.72	7.80	10.27	13.00	16.51	20.28
14 bars	1.54	2.80	4.34	6.16	8.40	11.06	14.00	17.78	21.84
15 bars	1.65	3.00	4.65	6.60	9.00	11.85	15.00	19.05	23.40

5.12   Plain concrete

a   The ACI Code does not recognize plain unreinforced concrete as a material to resist bending, except in footings, where these stresses may be used:

Extreme fiber stress in compression, $0.45f_c'$
Extreme fiber stress in tension, $0.03f_c'$

As bending stress is applied to any member of a material with a variation in ability to resist compression and tension as is indicated by the above allowable fiber stresses, the neutral axis changes position before failure occurs, until the area of the triangle of compressive stress is equal to the triangle of tensile stress. This is known as the theory of limit design. Without going into the derivation of the formula, it may be stated that from the

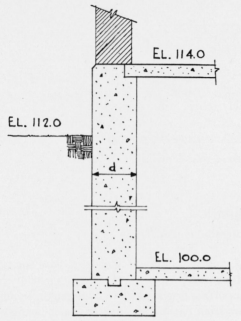

Fig. 5.2   **Plain Concrete Basement Retaining Wall**

above combination of allowable stresses, an equivalent modulus of rupture may be obtained, $f = 0.105f_c'$, by means of which a required section modulus may be found,

$$S = \frac{M}{f}$$

For a 3,000-lb concrete, $f = 315$ psi.

Further design criteria established by the ACI Code may be found in Sec. 1207 of the Code, Pedestals and Footings (Plain Concrete), as follows:

The allowable compressive unit stress on the gross area of a concentrically loaded pedestal shall not exceed $0.25f_c'$. Where this stress is exceeded, reinforcement shall be provided and the member designed as a reinforced concrete column.

The width and depth of a pedestal or footing of plain concrete shall be such that the tension in the concrete shall not exceed $.03f_c'$ and the average shearing stress shall not exceed $.02f_c'$ taken on sections as prescribed in Sec. 1204 and 1205 for reinforced concrete footings.

The two sections referred to are quoted in Table 8.3 for the design of reinforced-concrete foundations.

b Although it is not advisable to consider the use of unreinforced concrete for ordinary beam and slab design, there are certain parts of buildings or structures which may be of plain concrete, designed to resist bending; for example, the various parts of a retaining wall (as described in Art. 8.30), the offsets of a footing (as in Art. 8.11), and basement retaining walls (as in Art. 8.31). A problem in this third category will serve as an example of the use of these rules of design.

Problem Assume the basement retaining wall shown in Fig. 5.2. The resultant beam diagram is shown in Fig. 5.3. From similar triangles, the distance x may be determined from the equation

$$15x_1^2 = 617$$
$$x_1 = 6.41$$
$$x = 8.41$$
$$M = 617 \times 8.41$$
$$\underline{- 617 \times 2.14}$$
$$617 \times 6.27 = 3,870 \text{ ft-lb}$$
$$= 46,430 \text{ in.-lb}$$

Therefore, assuming a 3,000-psi concrete,

$$\text{Required } S = \frac{46,430}{315} = 147.4 = \frac{bd^2}{6}$$

or since $b = 12$ in., $S = 2d^2$.

$$d = \sqrt{\frac{147.4}{2}} = \sqrt{73.7} = 8.6 \text{ in.}$$

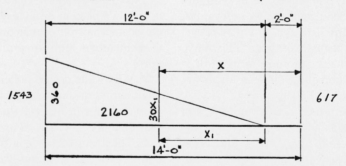

Fig. 5.3   **Beam Load Diagram—Basement Retaining Wall**

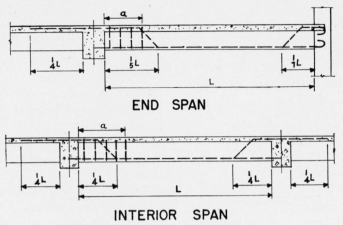

END SPAN

INTERIOR SPAN

Fig. 5.4   Typical Beam Reinforcement

For practical design, however, the minimum plain concrete wall thickness for the condition shown is 1 ft 1 in.

5.20   REINFORCED–CONCRETE BEAM DESIGN

a Reinforced-concrete beam design involves more computations than the design of steel beams. Because of the monolithic nature of concrete construction, beams are designed for continuity, and the moment at the end of the beam is reversed from the moment at the center of the beam.

In the design of a reinforced-concrete beam the following steps are necessary:

1. Compute bending moments and shears in accordance with the methods of Art. 3.10 for simple beams, or Art. 3.20 or 3.21 for continuous beams.

2. Determine the concrete-beam size by the method of Art. 5.20*b* or 5.21. (Frequently it is advisable for the economy of form reuse or for architectural requirements to determine one of several beam sizes for an entire area, and make all the beams this size. This may waste concrete but save more in form work.)

3. Check the assumed size of beam for shear by the method of Art. 5.30.

4. Compute the steel area required by means of Art. 5.20*b* and select the bars to furnish this steel, both for positive and negative moment. Positive moment through the center of the beam is provided for by furnishing sufficient straight and bent bars for the total positive area. Negative moment at the supports is provided for by bending up enough bars from each of the two adjacent beams so that the sum of bar areas at this point is sufficient for the negative area (see Fig. 5.4).

5. Compute the stirrups required, if any, and determine spacing by the method of Art. 5.30.

The recognized authoritative codes on reinforced-concrete design are the 1951 Code of the American Concrete Institute, and the 1941 Joint Committee Code. The allowable stresses and essential formulae of these codes are given in Arts. 1.22 and 5.11. The following restrictions from these two codes should be observed in all cases:

1. Wherever positive moment in a beam is indicated by the design, not less than $\frac{1}{2}$ percent or $0.005bd$ of the rectangular beam shall be used.

2. Negative reinforcement (top steel) not less than $\frac{1}{2}$ percent or $0.005bd$ of the rectangular beam shall be provided at the outer end of all members built integrally with their supports.

3. Where the design indicates negative moment across the entire span, the reinforcement need not be run beyond the point where the required steel is $0.0025bd$ or less.

4. The unsupported length of beam between lateral supports shall not exceed 32 times the compression flange.

Table 5.3   Minimum Beam Widths, in. (ACI Code)

Bar no.	Number of bars in single layer					Add for each added bar
	2	3	4	5	6	
4	$5\frac{3}{4}$	$7\frac{1}{4}$	$8\frac{3}{4}$	$10\frac{1}{4}$	$11\frac{3}{4}$	$1\frac{1}{2}$
5	6	$7\frac{3}{4}$	$9\frac{1}{4}$	11	$12\frac{1}{2}$	$1\frac{5}{8}$
6	$6\frac{1}{4}$	8	$9\frac{3}{4}$	$11\frac{1}{2}$	$13\frac{1}{4}$	$1\frac{3}{4}$
7	$6\frac{1}{2}$	$8\frac{1}{2}$	$10\frac{1}{4}$	$12\frac{1}{4}$	14	$1\frac{7}{8}$
8	$6\frac{3}{4}$	$8\frac{3}{4}$	$10\frac{3}{4}$	$12\frac{3}{4}$	$14\frac{3}{4}$	2
9	$7\frac{1}{4}$	$9\frac{1}{2}$	$11\frac{3}{4}$	14	$16\frac{1}{4}$	$2\frac{1}{4}$
10	$7\frac{3}{4}$	$10\frac{1}{4}$	$12\frac{3}{4}$	$15\frac{1}{4}$	$17\frac{3}{4}$	$2\frac{5}{8}$
11	8	11	$13\frac{3}{4}$	$16\frac{1}{2}$	$19\frac{1}{2}$	$2\frac{7}{8}$

5. The minimum clear distance between bars shall be the nominal bar diameter, but not less than 1 in. The side clearance for bars in beams, girders, and columns must be $1\frac{1}{2}$ in.; and for bars of over $\frac{5}{8}$-in. diameter in members exposed to the weather, not less than 2 in. The width thus determined may be the governing factor in determining the required beam width (see Table 5.3).

Table 5.3 shows minimum beam width when stirrups are used. If no stirrups are required, deduct $\frac{3}{4}$ in. from the figures shown.

b Since reinforced concrete is not a homogeneous material, the location of the neutral axis will vary, depending on the compression stress in the concrete and the tensile stress in the steel. The location of the neutral axis may be found from either of the following formulae

$$k = \sqrt{2pn + (pn)^2} - pn \qquad (5.1)$$

$$k = \frac{n}{m + n} \qquad (5.2)$$

The effective depth between centroids of compression and tension *jd* is easily found after *k* has been found.

$$j = 1 - \frac{k}{3} \qquad (5.3)$$

With reference to Art. 3.10, it will be seen that the external moment M is resisted by an internal moment couple of force P times the lever arm *jd*. This force in tension may be replaced by the product of a steel stress and a steel area, $f_s A_s$, and the resisting moment in tension is

$$M_s = f_s A_s j d \qquad (5.4)$$

The force P in compression may be replaced by the area of the triangle $\frac{1}{2} f_c k d$ multiplied by width b, or

$$M = \frac{1}{2} f_c k j b d^2 \qquad (5.5)$$

Since for any given combination of steel and concrete stresses, $\frac{1}{2} f_c k j$ is replaced by a constant R, Formula (5.5) becomes

$$M_c = R b d^2 \qquad (5.6)$$

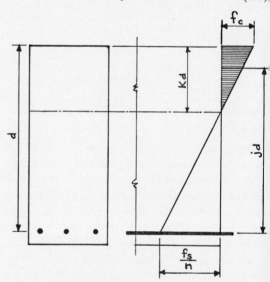

Fig. 5.5 Graphical Indication of Stresses—Concrete Beam

The majority of concrete-beam problems can be solved by the use of Formulae (5.4) and (5.6) above. For practical design purposes, j may be taken as 0.875. Constants for the various combinations of steel and concrete stresses ordinarily encountered in various codes are listed in Table 5.1. The constants given in this table are based on "balanced reinforcement"—that is, both steel and concrete are working to their maximum allowable working capacity. Within the limits of these constants, any change in steel or concrete will be only toward the side of safety and, therefore, design according to the methods here stated is sufficiently accurate.

Problem Design for moment only a rectangular concrete beam for a simple span of 20 ft to carry a uniform load of 1,200 lb per ft, using a 3,000-psi concrete and 1951 ACI stresses ($f_c = 1,350$, $f_c = 20,000$).

$$W = 20 \times 1,200 = 24,000 \text{ lb}$$

$$M = \frac{24,000 \times 20 \times 12}{8} = 720,000 \text{ in.-lb}$$

$$M_c = 720,000 = Rbd^2$$

From Table 5.1 $R = 236$.

$$bd^2 = \frac{720,000}{236} = 3,050$$

Use 12 × 16-in. net.

$$M_s = 720,000 = f_s A_s j d$$

From Table 5.1 $f_s j = 17,320$.

$$A_s = \frac{720,000}{17,320 \times 16} = 2.6 \text{ sq in.}$$

Use two No. 9 straight and one No. 7 bent, $A_s = 2.6$ sq in.

The computed depth d is from the top of the beam to the center line of the steel. Ordinary code requirement for cover of steel reinforcement in beams and girders is $1\frac{1}{2}$ in. The gross depth of the beam, therefore, is 16 in. (computed above) $+ \frac{1}{2}$ in. (half the depth of the bars) $+ 1\frac{1}{2}$-in. cover = 18 in. total depth.

c Occasionally it is necessary to solve a problem using special materials or stresses for which the constants given in Table 5.2 will not work. For example, suppose it is required to design a beam using a specially prepared aggregate with the characteristics $f_c' = 3,500$ and $E_c = 2,800,000$, and with standard steel stresses $f_s = 20,000$ and $E_s = 30,000,000$. Using $f_c = 0.45 f_c' = 1,575$,

$$m = \frac{20,000}{1,575} = 12.7 \quad \text{and} \quad n = \frac{30}{2.8} = 10.7$$

From Formula (5.2)

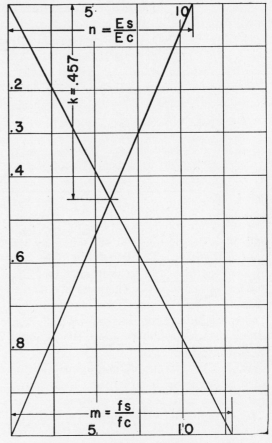

Fig. 5.6   Graphical Computation of k

$$k = \frac{n}{m + n} = \frac{10.7}{12.7 + 10.7} = \frac{10.7}{23.4} = 0.458$$

$$j = 1 - 0.153 = 0.847$$

The same result is obtained graphically in Fig. 5.6.

$$R = \tfrac{1}{2} f_c k j = \tfrac{1}{2} \times 1,575 \times 0.457 \times 0.847 = 305.2$$

Then for the problem given in 5, paragraph *b*,

$$bd^2 = \frac{720,000}{305.2} = 2,359$$

Assume 12 in. width; then

$$d = \sqrt{\frac{2,359}{12}} = \sqrt{192} = 14$$

Use 12 × 14-in. net.

$$A_s = \frac{720,000}{20,000 \times 0.847 \times 14} = 3.04$$

Use two No. 8 bent and two No. 8 straight. For $A_s = 3.16$, total depth = 14 in. (computed)

$+ \frac{1}{2}$ in. (half bar thickness) $+ 1\frac{1}{2}$-in. cover $=$ 16 in. Therefore the beam is 12×16 in.

A simple method of obtaining k graphically, based on Formula (5.2), is shown in Fig. 5.6. The use of the diagram is self-explanatory.

d Another form of problem is the determination of actual stresses in steel and concrete in a given beam under given load conditions.

Assume a 720,000-in.-lb moment in a 12×23-in. beam, 3,000-psi concrete, 1951 ACI Code, three 1-in. square bars. The net depth of beam is 21 in. and the steel percentage

$$p = \frac{3}{12 \times 21} = 0.012, \quad n = 10, \quad pn = 0.12$$

From Formula (5.1)

$$k = \sqrt{0.24 + 0.0144 - 0.12} = \sqrt{0.2544} - 0.12$$
$$= 0.504 - 0.12 = 0.384$$
$$j = 1 - 0.128 = 0.872$$

From Formula (5.4)

$$f_s = \frac{720,000}{3 \times 0.872 \times 21} = 13,100 \text{ psi}$$

From Formula (5.5)

$$f_c = \frac{720,000}{0.5 \times 0.384 \times 0.872 \times 12 \times 441} = 813 \text{ psi}$$

e Before any steel bar can develop its tensile strength it must develop sufficient bond strength to the concrete to equal the tensile value. Otherwise, the tensile value of that bar must be reduced in proportion to the reduced bond value. Ordinarily bond plays very little part in the design of any beam since sufficient anchorage is usually provided.

If it is required to compute the bond stress in any bar, the following formula may be used:

$$u = \frac{8V}{7\Sigma od}$$

The ACI Code specifies a bond stress for deformed bars of $0.07f_c'$ for top bars, $0.08f_c'$ for two-way footings, and $0.10f_c'$ for others. The critical point for negative steel is taken at the support, for positive steel at the point of inflection.

Let us check the unit bond stress in a continuous beam with a total uniform load of 24,000 lb, a net depth of 16 in., and with

two No. 7 and one No. 9 bars, assuming the point of inflection $\frac{1}{5}$ of the span from the support.

At this point $V = 0.3 \times 24,000 = 7,200$ lb. The perimeter of bars $= 5.5$ (two No. 7) $+ 3.54$ (one No. 9) $= 9.04$ in.

$$u = \frac{8 \times 7,200}{7 \times 9.04 \times 16} = 56.9 \text{ psi}$$

5.21 Concrete T beams

a Because floor slabs are ordinarily poured monolithic with the supporting beams, the more common condition is to treat the construction as a T-beam construction instead of rectangular beams. The only point of saving in the use of T-beam construction is in the fact that the compression may be developed in the combination of web and flange instead of the web alone. The constants change slightly but the amount of steel is the same as for rectangular beams, and the shear must be taken by the web only. Obviously, if the neutral axis comes within the flange, that is, if t/d is 0.375 or over, the beam is treated as a rectangular beam, but the width b used in computing the beam in compression may be the full flange width determined by the limitations of the ACI Code.

b The following sections quoted from the 1941 ACI Code may be taken as good practice in the design of T beams.

[From Sec. 705(*a*)] The effective flange width to be used in the design of symmetrical T beams shall not exceed one-fourth of the span length of the beam and its overhanging width on either side of the web shall not exceed 8 times the thickness of the slab nor one-half the clear distance to the next beam.

[From Sec. 705(*b*)] For beams having a flange on one side only, the effective overhanging flange width shall not exceed one-twelfth of the span length nor 6 times the thickness of the slab, nor one-half the clear distance to the next beam.

[From Sec. 705(*c*)] Where the principal reinforcement in a slab which is considered as the flange of a T-beam is parallel to the beam, transverse reinforcement shall be provided in the top of the slab, the spacing not to exceed 5 times the slab thickness nor more than 18 in.

[From Sec. 705(*d*)] Provision shall be made for the compressive stress at the support in continuous T-beam construction.

[From Sec. 705(e)]   This overhanging portion of the flanges shall not be considered in computing shear and diagonal tension.

[From Sec. 705(f)]   Isolated beams in which the T-form is used only to provide additional compression area, shall have a flange thickness not less than one-half the width of the web and a total flange width not more than 4 times the web thickness.

The following formulae may be used in the solution of T beams.

$$k = \frac{1}{1 + \frac{fs}{nf_c}} = \frac{pn + \frac{1}{2}\left(\frac{t}{d}\right)^2}{pn + \frac{t}{d}} \qquad (5.7)$$

$$kd = \frac{2ndA_s + bt^2}{2nA_s + 2bt}$$

$$d - jd = \frac{3kd - 2t}{2kd - t} \times \frac{t}{3}$$

$$j = \frac{6 - 6\left(\frac{t}{d}\right) + 2\left(\frac{t}{d}\right)^2 + \left(\frac{t}{d}\right)^3\left(\frac{1}{2pn}\right)}{6 - 3\left(\frac{t}{d}\right)}$$

$$= 1 - \frac{t}{d}\left(\frac{3k - 2t/d}{6k - 3t/d}\right) \qquad (5.8)$$

$$f_s = \frac{M}{A_s jd} = \frac{M}{pjbd^2}$$

$$f_c = \frac{f_s k}{n(1 - k)}$$

$$M_s = f_s A_s jd$$

$$M_c = f_c\left(1 - \frac{t}{2kd}\right)bt \times jd = Rbd^2 \qquad (5.9)$$

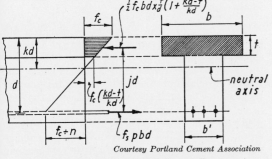

Courtesy Portland Cement Association

Fig. 5.7   Formulae for T-Beam Design

c   When the neutral axis lies in the web, the amount of compression in the web below the flange is commonly small compared with that in the flange and is neglected in the formulae.

The value of R of the formula may be selected from Table 5.4. Note that in using this

chart b is the flange width conforming with the limitations of Art. 5.21b.

Problem   Design for moment only a reinforced-concrete T beam for a moment of 1,600,000 in.-lb, using a beam with a total depth of 18 in. and an adjacent slab 4 in. thick, and assuming that all the limitations of Art. 5.21b will be met. Use 1951 ACI Code specifications for 3,000-psi concrete.

$$\frac{t}{d} = \frac{4}{16} = 0.25$$

From Table 5.4,

$$R = 207.5$$

$$b = \frac{1,600,000}{207.5 \times 256} = 30.1 \text{ in.}$$

$$A_s = \frac{1,600,000}{20,000 \times 0.886 \times 16} = 5.64 \text{ sq in.}$$

Use two No. 11 bars, $A = 3.16$, and two No. 10 bars, $A = 2.54$. A_s furnished $= 5.70$ sq in.

From Table 5.3 the minimum width of stem would be $13\frac{1}{2}$ in. Use 14-in. stem.

Table 5.4   Value of R for T Beams
(See Fig. 5.7)

t/d	$f_c' = 2,000,$ $f_c = 900$	$f_c' = 2,500,$ $f_c = 1,125$	$f_c' = 3,000,$ $f_c = 1,350$
0.06	49	61	73
0.08	62	78	94
0.10	75	94	113
0.12	87	108	130
0.14	97	122	146
0.16	107	134	160
0.18	116	145	173
0.20	123	154	185
0.24	136	170	204
0.28	145	181	218
0.32	152	190	228
0.36	156	195	234
0.40	157	196	236

Intermediate values may be interpolated.

5.22   Concrete beams reinforced for compression

a   Although it is more economical to use rectangular or T beams without compression reinforcement, sometimes isolated cases require that the beam be limited to a certain width and depth so that it is impracticable to get the b and d required. In such cases steel

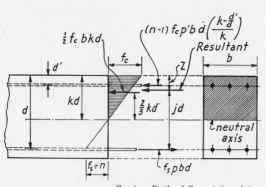

Courtesy Portland Cement Association

Fig. 5.8   Formulae for Double Reinforced Beams

reinforcement is used to obtain additional compressive value, but not over 2 percent of the area bd.

Accurate methods of computation for this problem are quite lengthy as may be noted from the formulae below, to be used in conjunction with Fig. 5.8. The ACI Code permits the compression reinforcement in a double reinforced beam to be taken at twice the tabular value, but not more than the allowable stress in tension.

$$k = \sqrt{2n\left(p + p'\frac{d'}{d}\right) + n^2\,(p + p')^2} \\ - n\,(p + p')$$

$$z = \frac{\frac{1}{3}k^3 d + 2p'nd'\left(k - \dfrac{d'}{d}\right)}{k^2 + 2p'n\left(k - \dfrac{d'}{d}\right)}$$

$$jd = d - z$$

$$f_c = \frac{6M}{bd^2\left[3k - k^2 + \dfrac{6p'n}{k}\left(k - \dfrac{d'}{d}\right)\left(1 - \dfrac{d'}{d}\right)\right]}$$

$$f_s = \frac{M}{pjbd^2} = nf_c\frac{1-k}{k} \qquad f'_s = nf_c\frac{k - \dfrac{d'}{d}}{k}$$

$$A_s = \frac{M}{f_s jd} \text{ or } pbd \qquad A_s' = p'bd$$

$$M = Kbd^2 \qquad\qquad d = \sqrt{\frac{M}{Kb}}$$

$$p = \frac{f_c}{f_s}\left[\frac{k}{2} + \frac{n-1}{k}\left(k - \frac{d'}{d}\right)p'\right]$$

$$K = f_c\left(\frac{k}{2} - \frac{k^2}{6} + \frac{n-1}{k}p'\left[(1-k)\left(k - \frac{d'}{d}\right) \\ + \left(k - \frac{d'}{d}\right)^2\right]\right)$$

b   Without going through these long formulae, the beam may be solved by the use of the curves in Fig. 5.9. The compression steel may be computed with sufficient accuracy from the formula

$$A_s' = \frac{M - Rbd^2}{2cd}$$

The value of c is selected from the proper curve.

Problem   Assume the same beam as in the preceding problem except that it must be a rectangular beam with no T. The rectangular beam is 14 in. wide, 18 in. total depth (16 in. net).

From these dimensions and from Fig. 5.9,

$$Rbd^2 = 236 \times 14 \times 256 = 845{,}800 \text{ in.-lb}$$
$$A_s' = \frac{1{,}600{,}000 - 845{,}800}{2 \times 7{,}400 \times 16} = 3.19 \text{ sq in.}$$

Use five No. 8.

$$p = \frac{3.19}{16 \times 14} = .0142 \text{ or } 1.42 \text{ percent}$$

c   The added compression area changes the effective depth of the beam jd, as will be noted from Fig. 5.8. This change is almost always on the safe side, however, and may be neglected. If it is necessary to compute this change, a sufficiently accurate result may be obtained from the formula

$$j_1 d = d - \frac{2 + \dfrac{kd}{3}}{2}$$

Based on this equation, the corrected area of tensile steel in the preceding problem may be found as follows:

$$j_1 d = 16 - \frac{2 + \dfrac{0.403 \times 16}{3}}{2} = 16 - \frac{4.15}{2} = 13.92$$

$$A_s = \frac{1{,}600{,}000}{20{,}000 \times 13.92} = 5.72 \text{ sq in.}$$

Use three No. 11 and one No. 10. $A_s = 5.96$ sq in.

5.30   SHEAR IN CONCRETE

a   Because reinforced concrete is nonhomogeneous and because the relations between vertical and horizontal shear are complicated,

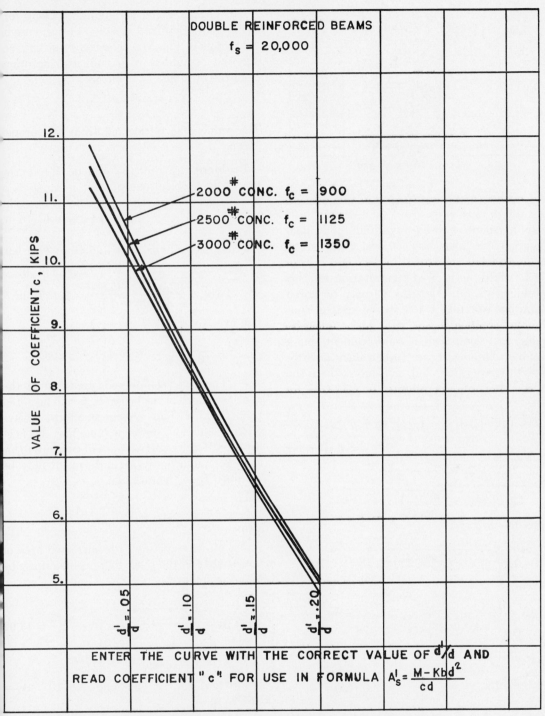

Fig. 5.9   Chart for Double Reinforced Beams

the ordinary conception of simple shear as considered in Art. 2.11 is not applicable to reinforced concrete. Instead, the subject is treated under the joint subject of shear and diagonal tension. Much of the design data, particularly with reference to diagonal tension and the use of stirrups, has been obtained from tests rather than pure theory.

The unit shearing stress in reinforced-concrete beams may be computed by the formula

$$v_c = \frac{V}{bjd}$$

With the value of $\frac{7}{8}$ for j, this formula for general use becomes,

$$v_c = \frac{8V}{7bd} = \frac{V}{0.875bd} \qquad (5.10)$$

The allowable stresses set up by the American Concrete Institute cover two conditions for beams (which are treated in this article), as well as one for flat slabs, and one for foundations, both of which are discussed in their respective articles. For beams with no web reinforcement (stirrups), $v_c = 0.03f_c'$. For beams with properly designed web reinforcement, $v_c = 0.12f_c'$.

The application of the above stresses in ordinary practice means that for a 3,000-psi concrete we use a fiber stress of 90 psi where no stirrups are used, and 360 psi through the length where stirrups are used.

b The ordinary method of checking for shear is to compute the unit shear in accordance with Formula (5.10). If this is over 90 psi for 3,000-psi concrete, design stirrups.

Problem To check the problem in Art. 5.20*b* for shear,

$$v = 12,000 \text{ lb}$$

$$v_c = \frac{8 \times 12,000}{7 \times 12 \times 16} = 71.4 \text{ psi}$$

Therefore stirrups are not needed (see Table 5.5).

c Theoretically, bent-up bars may be figured as stirrups, but the exact bend point, etc., must be computed in order to take advantage of this allowance. Actually, in most offices, this is disregarded and stirrups are designed to take care of diagonal tension wherever the v_c is in excess of 90 psi for 3,000-psi concrete. Ordinarily two-leg or U stirrups are used, as shown in Fig. 5.10, but where shear values are high, it may be advisable to use four-leg or W stirrups.

The allowable fiber stress in the stirrup is limited to 20,000 psi when the size of bar is such that bond and anchorage requirements

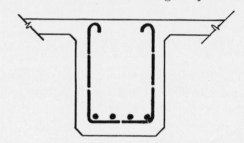

Fig. 5.10 Typical Stirrups

on the stirrup are within proper limits. Without explaining the derivation, this will require that without reduction of values, the stirrup with hooks must be used with the following minimum net depth beams, using 3,000-psi concrete.

Table 5.5 Allowable Shear, in Kips, on Concrete Beams Without Stirrups

Based on use of 3,000-psi concrete, $v_c = 90$ psi

Net d, in.	$b = 8$ in.	$b = 10$ in.	$b = 12$ in.	$b = 14$ in.	$b = 16$ in.
8	5.04	6.3			
10	6.3	7.88			
12	7.56	9.45	11.34		
14	8.82	11.03	13.23	15.44	
16	10.08	12.6	15.12	17.64	20.16
18	11.34	14.18	17.01	19.85	22.68
20	12.6	15.75	18.9	22.05	25.2
22	13.86	17.33	20.79	24.26	27.72
24	15.12	18.9	22.68	26.46	30.24
26		20.48	24.57	28.67	32.76
28		22.05	26.46	30.87	35.28
30		23.63	28.35	33.08	37.8
32		25.2	30.24	35.28	40.32

Stirrup No.	Min depth, in.
6	21
5	18
4	14
3	12
2	18 (plain bars)

If lesser depths are used, the allowable fiber stress in the stirrup must be reduced proportionately.

d The method of computing stirrups recommended by the American Concrete Institute and used in most building codes assumes that the concrete takes its full shear value, as given in Art. 1.22, and the steel stirrups take the remainder. The spacing of stirrups at any given point as obtained by this method is

$$s_1 = \frac{A_s f_v j d}{V_s} \qquad (5.11)$$

The hatched area in Fig. 5.11 represents graphically the shear resisted by stirrups computed by the above method.

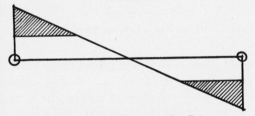

Fig. 5.11   Shear Diagram for Stirrups

Since for any size stirrup selected A_s represents the area of the two legs of the stirrup, f_v is taken as 20,000, and j is assumed at $\frac{7}{8}$ in., we may derive the following from Formula (5.11):

For No. 2 U Stirrups, $s_1 = \dfrac{1{,}750d}{V_s}$

For No. 3 U Stirrups, $s_1 = \dfrac{3{,}850d}{V_s}$

For No. 4 U Stirrups, $s_1 = \dfrac{7{,}000d}{V_s}$

For No. 5 U Stirrups, $s_1 = \dfrac{10{,}850d}{V_s}$

For No. 6 U Stirrups, $s_1 = \dfrac{15{,}400d}{V_s}$

Maximum spacing of stirrups should not exceed $\frac{1}{2}d$.

There are several graphical methods of determining stirrup requirements from shear diagrams (see Art. 3.12), but many engineers prefer to use the above method, using the Stirrup Dividend Table, Table 5.6. This table takes into account reduction of values where required in accordance with the last paragraph of Art. 5.30c.

e If the unit shearing stress for a 3,000-psi concrete beam computed by Formula (5.10) exceeds 90 psi, stirrups are required. Table 5.5 gives the allowable shear for a 3,000-psi concrete beam without stirrups. Values for beams not listed may be interpolated. To use Table 5.6 for computation of stirrups, subtract the shear value of the plain concrete beam from the end reaction to obtain V_s, the shear to be taken by stirrups. From Table 5.6, for d and the size stirrup to be used, select the proper stirrup dividend. The spacing at the end of the beam is this dividend divided by V_s. The first stirrup should be placed at the center of this spacing, and the second one a full spacing from it, but not over $\frac{1}{2}d$. The reduction in shear up to this point is subtracted from V_s, and a new spacing com-

Table 5.6   Stirrup Dividends

Net depth d, in.	No. 2 stirrup	No. 3 stirrup	No. 4 stirrup	No. 5 stirrup
8	6,220	20,530	32,000	38,580
10	9,720	32,000	50,000	60,280
12	14,000	46,200	72,000	86,800
14	19,060	53,900	98,000	118,140
16	24,900	61,600	112,000	154,310
18	31,500	69,300	126,000	195,300
20	35,000	77,000	140,000	217,000
22	38,500	84,700	154,000	238,700
24	42,000	92,400	168,000	260,400
26	45,500	100,100	182,000	282,100
28	49,000	107,800	196,000	303,800
30	52,500	115,500	210,000	325,500
32	56,000	123,200	224,000	347,200
34	59,500	130,900	238,000	368,900
36	63,000	138,600	252,000	390,600
38	66,500	146,300	266,000	412,300
40	70,000	154,000	280,000	434,000
42	73,500	161,700	294,000	455,700
44	77,000	169,400	308,000	477,400
46	80,500	177,100	322,000	499,100
48	84,000	184,800	336,000	520,800
50	87,500	192,500	350,000	542,500

puted based on the revised V_s, repeating this operation until V_s is zero.

Frequently it is accurate enough to compute a spacing, and use this spacing until the shear is reduced enough to use a greater predetermined spacing. Thus, assume that the spacing computed for end reaction is 6 in. Then compute the allowable shear for a 9-in. spacing, and carry the 6-in. spacing until this point is reached. Next, check the allowable shear for 12-in. spacing and carry 9-in. spacing until the new point is reached, and so on. If the load on the beam is concentrated, since the shear does not reduce except at points of concentrated load, the spacing from the reaction to the point of concentration will be the same with no change. Thus, if 6 in. is the computed spacing and the concentrated load is 4 ft out on the beam, the spacing will be one at 3 in. and seven at 6 in., making 45 in. to the last stirrup.

Problem Assume a T beam carrying 3,000 lb per ft (250 lb per in.), 15 ft long, and a central concentrated load of 20,000 lb, with a stem 16 in. wide, 16 in. net depth, 18 in. total depth, ACI Code for 3,000-psi concrete. Compute the required stirrups (Fig. 5.12).

Allowable V_c without stirrups $= 90 \times 16 \times 16 \times 0.875 = 20.16$ kips.

$$V = 32.5$$
$$V_c = \underline{20.16}$$
$$V_s = 12.34$$

Since the shear reduces at the rate of 3 kips per ft, stirrups will be required over a distance of

$$\frac{12.34}{3} = 4.11 \text{ ft}$$

With No. 3 U stirrups, from Table 5.6

$$s_1 = \frac{61.6}{12.34} = 5 \text{ in.}$$

Use $2\frac{1}{2}$ in. for the first stirrup and 5 in. for the second stirrup.

$$\frac{7.5}{12} \times 3 = 1.88$$

$$V_s = 12.34 - 1.88 = 10.46$$

$$s_3 = \frac{61.6}{10.46} = 5.9$$

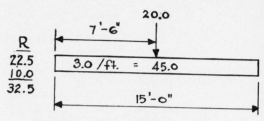

Fig. 5.12 Stirrup Design Problem

Use 6-in. spacing, reduction $= 1.5$.

$$10.46 - 1.5 = 8.96$$

$$s_4 = \frac{61.6}{8.96} = 6.9$$

Use 7-in. spacing, reduction $= 1.75$.

$$8.96 - 1.75 = 7.21$$

$$s_5 = \frac{61.6}{7.21} = 8.5$$

However, the maximum allowable spacing $= \frac{1}{2} \times 16 = 8$ in., so s_5 will be 8 in.

Using one space each at $2\frac{1}{2}$, 5, 6, 7, and 8 in., the total through the fifth stirrup space is 2 ft $- 4\frac{1}{2}$ in., or 2.37 ft. Since stirrups are required through a total length of 4.11 ft (see above), stirrups are required through an additional length of 1.74 ft beyond those listed above, or three additional spaces at 8 in. Therefore at each end we require eight No. 3 U stirrups spaced one at $2\frac{1}{2}$ in., one at 5 in., one at 6 in., one at 7 in., and four at 8 in. The total distance through which stirrups are used is 4 ft $4\frac{1}{2}$ in., or 4.37 ft.

5.40 SOLID ONE–WAY REINFORCED–CONCRETE SLABS

a For many years the most common type of fireproof floor construction has been the solid one-way reinforced-concrete slab. Under normal conditions it is most suitable and most economical for slabs ranging from 6 to $8\frac{1}{2}$ ft, although for light loads it may be economical up to 12 ft span. This type of slab is designed as a rectangular beam in accordance with the method of Art. 5.20, with the main reinforcement the short direction of the slab. At right angles to the main bars, shrinkage and temperature reinforcement is provided for to the extent of $0.002bd$ for floors and $0.0025bd$ for roofs. If the main steel area

Table 5.7   Area of Steel for Rods Spaced at Various Intervals

Square inches per linear foot of slab

Spacing o.c., in.	Rod No.								
	3	4	5	6	7	8	9	10	11
3	0.44	0.80	1.24	1.76	2.40	3.16	4.00	5.08	
$3\frac{1}{2}$	0.38	0.69	1.06	1.51	2.06	2.71	3.43	4.35	5.35
4	0.33	0.60	0.93	1.32	1.80	2.37	3.00	3.81	4.68
$4\frac{1}{2}$	0.29	0.53	0.83	1.17	1.60	2.11	2.67	3.39	4.16
5	0.26	0.48	0.74	1.06	1.44	1.90	2.40	3.05	3.74
$5\frac{1}{2}$	0.24	0.44	0.68	0.96	1.31	1.72	2.18	2.77	3.40
6	0.22	0.40	0.62	0.88	1.20	1.58	2.00	2.54	3.12
$6\frac{1}{2}$	0.20	0.37	0.57	0.81	1.11	1.46	1.85	2.34	2.88
7	0.19	0.34	0.53	0.75	1.03	1.35	1.71	2.18	2.67
$7\frac{1}{2}$	0.18	0.32	0.50	0.70	0.96	1.26	1.60	2.03	2.50
8	0.16	0.30	0.46	0.66	0.90	1.18	1.50	1.90	2.34
$8\frac{1}{2}$	0.15	0.28	0.44	0.62	0.85	1.12	1.41	1.79	2.20
9		0.27	0.41	0.59	0.80	1.05	1.33	1.69	2.08
$9\frac{1}{2}$		0.25	0.39	0.56	0.76	1.00	1.26	1.60	1.97
10		0.24	0.37	0.53	0.72	0.95	1.20	1.52	1.87

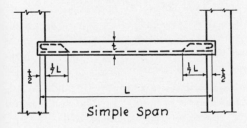

Simple Span

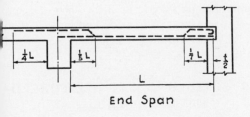

End Span

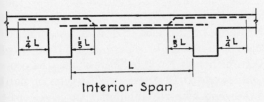

Interior Span

Fig. 5.13   Typical Concrete Slabs

required is not over 0.2 sq in. and the supporting members are steel beams, it is usually more economical to use welded wire-mesh reinforcement at an allowable stress of 30,000 psi,

which may be unrolled and placed with much less labor cost than bars. Table 5.7 will assist in selecting bars to furnish any given area of steel.

b If adjacent slab spans vary by not over 20 percent, the bending moment under uniform load conditions may be computed by means of coefficients in accordance with Table 5.8.

Table 5.8   Bending Moment in Slabs for Uniform Loads

Coefficients of wl^2

Length of spans	Number of spans	End spans		Intermediate spans	
		$+M$ at center	$-M$ at face of 2d support	$+M$ at center	$-M$ at face of support
Equal to or less than 10 ft	Two	$\frac{1}{14}$	$\frac{1}{9}$		
	More than two	$\frac{1}{14}$	$\frac{1}{10}$	$\frac{1}{16}$	$\frac{1}{12}$
Greater than 10 ft	Two	$\frac{1}{14}$	$\frac{1}{12}$		
	More than two	$\frac{1}{14}$	$\frac{1}{10}$	$\frac{1}{16}$	$\frac{1}{11}$

Problem   Design a slab to carry a total load of 200 psf on a continuous span of

10 ft 6 in., using 3,000-psi concrete and the ACI Code.

$$W = 10.5 \times 200 = 2,100$$

$$M = \frac{2,100 \times 10.5 \times 12}{11} = 24,054$$

$$d = \sqrt{\frac{24,054}{236 \times 12}} = \sqrt{8.5} = 2.92$$

Allow for $\frac{3}{4}$-in. cover plus half thickness of bar $= 3 + 1 = 4$. Use 4-in. slab.

$$A_s = \frac{24,054}{20,000 \times 0.875 \times 3} = 0.458 \text{ sq in.}$$

From Table 5.7 use No. 4 bars at 5 in. o.c.; $A_s = 0.48$.

Table 5.9 is useful for the selection of moment direct. It gives moment for simple, end, and continuous spans varying by 3-in. increments from 4 to 13 ft, and for 100, 150, and 200 psf. For other loads not listed, the moments given in the first series of tables for 100 psf may be multiplied by the correct multiplier. For example, for 165 psf, use 1.65 times the moment given for 100 psf.

c   If a slab is required to carry a concentrated load, the simplest method of design is a simplification of the Hardy Cross method of moment distribution, as described in Art. 3.21 and as given below. (Many codes, however, permit the weight of partitions to be spread as described in Art. 1.50*b*.)

The variation consists of determining the fixed end moment at the heavy end due to partition load, in accordance with the coefficient from Table 3.1, and using half of this moment added to the normal uniform load moment found by the coefficient method described in Art. 5.40*b*.

Problem   Design an intermediate slab on a span of 8 ft 6 in., carrying a total uniform load of 150 psf and a partition load of 400 lb per ft at right angles to the main reinforcement, at a point 2 ft 6 in. from the support (see Fig. 5.14).

For the uniform load,

$$W = 150 \times 8.5 = 1,275$$

$$M_1 = \frac{1,275 \times 8.5 \times 12}{12} = 10,837$$

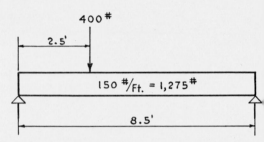

Fig. 5.14   Slab Carrying Concentrated Load

For the concentrated load, the position of the load is $2.5/8.5 = 0.29$ of span. From Table 5.

$$M_2 = \frac{0.146 \times 400 \times 8.5 \times 12}{2} = 2,980$$

The divisor 2 is an approximate moment distribution factor. The total moment to design for is $10,840 + 2,980 = 13,820$.

$$d = \sqrt{\frac{13,820}{236 \times 12}} = \sqrt{4.88} = 2.21$$

Add $\frac{3}{4}$ in. for cover, and for half the thickness of the bar,

$$\text{Total } t = 2.21 + 1 = 3.21 \text{ in.}$$

Use $3\frac{1}{2}$ in. slab.

$$A_s = \frac{13,820}{20,000 \times 0.875 \times 2.5} = 0.316 \text{ sq in.}$$

Use No. 4 bars, $7\frac{1}{2}$ in. o.c.; $A_s = 0.32$.

e   If there are a large number of slabs to design, it is profitable for the designer as well as the contractor to standardize them, using slabs such as those listed in Table 5.10. The slab is designated by means of a number and a letter—the number representing the gross thickness of the structural slab, the letter indicating the reinforcement. Thus a 4G slab is 4 in. thick reinforced with 4×16, $\frac{4}{9}$ welded wire mesh and is good for a moment of 6,120 in-lb. The area of steel required is also given in case it is desired to use bars instead of mesh for reinforcement. It is advisable that the designer understand the designation used for standard mesh reinforcement. The first two figures (4×16) indicate the spacing in inches of the main and cross reinforcement respectively, and the fractional number ($\frac{4}{9}$) indicates the gage of the main and cross wires in the mesh. Thus the reinforcement called for above, 4×16, $\frac{4}{9}$, calls for 4-gage wires

Table 5.9   Concrete Slabs—Required Moments

Span	Load = 100 psf				Load = 150 psf				Load = 200 psf			
	W	$WL/8$	$WL/10$	$WL/12$	W	$WL/8$	$WL/10$	$WL/12$	W	$WL/8$	$WL/10$	$WL/12$
4'0''	400	2,400	1,920	1,600	600	3,600	2,880	2,400	800	4,800	3,840	3,200
4'3''	425	2,710	2,160	1,810	638	4,050	3,240	2,700	850	5,420	4,330	3,610
4'6''	450	3,040	2,430	2,020	675	4,560	3,650	3,040	900	6,070	4,860	4,050
4'9''	475	3,380	2,710	2,250	713	5,070	4,060	3,380	950	6,770	5,410	4,510
5'0''	500	3,750	3,000	2,500	750	5,620	4,500	3,750	1,000	7,500	6,000	5,000
5'3''	525	4,130	3,310	2,760	788	6,210	4,970	4,140	1,050	8,260	6,600	5,510
5'6''	550	4,540	3,630	3,020	825	6,810	5,460	4,540	1,100	9,080	7,270	6,050
5'9''	575	4,960	3,960	3,300	862	7,440	5,950	4,960	1,150	9,920	7,950	6,610
6'0''	600	5,400	4,320	3,600	900	8,100	6,490	5,400	1,200	10,800	8,650	7,200
6'3''	625	5,860	4,680	3,910	938	8,730	7,050	5,860	1,250	11,720	9,370	7,820
6'6''	650	6,340	5,070	4,230	975	9,525	7,630	6,350	1,300	12,680	10,140	8,460
6'9''	675	6,840	5,470	4,560	1,013	10,260	8,210	6,840	1,350	13,680	10,940	9,120
7'0''	700	7,350	5,880	4,900	1,050	11,025	8,840	7,350	1,400	14,700	11,760	9,800
7'3''	725	7,880	6,310	5,260	1,088	11,850	9,490	7,900	1,450	15,750	12,620	10,500
7'6''	750	8,440	6,750	5,630	1,125	12,660	10,120	8,440	1,500	16,860	13,500	11,250
7'9''	775	9,020	7,210	6,010	1,162	13,500	10,800	9,000	1,550	18,000	14,420	12,010
8'0''	800	9,600	7,680	6,400	1,200	14,400	11,500	9,600	1,600	19,200	15,360	12,800
8'3''	825	10,210	8,170	6,810	1,238	15,300	12,240	10,200	1,650	20,400	16,330	13,600
8'6''	850	10,830	8,670	7,220	1,275	16,230	13,000	10,820	1,700	21,630	17,330	14,450
8'9''	875	11,480	9,180	7,650	1,313	17,250	13,800	11,500	1,750	22,900	18,380	15,300
9'0''	900	12,150	9,710	8,100	1,350	18,225	14,600	12,150	1,800	24,300	19,440	16,200
9'3''	925	12,820	10,250	8,560	1,388	19,275	15,400	12,850	1,850	25,700	20,510	17,100
9'6''	950	13,530	10,820	9,020	1,425	20,350	16,300	13,550	1,900	27,100	21,630	18,050
9'9''	975	14,250	11,410	9,500	1,462	21,450	17,200	14,300	1,950	28,500	22,810	19,020
10'0''	1,000	15,000	12,000	10,000	1,500	22,500	18,000	15,000	2,000	30,000	24,000	20,000
10'3''	1,025	15,750	12,610	10,500	1,538	23,600	18,920	15,750	2,050	31,500	25,200	21,000
10'6''	1,050	16,530	13,230	11,020	1,575	24,800	19,840	16,520	2,100	33,100	26,430	22,050
10'9''	1,075	17,350	13,860	11,560	1,613	26,000	20,810	17,340	2,150	34,630	27,730	23,100
11'0''	1,100	18,150	14,530	12,100	1,650	27,200	21,780	18,150	2,200	36,300	29,100	24,200
11'3''	1,125	19,000	15,200	12,660	1,688	28,450	22,680	19,000	2,250	37,900	30,380	25,300
11'6''	1,150	19,820	15,870	13,230	1,725	29,740	23,610	19,850	2,300	39,700	31,730	26,450
11'9''	1,175	20,710	16,580	13,810	1,762	31,060	24,840	20,700	2,350	41,420	33,130	27,600
12'0''	1,200	21,600	17,290	14,400	1,800	32,400	25,900	21,600	2,400	43,200	34,580	28,800
12'3''	1,225	22,500	18,010	15,020	1,838	33,750	27,000	22,500	2,450	45,000	36,000	30,000
12'6''	1,250	23,420	18,750	15,630	1,875	35,100	28,120	23,420	2,500	46,800	37,500	31,230
12'9''	1,275	24,400	19,520	16,250	1,913	36,500	29,300	24,400	2,550	48,800	39,100	32 500
13'0''	1,300	25,340	20,290	16,900	1,950	38,000	30,400	25,350	2,600	50 800	40,600	33,800

spaced 4 in. o.c. for the main reinforcement, and 9-gage wires spaced 16 in. o.c. for the cross wires.

f Various methods are used to simplify the construction of slabs so that the same mesh may be used over as many spans as possible. If there is unlimited choice of beam spacings, it will be found that if the end spans are made equal to 0.91 of the intermediate span, the moments for $WL/10$ in the end span and $WL/12$ in the intermediate span will be approximately equal. For instance, assume a roof of 60-ft length and allow for 4-in. bearing on the wall at each end. Select spans of between 7 ft 6 in. and 8 ft to use the same size mesh throughout. This will give a total of eight spans, or two end spans at $0.91L$ and six intermediate spans, or

$$7.82L = 60.67 \text{ ft}$$
$$L = 7.76$$

Use 7 ft 9 in. The end spans will be

$$\frac{60 \text{ ft 8 in.} - 46 \text{ ft 6 in.}}{2} = 7 \text{ ft 1 in.}$$

Using 100 psf total load, the intermediate moment from Table 5.9 is 6,010 in.-lb. The end-

Table 5.10   Reinforced Concrete Slabs—Allowable Moments

Inch-pounds per foot width
Using standard welded wire mesh, 3,000-psi concrete, $f_s = 30,000$ psi

Welded wire mesh		A_c	3 in.	3½ in.	4 in.	4½ in.	5 in.	5½ in.	6 in.
A	$4 \times 12, \frac{10}{12}$	.043	2,310						
B	$4 \times 12, \frac{9}{12}$	.052	2,800	3,500					
C	$4 \times 12, \frac{8}{12}$	.062	3,340	4,170					
D	$4 \times 16, \frac{7}{11}$	.074	3,980	4,980	5,970				
E	$4 \times 16, \frac{6}{10}$	.087	4,680	5,850	7,020	8,190	9,360		
F	$4 \times 16, \frac{5}{10}$	.101	5,430	6,790	8,150	9,510	10,870	12,230	
G	$4 \times 16, \frac{4}{9}$	.120	6,460	8,070	9,684	11,300	12,900	14,530	16,140
H	$4 \times 16, \frac{3}{8}$	.140	7,530	9,410	11,300	13,180	14,060	15,950	17,830
J	$4 \times 16, \frac{2}{8}$	.162	8,720	10,990	13,170	15,350	17,530	19,710	21,890
K	$2 \times 16, \frac{6}{10}$	.174	9,360	11,700	14,040	16,380	18,720	21,060	23,400
L	$2 \times 16, \frac{5}{10}$	.202	10,830	13,580	16,300	19,020	21,740	24,460	27,180
M	$2 \times 16, \frac{4}{8}$	.239	12,860	16,070	19,290	22,500	25,720	28,930	32,150
N	$2 \times 16, \frac{3}{8}$	.280		11,820	22,600	26,360	28,120	33,900	35,660
P	$2 \times 16, \frac{2}{8}$	.325			26,230	30,600	34,970	39,340	43,710
Q	$2 \times 16, \frac{1}{7}$	.377				35,500	40,580	45,650	50,720

span load is $7.08 \times 100 = 708$, and the end span moment is

$$\frac{708 \times 7.08 \times 12}{10} = 6,015 \text{ in.-lb}$$

Thus the same slab may be used for both end span and intermediate.

Sometimes the same mesh is used throughout, but the end-span forms are dropped ½ in. to increase the capacity of the steel. Thus if we assume 150 psf on 7 ft 9 in. spans throughout, both end span and intermediate, we will have an intermediate moment of 9,000 in.-lb and an end-span moment of 10,800 in.-lb. Referring to Table 5.10, we may use a $3K$ intermediate span and $3\frac{1}{2}K$ end span thus using the same mesh throughout.

Another method of providing for the increased moment is to use the same mesh throughout and increase the steel area in the same end span by adding ¼-in. round bars spaced as required to provide the extra area. Note that additional steel is required for negative moment only.

5.41   One-way concrete-joist floor construction

a   One-way concrete-joist floors are frequently used in hospital, school, or apartment-house construction. Precast-concrete joists,

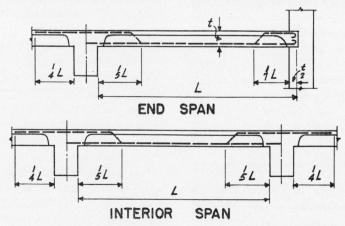

Fig. 5.15 Typical Concrete Joist Slabs

f which there are several types on the market, may be discussed more properly under rt 5.42. This discussion and the methods roposed are best fitted to use in metal-pan bbed floors—sometimes known as tin-pan onstruction—and one-way floors with block llers. Depth of metal pans runs from 8 to 4 in., and a top slab $2\frac{1}{2}$ or 3 in. thick is used o form a T beam. Block fillers are run from to 12 in. thick plus the top slab.

One of the lightest types of concrete floors esults from the use of metal-pan fillers between concrete joists. Numerous kinds of uch pans are available. Some are fabricated f light-gage material and are intended to be eft in place. Other pans are made of heavier netal and are removed when the forms are tripped, to be used again or returned to the wner, if leased. Both styles are furnished ith either straight or tapered closed ends. apered pans are highly desirable on long pans, because with their use the width of he joists is increased at points where such vidth is needed, namely, near the supports vhere the shearing stresses are the highest. The usual width of metal pans is 20 in., although 10-, 15-, and 30-in. pans are generally vailable. Figures 5.16 and 5.17 indicate this ype of construction.

Metal-pan ribbed floors reach their highest conomy on long spans with light loads. The veight is very light and the depth of the floor produces great rigidity. These floors are not o well suited to support concentrated loads, s the topping between joists is comparatively hin ($2\frac{1}{2}$ to 3 in.). Care must be taken to re-nforce the topping across construction joints o prevent them from opening.

Hollow filler blocks of lightweight concrete r clay tile laid in rows in the bottom of con-rete slabs constitute a form of ribbed slab. The dead load is considerably reduced in omparison with a solid slab of equal load-arrying capacity, although the total depth

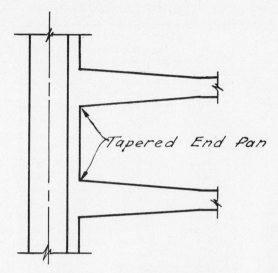

Fig. 5.17   Use of Tapered End Pans

of slab is increased. The width of the concrete joists, separating the rows of filler and encasing the reinforcement, may be made any desired size to meet the strength requirements. It is customary to include a solid concrete top of 2 in. or more in depth over the blocks. This serves the double purpose of providing a space for concealing small pipes and conduits, and also forms a T section with the joists, thus adding considerable strength to them. Introduction of filler blocks improves sound and heat insulation of a slab.

Although plaster may be applied directly to the slab, it has been noted that at times a slight discoloration takes place when clay-tile filler is used. This is caused by the use of materials of different densities and absorption qualities next to one another, and may be eliminated by placing the soffit pieces in the bottoms of the joists to form an all-tile ceiling.

To insure straight joists, care should be taken that the filler blocks are kept accurately in line. As the blocks are porous, they should be thoroughly sprinkled to prevent absorption of the water in the concrete, particularly in warm weather.

It is advisable to maintain a minimum joist width of 5 in. using metal pans and 4 in. using filler blocks, to facilitate the placing of bars.

b   The following sections quoted from the 1951 ACI Code may be taken as representing

Fig. 5.16   Section Through Metal Pan
Ribbed Floor

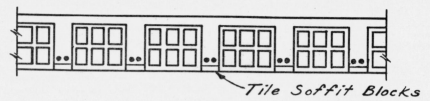

Tile Soffit Blocks

Fig. 5.18   Tile and Joist Ribbed Floor

good practice in the design of concrete-joist floor construction.

[From Sec. 708(*a*)]   Concrete joist floor construction consists of concrete joists and slabs placed monolithically with or without burned clay or concrete tile fillers. The joists shall not be farther apart than 30 in. face to face. The ribs shall be straight, not less than 4 in. wide, nor of a depth more than three times the width.

[From Sec. 708(*b*)]   When burned clay or concrete tile fillers of material having a unit compressive strength at least equal to that of the designed strength of the concrete in the joists are used, and the fillers so placed that the joints in alternate rows are staggered, the vertical shells of the fillers in contact with the joists may be included in the calculations involving shear or negative moment.

[From Sec. 708(*c*)]   The concrete slab over the fillers shall be not less than $1\frac{1}{2}$ in. thick, nor less in thickness than $\frac{1}{12}$ of the clear distance between joists. Shrinkage reinforcement shall be provided in the slab.

[From Sec. 708(*d*)]   Where removable forms or fillers not complying with Sec. 708(*b*) are used, the thickness of slab shall be not less than $\frac{1}{12}$ of the clear distance between joists and in no case less than 2 in. Such slab shall be reinforced at right angles to the joists.

c   Concrete-joist construction in general is subject to the design methods for T beams as described in Art. 5.21. In many instances, however, the layout is such that the coefficient method of design (Table 5.8) is not applicable, as, for example, in schools, where the classroom spans are approximately 23 ft, while the corridor span is only about 10 ft or less. Under such conditions it is necessary to compute the moment by methods of moment distribution as described in Art. 3.21. Since the maximum negative moment occurs with two adjacent spans loaded—whereas the maximum positive moment occurs with one span loaded and the adjacent spans unloaded—it is necessary to run through design calculations under the several possible load conditions and deter-

mine the combination of dead and live load which gives maximum moment conditions. simplification of this computation is given i Art. 5.41*d*.

After the maximum positive and negativ moments in each span have been determine select the joist and top slab required for th design, and the reinforcement in the joist. Table 5.11 is taken from the standard prac tice of the author's office. It is based on th use of 20-in.-wide metal forms.

In Table 5.11 the column $+M_c$ is the max imum positive moment in the joists as a beam; $-M_c$ is the maximum negative momen unless compression steel is used. The mo ment of inertia is given in case it is desire to compute stiffness factors. The weight give is the average weight per square foot for jois and top slab using 5-in.-wide joists and 20-in. wide metal forms. If block fillers are used th weight must be increased accordingly. I Tables 5.11 and 5.12 concrete joists are show thus: $12 + 2\frac{1}{2}$cd. This indicates 12-in.-dee pans with $2\frac{1}{2}$ in. top slab. The letters indicat reinforcement as tabulated. The first lette is the straight bar, the second, bent. An in dication such as $12 + 2\frac{1}{2}$(c/a indicates a (c top bar across the entire span, and an (a straight bottom bar. Except as otherwis noted, joists are 5 in. wide. A figure in paren theses, e.g., (8), indicates a joist widt which varies from the standard. The indica tion (t) after the size means tapered end pan to increase shear or negative-moment area.

d   As has been noted in paragraph *c*, th computation of maximum positive and nega tive moments for three-span symmetrica joists such as may be used in schools, hospi tals, etc., may be simplified by the use c curves. These curves are shown in Fig. 5.1 and are used in accordance with the followin, procedure.

Table 5.11   Moment in Concrete-Joist Spans

Inch-kips per foot of width of slab

Depth, in.	(a) No. 3	(b) No. 4	(c) No. 5	(d) No. 6	(e) No. 7	(f) No. 8	(g) No. 9	(h) No. 10	(j) No. 11	$+ M_c$	$- M_c$	Weight, psf
8 + 2	7.9	14.25	21.4	31.4	42.8	56.0	71.25	91.6	111.3	151.5	41.0	48
8 + 2½	8.35	15.1	22.65	33.2	45.3	59.1	75.5	97.0	117.0	181.0	46.0	54
0 + 2	9.75	17.6	26.4	38.9	52.8	69.0	88.0	113.0	138.0	207.0	63.5	53
0 + 2½	10.2	18.5	27.75	40.7	55.5	72.3	92.5	118.6	144.7	249.0	68.5	59
0 + 3	10.6	19.3	28.8	42.4	57.8	74.3	96.4	123.6	151.0	288.0	75.0	65
2 + 2	11.56	21.0	31.5	46.3	63.0	82.3	105.0	134.6	164.5	263.0	88.3	59
2 + 2½	12.0	21.8	32.7	48.2	65.4	85.6	109.0	139.8	170.8	317.0	95.5	65
2 + 3	12.5	22.6	33.9	50.0	67.8	89.1	113.0	145.0	177.0	370.0	103.0	71
4 + 2½	13.87	25.1	37.65	55.5	75.3	99.0	125.5	161.2	197.0	389.0	127.5	70
4 + 3	14.35	26.0	39.0	57.4	78.0	102.2	130.0	167.0	204.0	450.0	136.0	76

Table 5.12   Shear in Concrete-Joist Spans

Pounds per foot of width of slab

Depth, in.	4 in.	4½ in.	5 in.	5½ in.	6 in.	6½ in.	7 in.	7½ in.	8 in.	8½ in.	I^4 in. per joist
8 + 2	1,418	1,559	1,701	1,839	1,959	2,085	2,205	2,321	2,430	2,537	848.5
8 + 2½	1,496	1,646	1,796	1,941	2,068	2,200	2,328	2,450	2,565	2,678	967.0
0 + 2	1,733	1,906	2,078	2,247	2,394	2,548	2,695	2,837	2,970	3,100	1,408
0 + 2½	1,811	1,992	2,174	2,349	2,503	2,664	2,818	2,966	3,105	3,241	1,636
0 + 3	1,890	2,079	2,267	2,452	2,612	2,779	2,940	3,055	3,240	3,382	1,851
2 + 2	2,048	2,252	2,456	2,656	2,830	3,011	3,185	3,353	3,510	3,664	2,208
2 + 2½	2,126	2,339	2,552	2,758	2,938	3,127	3,308	3,482	3,645	3,805	2,492
2 + 3	2,205	2,426	2,645	2,860	3,047	3,243	3,430	3,611	3,780	3,946	3,790
4 + 2½	2,441	2,685	2,930	3,167	3,374	3,590	3,798	3,998	4,185	4,369	3,610
4 + 3	2,520	2,772	3,023	3,269	3,482	3,706	3,920	4,126	4,320	4,509	3,945

1. Compute ratio r of center span to side span.

2. Compute factor $K = $ (Side span/10)^2.

3. Enter the chart (Fig. 5.19) with the ratio r computed in step 1, and read the value of $-M_1$ fully loaded, $-M_2$ maximum, $-M_3$ side spans loaded, and $-M_4$ center span loaded.

4. Set down dead load per square foot on side span and center span. This load is on the span regardless of any variation of live-load condition. Set down separately the live load per square foot on side span and center span. This may be on classrooms or corridor separately or on both.

5. The maximum negative moment over the support occurs with two adjacent spans loaded, and dead load only on the third span. The maximum positive load occurs in the side spans with both side spans loaded, and dead load only on the corridor, and this condition of loading will also cause the maximum negative moment in the center span. The maximum positive moment in the center span (if the spans are such that positive moment can be obtained in the center span) will occur with the center span fully loaded and with dead load only on side spans.

Compute $-M$ for each of the above cases by multiplying $-M$ as selected in step 3 by $w/100$ for each of the cases noted, and by the factor K. The maximum net $+M$ in the side spans is $(WL/8) + (-M/2)$ and in the center span $(WL/8) + (-M)$.

Problem   A school has classroom joists 23 ft long with 9-ft corridor spans. The construction is 12 + 2½ slabs, using 5-in. joists, 25 in. on centers. The classroom finish weighs

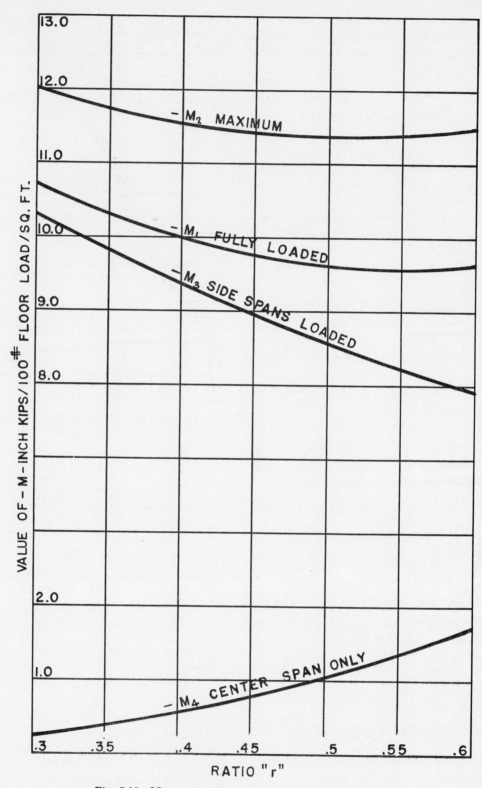

Fig. 5.19   Moments—Three-Span Symmetrical Slabs

15 psf, with a 10-psf ceiling. The corridor finish weighs 30 psf with a 10-psf ceiling. The classroom live load is 50 psf, and the corridor live load 80 psf. Design the joists.

$$\text{Ratio } r = \frac{9}{23} = 0.391$$
$$\text{Factor } K = 2.3^2 = 5.29$$

From Fig. 5.19

$$-M_1 = 10.03$$
$$-M_2 = 11.6$$
$$-M_3 = 9.4$$
$$-M_4 = 0.58$$

	Side spans	Center span
Dead loads:		
12 + 2½ slab	65	65
Finish	15	30
Ceiling	10	10
Total dead load	90	105
Live load	50	80
Total load	140	185

The maximum negative moment is

$$1.4 \times 11.6 = 16.24$$
$$+0.45 \times 0.58 = 0.26$$
$$\overline{1.85} \qquad 16.50 \times 5.29 = -87.3 \text{ in.-kips}$$

The maximum positive moment in side spans is obtained as follows. Maximum positive moment on simple span is

$$\frac{WL}{8} = \frac{140 \times 23 \times 23 \times 12}{8} = 111.1 \text{ in.-kips}$$

This is reduced by half the following:

$$1.05 \times 10.03 = 10.53$$
$$0.35 \times 9.4 = 3.29$$
$$\overline{1.40} \qquad 13.82 \times 5.29 = -73.1$$
$$+M \text{ in side span} = 111.1 - 36.55 = +74.55$$

The maximum positive moment on the center span as a simple span, with live plus dead load, is

$$\frac{WL}{8} = \frac{185 \times 9 \times 9 \times 12}{8} = 22.5 \text{ in.-kips}$$

For dead load only it is

$$\frac{105 \times 9 \times 9 \times 12}{8} = 12.76 \text{ in.-kips}$$

To check for negative moment at the center of the span,

$$M = -73.1 + 12.76 = -60.34$$

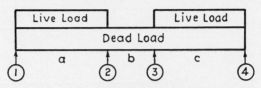

(a) For Maximum Moment In Spans "a" and "c". For Possible Negative Moment In Slab "b"

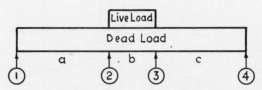

(b) For Maximum Moment In Span "b". For Possible Negative Moment In Spans "a" and "c"

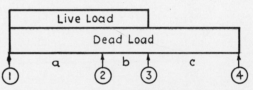

(c) For Maximum Negative Moment Shear And Reactions At Support "2"

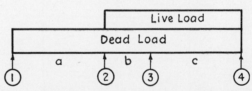

(d) For Maximum Negative Moment Shear and Reactions At Support "3"

Fig. 5.20 Possible Maximum Moment Conditions—Three-Span Slab

To check for possible positive moment, the negative moment at the ends of the span is

$$0.90 \times (-10.03) = -9.03$$
$$+0.95 \times (-0.58) = -0.57$$
$$\overline{\qquad\qquad\qquad -9.60 \times 5.29 = -50.8}$$

Therefore, with a minimum negative moment at the ends of 50.8 in.-kips and a maximum positive moment of 22.4, there can never be any net positive moment in the center of the span.

The moments to design for are,

$+M$ in side spans, $+74.55$ in.-kips
$-M$ at center supports, -87.3 in.-kips
$-M$ at center of corridor, 60.34 in.-kips

To furnish M in the corridor (referring to Table 5.11) will require one No. 7 top bar, which furnishes 65.4 in.-kips.

At the supports we need in addition

$$87.4 - 65.4 = 22.0 \text{ in.-kips}$$

This will require one No. 5 bar, which will be bent up from the side spans. This furnishes 32.7 in.-kips.

The side span will require in addition

$$74.55 - 32.7 = 41.85 \text{ in.-kips}$$

This will require one No. 6 bar, straight.

In accordance with the system of designation in Table 5.11, the side span will be designated $12 + 2\frac{1}{2}$dc, and the center span $12 + 2\frac{1}{2}$ e/a.

Although the calculations indicate no positive moment in the center span, it is good policy to put in a minimum-sized bar (No. 3) for possible erection stresses.

The computation of reactions takes into account internal moment also, as described in Art. 3.20d. If there were no such internal moment, the reactions would be half the load in each span, or for the side span,

$$R = \frac{140 \times 23}{2} = 1,610 \text{ lb per ft}$$

and for the center span,

$$R = \frac{185 \times 9}{2} = 833 \text{ lb per ft}$$

The correction for internal moment at the outer end is

$$\frac{73,100}{23 \times 12} = 265 \text{ lb}$$

and the corrected reaction is

$$1,610 - 265 = 1,345 \text{ lb}$$

The correction for internal moment at the inner end of the side span is

$$\frac{87,400}{23 \times 12} = 317$$

and the corrected reaction is

$$1,610 + 317 = 1,927 \text{ lb}$$

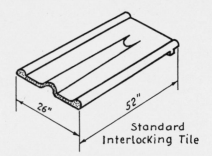

Fig. 5.21   Precast Concrete Roof Tile

Although it is not absolutely accurate, it is safe to assume that the reaction from the corridors is the uncorrected reaction of 833 lb, since it is hardly likely that there can be enough variation in these moments to affect materially a variation in load. The total load for which to design the corridor beam would therefore be

$$1,927 + 833 = 2,760 \text{ lb per ft}$$

5.42   Precast-concrete floors and roofs

a There are various patented precast floor and roof systems available, their economy and usability being determined largely by freight rates from the point of manufacture. In this category we may list four classes as most common:

1. Precast roof tile, which requires no roof finish of any kind (Fig. 5.21)
2. Short-span flat tongue-and-groove plank or channel-type slabs (Fig. 5.22)
3. Long-span cored plank (Fig. 5.23)
4. Precast-concrete joists (Fig. 5.24)

The various manufacturers publish load tables and specifications for application, and some of the manufacturers will bid on the ma-

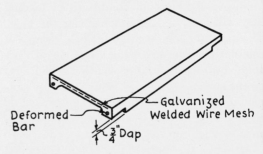

Fig. 5.22   Precast Channel-Type Concrete Slab

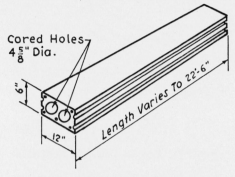

Fig. 5.23   Flexicore Concrete Plank

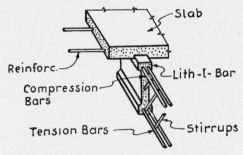

Fig. 5.24   Lith-I-Bar Concrete Joist Construction

terial erected in place. Only an actual bid from a contractor will give a comparison of cost with cast-in-place systems.

b Any precast system lacks stiffness in itself and requires more stiffness to be built into the frame than does a poured-in-place slab. Most precast systems do not provide lateral bracing for the top flange of steel beams, and frequently rod bracing must be installed with them. Each system has its economical limitations of span, and some systems are only economical if spans are kept uniform. The designer should investigate the requirements of the system before proceeding with the design.

To offset the disadvantages, precast systems save forming costs, are cleaner in installation, are faster to install provided delivery is made in time, are usually lighter in dead load, and can be installed regardless of freezing weather.

5.43   Kneed reinforced-concrete slabs

a Concrete slabs with a knee, similar to a stair slab and landing poured monolithically without support at the knee, are actually rigid frames, and under all conditions of loading they will have negative moment at the knee. The accurate computation of such a slab is a complex problem involving a number of variables, but a satisfactory solution which errs on the side of safety may be obtained by simple approximate methods. The method is largely graphical and involves the use of a moment diagram.

Although the method given here is applied to a slab with an upward knee as shown in

Fig. 5.25, step 1, it applies equally to a slab with a downward knee such as the opposite run in a flight of stairs.

b The steps in the computation of this slab are as follows.

1. In order to determine the position of the theoretical knee, draw the horizontal center line of the landing slab *bc* and the sloping center line of the slab supporting the stairs *ab*. The intersection of these two lines (*b*) determines the position of the knee (Fig. 5.25, step 1).

2. Compute the simple beam moment on the slab, allowing for full live and dead load on all parts of the slab, and lay out the moment diagram (Fig. 5.25, step 2). At the point where the line of the knee *b* cuts the moment diagram, lay off a negative moment *ef* beyond the curve of the moment diagram. This negative moment is 0.4 of the maximum positive moment *gh* on the simple span. Draw lines from the extreme outer point of the negative moment *f* to the two ends of the moment diagram. These lines, *af* and *fc*, become the new base lines of the moment diagram; the area intercepted on the original moment diagram represents positive moment on the span, the area outside the original moment diagram represents negative moment. These are indicated by the shaded area in Fig. 5.25, step 2. This gives the negative moment for which the slab must be designed, and the length through which negative steel must be provided. Negative bars should be developed in tension beyond this point.

3. Under some conditions of span or loading, the negative moment will not be as great

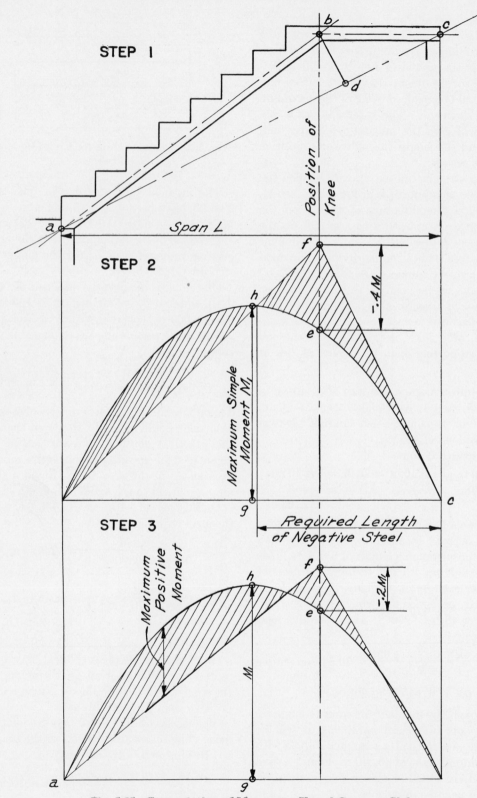

Fig. 5.25 Computation of Moments—Kneed Concrete Slab

as designed for in step 2; and since the maximum positive moment may result when the negative moment is a minimum, the same procedure as that given in step 2 should be followed through, except that the negative moment should be reduced to 0.2 of the maximum positive moment. The intercepts thus obtained will give the maximum positive moment, and the length through which positive moment occurs.

4. If a straight line be drawn between the two points of support (*ac* in Fig. 5.25, step 1), it indicates the direction of thrust on the supports of an upward knee, or pull on the supports of a downward knee. The amount of this stress is obtained by dividing the maximum negative moment found in step 2 by the height *bd* perpendicular to the line *ac*. By means of a vector analysis the stress may be divided into vertical and horizontal components, or it may be taken out at the end of the supporting span by means of ties or struts.

Problem   Assume the stair slab shown in Fig. 5.25, step 1, with eight risers at $7\frac{1}{2}$ in., using 10-in. runs and a 4-ft landing. Design for a live load of 125 psf.

The span *L* becomes

Seven treads at 10 in. = 70 in. = 5 ft 10 in.
Landing   = 4 ft
Span   = 9 ft 10 in.

Assume a 4-in. slab having a constant dead load of 50 psf. In addition, spread the load of the steps through a length of 6 ft 8 in. This load is made up of eight triangular prisms of concrete, each $7\frac{1}{2}$ in. high by 10 in. long, or 2.08 cu ft of concrete, which would weigh 312 lb, or 48 psf. Add to these the live load of 125 psf.

$$M = \frac{4.78 \times 12 \times 1{,}065}{2} = 30{,}540 \text{ on simple}$$
$$\text{span}$$

$$-M = 0.4 \times 30{,}540 = 12{,}200 \text{ in-lb}$$

Although the moment diagram is made up of segments of several parabolas, it will be accurate enough to plot a single parabola with a maximum height of 30,540 in.-lb and a span of 9.83 ft in order to obtain maximum positive and negative moments.

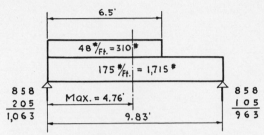

Fig. 5.26   Load Diagram for Kneed Concrete-Slab Problems

The moment diagrams in Fig. 5.25, steps 2 and 3, have been drawn to such a scale that M_1 is 30,540 in.-lb, $-0.4M_1$ is 12,200 in.-lb, and $-0.2M_1$ is 6,100 in.-lb. The maximum positive moment scaled from the diagram in step 3 is 11,250 in.-lb.

On the basis of a positive moment of 11,250 in.-lb and a negative moment of 12,160 in.-lb, using 3,000-psi concrete with ACI Code, *K* is 236, and the minimum slab thickness may be computed thus:

$$d = \sqrt{\frac{12{,}200}{236 \times 12}} = \sqrt{4.3} = 2.1 \text{ in. net}$$

Therefore, allowing for proper coverage, a $3\frac{1}{2}$-in. slab could be used. However, there are the practical considerations of getting two layers of steel—positive and negative moment resistance—in the slab, which would make it more practical to use a 4-in. minimum slab.

On the basis of a 4-in. slab of 3 in. net depth, the steel required would be

$$-A_s = \frac{12{,}200}{0.866 \times 20{,}000 \times 3} = 0.235 \text{ sq in.} =$$
$$\text{No. 3 at } 5\frac{1}{2} \text{ in. o.c.}$$

$$+A_s = \frac{11{,}250}{0.866 \times 20{,}000 \times 3} = 0.216 \text{ sq in.} =$$
$$\text{No. 3 at 6 in. o.c.}$$

The moment diagram in step 3 indicates that a small amount of positive steel may be required throughout almost the entire length of the span, and it is advisable to extend half the positive steel through this area.

The thrust or direct pull may be computed next. The scaled distance *bd* on the diagram is 1 ft 5 in., or 17 in. Therefore

$$H = \frac{12{,}200}{17} = 718 \text{ lb per ft width}$$

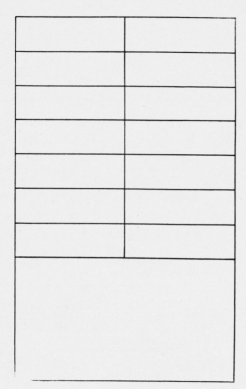

Fig. 5.27   Plan for Kneed Concrete-Slab Problem

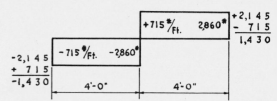

Fig. 5.28   Thrust Diagram—Kneed-Concrete-Slab Problems

Assume that the stairs are 4 ft wide for each flight, as shown in plan in Fig. 5.27. The resultant loads and reactions are shown in Fig. 5.28. To carry the thrust for the run from the landing down, a tensile area of 1,436/20,000 = 0.07 sq in. will be required. Use one No. 3 rod buried in the stair partition.

To carry the inward thrust on the run from the landing up, a compression member capable of carrying 1,436 lb on an unsupported length of 11 ft will be required. For this a member with $l/r = 1.1$ will be required if we use 120 as a minimum or 0.61 if we use 200 as the minimum. Even on this latter basis, it would require a standard $1\frac{1}{2}$-in. pipe, which would be stressed to only 1,436/0.799 = 1,790 psi in compression. It might sometimes be better to pour a concrete curb to take this thrust and use this curb as the base of the stair wall.

The final detail of the stairs is shown in Fig. 5.29. This figure indicates several points

relative to the reinforcement which should be noted for stair slabs. Reinforcement required to pass a reentrant angle should not be merely bent around the corner, since under tension it has a tendency to straighten out and spall off the concrete. It is, therefore, carried through and hooked beyond the reentrant angle as is indicated in Fig. 5.29. Also, it is advisable for the protection of the nosing to put a single nosing bar in the nosing of each tread.

5.50 TWO–WAY CONCRETE SLABS

a   One of the most popular of the newer types of floor systems is the so-called "two-way slab." This is a floor slab reinforced in two directions, with supporting beams or walls on all four sides, and is not to be confused with the "flat-slab system," whicn is a system of girderless slabs. The slabs may be either solid concrete or concrete ribs with tile or concrete-block fillers. The system using 16-in. square tile fillers, either with or without topping, is known as the Shuster system and is marketed by the Whitacre Fireproofing Co. The system using specially shaped concrete-block fillers is known as the Republic system and is sold by the Republic Fireproofing Co. In these systems using fillers, the reinforcement is concentrated in the ribs, approximately 2 ft apart. The shear is taken care of by widening the ribs at the ends, by means of using narrower fillers. Usually, only straight bars are used—straight bottom bars from beam to beam and straight top bars from quarter point to quarter point. Only bars at the end of the span are hooked at the outer end.

This type of construction becomes more efficient as it approaches a square. As the ratio of sides approaches 2:1, the slab ap-

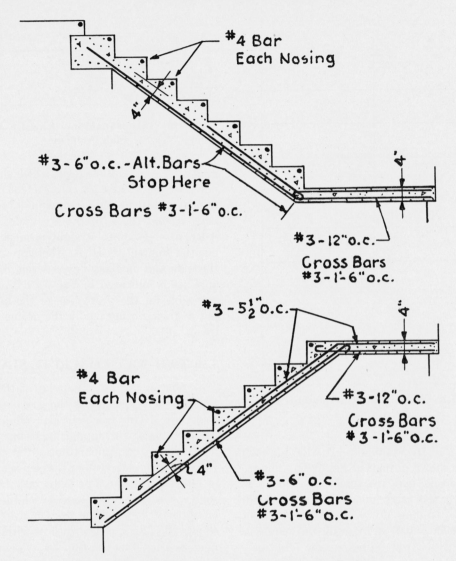

#4 Bar
Each Nosing

#3 - 6" o.c. - Alt. Bars
Stop Here

Cross Bars #3 - 1-6" o.c.

#3 - 12" o.c.
Cross Bars
#3 - 1-6" o.c.

4"

#3 - 5½" o.c.

#4 Bar
Each Nosing

#3 - 12" o.c.
Cross Bars
#3 - 1-6" o.c.

4"

#3 - 6" o.c.
Cross Bars
#3 - 1-6" o.c.

Fig. 5.29   Final Design—Kneed-Concrete-Slab Problem

proximates a one-way slab. The slab is well suited to carry heavy concentrations through plate action.

b There are several methods of design given in the 1951 ACI Code, only one of which will be given here. Design methods are given in Sec. 709 of the ACI Code, from which the following is abstracted.

The slab may be supported by walls or beams on all four sides, but if not securely attached to supports, special reinforcement must be provided in both top and bottom of slab for a distance in each direction from the corner of $\frac{1}{5}$ of the longest span. The reinforcement in the top of the slab shall be parallel to the diagonal from the corner, the reinforcement in the bottom shall be at right angles to the diagonal. The reinforcement in each band shall be of equivalent size and spacing to that required for the maximum positive moment in the slab.

In no case shall the slab thickness be less than 4 in. nor less than the perimeter of the slab divided by 180. The spacing of reinforcement shall be not more than three times the slab thickness, and the ratio of reinforcement shall be at least .0025.

The slab may be considered as consisting of strips in each direction as follows: A middle strip one-half panel in width, extending through the panel in the direction in which moments are considered.

A column strip occupying the two quarter-panels outside the middle strip.

Where the ratio of short to long span is less than 0.5, the middle strip in the short direction shall be considered as having a width equal to the difference between the long and short span, the remaining area representing the two column strips.

The critical section for positive moment shall be taken along the center line of panel, for negative moment at the face of supporting beams.

The bending moment for the middle strips shall be computed from the formula

$$M = CwS^2$$

where C is the coefficient from Table 5.50(b), w is the total unit load per square foot, and S is the short span in feet, the resulting moment being in foot units. Note that all moments are based on the short span.

The average moments per foot of width in the column strip shall be $\frac{2}{3}$ of the corresponding moment in the middle strip. In determining the spacing of the reinforcement in the column strip, the moment may be assumed to vary from a maximum at the band line to a minimum at the edge of the panel.

Where the negative moment on one side of a support is less than .8 of that on the other side,

Table 5.13   Two-Way Slab Moment Coefficients

	Short span*						Long span (all values of r)
	$r = 1.0$	$r = 0.9$	$r = 0.8$	$r = 0.7$	$r = 0.6$	$r = 0.5$ and less	
Case 1—Interior Panels							
Negative moment at edge	.033	.040	.048	.055	.063	.083	.033
Positive moment at midspan	.025	.030	.036	.041	.047	.062	.025
Case 2—One Edge Discontinuous							
Negative moment at continuous edge	.041	.048	.055	.062	.069	.085	.041
Negative moment at discontinuous edge	.021	.024	.027	.031	.035	.042	.021
Positive moment at midspan	.031	.036	.041	.047	.052	.064	031
Case 3—Two Edges Discontinuous							
Negative moment at continuous edge	.049	.057	.064	.071	.078	.090	049
Negative moment at discontinuous edge	.025	.028	.032	.036	.039	.045	.025
Positive moment at midspan	037	.043	.048	.054	.059	.068	.037
Case 4—Three Edges Discontinuous							
Negative moment at continuous edge	.058	.066	.074	.082	.090	.098	.058
Negative moment at discontinuous edge	.029	.033	.037	.041	.045	.049	.029
Positive moment at midspan	.044	.050	.056	.062	.068	.074	.044
Case 5—Four Edges Discontinuous							
Negative moment at edge	.033	.038	.043	.047	.053	.055	.033
Positive moment at midspan	050	.057	.064	.072	.080	.083	.050

*r = ratio of short span to long span.

Table 5.14   Design of Two-Way Concrete Slabs

	C	W	S^2	M ($\times$ 12)	Adjusted M	A_s	Reinforcement
A3	− .028	150	324	− 16,330		− .207	No. 3, 6 in. o.c.
	+ .043	150	324	+ 25,080		+ .318	No. 4, $5\frac{3}{4}$ in. o.c.
	− .057	150	324	− 33,240		− .42	No. 4, $4\frac{1}{2}$ in. o.c.
A2	− .057	150	324	− 33,240		− .42	No. 4, $4\frac{1}{2}$ in. o.c
	+ .043	150	324	+ 25,080	[.78]	+ .318	No. 4, $5\frac{3}{4}$ in. o.c
	− .048	150	324	− 27,990	− 21,540	− .274	No. 3, $4\frac{3}{4}$ in. o.c.
A1	− .049	150	100	− 8,620	− 15,170	− .192	No. 3, $4\frac{3}{4}$ in. o.c.
	+ .037	150	100	+ 6,660	[.75]	+ .135	No. 3, 9 in. o.c.
	− .025	150	100	− 4,500		− .135	No. 3, 9 in. o.c.

Minimum steel = 0.0025 × 4.5 × 12 = 0.135

Table 5.15   Flat-Slab Moment Coefficients

| | $M = CM$ coefficient C | | |
	Positive	Interior Negative	Exterior Negative
Moments in interior flat-slab panel			
With drop panel			
Column strip	+ 0.20	− 0.50	
Middle strip	+ 0.15	− 0.15	
Without drop panel			
Column strip	+ 0.22	− 0.46	
Middle strip	+ 0.16	− 0.16	
Moments in exterior flat-slab panel			
With drop panel			
Column strip	+ 0.25	− 0.55	− 0.45
Middle strip	+ 0.19	− 0.165	− 0.10
Without drop panel			
Column strip	+ 0.28	− 0.50	− 0.41
Middle strip	+ 0.20	− 0.176	− 0.10
Moments in panels with marginal beams or walls			
Half column strip adjacent to and parallel with beams or walls			
With drop panel, column strip*	+ 0.05	− 0.125	
Without drop panel, column strip*	+ 0.055	− 0.115	
With drop panel, column strip†	+ 0.10	− 0.25	
Without drop panel, column strip†	+ 0.11	− 0.23	
Moment across beams or wall			
With drop panel, middle strip*		0.195	
Without drop panel, middle strip*		0.208	
With drop panel, middle strip†		0.15	
Without drop panel, middle strip†		0.16	

*Applies to marginal beams with a depth greater than $1\frac{1}{2}$ times the slab thickness, or to a bearing wall.
†Applies to beams with a depth $1\frac{1}{2}$ times the slab thickness or less.

$\frac{2}{3}$ of the difference may be distributed in proportion to the relative stiffnesses of the slabs. If an intermediate panel is less than .6 of the span either side of it, it should be investigated for possibility of negative moment across the entire span

c The load on supporting beams for a two-way rectangular panel may be assumed as the load within the tributary areas of the panel bounded by the intersection of 45-deg lines from the corners with the median line of the panel parallel to the long side. The bending moment may be determined approximately by using an equivalent uniform load per lineal foot of beam for each panel supported, as follows:

For the short beam, $\dfrac{wS}{3}$

For the long beam, $\dfrac{wS}{3}\dfrac{(3 - r^2)}{2}$

d The plan of a floor to be designed as a two-way slab to carry a total load of 150 psf is shown in Fig. 5.30. The panels are designated by a number and a letter. Having sketched out the plan and put down the dimensions in each direction, compute r, the ratio of short to long span for each panel, and set it down. From Table 5.13 select (or interpolate) and set down the value of C and the value of S^2, the short span.

The design of the complete floor is too lengthy to set down the whole problem, but the computation of one band across panel A is given in Fig. 5.30. The maximum moment, 33,240, would require a slab thickness of

$$d = \sqrt{\frac{33,240}{12 \times 236}} = 3.46 \text{ in. net}$$

or $4\frac{1}{2}$ in. gross. The requirement of $\frac{1}{180}$ of perimeter would require 5.1 in. total depth, or

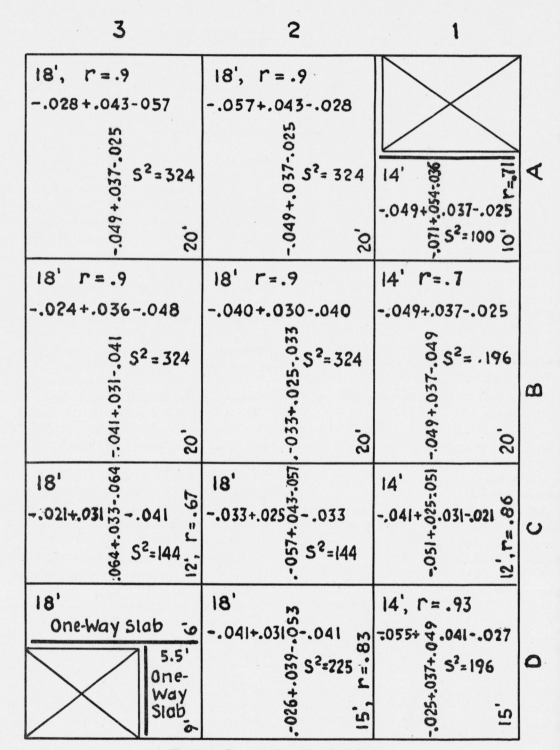

Fig. 5.30 Plan for Two-Way Slab Problem

a 5½-in. slab. On this basis, the steel is computed based on a net depth of 4½ in.

Two-thirds of the variation in negative moment from panel A2 to A1 is adjusted in accordance with stiffness factors. Using the
stiffness factor of 1 for a 14-ft span, it is reduced to 0.75 because it is an end span, and
$\frac{14}{18} = 0.78$ is the stiffness factor for the interior
18-ft panel (see Art. 3.21b). Minimum steel
governs the steel area in panel A1.

5.51 Flat slab

a According to the ACI Code a flat slab
is defined as a reinforced-concrete slab supported by columns with or without flaring
heads or column capitals, with or without de-
pressed or drop panels, and generally without
beams or girders. Two methods of design are
recognized, (1) the design as continuous bents
on accepted rigid-frame design methods, and
(2) for ordinary cases within the following limitations, the accepted coefficient method.
Three limitations for this method will apply:

1. The ratio of length to width of panel is
not to exceed 1.33.

2. The slab is to be continuous for at least
three panels in each direction.

3. Adjacent span lengths in each direction
are to vary by not more than 20 percent of the
shorter span.

Only the coefficient method will be discussed
in this article. The continuous-bent method
may be obtained from Sec. 1002 of the 1951
edition of ACI Code.

b In flat slabs designed under the coefficient method the basic moment M_o, the numerical sum of positive and negative moments
in the direction of either side of an interior
rectangular panel, is found as follows:

$$M_o = 0.09WL\left(1 - \frac{2c}{3L}\right)^2$$

where W is the load on the entire panel, L the
length in the direction under consideration,
and c the diameter or width of column capital
or splayed head at the underside of the slab
or drop panel. For the special condition usually used, where $c = 0.225L$, $M_o = 0.065WL$.

In computing compression due to bending,
three-fourths of the width of strip or of drop

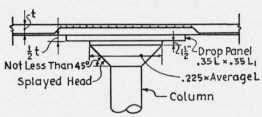

Fig. 5.31   Typical Section Through Flat Slab

panel shall be used. Tensile reinforcement
may be distributed over the entire width.

In computing moments, the slab shall be
divided into column strip and middle strip,
each half the distance between column centers, as shown in Fig. 5.32. The slab thickness
shall be not less than $L/40$ with drop panels
or $L/36$ without drop panels. The thickness
of drop panel below the slab shall be not more
than one-fourth the distance from the edge
of the column capital to the edge of the drop
panel. It will be found that the dimension
ratios shown in Fig. 5.31 are quite satisfactory for design. Openings may be cut through
a flat slab if provision is made for total positive and negative bending moments required.

The design must comply with the requirements to resist bending moment, in accordance with the coefficients of Table 5.15, and
to provide for shear.

The shearing unit stress on a vertical sec-
tion at a distance $t_2 - 1\frac{1}{2}$ in. beyond the edge
of the column capital or splayed head and
parallel and concentric with it shall not exceed
the following values:

1. $0.03f_c'$ when at least 50 percent of the total negative reinforcement in the column strip
passes directly over the column capital.

2. $0.025f_c'$ with 25 percent or less.

3. For intermediate percentages, interpolate.

The shearing unit stress on vertical sections
at a distance $t_3 - 1\frac{1}{2}$ in. beyond the edge of
the drop panel and parallel with them shall
not exceed $0.03f_c'$. At least 50 percent of the
cross-sectional area of the negative reinforcement in the column strip must be within the
width of strip directly above the drop panel.

In the above, t_2 is the thickness of slab without drop panels, or through drop panels, where
such are used, and t_3 is the thickness of slab

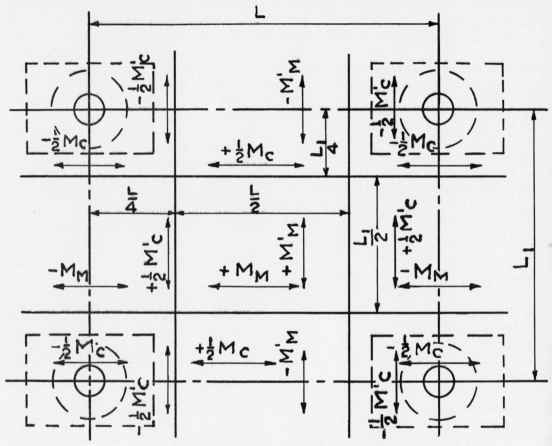

Fig. 5.32   Typical Plan of Flat Slab Bay

outside drop panels where they are used. Values for t_2 and t_3 may be substituted for d in the shear formula.

Problem   To illustrate the design of flat slabs, assume an interior panel 22 × 20 ft to carry a live load of 150 psf. The slab has no floor finish or ceiling but has drop panels. For preliminary design assume an 8-in. slab, weight 96 psf, total $w = 246$ psf.

For the proportions shown in Fig. 5.31, average span is 21 ft, drop panel 7 ft × 7 ft 9 in., splayed head 4 ft 9 in. diameter; the drop panel will be 4 in. deeper than the floor slab.

Total load on panel 22 × 20 × 246 $= 108,240$ lb
Less load inside shear line of drop panel $= (7 + 1.08)(7.75 + 1.08) \times 246 = -17,564$ lb
Net area in shear on slab $= \overline{91,676}$ lb

The shear at edge of drop panel is:

$$v = \frac{91,676}{406 \times 8 \times 0.875} = 32 \text{ psi}$$

Total load on panel $= 108,240$ lb
Less load inside splayed head $= (4.75 + 1.75)$ circle $= 33.18 \times 246 = \underline{-8,162}$ lb
$100,078$ lb

The shear at edge of splayed head is:

$$v = \frac{100,078}{245 \times 12 \times 0.875} = 40.6 \text{ psi}$$

Both of the above unit shear values are well within the allowable shearing stress for flat slabs, so the assumed thickness is satisfactory for shear.

The basic moment in the longer direction is

$$M_o = 0.065 \times 22 \times 12 \times 108,240$$
$$= 1,855,000 \text{ in.-lb}$$
$$-M_c = 0.5 \times 1,855,000 = 927,500 \text{ in.-lb}$$
$$+M_c = 0.2 \times 1,855,000 = 371,000 \text{ in.-lb}$$
$$\pm M_m = 0.15 \times 1,855,000 = 278,250 \text{ in.-lb}$$

For $\pm M_m$ and for $+M_c$, $d = 7$ in. net
For $-M_c$, $d = (8 + 4) - 1 = 11$ in. net

$$-A_{sc} = \frac{927.5}{17.5 \times 11} = 4.84 \text{ sq in.} = 25 \text{ No. } 4$$

$$+A_{sc} = \frac{371}{17.5 \times 7} = 3.05 \text{ sq in.} = 16 \text{ No. } 4$$

$$\pm A_{sm} = \frac{278.25}{17.5 \times 7} = 2.27 \text{ sq in.} = 12 \text{ No. } 4$$

By putting in each column band seven straight and nine bent bars lapped to the quarter point of the adjacent panel, we will provide 18 bars over the column head and 16 for positive moment in the column band. We will add seven straight bars in the top over the column to provide 25 total. Similarly six straight and six bent in the middle band will provide 12 for positive and 12 for negative moment.

The basic moment in the short direction will be

$$M_o = \tfrac{20}{22} \times 1,855,000 = 1,686,000 \text{ in.-lb}$$
$$-M_c = 843,000 \text{ in.-lb}$$
$$+M_c = 337,200 \text{ in.-lb}$$
$$\pm M_m = 253,000 \text{ in.-lb}$$

Since these bars cannot occupy the same plane as the bars in the longer direction, the net depths are $\frac{1}{2}$ in. less, or $6\frac{1}{2}$ and $10\frac{1}{2}$ in. respectively.

$$-A_{sc} = \frac{843}{17.5 \times 10.5} = 4.58 \text{ sq in.} = 23 \text{ No. } 4$$
(add 7 No. 4 straight top bars)

$$+A_{sc} = \frac{337.2}{17.5 \times 6.5} = 2.96 \text{ sq in.} = 15 \text{ No. } 4$$
(7 straight, 8 bent)

$$\pm A_{sm} = \frac{253}{17.5 \times 6.5} = 2.23 \text{ sq in.} = 12 \text{ No. } 4$$
(6 straight, 6 bent)

Normally, compression in the concrete does not control flat-slab design. We will check this problem to indicate this. The ACI Code specifies that $\frac{3}{4}$ of the width of the strip shall be used in computing compressive stress, except that $\frac{3}{4}$ of the width of the drop panel shall be used in computing compressive strength over the columns.

Thus, using $K = 157$ for 2,000-psi concrete, the allowable moment for the 8-in. slab in the long direction will be

$$M = 0.75 \times 157 \times 120 \times 49 = 692,000 \text{ in.-lb}$$

and for the drop panel

$$M = 0.75 \times 157 \times 84 \times 121 = 1,210,000 \text{ in.-lb}$$

Therefore compressive stress may be disregarded.

c Under certain conditions there is an application of the flat-slab system to short spans which may be found particularly useful and economical. This application (which actually is a variation of the flat-slab requirements) is quoted from a proposed local building code:

In flat slabs without drop panels where t is greater than $.05L$, a continuous mat of reinforcement sufficient for the total positive moments of the panel may be used in the bottom of the slab and a mat of reinforcement sufficient for the total negative moments of the panel may be used over each supporting column in the top of the slab. The reinforcement in the mats for positive moment shall be spliced only on column center lines, and shall lap not less than 40 diameters of the bars. The reinforcement in the mats for negative moments shall extend not less than $.3L$ in each direction from the column center lines.

Obviously this use of the flat slab is intended for short spans. It has been used in the space under the first floor of school buildings, where column spacing of 10 to 12 ft in each direction does not interfere with the use of this space for pipes or plenum chambers.

5.52 Reinforced-concrete slabs on the ground

a Reinforcement in slabs on compacted or undisturbed earth of uniform bearing value does not contribute enough to load-carrying capacity to influence the design. However, it is good practice to put reinforcement in the slab for the purpose of preventing unsightly shrinkage cracks, and the area of reinforcement per foot width in each direction should be $A_s = wL/25,000$.

b Under certain unusual conditions, reinforced-concrete slabs on the ground may be computed as flat slabs or two-way slabs, in accordance with Art. 5.50 or 5.51.

The first of these conditions is a slab supported on filled ground, particularly a floor designed to carry heavy live loads, such as heavy-duty machine-shop floors or heavy warehouses.

A second condition where a slab of this type must be used is to resist the uplift of water pressure. In the design for this condition, the dead weight of the concrete slab is subtracted from the pressure head per square foot, and the slab is designed to resist the difference. If the head to be designed against is great, it may be necessary to provide additional dead load in the slab to assist the dead load of the structure above in resisting the uplift.

Obviously, since slabs and beams on the ground are formed by the earth, it is advisable to form beams and footings using sloping sides. For waterproofing, a subslab is often used, on which waterproofing is laid, and the supporting slab laid over the waterproofing. Remember that the load on a waterproofing slab is a load upward and the location of the steel reinforcement is reversed—the positive-moment steel being located in the top of the slab and the negative moment in the bottom.

A typical problem will illustrate the use of this type of construction to resist the uplift of water pressure.

Problem Assume a column spacing of 20 ft in each direction (an ideal situation for flat-slab construction). Design a slab to resist a water pressure of 6 ft of head. The columns carry a load of 200 kips on soil with a carrying capacity of 6,000 psf. From Tables 8.2 and 8.3, we find that the foundation required is 6 ft square and 1 ft 5 in. thick. The slab is designed in accordance with the flat-slab formulae given in Art. 5.51. The design load per square foot is arrived at as follows:

Upward load = 6-ft head × 62.5 = 375

Dead load: 3   in. subfloor
              $1\frac{1}{2}$ in. finish
              $\underline{6\ \ \text{in. slab (assumed)}}$
              $10\frac{1}{2}$ in. total   = 125

Net design load   = 250 psf

The foundation in this instance must serve both as a foundation and as an inverted splayed head, and its depth must be either the depth required for the footing or for the splayed head adjacent to the column, whichever is the greater. Using the splayed-head dimension ratio shown on Fig. 5.31, the desirable width of splayed head for the span is $0.225 \times 20 = 4.5$ ft. Since the splayed head must be below the slab, this is the side of the square at the bottom of the footing.

Assuming an 18-in. column, the depth of splay at 45 deg is $\dfrac{4.5 - 1.5}{2} = 1.5$ ft, or 18 in. To this should be added the depth of the shoulder to arrive at the total depth—2 in. plus the depth of slab, assumed at 6 in., thus giving a total depth of footing design of 26 in. This will undoubtedly satisfy conditions either for footing design under full live and dead load without uplift or for flat slab designed for uplift and dead load only. Assuming a 45-deg slope for the excavation, the side of square for punching shear in the slab is $4.5 + 1.5 + 1.5 = 7.5$.

The total uplift load per bay = $250 \times 20 \times 20 = 100,000$ lb.

The shear is taken at a distance d outside the splay, and with a 6-in. slab we may use $4\frac{1}{2}$ in. net for d; or the area to be deducted for shear is (7 ft 6 in. + 9 in.) square, and the load on this area to be deducted for shear is $8.25 \times 8.25 \times 250 = 17,015$. The net shear is $100,000 - 17,015 = 82,985$ lb.

The unit shear on a perimeter 99 in. square is

$$v = \frac{82,985}{99 \times 4 \times 4.5 \times 0.875} = 53.2\ \text{lb}$$

which is within the allowable.

The design of reinforcement is in accordance with the method of Art. 5.51.

The depth of the splayed head for a column under these conditions would be

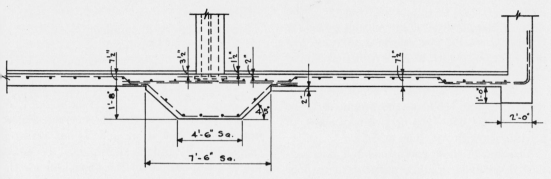

Fig. 5.33   Flat Slab Reinforced Against Water Pressure

Depth of slab $= 7\frac{1}{2}$ in.
Depth of shoulder $= 2$ in.
Depth of splay, assuming an 18-in. column

$$= \frac{4 \text{ ft } 6 \text{ in.} - 1 \text{ ft } 6 \text{ in.}}{2} = 1 \text{ ft } 6 \text{ in.} = \frac{18 \text{ in.}}{27\frac{1}{2} \text{ in.}}$$

$$= 2 \text{ ft } 3\frac{1}{2} \text{ in.}$$

Therefore, since this is the greater of the two depths, it should be used. Figure 5.33 shows a section through the construction.

c A slab on filled ground is frequently combined with pile foundations because of the nature of the subsoil. Although the column spacing is frequently satisfactory for flat-slab construction (a ratio of not over $1\frac{1}{3}$ to 1), many installations are not suited to flat-slab column spacing—for example, machine shops, which are often equipped with crane spans and other irregular conditions. Beams laid in trenches, either as one-way or two-way slab systems, are quite satisfactory for this condition, as indicated in the accompanying plan and beam sections (Fig. 5.34).

5.60   GYPSUM SYSTEMS

a Because in some areas they fill certain needs at a low cost, and because the sales-promotion work has been well handled, gypsum floor and roof slabs have come into fairly common use in sections where freight rates do not work against them. Their chief advantages may be summed up as follows: (1) light weight; (2) low cost; (3) good fire resistance; (4) if precast, can be applied in winter; (5) if precast, can be used satisfactorily for sloping roofs; and (6) if precast, can

be nailed, and nails will hold reasonably well The chief arguments against its use seem to be: (1) its lack of strength renders it undesirable for heavy or concentrated loads; (2) if not properly protected during construction it will soften and disintegrate in wet weather; (3) all precast systems lack the ability to stiffen the structure.

b All gypsum systems are sold and installed by specialists, and the details, load tables, and other data are available from their catalogs and from their salesmen. The long-span poured-in-place systems (spans up to about 7 ft 6 in.) are designed on the basis of the suspension-bridge principle, and the end-bay steel must be braced to provide anchorage (see Fig. 5.35). The long-span precast may be designed on the same principle, or it may be of rigid-channel type (Fig. 5.36) or tongue-and-groove plank sections. With either type of precast system, the steel beams must have the top flange braced to reduce the l/b of the beam, since the slab does not furnish lateral support for the beam. Gypsum planks, either 2 or $2\frac{1}{2}$ in. thick, usually with tongue-and-groove metal edges (Fig. 5.37), are one of the most common forms of long-span gypsum slabs; and although the metal clips by means of which the slab is clamped to the beam do furnish considerable lateral support to the top flange of the beam, there are many building departments which still require the additional lateral bracing of tie rods. The short-span roof systems, usually 30- or 32-in. span (Figs. 5.38 and 5.39), either precast or cast in place on plasterboard forms, are supported on steel

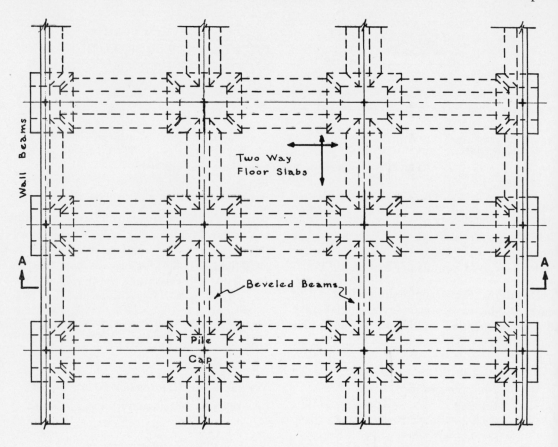

PLAN

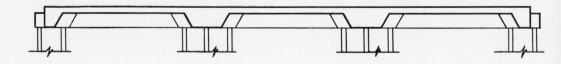

SEC. A-A

Fig. 5.34 Supported First-Floor Slabs

T sections or rail sections, which are usually furnished by the gypsum contractor and welded to steel beams about 7 or 8 ft apart. These welded T sections in themselves will furnish adequate lateral bracing to the steel beams.

c Most of the design data for gypsum systems is found in the manufacturer's catalogs. The load capacity of gypsum slabs or planks is tabulated for various spans. Similarly the maximum span of Ts or rails for the short-span systems is usually given in the manufacturer's catalogs, although it may sometimes be necessary to use standard Ts as listed below instead of the rail Ts or other sections sold by the manufacturer.

Since some form of short-span system is most commonly used, a problem and tables of

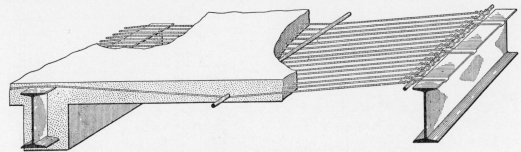

Fig. 5.35   Long-Span Poured-in-Place Gypsum Slab

capacities of the T and rail sections ordinarily used are included here. Note that in Table 5.17 the weight of supporting rails is given in pounds per yard (as is common practice for rails) instead of pounds per foot as for Ts.

Problem   Select the required T or rail to carry a 2-in. cast-in-place gypsum slab with 6 psf roof covering and 30 psf roof load plus suspended ceiling, spacing of beams to be 7 ft 6 in.

Roof load	= 30
2-in. gypsum slab	= 8
Roofing	= 6
Ceiling	= 10
Steel	= 3
	57 psf

From Table 5.17 select 12-lb rail.

5.70   TILE–ARCH CONSTRUCTION

Although tile-arch construction cannot be classed as concrete floor slab, the fact that it is a competing fireproof construction—or, more

properly, was a competing construction—is perhaps sufficient reason to discuss it in this sequence. Because of excessive cost, it is seldom used nowadays, and most tile-arch construction uses flat arches, as indicated in Fig. 5.40. It is desirable for the sake of fin-

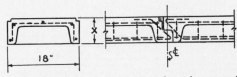

Cross Section   Part Longitudinal Sect'n

Fig. 5.36   Channel-Type Gypsum Slab

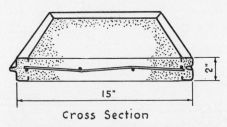

Cross Section

Fig. 5.37   Gypsteel Plank

Table 5.16   Capacity of Ts for Short-Span Gypsum Systems

Weight, pounds per foot

Span	4.1 lb	4.9 lb	5.5 lb	6.4 lb	6.7 lb	7.5 lb	8.9 lb	10.8 lb
5'0"	66.25	85.0	103.75	122.5				
5'6"	55.0	70.0	85.0	101.5	127.5			
6'0"		58.75	71.25	83.75	106.25	121.25		
6'6"			60.0	71.25	90.0	102.50	118.75	133.75
7'0"				61.25	77.5	87.5	102.50	115.0
7'6"					67.5	77.5	88.75	98.75
8'0"					58.75	66.25	76.25	86.25
8'6"						58.75	76.5	76.25
9'0"							60.0	67.5

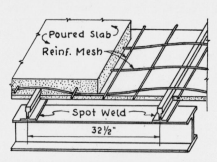

Fig. 5.38   Short-Span Poured-in-Place Gypsum Slab

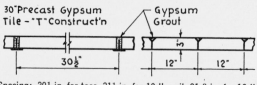

Spacing: 30½ in. for tees, 31⅛ in. for 12-lb rail, 31⅜ in. for 16-lb rail, and 31½ in. for 20-lb rail

Fig. 5.39   30-in. Gypsum-Tile T Construction

ished ceiling to have the arch fill the depth of the beam as shown. However, occasionally the beams are shallower than the arch, and the beams are then kept flush bottom with those of the economical depth. Deeper beams are used with a starting block of the proper depth on which the arch is started, as shown in Fig. 5.40.

When arch blocks are the same depth as the beams, they are usually laid to project 1½ in. below the bottom of the beams, and the space above the arch is filled in with lean concrete in which conduits, pipes, etc., can be laid.

Table 5.18 is a manufacturer's standard table of flat terra-cotta arches, giving the safe load in pounds per square foot and allowing a factor of safety of 7.

Tile arches produce side thrust on the floor beams. This thrust is taken up by tie rods between the beams. With flat arches, ¾-in.

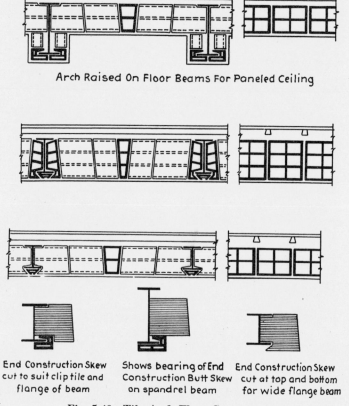

Arch Raised On Floor Beams For Paneled Ceiling

End Construction Skew cut to suit clip tile and flange of beam

Shows bearing of End Construction Butt Skew on spandrel beam

End Construction Skew cut at top and bottom for wide flange beam

Fig. 5.40   Tile-Arch Floor Construction

ound tie rods spaced not over 15 times the
beam flange width will usually be sufficient.
The thrust may be obtained from the formula

$$H = \frac{3wL^2}{2R}$$

where H is the thrust per foot length of beam,
w the total live and dead load per square foot,
L the arch span in feet, and R the rise of the
arch in inches, which may be taken as the arch
depth less 2.4. The maximum spacing is the

tensile value of one rod at the root of the
thread divided by H.

Table 5.18   Flat Terra-cotta Arches

Allowable load, psf

Span of arch	Depth of arch blocks, inches					
	6	7	8	9	10	12
	Area of arch blocks, square inches					
	31	34	37	40	43	49
3′0″	458	588	735	901	1,084	1,487
3′3″	386	496	622	763	916	1,262
3′6″	330	424	531	653	785	1,083
3′9″	284	365	459	565	679	938
4′0″	247	318	399	493	593	820
4′3″	216	278	350	433	521	722
4′6″	190	245	309	382	461	640
4′9″	168	217	274	340	410	571
5′0″	149	193	244	304	367	511
5′3″		172	218	272	330	460
5′6″		154	196	245	297	416
5′9″		139	176	222	269	378
6′0″			159	201	244	344
6′3″			144	183	222	314
6′6″			131	166	203	287
6′9″				152	186	264
7′0″				139	170	243
7′6″					144	206
8′0″						177
8′6″						153
9′0″						132

Table 5.17   Capacity of Rails for Short-Span Gypsum Systems

Weight, pounds per yard

Span	12 lb	16 lb	20 lb
5′0″	132.5		
5′6″	110.0		
6′0″	92.5		
6′6″	77.5	125	
7′0″	67.5	107.5	
7′6″	58.75	93.75	132.5
8′0″		80.0	116.25
8′6″		72.5	102.5
9′0″		63.75	90.0
9′6″		56.25	81.25
10′0″			72.5
10′6″			65.0
11′0″			60.0

6

Timber and Other Materials in Bending

6.10 TIMBER BEAMS AND JOISTS

a Wooden beams are used in building construction as joists or girders carrying a floor or roof load. Strength limitations prevent their use for very heavy loads or very long spans. For ordinary structural uses in the eastern United States, most residence joist and rafter designs are based on the use of eastern hemlock or short-leaf yellow pine. Heavier designs such as factory floors, etc., are frequently based on the use of long-leaf yellow pine or Douglas fir. Building codes vary greatly in the allowable stresses on these materials.

The stresses recommended by the Forest Products Laboratory of the U.S. Department of Agriculture are being accepted more and more by building departments. Many codes, however, list so many classifications for grade and for moisture conditions that they are confusing. Table 1.1 shows the allowable stresses in the grades ordinarily used in building-construction work. This list also assumes a "continuously dry" condition, and, therefore, is not applicable to bridge work.

It is the practice of the lumber industry to rate lumber sizes on a series of nominal standard sizes which are slightly in excess of the actual sizes. Table 1.11 lists the lumber sizes as nominal sizes, but gives also the actual dressed size, and the section moduli have been figured on the basis of actual size.

b The factors controlling the selection of a wood beam are (1) strength in bending, determined by section modulus, (2) horizontal shearing stress, and (3) deflection. In addition, when the beam under consideration is a joist, the spacing must be set to take standard lath, which is 48 in. long. The spacing for floors is usually either 12 or 16 in. and for roofs either 16 or 24 in. With a fairly heavy load, crushing of the beam may occur at the bearing because the allowable bearing on the side grain of a timber is low—only about one-third of the allowable end-grain bearing.

The bending moment on a wood beam should be figured in the manner described in Art. 3.10. The section modulus required may then be obtained by dividing the moment in inch-pounds by the allowable unit fiber stress, and the beam selected from Table 1.11. If the designer has a number of joists or beams to figure, he may make up his own formula for obtaining S direct from load and span in feet. For 1,200-psi fiber stress, the commonest now in use for short-leaf yellow pine, $S = 1.25WL$. For 1,600-psi fiber stress, commonly used for long-leaf yellow pine or structural-grade Douglas fir, $S = 0.94WL$.

The most commonly used structural material, wood, is frequently subjected to abuse through failure to design properly for loads from above. Occasionally loads from above are carried down through bearing partitions to a line of joists below without making provision for the concentrated loads (see Fig. 6.1).

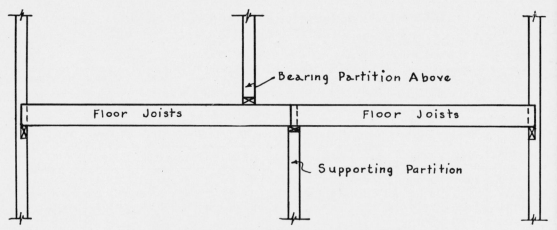

Fig. 6.1   A Frequently Overlooked Joist Load

Problem Select short-leaf yellow pine floor joists for a 17-ft span in a residence, total floor load 60 psf. Based on 1 ft width,

$$W = 17 \times 60 = 1{,}020$$
$$S = 1.25 \times 1.02 \times 17 = 21.7$$

Use 2×10, 12 in. o.c. $(S = 24.4)$,
or 2×12, 16 in. o.c.

$$\left(S = 35.8, \text{ or } \frac{35.8}{1.33} = 26.9 \text{ per ft width}\right).$$

The 2×10 would require

$$\frac{2 \times 10}{12} = 1.67 \text{ bd ft per sq ft}$$

The 2×12 would require

$$\frac{2 \times 12}{12 \times 1.33} = 1.5 \text{ bd ft per sq ft}$$

Therefore, other things being equal, it would probably be cheaper, and certainly stiffer to use the 2×12 (see Table 6.1).

Problem The engineer is frequently confronted with a problem of this type: What load per square foot may be placed on a warehouse floor of 4×12 long-leaf yellow pine joists 24 in. o.c. on a 16 ft span? The simplest method is to assume 100 psf total load and design a beam, then from the ratio of section modulus required compute allowable load. Assuming 100 psf,

$$W = 2 \times 16 \times 100 = 3{,}200$$

Assume 1,600-psi fiber stress.

$$S = 0.94 \times 3.2 \times 16 = 48.1 \text{ required}$$
$$79.9 \text{ furnished}$$

The allowable load is

$$W = \frac{79.9}{48.1} \times 100 = 166 \text{ psf total}$$

c In short beams or beams having a heavy concentration near the end, as in Fig. 6.1, the safe unit stress in horizontal shear may be the governing factor. The maximum unit horizontal shear at any point is 1.5 times the total shear at that point divided by the cross-sectional area. Applying this rule to the problem stated above,

$$f_{hs} = 1.5 \times \frac{1{,}600 \times \dfrac{79.9}{48.1}}{3.625 \times 11.5} = 95.6 \text{ psi}$$

This is within the allowable unit shear given in Table 1.1, so the result of the problem need not be revised.

d If the span in feet is in excess of 1.5 times the depth in inches, deflection may control the selection of a timber joist or beam and should be checked. Deflection may be computed by the regular deflection formula, but for simpler application the following formula, based on the standard formula for deflection of a uniformly distributed loaded beam, may be derived, using deflection in inches and span in feet.

$$\Delta = \frac{15fL^2}{Ec}$$

In case of steel or concrete under a given load on a span, the beam will take a deflection and, within the elastic limit, when the load is removed the beam will assume its original po-

Table 6.1 Floor Joists for 12-in. and 16-in. Spacing

Designed for live load and dead load.

Fiber stress of 1,200 psi, shear of 125 psi.

Where several sizes of joists are possible, they are given so that the most economical size may be selected. Narrower-faced joists result in a saving of wall height.

D.L. (dead load) includes weight of joist, 1-in. subfloor, and 1-in. finish floor.

A 10-psf plastered ceiling can be provided for by selecting the size for a 10-psf heavier live load.

Span, feet	30 psf + D.L.		40 psf + D.L.		50 psf + D.L.		60 psf + D.L.		70 psf + D.L.	
	12 in.	16 in.	12 in.	16 in.	12 in.	16 in.	12 in.	16 in.	12 in.	16 in.
9	2 × 6	2 × 6	2 × 6	2 × 6	2 × 6	2 × 6	2 × 6	2 × 8	2 × 6	2 × 8
10	2 × 6	2 × 6	2 × 6	2 × 6	2 × 6	2 × 8	2 × 8	2 × 8	2 × 8	2 × 8
11	2 × 6	2 × 6	2 × 6	2 × 8	2 × 8	2 × 8	2 × 8	2 × 8	2 × 8	2 × 10
										3 × 8
12	2 × 6	2 × 8	2 × 8	2 × 8	2 × 8	2 × 8	2 × 8	2 × 10	2 × 8	2 × 10
										3 × 8
13	2 × 6	2 × 8	2 × 8	2 × 8	2 × 8	2 × 10	2 × 8	2 × 10	2 × 10	2 × 10
						3 × 8		3 × 8	3 × 8	3 × 8
14	2 × 8	2 × 8	2 × 8	2 × 10	2 × 8	2 × 10	2 × 10	2 × 10	2 × 10	2 × 12
				3 × 8		3 × 8	3 × 8	3 × 8	3 × 8	3 × 10
15	2 × 8	2 × 8	2 × 8	2 × 10	2 × 10	2 × 10	2 × 10	2 × 12	2 × 10	2 × 12
				3 × 8	3 × 8	3 × 8	3 × 8	3 × 10	3 × 8	3 × 10
16	2 × 8	2 × 10	2 × 10	2 × 10	2 × 10	2 × 12	2 × 10	2 × 12	2 × 12	2 × 12
		3 × 8	3 × 8	3 × 8	3 × 8	3 × 10	3 × 8	3 × 10	3 × 10	3 × 10
17	2 × 8	2 × 10	2 × 10	2 × 10	2 × 10	2 × 12	2 × 12	2 × 12	2 × 12	2 × 14
		3 × 8	3 × 8	3 × 8	3 × 8	3 × 10	3 × 10	3 × 10	3 × 10	3 × 10
18	2 × 10	2 × 10	2 × 10	2 × 12	2 × 10	2 × 12	2 × 12	2 × 14	2 × 12	2 × 14
	3 × 8	3 × 8	3 × 8	3 × 10	3 × 8	3 × 10	3 × 10	3 × 10	3 × 10	3 × 12
										4 × 10
19	2 × 10	2 × 10	2 × 10	2 × 12	2 × 12	2 × 12	2 × 12	2 × 14	2 × 14	2 × 14
	3 × 8	3 × 8	3 × 8	3 × 10	3 × 10	3 × 10	3 × 10	3 × 12	3 × 10	3 × 12
								4 × 10		4 × 10
20	2 × 10	2 × 12	2 × 12	2 × 12	2 × 12	2 × 14	2 × 12	2 × 14	2 × 14	2 × 16
	3 × 8	3 × 10	3 × 10	3 × 10	3 × 10	3 × 12	3 × 10	3 × 12	3 × 12	3 × 12
						4 × 10		4 × 10	4 × 10	
21	2 × 10	2 × 12	2 × 12	2 × 14	2 × 12	2 × 14	2 × 14	2 × 16	2 × 14	2 × 16
	3 × 8	3 × 10	3 × 10	3 × 10	3 × 10	3 × 12	3 × 12	3 × 12	3 × 12	3 × 14
				4 × 10	4 × 10		4 × 10		4 × 10	4 × 12
22	2 × 10	2 × 12	2 × 12	2 × 14	2 × 14	2 × 14	2 × 14	2 × 16	2 × 14	2 × 16
	3 × 8	3 × 10	3 × 10	3 × 12	3 × 10	3 × 12	3 × 12	3 × 12	3 × 12	3 × 14
				4 × 10		4 × 10	4 × 10		4 × 10	4 × 12
23	2 × 12	2 × 12	2 × 12	2 × 14	2 × 14	2 × 16	2 × 14		2 × 16	
	3 × 10	3 × 10	3 × 10	3 × 12	3 × 12	3 × 12	3 × 12	3 × 14	3 × 12	3 × 14
				4 × 10	4 × 10		4 × 10	4 × 12		4 × 12
24	2 × 12	2 × 14	2 × 14	2 × 14	2 × 14	2 × 16	2 × 16		2 × 16	
	3 × 10	3 × 10	3 × 10	3 × 12	3 × 12	3 × 14	3 × 12	3 × 14	3 × 14	3 × 16
				4 × 10	4 × 10	4 × 12	4 × 10	4 × 12	4 × 12	
25	2 × 12	2 × 14	2 × 14	2 × 16	2 × 14	2 × 16	2 × 16		2 × 16	
	3 × 10	3 × 12	3 × 12	3 × 12	3 × 12	3 × 14	3 × 12	3 × 14	3 × 14	3 × 16
		4 × 10	4 × 10		4 × 10	4 × 12		4 × 12	4 × 12	
26	2 × 12	2 × 14	2 × 14	2 × 16	2 × 16		2 × 16			
	3 × 10	3 × 12	3 × 12	3 × 14	3 × 12	3 × 14	3 × 14	3 × 16	3 × 14	3 × 16
		4 × 10	4 × 10	4 × 12		4 × 12	4 × 12		4 × 12	

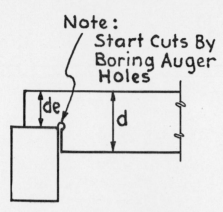

Fig. 6.2   Notched End of Joist

sition. This is not strictly true with wood. If a timber is loaded excessively with a constant load, it will deflect and the deflection will continue to increase under the same load, even within the elastic limit of the material. Then, when the load has been removed, it will be found that the material has taken a permanent set or deflection.

Problem   Check the deflection on a joist figured in paragraph *b* using the 12-in. joist.

$$f = \frac{21.7}{26.9} \times 1{,}200 = 968 \text{ psi}$$

$$\Delta = \frac{15 \times 968 \times 17^2}{1{,}600{,}000 \times 5.75} = 0.456 \text{ in.}$$

The permissible $\Delta = 17/3$ in.$0 = 0.567$ (see Table 6.2).

e   It is sometimes necessary to determine the strength of a wood beam which is notched, either for the passage of pipes or for bearing at the end. If the notch is at or near the center of the beam, the least net depth should be used in determining the strength of the beam in bending.

If the beam is notched on the lower side at the ends, the strength of a short, relatively deep beam or joist should be checked for end shear using the formula

$$V = \left(\tfrac{2}{3}\right) \frac{b d_e^2 v}{d}$$

where d is the total depth, d_e the end depth, and v the allowable horizontal-shear unit stress (Fig. 6.2).

f   Since by far the commonest form of wood construction problem to be encountered is the selection of a wood floor joist, Table 6.1 has been included to enable the designer to select the joist size directly. This table is taken from the Southern Pine Manual of Standard Wood Construction.

For a simpler approach to the problem of deflection of a wood joist, Table 6.2 has been included. This table is also taken from the Southern Pine Manual of Standard Wood Construction.

Table 6.2   Floor Joists Based on Deflection

Designed for live load and dead load.
Spans limited to deflection of $\frac{1}{360}$ of span.
D.L. (dead load) includes weight of joist, 1-in. subfloor, and 1-in. finish floor.
A 10-psf plastered ceiling can be provided for by selecting the size for a 10-psf heavier live load.

	30 psf + D.L.		40 psf + D.L.		50 psf + D.L.	
	12 in. o.c.	16 in. o.c.	12 in. o.c.	16 in. o.c.	12 in. o.c.	16 in. o.c.
2 × 6	11′6″	10′7″	10′7″	9′8″	10′0″	9′1″
2 × 8	15′2″	14′1″	14′1″	12′11″	13′2″	12′1″
3 × 8	17′6″	16′3″	16′3″	14′11″	15′4″	14′0″
2 × 10	19′1″	17′9″	17′9″	16′3″	16′8″	15′3″
3 × 10	21′11″	20′5″	20′5″	18′9″	19′3″	17′8″
2 × 12	23′0″	21′4″	21′4″	19′6″	20′1″	18′4″
3 × 12	23′11″	24′6″	24′6″	22′7″	23′2″	21′3″
2 × 14	26′9″	24′11″	24′11″	22′11″	23′5″	21′6″

6.20 CAST–IRON LINTELS

a Cast-iron lintels were extensively used at one time but rarely nowadays. The principles used in computation of lintel sections, however, are those used in other cast-iron sections, such as special bases, castings, etc., and it would be advisable to consider the problem of their design. The cross section generally used is either a single or double T, as shown in Fig. 6.3. It is often deeper in the center of the span than at either end and may have a reinforcing rib at the center, as shown in Fig. 6.4.

b The steps in computing the strength of a lintel are as follows: (1) With the section and shape given, by the methods of Art. 1.31, compute the position of the neutral axis and the moment of inertia about the neutral axis, and from the results thus obtained compute *S*, the section modulus. (2) Having *S* and the span, and using a modulus of rupture of 3,000 psi, the capacity of the lintel may be computed as described in Art. 3.10. This method of procedure has assumed that the problem involved is the determination of capacity for a given lintel, since it is somewhat unlikely that an engineer would design a new lintel of cast iron nowadays.

Problem A cast-iron lintel of an inverted T shape (Fig. 6.3) has a flange 7 in. wide and a web 4 in. high (net). It is of $\frac{5}{8}$-in. thick metal throughout. Assume that it is required to span a window 4 ft 6 in. and to carry an 8-in. brick wall 5 ft high. Check the lintel to carry this load.

To simplify computation, we will use the center of the flange as a trial axis.

	A	$\bar{y}$	Ay	Ay^2	I_0
Flange	4.375	0	0	0	0.1425
Web	2.5	2.3125	5.78	13.4	3.33
	6.875		5.78	13.4	3.4725
					13.4
					16.8725

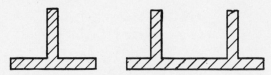

Fig. 6.3 Sections Through Cast-Iron Lintels

$$\bar{y} = \frac{5.78}{6.875} = 0.841$$

$$c = 4.3125 - 0.841 = 3.4715 \text{ in.}$$

$$I_0 = 16.8725 - (6.875 \times 0.841^2)$$
$$= 16.8725 - 4.86 = 12.0125$$

$$S = \frac{12.0125}{3.4715} = 3.46 \text{ furnished}$$

$$W = 5 \times 80 \times 4.5 = 1,800$$

$$M = \frac{1,800 \times 4.5 \times 12}{8} = 12,150$$

$$S \text{ required} = \frac{12,150}{3,000} = 4.05$$

Therefore lintel cannot be used.

6.30 ALUMINUM SECTIONS

Aluminum sections, because of their cost, are used in building construction only for ornamental metal structures and other special conditions. Since the allowable fiber stress to be used is dependent on the alloy used, no such stress can be given in an article of this kind. Moreover, although the sections and properties of these sections generally available follow the pattern of steel sections in angles up to $6 \times 6 \times \frac{3}{4}$ in., in I-beam size up to 12 in. (American standard beam), in channel size up to 12 in., and in H beams up to 8×8, there is enough variation in properties and in materials available so that the designer should check with the manufacturer before proceeding with the design. As to method of design, the procedure in general follows the procedure used in design of structural steel, after the allowable stress and sections available have been determined.

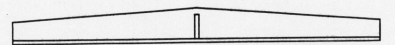

Fig. 6.4 Tapered Cast-Iron Lintel—Elevation

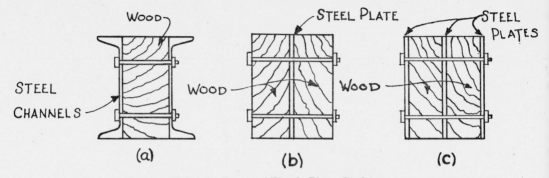

Fig. 6.5   Types of Flitch-Plate Girders

6.40   FLITCH–PLATE OR COMBINATION BEAMS

a   Formula (2.3) may be written $\delta = f/E$. Therefore if two materials work to resist the same type of stress in unison,

$$\delta = \frac{f_1}{E_1} = \frac{f_2}{E_2} \quad \text{or} \quad f_1 = \left(\frac{E_1}{E_2}\right)f_2 \quad \text{or} \quad f_1 = nf_2$$

In other words, if two materials having different moduli of elasticity are used together, they do not both work to the limit of their stress, but each carries stress in proportion to the above formula.

Problem   Let us assume that an 8×12 long-leaf yellow pine beam is reinforced by the addition of two 12-in. 27-lb channels properly bolted together. What percentage is added to the strength of the wood beam?

Assume $E_{yp} = 1,600,000$, $E_s = 30,000,000$, and $n = 30/1.6 = 18.75$.

If $f_{yp} = 1,600$, $f_s = 30,000$, which would overstress the steel. Therefore, if f_s is kept to $20,000$, $f_{yp} = 1,067$.

On the basis of long-leaf yellow pine only,

$$M = 1,600 \times 165 = 264,000 \text{ in.-lb}$$

The combined girder will carry

$$
\begin{aligned}
1,067 \times 165 &= 176,000 \\
20,000 \times 42.8 &= \underline{856,000} \\
&\ 1,032,000 \\
&-\ \underline{264,000} \\
\text{Increase} &= 768,000 \text{ in.-lb}
\end{aligned}
$$

$$\text{Percent increase} = \frac{768.5}{264} = 291 \text{ percent}$$

b   The above type of beam, using two wood beams on either side of a vertical steel or wrought-iron plate, properly bolted, was used quite extensively until steel beams were developed, and was known as a flitched beam or flitch-plate girder. Occasionally nowadays this method may be found economical to reinforce a steel beam by the addition of two wood beams, or to reinforce a wood beam by the addition of two steel channels or plates. It should be noted also that this method may only be used if the component parts are of equal depth.

6.50   COMPOSITE BEAMS

a   The following taken from the AISC Code will govern the design of composite beams of rolled steel completely encased in concrete.

(a) Definition.   The term "composite beam" shall apply to any rolled or fabricated steel floor beam entirely encased in a poured concrete haunch at least four inches wider at its narrowest point than the flange of the beam, supporting a concrete slab on each side without openings adjacent to the beam; provided that the top of the beam is at least $1\frac{1}{2}$ inches below the top of the slab and at least 2 inches above the bottom of the slab; provided that a good grade of stone or gravel concrete, with Portland cement, is used; and provided that the concrete haunch has adequate mesh, or other reinforcing steel, throughout its whole depth and across its soffit.

(b) Design Assumptions.   Composite beams may be figured on the assumption that:

(1) The steel beam carries unassisted all dead loads prior to the hardening of the concrete, with due regard for any temporary support provided, and

(2) The steel and concrete carry by joint action all loads, dead and live, applied after the hardening of the concrete.

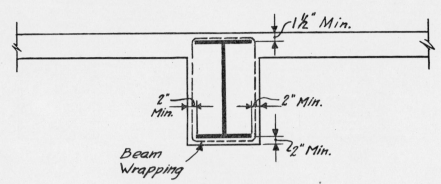

Fig. 6.6   Composite Beam

(c) *Unit Stresses.* The total tensile unit stress in he extreme fibre of the steel beam thus computed hall not exceed 20,000 pounds per square inch. Section 15(a)]

The maximum stresses in the concrete, and the atio of Young's moduli, for steel and concrete, hall be prescribed by the specifications governing he design of reinforced concrete for the structure.

(d) *End Shear.* The web and the end connections f the steel beam shall be designed to carry the otal dead and live load, except as this may be re-uced by the provision of proper support.

b A proposed method of approach is to reat the top concrete slab of an assumed vidth of 15 times the thickness as a part of he beam, and, since concrete does not resist ension as well as steel, to disregard all other oncrete. This concrete is converted to equiv-lent steel area by dividing by n, and the sec-ion modulus is computed. Note that "15 imes the thickness" is an arbitrary figure hav-ng no relation to n. Since the steel is bonded o the concrete throughout the entire perime-er of the beam, horizontal shear between steel nd concrete may be disregarded.

Problem   Assume an 18 WF 50, as shown n Fig. 6.6, with a 4-in.-thick concrete slab. Vhat is the comparative strength of this ombination figured as a composite beam, vith the beam treated as a simple steel beam aterally supported?

Assume $n = 15$. The concrete may be con-erted into equivalent steel and the method f Art. 1.31 (f and g) used.

The concrete to be considered is $15 \times 4 =$ 50 in. wide and 4 in. thick. The equivalent teel area is

$$\frac{\text{Concrete area}}{n} = \frac{60 \times 4}{15} = 16 \text{ sq in.}$$

The equivalent steel I is

$$\frac{I_c}{n} = \frac{60 \times 4^3}{12 \times 15} = 21.3$$

Using the center line of the steel beam as a reference axis, we may tabulate the results:

	A	y	Ay	Ay^2	I
Concrete	16	8.5	136	1,155	21.3
Steel	14.71		0	0	800.6
	30.71		136	1,155	821.9
					1,155
					1,976.9

$$\bar{y} = \frac{136}{30.71} = 4.43 \text{ in. above center of}$$
$$18\text{-in. beam}$$

$$c = 4.43 + 9 = 13.43$$

$$A\bar{y}^2 = A\bar{y} \times y = 136 \times 4.43 = 602.5$$

I about axis of beam $\qquad = 1,976.9$

$\qquad\qquad\qquad\qquad\qquad\qquad - 602.5$

I about combined neutral axis $= 1,374.4$

$$S = \frac{1,374.4}{13.43} \qquad\qquad = 102.3$$

$- S$ of original beam $= - 89.0$

Increase in strength $\quad = \quad 13.89$ percent

c   Equivalent section moduli for composite beams are included in Table 1.6. Since the minimum slab which would be used under such condition is $3\frac{1}{2}$ in. thick, these tables are based on a $3\frac{1}{2}$-in. slab of 3,000-psi concrete. A thicker slab or concrete of another mix will vary this table slightly, although the variation is so small in any but the smaller-sized beams as to be negligible.

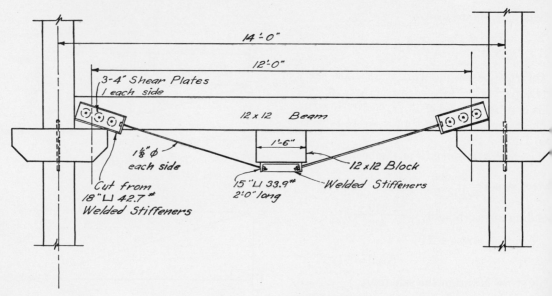

Fig. 6.7   Trussed Beams

6.60   TRUSSED BEAM

Although a trussed beam—or as it is commonly called by carpenters, a belly-rod truss —might more properly be treated as a truss, the common use to which it is put nowadays makes it more logical to classify it as a beam. Formerly it was a form of combination wood and wrought-iron truss, using a wood beam for the top chord and bent rods to form an inverted king-post or queen-post truss. It was used for spans or loads which were too great for the economic use of a single wooden beam.

Nowadays, however, the use of trussed beams is largely limited to strengthening a wood beam which is overloaded, cracked, or sagging, or where it is desirable to provide for additional beam capacity. They are seldom used in the design of a new building, since the cost of labor involved is greater than that of a structural-steel beam of equal or greater capacity. For this reason, the discussion of the problem presented here will be limited to the installation of belly-rods for strengthening an existing beam, which may, because of practical considerations, be somewhat different from the design for a new building.

Problem   Assume a 12 × 12 beam in place in a building on a span of 12 ft center to center of support on timber bolsters, as shown in Fig. 6.7. This beam is of 1,200-psi-stress southern pine and is carrying 16 ft of floor at a total load of 150 psf.

$$W = 12 \times 16 \times 150 = 28,800 \text{ lb}$$
$$M = \frac{28,800 \times 12 \times 12}{8} = 518.4 \text{ in.-kips}$$

The section modulus of a 12 × 12 from Table 1.11 is 253. Therefore the stress in the beam is 518,400/253 = 2,049 psi, which exceeds the allowable limit.

Whatever method of correction is used must permit installation in a practical manner. The method indicated here has been used satisfactorily. Undoubtedly a number of other satisfactory details could be worked out.

In order to turn up the nut on the tension rods, they are connected into a 15-in. channel under the 12 × 12-in. strut block. The truss depth is, therefore,

Half the beam depth	= 5.75
12 × 12-in. block	= 11.5
To gage line of 15-in. channel =	2
	19.25 in.

The truss and stress diagrams are as shown in Fig. 6.8. Because of the width of the strut, it is indicated as two members, and the truss becomes an inverted queen-post truss.

The panel-point load is

$$\frac{79.5}{2 \times 12} \times 16 \times 150 = 7{,}950 \text{ lb}$$

On this basis, the two truss rods carry 7.4 kips, or 13.7 kips each (see Art. 10.10b). This requires an area of $13.7/20 = 0.685$ sq in. each at the root of the thread, or $1\frac{1}{8}$-in. rods (see Table 2.4).

To check the strength of the beam,

$$\text{Direct stress} = \frac{26{,}600}{132.25} = 201$$

$$\text{Bending stress (roughly)} = \frac{2{,}049}{4} = \underline{512}$$

(original stress $\div 2^2$)

$$\text{Total} = 713$$

This stress is within the safe limit.

The channel into which the rods frame at the bottom should be strengthened by welding in stiffeners to prevent the thin web from deflecting away from the strut block and permitting the flange to bend.

The greatest problem in detail is the anchorage of the upper end of the rods to the beam. This is accomplished by means of shear plates. Shear plates are a variation of split-ring connectors, described in Art. 9.33. The information relative to their design is obtained from "Teco Design Manual," of the Timber Engineering Co., Washington, D.C. From the load diagram, the angle with the grain is approximately 18 deg, and for group B lumber the approximate value of one ring would be

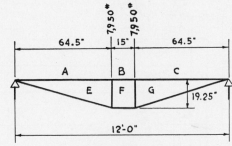

Truss Diagram

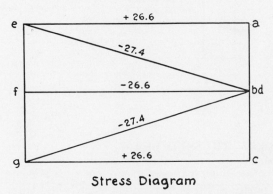

Stress Diagram

Fig. 6.8   Stress Diagram—Trussed Beam

5,000 lb. It would, therefore, require three shear plates to develop the stress in each rod, and they would be carrying 91 percent of their capacity. On this basis, the minimum edge distance is $2\frac{3}{4}$ in. and spacing is 7 in. The connecting member may be cut from 15-in. channel and strengthened with welded stiffeners as described for the bottom channel.

7

Columns

.10 STEEL COLUMNS

a In Art. 2.12 attention was called to the
fact that in all steel columns direct compression is combined with some buckling, and
therefore we cannot adopt a single unit stress
that applies to all columns. The ratio l/r—
the length between lateral supports divided
by the radius of gyration of the section—is
the factor on the basis of which the allowable
stress is reduced. In paragraph *b* below, the
generally accepted AISC formula is given.

Furthermore, loads applied to steel columns are frequently not concentric or balanced,
and this eccentricity must also be taken into
account in steel-column design.

There are for each column section two radii
of gyration corresponding to the two axes of
the column. Ordinarily the only *r* in which
we are interested is the lesser. However, a
column may be braced in the weak direction
and skip a story in the strong direction, and
in this case both l/r ratios must be considered.
The column-load tables (Tables 7.2 and 7.3)
give the ratio of the greater to the lesser *r*,
and by dividing the greater length by this
ratio, the allowable load may be selected directly by reading opposite the resulting length
or the lesser length, whichever is the greater.

Before the use of wide-flange sections, column sections were built up in various ways,
the preferred section finally developing into
a web plate with four angles, and sometimes
cover plates. Nowadays, until loads run to
over 1,500 kips, ordinary rolled wide-flanged
sections are satisfactory.

For light-load columns occurring in such a
location that the beams may frame on top of
the column, standard steel-pipe columns are
frequently used. They are economical in that
the maximum radius of gyration is obtainable
from a given area when all the area is at the
maximum distance from the center of gravity.
They are impractical, however, when it becomes necessary to connect steel to the curved
surface. This practically limits their usability to basement columns of houses and to
store-front columns and similar one-story locations. Capacities of pipe columns are given
in Table 7.4. Connections and base plates
may be obtained by welding top and bottom
plates as required. If the loads are not near
the capacity of the column, ordinary screwed
flanges may be used for connections, but it
should be kept in mind that threading takes
area away from the column and that there is
danger of the flange catching an insufficient
number of threads to develop the load.

Attention is called to possible load reduction as given in Art. 1.50*c*.

b In the absence of other code requirements governing the design of steel columns,
the following sections from the AISC Code
will govern the design of columns.

[From Section 12(*a*)] Members subject to both
axial and bending stresses shall be so proportioned
that the quantity $f_A/F_A + f_B/F_B$ shall not exceed
unity, in which the lower case letters represent actual computed fibre stresses, and the upper case
letters represent the permissible stresses, the subscript "*A*" representing axial stresses due to direct
loads and "*B*" bending stresses due to moment in
the column.

[From Section 15(a)] The allowable stress in compression on the gross section for axially loaded columns with l/r not greater than 120,

$$= 17,000 - 0.485 \ (l/r)^2.$$

[From Section 16(a)] The ratio of unbraced height to least radius of gyration l/r for main compression members shall not exceed 120.

[From Section 16(b)] The slenderness of a main compression member may exceed 120, but not 200, provided that it is not ordinarily subject to shock or vibrating loads, and provided that its unit stress under full design loading shall not exceed the following fraction of that stipulated under Section 15(a) for its actual ratio l/r: $1.6 - (l/200r)$.

[From Section 18(c)] The thickness of the outstanding legs of flanges shall be not less than $\frac{1}{16}$ of the outstanding width for columns.

[From Section 18(d)] In compression members the unsupported width of web, cover or diaphragm plates between the nearest lines of rivets or welds, or between the roots of the flanges in case of rolled sections, shall not exceed 40 times the thickness.

When the unsupported width exceeds this limit, but a portion of its width no greater than 40 times the thickness would satisfy the stress requirements, the member will be considered acceptable.

The unsupported width of cover plates perforated with a succession of access holes, only the least net width across holes being assumed available to resist compression, may exceed 40, but shall not exceed 50, times the thickness.

c To illustrate the method of design, select the wide-flange column to carry a concentric load of 250,000 lb on a story height of 15 ft using the AISC formula.

It is not necessary to compute the area required to solve a problem of this type. By referring to Table 7.3 we find at 15 ft that any of the following columns will carry 250 kips: 8 WF 67, 10 WF 60, 12 WF 65, or 14 WF 61. Since there are no limitations, the most economical, 10 WF 60, may be selected.

Let us assume that the column is braced the weak way at 15 ft height, but in the other direction it is braced at 29 ft height. From Table 7.3 we find the ratio for the 10 WF 60 selected is 1.72. To check the column selected, the equivalent height in the table is 29/1.72 = 16.9 ft. Therefore it would be necessary to go to the 10 WF 66 if the 10-in. column were to be used.

A similar check on the 14 WF 61 gives the equivalent height in the table = 29/2.44 =

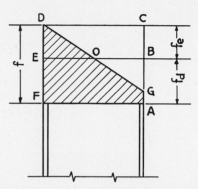

Fig. 7.1 Representation of Stresses on Column Section

11.9 ft. Therefore the economical column under this condition would be 14 WF 61.

Problem A column 10 ft high supports central load of 135,000 lb. Pick a rolled-steel section by the formula $16,000 - 70l/r$, maximum $l/r = 100$. (From a state license examination.)

Although the formula is not the AISC formula, the tables referred to may be used in the selection of a trial column. The 8 WF 3 is listed at 139 kips for a 10-ft height. The least r is 2.01. Therefore $l/r = 120/2.01 = 59.6$. Then $f_c = 16,000 - (70 \times 59.6) = 11,828$ psi.

$$\text{Required } A_s = \frac{135,000}{11,828} = 11.4 \text{ sq in.}$$

Next try 8 WF 40, $A_s = 11.76$ sq in., least $r = 2.04$. $l/r = 120/2.04 = 58.8$

$$f_c = 16,000 - (70 \times 58.8) = 11,88$$

$$\text{Required } A_s = \frac{135,000}{11,844} = 11.35 \text{ sq in.}$$

Therefore 8 WF 40 is satisfactory.

d There are several conditions under which it becomes necessary to design a steel column for eccentricity or a combination of bending and direct stress. Figure 7.1 indicates graphically the stress on a column due to combined stresses. The rectangle *ABEF* indicates the total direct stress load on the column, equal to Af_d. The compression area *ODE* and the corresponding tensile area *OBG* indicate the effect of bending. The simplest way to design for the combined stress is to convert the moment into an equivalent direct stress, *BCDE*

Table 7.1 Allowable Stresses for Compression Members

ALLOWABLE STRESSES PER SQUARE INCH

FOR

COMPRESSION MEMBERS

Main and Secondary Members, l/r not over 120, $f = 17000 - 0.485\left(\dfrac{l}{r}\right)^2$						Secondary Members, l/r 121 to 200, $f = \dfrac{18000}{1 + \dfrac{l^2}{18000 r^2}}$				Main Members, l/r 121 to 200, $Do \times \left(1.6 - \dfrac{l/r}{200}\right)$			
$\dfrac{l}{r}$	Unit Stress ksi.	$\dfrac{l}{r}$	Unit Stress ksi.	$\dfrac{l}{r}$	Unit Stress ksi.	$\dfrac{l}{r}$	Unit Stress ksi.	$\dfrac{l}{r}$	Unit Stress ksi.	$\dfrac{l}{r}$	Unit Stress ksi.	$\dfrac{l}{r}$	Unit Stress ksi.
1	17.00	41	16.19	81	13.82	121	9.93	161	7.38	121	9.88	161	5.87
2	17.00	42	16.14	82	13.74	122	9.85	162	7.32	122	9.75	162	5.78
3	17.00	43	16.10	83	13.66	123	9.78	163	7.27	123	9.63	163	5.71
4	16.99	44	16.06	84	13.58	124	9.71	164	7.22	124	9.52	164	5.63
5	16.99	45	16.02	85	13.50	125	9.64	165	7.16	125	9.40	165	5.53
6	16.98	46	15.97	86	13.41	126	9.56	166	7.11	126	9.27	166	5.47
7	16.98	47	15.93	87	13.33	127	9.49	167	7.06	127	9.16	167	5.40
8	16.97	48	15.88	88	13.24	128	9.42	168	7.01	128	9.04	168	5.33
9	16.96	49	15.84	89	13.16	129	9.35	169	6.96	129	8.93	169	5.25
10	16.95	50	15.79	90	13.07	130	9.28	170	6.91	130	8.82	170	5.18
11	16.94	51	15.74	91	12.98	131	9.22	171	6.86	131	8.71	171	5.11
12	16.93	52	15.69	92	12.90	132	9.15	172	6.81	132	8.60	172	5.04
13	16.92	53	15.64	93	12.81	133	9.08	173	6.76	133	8.49	173	4.97
14	16.91	54	15.59	94	12.72	134	9.01	174	6.71	134	8.38	174	4.90
15	16.89	55	15.53	95	12.62	135	8.94	175	6.66	135	8.27	175	4.83
16	16.88	56	15.48	96	12.53	136	8.88	176	6.62	136	8.17	176	4.77
17	16.86	57	15.42	97	12.44	137	8.81	177	6.57	137	8.06	177	4.70
18	16.84	58	15.37	98	12.34	138	8.75	178	6.52	138	7.96	178	4.63
19	16.83	59	15.31	99	12.25	139	8.68	179	6.48	139	7.86	179	4.57
20	16.81	60	15.25	100	12.15	140	8.62	180	6.43	140	7.76	180	4.50
21	16.79	61	15.20	101	12.05	141	8.55	181	6.38	141	7.65	181	4.43
22	16.77	62	15.14	102	11.95	142	8.49	182	6.34	142	7.56	182	4.37
23	16.74	63	15.08	103	11.86	143	8.43	183	6.29	143	7.46	183	4.31
24	16.72	64	15.01	104	11.75	144	8.36	184	6.25	144	7.36	184	4.25
25	16.70	65	14.95	105	11.65	145	8.30	185	6.20	145	7.26	185	4.19
26	16.67	66	14.89	106	11.55	146	8.24	186	6.16	146	7.17	186	4.13
27	16.65	67	14.82	107	11.45	147	8.18	187	6.12	147	7.08	187	4.07
28	16.62	68	14.76	108	11.34	148	8.12	188	6.07	148	6.98	188	4.01
29	16.59	69	14.69	109	11.24	149	8.06	189	6.03	149	6.89	189	3.95
30	16.56	70	14.62	110	11.13	150	8.00	190	5.99	150	6.80	190	3.89
31	16.53	71	14.56	111	11.02	151	7.94	191	5.95	151	6.71	191	3.84
32	16.50	72	14.49	112	10.92	152	7.88	192	5.91	152	6.62	192	3.78
33	16.47	73	14.42	113	10.81	153	7.82	193	5.86	153	6.53	193	3.72
34	16.44	74	14.34	114	10.70	154	7.77	194	5.82	154	6.45	194	3.67
35	16.41	75	14.27	115	10.59	155	7.71	195	5.78	155	6.36	195	3.61
36	16.37	76	14.20	116	10.47	156	7.65	196	5.74	156	6.27	196	3.56
37	16.34	77	14.12	117	10.36	157	7.60	197	5.70	157	6.19	197	3.51
38	16.30	78	14.05	118	10.25	158	7.54	198	5.66	158	6.11	198	3.45
39	16.26	79	13.97	119	10.13	159	7.49	199	5.62	159	6.03	199	3.40
40	16.22	80	13.90	120	10.02	160	7.43	200	5.59	160	5.94	200	3.35

Table 7.2   Allowable Loads—Cover-plated Columns

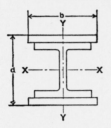

COVER PLATED
COLUMNS

ALLOWABLE CONCENTRIC LOADS
IN KIPS

Unbraced Length Feet	14 WF 320 CORE SECTION								
	Cover Plates: Width and Thickness, Inches								
	24x3⅝	24x3½	24x3⅜	24x3¼	24x3⅛	24x3	23x3	23x2⅞	23x2¾
8	4526	4424	4323	4221	4120	4018	3915	3818	3720
9	4517	4415	4314	4213	4112	4010	3906	3810	3712
10	4507	4406	4305	4204	4103	4002	3897	3801	3703
11	4497	4396	4295	4193	4093	3992	3887	3791	3693
12	4485	4384	4283	4183	4082	3981	3875	3780	3682
13	4472	4372	4272	4171	4070	3970	3864	3768	3670
14	4459	4359	4258	4158	4058	3957	3850	3755	3658
15	4445	4344	4244	4144	4044	3944	3836	3741	3644
16	4429	4329	4229	4129	4029	3929	3821	3726	3630
17	4413	4312	4213	4113	4013	3913	3805	3710	3614
18	4395	4295	4196	4096	3997	3897	3788	3693	3597
19	4376	4277	4178	4079	3980	3880	3770	3676	3580
20	4357	4257	4159	4060	3961	3862	3751	3657	3561
21	4336	4237	4139	4041	3942	3843	3731	3637	3542
22	4314	4216	4118	4020	3921	3823	3710	3617	3522
23	4292	4194	4096	3998	3901	3802	3689	3595	3501
24	4268	4170	4074	3976	3879	3781	3665	3572	3478
25	4243	4146	4049	3952	3856	3758	3641	3548	3456
26	4218	4121	4024	3928	3832	3734	3616	3524	3432
27	4191	4095	3998	3903	3807	3710	3590	3499	3407
28	4163	4067	3972	3877	3781	3684	3564	3473	3382
29	4135	4040	3944	3849	3754	3658	3537	3446	3355
30	4105	4010	3916	3821	3726	3631	3507	3417	3327
32	4043	3948	3854	3761	3668	3573	3446	3357	3268
34	3976	3883	3791	3699	3605	3512	3383	3294	3206
36	3906	3813	3722	3632	3539	3447	3314	3226	3140
38	3832	3741	3651	3560	3471	3379	3243	3157	3071
40	3752	3662	3575	3485	3398	3307	3167	3081	2979
42	3671	3582	3494	3408	3320	3231	3088	3002	2920
44	3585	3496	3412	3325	3239	3151	3003	2919	2839
46	3493	3408	3323	3238	3154	3066	2915	2833	2754
48	3399	3316	3233	3148	3065	2979	2824	2742	2665
50	3301	3217	3136	3056	2973	2888	2728	2650	2573
PROPERTIES									
Wt. per Foot	912	891	871	850	830	810	789	770	750
Depth d	24	23¾	23½	23¼	23	22¾	22¾	22½	22¼
Width b	24	24	24	24	24	24	23	23	23
Ratio r_x/r_y	1.50	1.49	1.49	1.48	1.47	1.47	1.52	1.51	1.50
Bending } B_x	.143	.144	.145	.146	.147	.148	.149	.150	.151
Factors } B_y	.322	.324	.327	.329	.332	.334	.346	.349	.352

Note: Leftmost margin label reads vertically "Unbraced length with respect to least radius of gyration"

Table 7.2   Allowable Loads—Cover-plated Columns (*Continued*)

COVER PLATED
COLUMNS

ALLOWABLE CONCENTRIC LOADS
IN KIPS

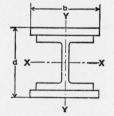

Unbraced Length Feet	14 W^F 320 CORE SECTION								
	Cover Plates: Width and Thickness, Inches								
	22x2¾	22x2⅝	22x2½	22x2⅜	22x2¼	22x2⅛	22x2	22x1⅞	22x1¾
8	3625	3532	3439	3346	3253	3160	3067	2974	2881
9	3617	3524	3431	3338	3245	3152	3060	2967	2874
10	3607	3514	3422	3329	3237	3144	3051	2958	2865
11	3597	3504	3412	3319	3227	3134	3042	2949	2857
12	3585	3493	3401	3308	3216	3124	3031	2939	2846
13	3573	3481	3389	3297	3204	3112	3020	2928	2835
14	3560	3468	3376	3284	3192	3100	3008	2916	2824
15	3545	3454	3362	3271	3179	3087	2995	2903	2812
16	3530	3439	3347	3256	3164	3073	2981	2890	2798
17	3513	3423	3331	3240	3149	3058	2967	2875	2784
18	3496	3405	3314	3224	3133	3042	2951	2860	2769
19	3477	3387	3297	3206	3116	3025	2935	2844	2753
20	3458	3368	3278	3188	3098	3007	2918	2827	2736
21	3438	3348	3258	3169	3079	2989	2899	2809	2718
22	3416	3327	3238	3149	3059	2969	2880	2790	2699
23	3394	3305	3216	3128	3038	2949	2860	2770	2680
24	3370	3282	3194	3106	3016	2928	2839	2750	2660
25	3346	3259	3170	3083	2993	2905	2817	2728	2639
26	3321	3234	3146	3058	2970	2882	2794	2705	2617
27	3295	3208	3120	3033	2946	2858	2771	2682	2594
28	3267	3181	3093	3007	2920	2833	2746	2658	2570
29	3239	3153	3065	2980	2894	2807	2721	2633	2546
30	3209	3124	3037	2953	2866	2781	2694	2607	2520
32	3148	3064	2978	2895	2809	2724	2639	2552	2466
34	3082	2999	2914	2833	2747	2664	2580	2494	2409
36	3014	2932	2847	2766	2683	2601	2518	2433	2349
38	2940	2860	2776	2697	2616	2533	2452	2369	2285
40	2862	2783	2701	2624	2543	2462	2382	2299	2217
42	2781	2703	2623	2547	2467	2387	2309	2228	2147
44	2695	2620	2540	2466	2387	2310	2232	2152	2072
46	2605	2532	2454	2380	2304	2228	2152	2072	1996
48	2513	2440	2364	2292	2216	2142	2067	1990	1914
50	2415	2344	2270	2200	2127	2054	1980	1905	1828
PROPERTIES									
Wt. per Foot	731	713	694	675	657	638	619	601	582
Depth d	22¼	22	21¾	21½	21¼	21	20¾	20½	20¼
Width b	22	22	22	22	22	22	22	22	22
Ratio r_x/r_y	1.56	1.55	1.54	1.54	1.53	1.52	1.52	1.51	1.51
Bending { B_x	.152	.153	.154	.155	.156	.157	.159	.160	.161
Factors } B_v	.363	.366	.370	.374	.377	.382	.386	.391	.397

Note: "Unbraced length with respect to least radius of gyration" appears as a vertical label along the left side of the table.

Table 7.2   Allowable Loads—Cover-plated Columns (*Continued*)

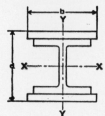

COVER PLATED
COLUMNS

ALLOWABLE CONCENTRIC LOADS
IN KIPS

Unbraced Length Feet	14 WF 320 CORE SECTION							
	Cover Plates: Width and Thickness, Inches							
	22x1⅝	22x1½	20x1½	20x1⅜	20x1¼	18x1¼	18x1⅛	18x1
8	2788	2695	2590	2506	2422	2334	2259	2183
9	2781	2688	2583	2498	2414	2326	2251	2175
10	2773	2680	2574	2490	2406	2317	2242	2166
11	2764	2671	2564	2480	2397	2307	2232	2157
12	2754	2662	2554	2470	2386	2297	2221	2147
13	2743	2651	2543	2459	2375	2285	2210	2135
14	2732	2640	2530	2447	2364	2272	2197	2123
15	2720	2628	2517	2434	2351	2258	2184	2110
16	2706	2615	2503	2420	2337	2243	2169	2096
17	2692	2601	2488	2405	2323	2228	2154	2081
18	2678	2587	2472	2390	2308	2211	2138	2065
19	2662	2571	2455	2373	2291	2194	2121	2048
20	2645	2555	2437	2355	2274	2175	2103	2030
21	2628	2538	2418	2337	2256	2156	2083	2012
22	2610	2520	2399	2317	2238	2135	2063	1993
23	2590	2501	2379	2297	2218	2114	2043	1972
24	2570	2482	2357	2276	2197	2092	2021	1951
25	2550	2461	2335	2255	2176	2069	1998	1928
26	2528	2440	2312	2232	2154	2045	1975	1906
27	2506	2418	2288	2208	2130	2020	1950	1882
28	2482	2395	2263	2183	2106	1994	1924	1857
29	2458	2371	2237	2158	2080	1967	1898	1831
30	2433	2347	2209	2131	2054	1939	1870	1804
32	2380	2295	2153	2075	2000	1880	1813	1748
34	2324	2239	2094	2017	1942	1817	1751	1688
36	2265	2182	2029	1954	1881	1751	1687	1625
38	2202	2120	1962	1888	1816	1681	1618	1558
40	2135	2054	1890	1817	1748	1607	1545	1488
42	2066	1987	1816	1744	1676	1529	1469	1413
44	1994	1915	1738	1668	1601	1447	1390	1335
46	1918	1839	1655	1587	1522	1359	1302	1251
48	1838	1761	1570	1502	1437	1272	1218	1169
50	1755	1680	1476	1410	1349	1189	1138	1091
PROPERTIES								
Wt. per Foot	563	544	524	507	490	473	458	442
Depth d	20	19¾	19¾	19½	19¼	19¼	19	18¾
Width b	22	22	20	20	20	18	18	18
Ratio r_x/r_y	1.50	1.50	1.59	1.58	1.58	1.66	1.65	1.64
Bending $\{$ B_x	.162	.164	.166	.168	.169	.172	.173	.175
Factors $\}$ B_y	.403	.410	.424	.430	.436	.439	.444	.449

Loads below heavy lines are for main members with l/r ratios between 120 and 200.

The figure at left shows the cross-section with dimensions labeled b (width at top, between Y axis), d (depth, vertical), and X-X and Y-Y axes.

Table 7.3 Allowable Loads—WF Column Sections

14

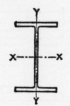

COLUMNS
WF SHAPES

ALLOWABLE CONCENTRIC LOADS
IN KIPS

Unbraced Length Feet	Nominal Depth and Width—Weight per Foot								
	14 x 16								
	426	398	370	342	*320	314	287	264	246
6	2113	1973	1834	1696	1586	1556	1422	1308	1219
7	2107	1967	1829	1691	1582	1551	1418	1304	1215
8	2100	1960	1823	1685	1576	1546	1413	1299	1211
9	2092	1953	1816	1678	1569	1540	1407	1294	1206
10	2083	1945	1808	1671	1562	1533	1400	1288	1200
11	2073	1936	1799	1663	1554	1525	1393	1281	1194
12	2062	1925	1789	1654	1546	1516	1386	1274	1187
13	2051	1914	1779	1644	1536	1507	1377	1266	1179
14	2038	1902	1768	1633	1526	1497	1368	1258	1171
15	2025	1889	1755	1622	1515	1487	1358	1249	1163
16	2011	1876	1742	1610	1503	1476	1348	1239	1154
17	1995	1862	1729	1597	1491	1463	1337	1228	1144
18	1979	1846	1714	1584	1478	1450	1325	1217	1133
19	1962	1830	1699	1569	1464	1437	1312	1205	1122
20	1944	1813	1683	1554	1449	1423	1299	1193	1110
21	1925	1794	1666	1538	1434	1408	1285	1180	1098
22	1905	1775	1648	1521	1417	1392	1270	1166	1085
23	1884	1756	1629	1503	1400	1376	1255	1152	1072
24	1862	1736	1610	1485	1382	1359	1239	1137	1058
25	1839	1714	1589	1466	1364	1341	1223	1122	1044
26	1815	1691	1567	1446	1345	1322	1205	1106	1029
27	1790	1668	1545	1425	1324	1303	1187	1089	1013
28	1765	1643	1522	1404	1303	1283	1168	1071	996
29	1738	1619	1499	1381	1282	1261	1149	1053	979
30	1711	1593	1474	1358	1260	1240	1130	1035	962
32	1653	1538	1423	1310	1213	1195	1087	995	925
34	1593	1480	1367	1259	1163	1147	1043	954	886
36	1528	1419	1309	1203	1110	1095	995	910	844
38	1458	1354	1247	1146	1054	1041	945	863	800
40	1386	1285	1183	1085	995	984	892	814	753

PROPERTIES									
Depth	$18\frac{3}{4}$	$18\frac{1}{4}$	18	$17\frac{1}{2}$	$16\frac{3}{4}$	$17\frac{1}{4}$	$16\frac{3}{4}$	$16\frac{1}{2}$	$16\frac{1}{4}$
Width	$16\frac{3}{4}$	$16\frac{5}{8}$	$16\frac{1}{2}$	$16\frac{3}{8}$	$16\frac{3}{4}$	$16\frac{1}{4}$	$16\frac{1}{8}$	16	16
Ratio r_x/r_y	1.67	1.66	1.66	1.65	1.59	1.64	1.63	1.63	1.62
Bending B_x	.177	.178	.179	.180	.191	.180	.181	.182	.182
Factors B_y	.443	.447	.451	.456	.481	.459	.464	.467	.470

*Column Core Section.

(Left margin: Unbraced length with respect to least radius of gyration)

Table 7.3 Allowable Loads—WF Column Sections (*Continued*)

COLUMNS 14

WF SHAPES

ALLOWABLE CONCENTRIC LOADS IN KIPS

Unbraced Length Feet		Nominal Depth and Width—Weight per Foot 14 x 16									
		237	228	219	211	202	193	184	176	167	158
Unbraced length with respect to least radius of gyration	6	1174	1130	1084	1046	1001	956	911	871	827	783
	7	1171	1126	1081	1042	998	953	908	868	824	780
	8	1166	1122	1077	1038	994	949	904	865	821	777
	9	1161	1117	1072	1034	989	945	900	861	817	774
	10	1156	1112	1067	1029	984	940	896	857	813	770
	11	1150	1106	1061	1024	979	935	891	852	809	766
	12	1143	1100	1055	1018	973	930	886	847	804	761
	13	1136	1093	1049	1011	967	924	880	842	799	756
	14	1128	1086	1041	1004	960	917	874	836	793	750
	15	1120	1078	1033	996	953	910	867	829	787	744
	16	1111	1069	1025	988	945	903	860	822	780	738
	17	1101	1060	1016	980	937	895	852	815	773	731
	18	1091	1050	1007	971	928	886	844	807	765	724
	19	1081	1040	997	961	919	877	836	799	757	717
	20	1070	1029	986	951	909	868	827	790	749	709
	21	1058	1017	975	940	899	858	817	781	741	701
	22	1045	1005	963	928	888	848	807	771	731	692
	23	1032	993	951	916	877	837	797	761	722	683
	24	1019	980	938	904	865	825	786	751	712	673
	25	1005	966	925	892	853	813	775	740	701	663
	26	990	952	911	878	840	801	763	728	690	653
	27	975	937	897	864	826	788	751	716	679	642
	28	959	927	882	850	812	775	738	704	667	631
	29	942	906	867	835	798	761	725	691	655	619
	30	925	889	851	819	783	747	711	678	643	607
	32	890	854	818	787	752	717	683	651	616	582
	34	851	818	782	753	719	685	652	621	588	556
	36	811	779	744	716	684	651	619	589	558	527
	38	769	738	704	678	646	616	585	557	527	497
	40	724	694	662	637	607	578	549	522	493	465

PROPERTIES

Depth	16⅛	16	15⅞	15¾	15⅝	15½	15⅜	15¼	15⅛	15
Width	15⅞	15⅞	15⅞	15¾	15¾	15¾	15⅝	15⅝	15⅝	15½
Ratio r_x/r_y	1.62	1.61	1.62	1.61	1.61	1.61	1.61	1.60	1.60	1.60
Bending Factors B_x	.182	.182	.183	.183	.183	.183	.183	.184	.184	.183
Bending Factors B_y	.472	.473	.475	.477	.477	.479	.480	.483	.485	.485

Table 7.3   Allowable Loads—WF Column Sections (*Continued*)

14

COLUMNS
WF SHAPES

ALLOWABLE CONCENTRIC LOADS IN KIPS

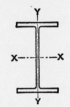

Unbraced Length Feet	Nominal Depth and Width—Weight per Foot									
	14 x 16			14 x 14½						
	150	142	*320	136	127	119	111	103	95	87
6	742	705	1586	673	628	589	549	509	470	430
7	740	702	1582	670	626	587	547	507	468	428
8	737	699	1576	667	623	584	545	505	466	426
9	734	696	1569	664	620	581	542	502	464	424
10	730	693	1562	660	616	578	539	499	461	422
11	726	689	1554	656	612	574	535	496	458	419
12	722	685	1546	651	608	570	531	493	455	416
13	717	680	1536	646	603	566	527	489	451	413
14	712	675	1526	641	598	561	523	485	447	409
15	706	670	1515	635	593	556	518	480	443	405
16	700	664	1503	629	587	551	513	475	439	401
17	694	658	1491	623	581	545	508	470	434	397
18	687	652	1478	616	575	539	502	465	429	392
19	680	645	1464	609	568	532	496	459	424	387
20	672	638	1449	601	561	525	490	453	418	382
21	664	630	1434	593	553	518	483	447	412	377
22	656	622	1417	585	545	511	476	441	406	372
23	647	614	1400	576	537	503	469	434	400	366
24	638	605	1382	567	528	495	461	427	393	360
25	629	596	1364	557	519	486	453	419	386	353
26	619	536	1345	547	510	477	444	411	379	346
27	609	576	1324	537	500	468	435	403	372	339
28	598	566	1303	526	490	459	426	395	364	332
29	587	555	1282	515	480	449	417	386	356	325
30	575	544	1260	503	469	438	408	377	347	317
32	552	522	1213	478	446	417	387	358	330	301
34	526	497	1163	453	421	394	366	338	311	284
36	499	471	1110	425	396	370	343	317	291	265
38	470	443	1054	395	368	343	317	293	269	246
40	439	414	995	365	339	317	293	270	249	226

PROPERTIES										
Depth	14⅞	14¾	16¾	14¾	14⅝	14½	14⅜	14¼	14⅛	14
Width	15½	15½	16¾	14¾	14¾	14⅝	14⅝	14⅝	14½	14½
Ratio r_x/r_y	1.60	1.59	1.59	1.67	1.67	1.67	1.67	1.67	1.66	1.66
Bending { B_x	.184	.185	.191	.185	.185	.185	.185	.185	.186	.185
Factors { B_y	.487	.491	.481	.519	.520	.521	.525	.525	.529	.530

(Left margin, vertical) Unbraced length with respect to least radius of gyration

*Column Core Section.
Loads below heavy lines are for main members with l/r ratios between 120 and 200.

Table 7.3   Allowable Loads—WF Column Sections (*Continued*)

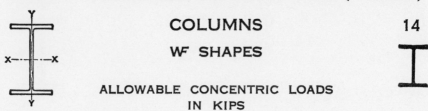

COLUMNS   14
WF SHAPES

ALLOWABLE CONCENTRIC LOADS IN KIPS

Unbraced Length Feet	Nominal Depth and Width—Weight per Foot							
	14 x 12		14 x 10			14 x 8		
	84	78	74	68	61	53	48	43
6	413	384	361	332	297	254	230	206
7	411	382	358	329	295	251	227	203
8	408	379	354	325	292	246	223	199
9	405	376	350	321	288	241	218	195
10	401	372	345	317	284	235	213	190
11	397	368	340	312	280	229	207	185
12	393	364	334	307	275	222	201	179
13	388	360	328	301	270	215	194	173
14	383	355	321	295	264	207	187	166
15	378	350	314	288	258	199	179	159
16	372	344	307	281	252	190	171	152
17	366	338	299	273	245	180	162	144
18	359	332	290	265	238	169	152	135
19	352	326	281	257	230	158	142	126
20	345	319	271	248	222	146	131	116
21	337	312	261	238	213	135	121	107
22	329	304	250	228	204	125	112	98
23	320	296	239	218	195	115	104	90
24	311	288	228	207	185	106	95	83
25	302	279	215	195	174	97	87	77
26	292	270	202	184	164	90	80	70
27	282	260	190	172	154	82	74	64
28	272	250	179	162	144	75	67	59
29	261	240	168	152	135	69	61	54
30	250	230	157	142	127	63	56	49
32	226	207	139	125	112	52		
34	204	188	121	109	97			
36	184	169	106	96	85			
38	166	152	93	83	74			
40	149	136	80	72	64			
PROPERTIES								
Depth	14⅛	14	14¼	14	13⅞	14	13⅞	13⅝
Width	12	12	10⅛	10	10	8	8	8
Ratio r_x/r_y	2.03	2.03	2.44	2.45	2.44	3.07	3.07	3.08
Bending B_x	.189	.189	.194	.194	.195	.200	.201	.202
Factors B_y	.659	.665	.821	.830	.834	1.090	1.102	1.119

(Unbraced length with respect to least radius of gyration)

Loads below heavy lines are for main members with l/r ratios between 120 and 200.

Table 7.3   Allowable Loads—WF Column Sections (*Continued*)

12   COLUMNS

WF SHAPES

ALLOWABLE CONCENTRIC LOADS IN KIPS

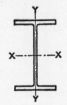

Unbraced Length Feet	Nominal Depth and Width—Weight per Foot										
	12 x 12										
	190	161	133	120	106	99	92	85	79	72	65
6	936	794	655	591	522	487	453	418	388	354	320
7	932	790	651	588	519	484	450	416	386	352	318
8	926	785	647	584	516	481	447	413	384	350	316
9	920	779	643	580	512	477	444	410	381	347	313
10	913	773	638	575	508	473	440	406	378	344	310
11	905	766	632	570	503	469	436	402	374	341	307
12	896	759	626	564	498	464	431	398	370	337	304
13	887	751	619	558	492	459	426	393	366	333	300
14	877	742	611	551	486	453	421	388	361	328	296
15	866	733	603	544	480	447	415	383	356	324	292
16	855	723	595	536	473	440	409	377	350	319	288
17	843	712	586	528	465	433	402	371	344	314	283
18	830	701	576	519	457	426	395	365	338	308	278
19	816	689	566	510	449	418	388	358	332	302	272
20	802	676	555	500	440	410	380	351	325	296	266
21	787	663	544	489	431	401	372	343	318	289	260
22	771	649	532	478	421	392	364	335	310	282	254
23	754	634	520	467	411	382	355	327	302	275	248
24	737	619	507	455	400	372	346	318	294	268	241
25	719	603	494	443	389	362	336	309	286	260	234
26	700	587	480	430	378	351	326	300	277	252	226
27	680	570	466	417	366	340	315	290	268	243	218
28	660	552	451	403	354	328	304	280	258	234	210
29	639	534	435	389	341	316	293	269	248	225	202
30	617	515	419	374	327	303	281	258	238	216	193
32	571	475	384	341	299	276	255	235	215	196	175
34	521	431	348	310	271	250	232	212	196	176	158
36	474	392	316	281	245	226	209	192	177	160	142
38	431	356	286	255	222	204	189	173	159	144	128
40	392	322	260	230	200	184	170	156	143	130	115
PROPERTIES											
Depth	14⅜	13⅞	13⅜	13⅛	12⅞	12¾	12⅝	12½	12⅜	12¼	12⅛
Width	12⅝	12½	12⅜	12⅜	12¼	12¼	12⅛	12⅛	12⅛	12	12
Ratio r_x/r_y	1.79	1.78	1.77	1.76	1.76	1.76	1.75	1.75	1.75	1.75	1.75
Bending B_x	.212	.213	.214	.216	.216	.216	.216	.216	.217	.217	.217
Factors B_y	.600	.610	.620	.631	.634	.637	.641	.642	.649	.653	.657

Loads below heavy lines are for main members with l/r ratios between 120 and 200.

Table 7.3   Allowable Loads—WF Column Sections (*Continued*)

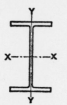

COLUMNS   12-10

W^F SHAPES

ALLOWABLE CONCENTRIC LOADS
IN KIPS

Unbraced Length Feet	Nominal Depth and Width—Weight per Foot						
	12 x 10		12 x 8			10 x 10	
	58	53	50	45	40	112	100
6	283	258	240	216	192	548	490
7	281	256	237	213	189	544	486
8	278	254	233	209	186	539	482
9	275	251	228	205	182	534	477
10	271	248	223	200	178	528	471
11	267	244	218	195	174	521	465
12	263	240	212	190	169	513	458
13	258	235	205	184	163	505	451
14	253	230	198	177	157	496	443
15	247	225	190	170	151	487	434
16	241	220	182	162	144	477	425
17	235	214	173	154	137	466	416
18	229	208	163	145	129	455	406
19	222	201	154	136	121	443	395
20	214	194	142	127	113	431	383
21	206	187	132	117	104	417	371
22	198	179	122	108	96	403	359
23	190	171	113	100	89	389	346
24	181	163	104	92	81	374	332
25	172	154	96	84	75	358	317
26	161	145	88	78	69	341	302
27	152	136	81	71	63	324	286
28	143	128	75	65	58	306	270
29	134	120	68	60	53	289	256
30	126	113	63	55	49	273	241
32	111	99	53	46	41	243	214
34	98	87				216	190
36	86	76				191	168
38	75	66				169	148
40	65	58				149	131
PROPERTIES							
Depth	12¼	12	12¼	12	12	11⅜	11⅛
Width	10	10	8⅛	8	8	10⅜	10⅜
Ratio r_x/r_y	2.10	2.11	2.64	2.65	2.64	1.75	1.74
Bending {B_x	.218	.221	.227	.227	.227	.261	.262
Factors {B_y	.797	.812	1.051	1.068	1.070	.728	.738

Unbraced length with respect to least radius of gyration

Loads below heavy line are for main members with *l/r* ratios between 120 and 200.

Table 7.3 Allowable Loads—WF Column Sections (*Continued*)

10
COLUMNS
WF SHAPES
ALLOWABLE CONCENTRIC LOADS
IN KIPS

Unbraced Length Feet	Nominal Depth and Width—Weight per Foot									
	10 x 10							10 x 8		
	89	77	72	66	60	54	49	45	39	33
6	436	377	352	323	294	264	239	217	188	159
7	432	374	349	320	291	262	237	214	185	156
8	428	370	346	317	288	259	235	210	182	153
9	424	366	342	313	285	256	232	206	178	150
10	419	362	338	309	282	253	229	202	175	147
11	413	357	333	305	278	250	226	197	170	143
12	407	352	328	301	274	246	222	192	166	139
13	401	346	323	296	269	242	218	186	160	135
14	394	340	317	290	264	237	214	180	155	130
15	386	333	310	284	258	232	210	173	149	125
16	378	326	303	278	252	227	205	166	143	119
17	369	318	296	271	246	221	200	158	136	113
18	360	310	289	264	240	215	194	150	129	107
19	350	301	281	257	233	209	188	142	121	100
20	340	292	272	249	226	202	182	133	113	92
21	329	282	263	240	218	195	176	123	105	86
22	317	272	253	231	210	188	169	114	97	79
23	305	261	243	222	202	180	162	106	90	73
24	293	250	233	213	193	172	155	98	83	68
25	280	239	222	203	183	164	147	90	76	62
26	267	227	211	192	174	156	139	84	71	57
27	252	214	199	181	164	146	131	77	65	53
28	237	202	187	171	154	138	123	71	60	48
29	224	191	176	161	145	130	116	65	55	44
30	212	180	167	152	137	122	109	60	50	40
32	188	159	148	134	121	108	96	50	42	34
34	167	140	130	118	106	96	85			
36	147	124	115	105	94	84	74			
38	130	109	101	92	83	73	65			
40	113	95	88	80	72	64	57			

PROPERTIES										
Depth	$10\frac{7}{8}$	$10\frac{5}{8}$	$10\frac{1}{2}$	$10\frac{3}{8}$	$10\frac{1}{4}$	$10\frac{1}{8}$	10	$10\frac{1}{8}$	10	$9\frac{3}{4}$
Width	$10\frac{1}{4}$	$10\frac{1}{4}$	$10\frac{1}{8}$	$10\frac{1}{8}$	$10\frac{1}{8}$	$10\frac{1}{8}$	10	8	8	8
Ratio r_x/r_y	1.73	1.73	1.72	1.72	1.72	1.71	1.71	2.17	2.16	2.16
Bending $\{B_x$	.263	.263	.264	.263	.263	.263	.264	.270	.275	.277
Factors $\{B_y$	.744	.753	.759	.761	.765	.767	.774	.995	1.025	1.055

Loads below heavy line are for main members with *l*/r ratios between 120 and 200.

Table 7.3 Allowable Loads—WF Column Sections (*Continued*)

COLUMNS 8

WF SHAPES

ALLOWABLE CONCENTRIC LOADS
IN KIPS

Unbraced Length Feet	Nominal Depth and Width—Weight per Foot							
	8 x 8						8 x 6½	
	67	58	48	40	35	31	28	24
6	324	280	232	193	169	149	132	113
7	320	277	229	190	167	147	129	111
8	315	273	225	187	164	145	126	108
9	310	268	221	184	161	142	122	105
10	304	263	217	180	158	139	118	101
11	298	257	212	176	154	136	114	97
12	291	251	207	172	150	132	108	93
13	283	244	201	167	146	128	103	88
14	275	237	195	161	141	124	96	83
15	266	229	189	155	136	120	90	77
16	256	221	182	149	131	115	83	71
17	246	212	174	143	125	110	77	65
18	236	202	166	136	119	104	69	59
19	224	192	158	129	112	98	64	54
20	212	182	149	121	105	92	58	49
21	200	171	139	112	98	86	52	44
22	186	159	129	105	91	79	47	40
23	174	148	120	97	84	73	43	36
24	161	137	112	89	78	68	39	32
25	150	128	104	83	72	62	35	29
26	139	118	96	77	67	57	31	26
27	129	109	89	71	62	53	28	
28	120	102	82	65	57	49		
29	111	94	76	61	52	46		
30	102	87	70	56	48	42		
31	95	80	64	51	44	38		
32	87	73	60	47	41	35		
33	81	68	54	43	37	32		
34	74	62	50	40				
35	68	57						
PROPERTIES								
Depth	9	8¾	8½	8¼	8⅛	8	8¹⁄₁₆	7⅞
Width	8¼	8¼	8⅛	8⅛	8	8	6½	6½
Ratio r_x/r_y	1.75	1.74	1.74	1.73	1.72	1.73	2.13	2.12
Bending $\{B_x$	.326	.328	.327	.331	.331	.333	.337	.339
Factors $\}B_y$	.921	.937	.941	.972	.972	.991	1.244	1.261

Unbraced length with respect to least radius of gyration

Loads below heavy line are for main members with l/r ratios between 120 and 200.

Table 7.4   Allowable Loads—Steel Pipe Columns

COLUMNS

STEEL PIPE

ALLOWABLE CONCENTRIC LOADS IN KIPS

For Dimensions and Designing Properties of Pipe see Page 139.

STANDARD

Unbraced Length Feet	Nominal Diameter—Weight per Foot										
	12		10			8		6	5	4	3½	3
	49.56	43.77	40.48	34.24	31.20	28.55	24.70	18.97	14.62	10.79	9.11	7.58
6	246	217	200	169	154	140	121	92	70	50	42	33
8	244	216	199	168	153	138	120	90	68	47	38	30
10	243	214	196	166	151	136	118	86	64	44	35	26
12	240	212	194	164	149	133	115	82	61	40	30	21
14	237	210	190	161	147	129	112	79	56	34	25	18
16	234	207	187	158	144	125	109	74	51	30	22	16
18	231	204	182	154	141	121	105	69	45	26	19	13
20	227	200	178	151	137	115	100	63	41	23	17	
22	222	196	172	146	133	109	95	56	37	21	15	

EXTRA STRONG

Unbraced Length Feet	Nominal Diameter—Weight per Foot							
	12	10	8	6	5	4	3½	3
	65.42	54.74	43.39	28.57	20.78	14.98	12.51	10.25
6	325	271	213	139	99	70	58	45
8	323	268	210	135	96	65	53	40
10	320	265	206	131	91	60	47	35
12	317	261	201	125	85	54	40	28
14	313	257	196	119	79	47	34	24
16	309	252	189	112	71	40	30	21
18	304	246	182	103	63	36	26	18
20	299	239	173	94	56	32	23	
22	293	232	164	84	51	28		
24	286	224	155	77	46	25		

DOUBLE EXTRA STRONG

Unbraced Length Feet	Nominal Diameter—Weight per Foot					
	8	6	5	4	3½	3
	72.42	53.16	38.55	27.54	22.85	18.58
6	355	257	183	130	103	80
8	350	249	176	118	93	70
10	343	240	165	108	82	59
12	334	228	154	94	68	48
14	324	213	140	79	58	40
16	312	200	125	70	50	34
18	299	182	109	61	43	
20	284	163	98	54	38	
22	269	147	88	47		
24	250	135	80			
26	230	124	72			

Loads below heavy line are for secondary members with l/r ratios between 120 and 200.

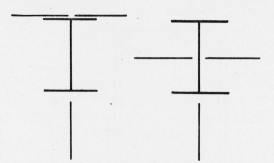

Figs. 7.2–7.3 Application of Eccentric Loads to Columns

equal to Af_e, which is added to the total direct stress. This conversion is performed by multiplying the moment in inch-pounds by a bending factor B in the column-load tables (Tables 7.2 to 7.4). There are two bending factors, one about each axis. If there is moment about both axes, the correct equivalent direct load to use is the sum of the loads.

In accordance with Sec. 6(a) of the AISC Code, the stress obtained by the method herein described is less than the permissible stress (see paragraph b above), but usually the variation is so slight that it may be disregarded.

e The commonest conditions under which bending must be figured in columns are offset beams (Fig. 7.2), as for wall columns; unbalanced loads (Fig. 7.3); and the brackets on the side of a mill-building column for carrying a crane load. Another condition is in connection with wind bracing.

To illustrate the application of this rule, assume the column shown in Fig. 7.3 to be loaded from above to 150 kips; two balanced loads on the beams framing to the web of the column of 15 kips each; and a load to the one flange of the column of 20 kips—a total load of 200 kips at the floor in question, with a 16-ft-clear story height. There is no definite rule about the point of application of load. It may be assumed to bear at the center of seat angle, or 2 in. off the face of column. If this condition occurs at the roof or at the floor where the column does not run through, the column section below must resist the full bending. If it occurs at the floor where the column runs through, the bending is assumed

to be resisted half above and half below the floor. Although the direct stress carries through from floor to floor, the eccentricity affects only the floor in which it occurs.

For the column described, let us assume a 10 WF 49. Then $B = 0.264$.

Equivalent direct stress
$$= \frac{0.264 \times 7 \times 20,000}{2} = 18,480$$

Direct stress $= 200,000$

$\overline{218,480}$

At 16 ft the 10 WF 49 is good for 205 kips, so it would be necessary to use the 10 WF 54. It is not necessary to recheck the equivalent direct stress, because B varies only slightly.

There is a characteristic of the bending factor which simplifies the first assumption of column size where the only eccentricity is an unbalanced load. As has been stated above, the load is assumed to be applied 2 in. off the face of the column. If we assume any floor below the top of the column, the moment is divided by 2. By reference to the load tables of 8-in. columns, it will be noted that the bending factors in the two directions are approximately $\frac{1}{3}$ and 1. The moment the weak way of the column, axis y-y or 2-2, is the unbalanced load times 2 in. divided by 2, or it is the amount of the unbalanced load, and the equivalent direct load is therefore approximately the unbalanced load times the bending factor 1. Similarly for the axis x-x or 1-1, the moment is the unbalanced load times a lever arm of 6 in. divided by 2, or it is 3 times the unbalanced load; and since the bending factor is approximately $\frac{1}{3}$, the equivalent direct load is almost the unbalanced load. Therefore, the direct load plus equivalent direct load is the sum of all direct loads plus the unbalanced loads. Since the bending factors are less for 10-, 12-, and 14-in. columns than for 8-in. columns, the assumption just described is on the safe side for all columns from 8×8 up. This simple rule applies only to unbalanced loads, as indicated by the framing in Fig. 7.3, where the beams frame to column center lines, but in multistory buildings this is the condition of eccentricity most frequently encountered.

f   The second form of eccentric load mentioned is that of a bracket on the side of a column, as in Fig. 7.4. An analysis made by R. Fleming over 30 years ago is probably the best approach to this problem.

Referring to Figs. 7.5 and 7.6, we may consider that the moment Pe is resisted by a moment couple Wc, or $W = Pe/c$. Subscript b may be used for the base of the column and t for the top. If the column is considered to have a free end at top and bottom (Fig. 7.7) as it would be with a triangular truss and no knee brace at the top, and anchor bolts on the center lines only, the following formulae may be used:

$$M_t = M_b = 0, \quad R_t = R_b = -\frac{Pe}{l}$$

$$M_1 = \frac{Ped}{l}$$

$$M_2 = -\frac{Pea}{l}$$

If the ends are considered fixed, the following formulae may be used:

$$M_b = \frac{W}{l^3}\left[-d^2(l-d) + a(l-a)^2\right]$$

$$R_b = \frac{W}{l^3}\left[d^2(3l-2d) - (2a+l)(l-a)^2\right]$$

$$M_t = \frac{W}{l^3}\left[-(l-d)^2 d + a^2(l-a)\right]$$

$$R_t = \frac{W}{l^3}\left[(l-d)^2(l+2d) - a^2(3l-2a)\right]$$

$$M_1 = \frac{W}{l^3}\left[- d(l-d)^2 + a^2(l-a)\right.$$
$$\left. + \frac{d}{l}(l-d)^2(l+2d) - \frac{d}{l}a^2(3l-2a)\right]$$

$$M_2 = \frac{W}{l^3}\left[-d^2(l-d) + a(l-a)^2\right.$$
$$\left. + \frac{a}{l}d^2(3l-2d) - \frac{a}{l}(l-a)^2(2a+1)\right]$$

In developing these end moments, the moment at the base must be provided for by anchorage—the moment couple between the center of one flange and the opposite anchor bolt, multiplied by the value of the anchor bolt at the root of the thread in tension. The moment at the top must be provided for by a knee brace to the column, or by a square-ended truss.

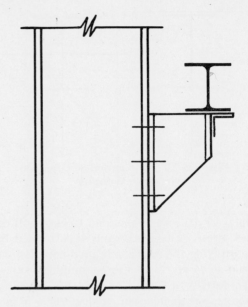

Fig. 7.4   Detail of Crane Support on Column

Brackets such as those treated above are unsatisfactory for crane loads of over 20 kips, and there are two methods used to take care of such conditions. We may use either two columns battened together as indicated in Fig. 7.9—each column carrying its own direct load, and the through column carrying the bending due to lateral moment of the crane— or a spliced column with a shallow column section carrying the roof, and a wide flange beam, like a 21 WF or 24 WF below the splice, as shown in Fig. 7.10.

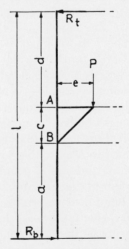

Fig. 7.5   Column Stresses Due to Crane Support

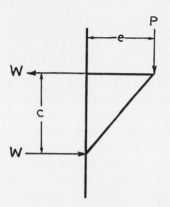

Fig. 7.6   Line Diagram of Crane Load on Column

g   The use of a traveling crane in a building usually combines another form of column bending with that discussed in paragraph (*f*) above. As the crane load is moved across the building, it puts a tractive effort into the crane bridge which is transmitted as a kick against the column. This is usually taken as 20 percent of the weight of the traveling crab plus load, and is applied to the column as a direct load at the line of the top of the bracket, or if the top of the crane girder is braced to the column, at this line.

If a simple column with a bracket is used, the moment and reactions are found as for an ordinary beam. If the column is of different size above and below the crane girder as in

Fig. 7.10, the best method of approach is the indirect Hardy Cross method, as described in Art. 3.21*g*.

h   The problem of designing columns for wind bracing is treated under the heading of wind bracing for mill buildings in Art. 10.21 and multistory buildings in Art. 10.22.

i   For multistory columns it is advisable for a designer to standardize on a form for loads and calculations. This statement applies to all types of calculations, but it is most important in column design.   Figure 7.11

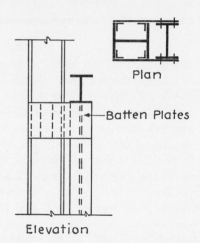

Fig. 7.9   Dual Column to Support Crane

shows the form used in the author's office. A typical six-story and roof office building is set up on this form. For each story the load is set down on the form as applied, in order from the top (as the floor plan is laid out) right side, bottom, and left side. The length to floor below is set down and the moment in each direction.

It is common practice to splice columns at alternate floors and, if there are an odd number of stories, as in this problem, it is better to make the splice above the first floor. Ordinarily, all columns should be spliced at the same floors, instead of staggering splices. The splice point should be located about 1 ft 6 in above the floor line. In this particular problem, the splices would be located above the odd numbered floors. These conditions may be varied by wind bracing.

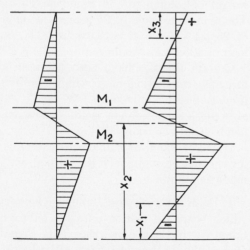

Figs. 7.7–7.8   Moment Diagram Due to Crane Load on Column

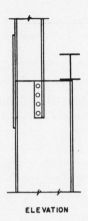

ELEVATION

Fig. 7.10   Spliced Column to Support Crane

We set down first the beam reactions for the roof and for the 6th floor taken from the calculations for beams. The sum of these loads is 103.5 kips. The approximate weight of column to add in for this load from the formula in Art. 1.50c is $60 + (0.4 \times 103.5) = 101.4$ lb per foot. We will therefore add in 1.5 kips for the roof column, and 1.2 kips for the sixth floor. The top tier is therefore designed for a total load of 107.2 kips plus an unbalance of 16.5, or 123.7 kips on a height of 12 feet. From Table 7.3, this would require an 8 WF 31.

The fifth and fourth floor loads from beam reactions are the same as the sixth, and the approximate total load at the fourth floor is found to be $107.2 + 59.7 + 59.7$ or 226.5. The weight to allow for columns will therefore be $60 + (0.4 \times 226.5) = 150.6$ lb per foot, or 1.8 kips per story. This is 0.6 kips greater than the load from the sixth floor, so we may add this to 59.7, or take down a total load per floor of $59.7 + 0.6 = 60.3$. However, in accordance with paragraph a above, we may start reducing the live load. The live load in this design is 50 psf on an area of 400 sq ft, or a total live load of 20 kips. The reduction on the fifth floor is 5 percent, or 1 kip. On the fourth floor, the reduction is 10 percent, or 2 kips. Adding in for unbalanced load, the equivalent total load is $224.8 + 16.5 = 241.3$ kips. The economical column for this is 10 WF 54.

We may assume about the same load increase from the third and second floors as from the fifth and fourth floors, or an approximate total load at the second floor of 342 kips. The weight per foot of column would be $60 + (0.4 \times 342) = 265.2$ lb per foot. Thirteen feet of this load is 3.5 kips, or 1.7 heavier than the fourth floor, or 62.0 kips, but the live load reduction is 15 percent of 3 kips, and for the second 20 percent or 4 kips.

The load on the second floor is applied in a slightly different manner from those on the typical floor. Although the reactions are the same, the moment differs because of the point of application of load. For a load of 341.8 kips on 14 ft height, the economical column would be 12 WF 79. The 10.0-kip load would be applied on a lever arm of $6 + 2 = 8$ in. The moment about axis 1-1 would therefore be

$$
\begin{aligned}
10.0 \times 8 &= 80 \\
-48.5 \times 6 &= \underline{-291} \\
\text{Net} &= -211
\end{aligned}
$$

The equivalent direct load would be

$$\frac{211 \times 0.217}{2} = 22.9$$

The unbalance in the other direction is 6.5, so the total direct load would be $341.8 + 29.4 = 371.2$ kips. This would require a 12 WF 85.

The first floor is designed for 100 psf live load and there is no eccentricity. The approximate total load is $341.8 + 90 = 431.8$ kips. The weight of column to add would be 3.3 kips. The reduction would be 25 percent of 100 psf, or 25 psf $\times$ 400 sq ft = 10.0 kips. The total load of 425.1 kips would require a 12 WF 92.

Certain liberties have been taken in the foregoing calculation, but it will be found that if every possible refinement were made, probably not a single column section in the entire height would be changed.

It will be found that time will be saved and fewer errors encountered if the calculations are made as follows.

1. From the work sheet—the plan layout on which beam calculation numbers have been noted—write down before each T, R, B, and L (top, right, bottom, left) for each floor the calculation number, and sketch odd moment

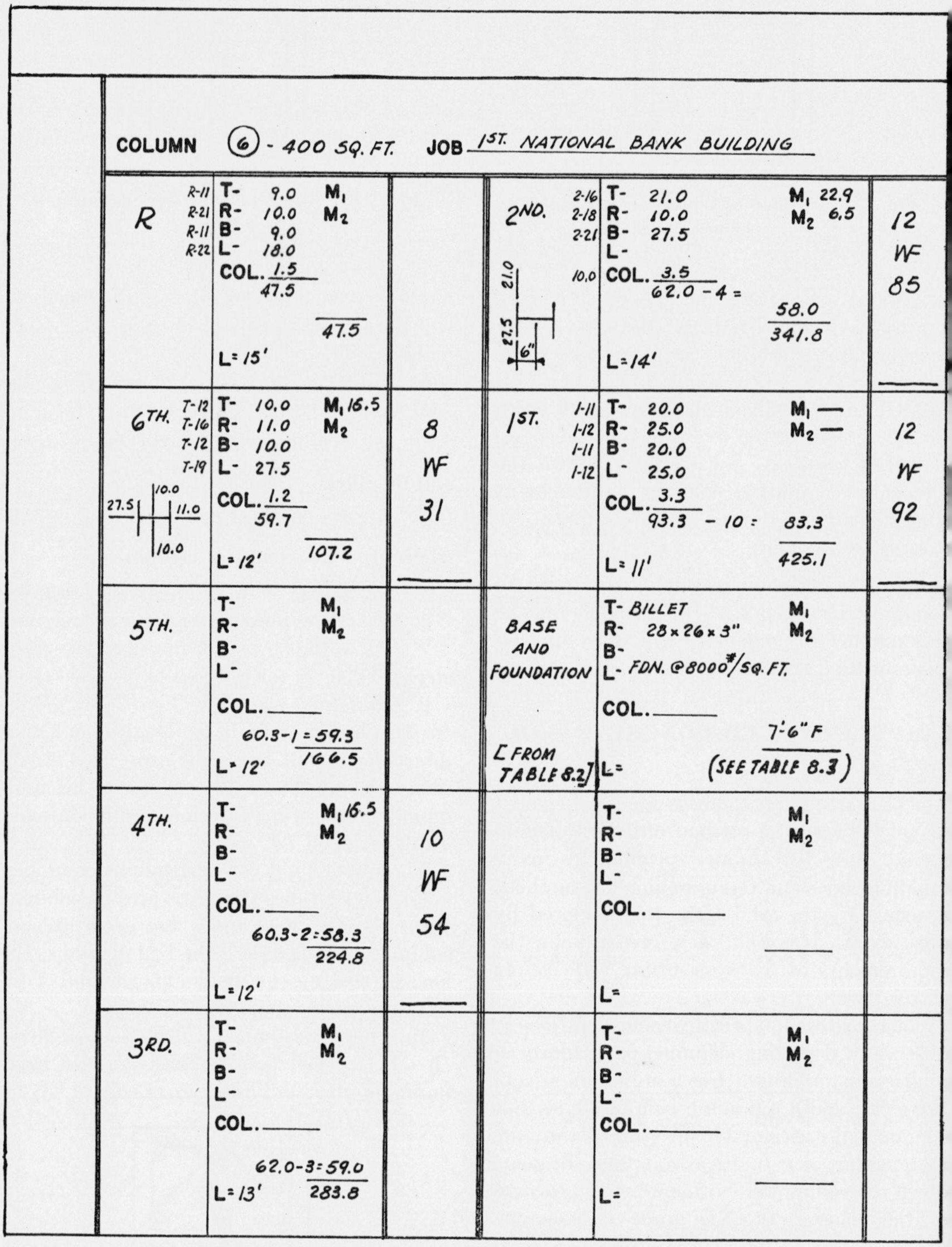

COLUMN ⑥ - 400 SQ. FT.		JOB 1ST. NATIONAL BANK BUILDING	

R   R-11 **T-** 9.0 **M₁**
 R-21 **R-** 10.0 **M₂**
 R-11 **B-** 9.0
 R-22 **L-** 18.0
   COL. *1.5*
    47.5
 	
      47.5
 	
 L= 15'
		2ND. 2-16 **T-** 21.0 **M₁** 22.9
		 2-18 **R-** 10.0 **M₂** 6.5
		 2-21 **B-** 27.5
		   L-
		 10.0 **COL.** *3.5*
		    62.0 - 4 =
		          58.0
		          341.8
		 L= 14'
			12
			 WF
			 85

6TH.   T-12 **T-** 10.0 **M₁** 16.5
 T-16 **R-** 11.0 **M₂**
 T-12 **B-** 10.0
 T-19 **L-** 27.5
   COL. *1.2*
    59.7
     107.2
 L= 12'
	8
	 WF
	 31
		1ST. 1-11 **T-** 20.0 **M₁** —
		 1-12 **R-** 25.0 **M₂** —
		 1-11 **B-** 20.0
		 1-12 **L-** 25.0
		   COL. *3.3*
		    93.3 - 10 = 83.3
		           425.1
		 L= 11'
			12
			 WF
			 92

5TH.   **T-**   **M₁**
 R-   **M₂**
 B-
 L-
 	
 COL. ____
  60.3-1 = 59.3
 L= 12'   166.5
		BASE
		 AND
		 FOUNDATION
		
		 [FROM
		 TABLE 8.2]
			T- BILLET **M₁**
			 R- 28 × 26 × 3" **M₂**
			 B-
			 L- FDN. @ 8000#/SQ.FT.
			
			 COL. ____
			       7'-6" F
			 L= (SEE TABLE 8.3)	

4TH.   **T-**   **M₁** 16.5
 R-   **M₂**
 B-
 L-
 	
 COL. ____
  60.3-2 = 58.3
    224.8
 L= 12'
	10
	 WF
	 54
			T- **M₁**
			 R- **M₂**
			 B-
			 L-
			
			 COL. ____
			
			 L=	

3RD. **T-** **M₁** **R-** **M₂** **B-** **L-** **COL.** ____ 62.0-3 = 59.0 **L**= 13' 283.8			**T-** **M₁** **R-** **M₂** **B-** **L-** **COL.** ____ **L**=	

Fig. 7.11 **Column Calculation Sheet**

Fig. 7.12　Section of Concrete Column—
4 Bars

Fig. 7.13　Section of Concrete Column—
6 Bars

conditions, as for the second floor in the problem we have considered. At the top of each sheet set down the floor area carried by the column.

2. Go through all calculations and set down the reactions and the live load for each floor.

3. Run the loads down and set down the moments, computing column allowances as the loads are run down.

4. Select the sizes.

It is wise to follow through step 1 with all columns, then step 2 with all, and so on. In this manner discrepancies will show up and errors will be avoided.

7.20　REINFORCED–CONCRETE COLUMNS

a Unfortunately there is wide disagreement as yet between the method of design of reinforced concrete columns specified by many building codes and the more modern methods specified by the ACI Code and adopted by most cities. It is well, therefore, to know the requirements of the appropriate code before starting work.

There are certain practical considerations to observe in designing columns, particularly in multistory buildings. Use a minimum area of 120 sq in. and a minimum side of 10 in. Use commercial sizes and 2-in. intervals for square, rectangular, or cylindrical columns. In going down the column, do not decrease (1) the size of the column, (2) the grade of concrete, (3) the number of bars, or (4) the size of bars. Throughout any one story, do not change the grade of concrete in the column.

Since it is generally accepted as being the best practice, and since it is the standard

method to which codes are being changed, we will design on the basis of 1951 ACI Code methods.

b 1. The *permissible axial load P* by the ACI Code for tied columns is

$$P = 0.180 f_c' A_g + 0.8 f_s A_s \qquad (7.1)$$

and for spirally reinforced columns

$$P = 0.225 f_c' A_g + f_s A_s \qquad (7.2)$$

where A_g = gross area of column

A_s = area of longitudinal reinforcement
f_c' = compressive strength of concrete
f_s = 16,000 psi for intermediate-grade steel, 20,000 psi for rail and hard-grade steel.

2. *Limitations applying to vertical reinforcement.* The lower limit for longitudinal reinforcement is 0.01 times the gross area of column section. The load carried by the minimum amount of reinforcement is tabulated in Tables 7.5 and 7.7.

The upper limit for longitudinal reinforcement is 0.04 times the gross area of columns with ties and 0.08 times the gross area of columns with spirals. For tied columns, the load carried by the maximum amount of reinforcement is tabulated in Table 7.5.

In spiral columns, with $1\frac{1}{4}$ in. square (No. 11) as the largest bar size used, the maximum numbers of bars is governed not by the

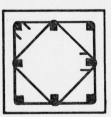

Fig. 7.14　Section of Concrete Column—
8 Bars

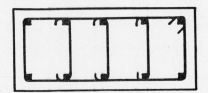

**Fig. 7.15 Section of Concrete Column—
Alternate Method of Tie Arrangement**

maximum ratio, 0.08, but by the minimum spacing allowed. Not less than six bars shall be used in columns with spirals.

The minimum center-to-center spacing permitted in the ACI regulations is $2\frac{1}{2}$ times the diameter for round bars, 3 times the side dimension for square bars; and the minimum clear spacing between bars is $1\frac{1}{2}$ in. or $1\frac{1}{2}$ times the maximum size of aggregate used.

The maximum number of bars given in Table 7.9 is governed by the space required to accommodate the increased number of bars at lapped splices and is for a single ring of bars. Where necessary, additional bars as indicated in Table 7.9 may be placed in an inner ring. It is considered permissible to place a bar close to a dowel (or bar from below) in the relative position shown in Fig. 7.17, and to take the minimum clear spacing between adjacent splices (each consisting of a bar and a dowel) the same as specified between bars in the preceding paragraph.

3. Where *lapped splices in deformed column bars* are used with 3,000-psi concrete or better, 20 diameters of bar should be used. Welded splices may be used instead of lapped splices, and where the bar diameter exceeds $1\frac{1}{2}$ in. welded splices are preferred. A welded splice is one in which the bars are butted and welded to develop in tension the yield-point stress of the bar.

4. *Lateral ties.* For bar sizes No. 6 and larger and columns with side dimension of 12 in. and larger, the minimum amount of tie reinforcement permitted by the ACI regulations requires No. 2 bars, spaced 12 in. o.c. For No. 5 bars, use No. 2 bars at 10 in. o.c. The maximum dimensions permitted by the Code for a principal column are 10 in. for thickness and 120 sq in. for area. With a 10-in. thickness, ties of No. 2 at 10 in. o.c. are required

regardless of the size of longitudinal bars. It is further specified that every longitudinal bar have lateral support equivalent to that provided by a 90-deg corner of a tie.

5. *Spiral reinforcement.* Load-carrying capacity according to Formula (7.2) above is based on gross area of concrete including the shell outside the spiral, but Formula (7.2) does not contain any term for the spiral reinforcement. The theory underlying the determination of spiral as expressed in Formula (7.3) is that spiral reinforcement should be furnished slightly in excess of the strength of the shell.

The minimum ratio of spiral reinforcement p' required by the ACI regulation is

$$p' = 0.45 \left(\frac{A_g}{A_c} - 1\right)\frac{f_c'}{f_s'} \qquad (7.3)$$

where p' = ratio of volume of spiral to volume of concrete core. The core diameter is the dimension out-to-out of spiral.

A_g = gross area of column

A_c = area within the spiral

f_c' = compressive strength of concrete

f_s' = 40,000 psi for hot-rolled rods of intermediate-grade steel; 60,000 psi for cold-drawn wire

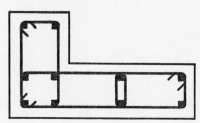

**Fig. 7.16 Typical Arrangement of Corner
Columns**

The p' value should never be less than 0.0112 for hot-rolled rods of intermediate-grade steel, nor less than 0.0075 for cold-drawn wire.

Note from Formula (7.3) that only one spiral ratio, p', belongs to each group of values of A_g/A_c, f_c', and f_s'. Spiral data may, therefore, be tabulated as in Table 7.10. The following Code provisions apply to spacing between adjacent loops in spirals: center-

Table 7.5   Allowable Loads—Tied Concrete Columns

Maximum loads, in kips, on concrete and limiting loads, in kips, on longitudinal reinforcement.
Use in connection with Eq. (7.1).

Column size, in.	Gross area A_g	Load on longitudinal reinforcement				Load on concrete		
		Intermediate grade		Hard grade		Values of $0.180f_c' \times A_g$ kips		
						Concrete strength: f_c'		
		Min. load	Max. load	Min. load	Max. load	2,000	2,500	3,000
10 × 12	120	15	61	19	77	43	54	65
10 × 14	140	18	72	22	90	50	63	76
10 × 16	160	20	82	26	102	57	72	86
10 × 18	180	23	92	29	115	65	81	97
12 × 12	144	18	74	23	92	52	65	78
12 × 14	168	21	86	26	106	60	75	91
12 × 16	192	24	98	30	119	69	86	104
12 × 18	216	28	111	33	133	78	97	117
12 × 20	240	31	123	37	147	86	108	130
14 × 14	196	25	100	31	125	70	88	106
14 × 16	224	29	115	36	143	81	101	121
14 × 18	252	32	129	40	161	91	113	136
14 × 20	280	36	143	45	179	101	126	151
14 × 22	308	39	158	49	197	111	139	166
16 × 16	256	33	131	41	164	92	115	138
16 × 18	288	37	147	46	184	104	130	155
16 × 20	320	41	164	51	205	115	144	173
16 × 22	352	45	180	56	225	127	158	190
16 × 24	384	49	197	61	246	138	173	207
18 × 18	324	41	166	52	207	117	146	175
18 × 20	360	46	184	58	230	130	162	194
18 × 22	396	51	203	63	253	143	178	214
18 × 24	432	55	221	69	276	156	194	233
18 × 26	468	60	239	75	299	168	211	253
20 × 20	400	51	205	64	256	144	180	216
20 × 22	440	56	225	70	282	158	198	238
20 × 24	480	61	246	77	307	173	216	259
20 × 26	520	66	266	83	333	187	234	281
20 × 28	560	72	287	90	358	202	252	302
22 × 22	484	62	248	77	310	174	218	261
22 × 24	528	68	270	84	338	190	238	285
22 × 26	572	73	293	92	366	206	257	309
22 × 28	616	79	315	99	394	222	277	333
24 × 24	576	74	295	92	369	207	259	311
24 × 26	624	81	324	100	399	225	281	337
24 × 28	672	88	364	108	430	242	302	363
26 × 26	676	91	364	114	456	243	304	365
26 × 28	728	98	393	123	491	262	328	393
28 × 28	784	100	400	125	500	282	353	423
30 × 30	900	115	461	144	576	324	405	486
32 × 32	1,024	131	524	164	656	369	461	553
34 × 34	1,156	148	590	184	738	416	520	624
	1,000	128	512	160	640	360	450	540

Table 7.6   Allowable Loads—Reinforcement in Tied Columns

Load in kips on longitudinal reinforcement $(0.8f_s A_s)$. Use in connection with Eq. (7.1).

No. bars	Columns with ties							No. bars
	Size of bars							
	No. 5	No. 6	No. 7	No. 8	No. 9	No. 10	No. 11	
Intermediate grade steel: $f_s = 0.8 \times 16{,}000 = 12{,}800$								
4	15	23	31	40	51	66	80	4
6	23	34	46	60	77	98	120	6
8	31	45	61	80	102	131	160	8
10	37	56	75	100	128	164	200	10
12	46	66	92	120	154	197	240	12
14	54	79	107	140	179	229	280	14
16	61	90	123	159	205	262	320	16
18	68	101	136	179	230	295	360	18
20	75	113	150	199	256	328	400	20
22	83	124	167	219	282	360	440	22
24	92	135	184	239	307	393	480	24
Rail or hard grade steel: $f_s = 0.8 \times 20{,}000 = 16{,}000$								
4	19	28	38	50	64	82	100	4
6	29	42	57	75	96	123	150	6
8	38	56	77	100	128	164	200	8
10	48	70	96	125	160	205	250	10
12	57	84	115	149	192	246	300	12
14	67	98	134	174	224	287	350	14
16	77	112	154	199	256	328	400	16
18	86	127	173	224	288	369	450	18
20	96	141	192	249	320	409	500	20
22	106	155	211	274	352	450	550	22
24	115	169	230	299	384	491	600	24

Courtesy Portland Cement Association

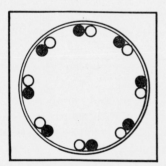

**Fig. 7.17   Arrangement of Reinforcement —
Spirally Reinforced Columns**

to-center spacing not to exceed one-sixth of the core diameter; clear spacing not to exceed 3 in.; clear spacing to be not less than $1\frac{3}{8}$ in. or $1\frac{1}{2}$ times maximum aggregate size. Spirals

meeting all these requirements are given in Table 7.10.

Standard practice in shops where spirals are coiled may result in different minimum core diameters that can be made conveniently with various sizes of rods. In Table 7.10 minimum core diameter has been taken as 12 in. for No. 4 rods, 15 in. for No. 5 rods, and 18 in. for No. 6 rods. It should be noted that some of the spirals in the tables are not collapsible.

6. *Review of column sections.* In alterations or extensions of buildings already constructed, problems may arise concerning safe loads permitted by ACI regulations on existing spiral columns designed according to other code requirements.

The first step in reviewing a column section

Table 7.7   Allowable Loads—Spirally Reinforced Concrete Columns

Maximum load, in kips, on concrete and limiting loads, in kips, on longitudinal reinforcement.
Use in connection with Eq. (7.2).

Square		Load on longitudinal reinforcement				Load on concrete		
		Intermediate grade		Hard grade		Values of $0.225f_c' A_g$, kips		
						Concrete strength: f_c'		
Column size, in.	Gross area A_g	Min. load	Max. load	Min. load	Max. load	2,000	2,500	3,000
14	196	31	122	39	152	88	110	132
16	256	41	150	51	187	115	144	173
18	324	52	200	65	250	146	182	219
20	400	64	225	80	281	180	225	270
22	484	77	250	97	312	218	272	327
24	576	92	275	115	343	259	324	389
26	676	108	300	135	374	304	380	456
28	784	125	349	157	437	353	441	529
30	900	144	374	180	468	405	506	607
32	1,024	164	399	205	499	461	576	691
34	1,156	185	424	231	531	520	650	780
	1,000	160		200		450	562	675

Round		Load on longitudinal reinforcement				Load on concrete		
		Intermediate grade		Hard and rail grade		Values of $0.225f_c' A_g$, kips		
						Concrete strength: f_c'		
Column size, in.	Gross area A_g	Min. load	Max. load	Min. load	Max. load	2,000	2,500	3,000
14	153.9	25	122	31	152	69	86	104
16	201.1	32	150	40	187	90	113	135
18	254.5	41	200	51	250	114	143	171
20	314.2	50	225	63	281	141	176	211
22	380.1	61	250	76	312	170	213	256
24	452.4	72	275	90	343	203	254	305
26	530.9	85	300	106	374	238	298	358
28	615.8	99	349	123	437	276	346	415
30	706.9	113	374	141	468	318	397	477
32	804.2	129	399	161	499	361	452	542
34	907.9	145	424	182	531	408	510	612

Courtesy Portland Cement Association

with given properties is to compute the ratio of spiral reinforcement p' in the column. If the computed value of p' is equal to or greater than the value of p' required by Formula (7.3), the permissible load may be determined from Formula (7.2).

In general, the computed value of p' will be smaller than that required by Formula (7.3). The permissible load may therefore be taken as the greater value of the two loads obtained by considering the column (1) as a tied col-

umn, the spiral acting simply as ties, or (2) as a spiral column with reduced gross area.

In Case (2), the reduced gross area A_g' may be determined as

$$A_g' = \left(1 + \frac{p'}{0.45} \times \frac{f_s'}{f_c'}\right) A_c \qquad (7.4)$$

in which p' is the computed spiral ratio and A_c the actual core area. Formula (7.4) is obtained from Formula (7.3), and A_g' includes the core area plus a shell corresponding to the

Table 7.8   Allowable Loads—Reinforcement in Spiral Columns

Load in kips on longitudinal reinforcement ($f_s A_s$). Use in connection with Eq. (7.2).

No. bars	Size of bars							No. bars
	No. 5	No. 6	No. 7	No. 8	No. 9	No. 10	No. 11	
Intermediate grade steel: $f_s = 16,000$ psi								
6	30	42	58	76	96	122	150	6
7	35	49	67	88	112	142	175	7
8	40	56	77	101	128	163	200	8
9	45	63	86	114	144	183	225	9
10	50	70	96	126	160	203	250	10
11	55	77	106	139	176	224	275	11
12	60	84	115	152	192	244	300	12
13	64	92	125	164	208	264	324	13
14	69	99	134	177	224	285	349	14
15	74	106	144	190	240	305	374	15
16	79	113	154	202	256	325	399	16
17	84	120	163	215	272	346	424	17
18	89	127	173	228	288	366	449	18
19	94	134	182	240	304	386	474	19
20	99	141	192	253	320	406	499	20
21	104	148	202	266	336	427	524	21
22	109	155	211	278	352	447	549	22
23	114	162	221	291	368	467	574	23
24	119	169	230	303	384	488	599	24
25	124	176	240	316	400	508	624	25
Rail or hard grade steel: $f_s = 20,000$ psi								
6	37	53	72	95	120	152	187	6
7	43	62	84	111	140	178	219	7
8	50	70	96	126	160	203	250	8
9	56	79	108	142	180	229	281	9
10	62	88	120	158	200	254	312	10
11	68	97	132	174	220	279	343	11
12	74	106	144	190	240	305	374	12
13	81	114	156	205	260	330	406	13
14	87	123	168	221	280	356	437	14
15	93	132	180	237	300	381	468	15
16	99	141	192	253	320	406	499	16
17	105	150	204	269	340	432	531	17
18	112	158	216	284	360	457	562	18
19	118	167	228	300	380	483	593	19
20	124	176	240	316	400	508	624	20
21	130	185	252	332	420	534	655	21
22	136	194	264	348	440	559	686	22
23	143	202	276	364	460	584	718	23
24	149	211	288	379	480	610	749	24
25	155	220	300	395	500	635	780	25

Courtesy Portland Cement Association

Table 7.9 Maximum Number of Bars in Spiral Columns

At lapped splices in outer ring (*O*) and in inner ring (*I*) if area required is greater than that obtainable in outer ring only.

Column size, in., $1\frac{1}{2}$ in. protection	Bar size														Column size, in., 2 in. protection
	No. 5		No. 6		No. 7		No. 8		No. 9		No. 10		No. 11		
	O	*I*	*O*	*I*	*O*	*I*	*O*	*I*	*O*	*I*	*O*	*I*	*O*	*I*	
14	11		10		9		8		7		6				15
16	13	8	11	7	10	6	9	5	8	4	7		6		17
18	15	10	13	9	12	8	11	7	10	5	8	4	8		19
20	17	12	15	11	14	9	13	8	11	6	10	5	9	4	21
22	19	14	17	13	16	11	15	10	13	8	11	6	10	5	23
24	21	16	19	15	18	13	16	12	14	9	12	8	11	6	25
26	23	19	21	17	20	15	18	13	16	11	14	9	12	8	27
28	26	21	24	19	22	17	20	15	17	13	15	11	14	9	29
30	28	23	26	21	24	19	22	17	19	14	17	12	15	10	31
32	30	26	28	23	26	21	24	19	21	16	18	13	16	11	33
34	33	28	30	25	27	23	25	21	22	17	19	15	17	13	35

Courtesy Portland Cement Association

Table 7.10 Rolled-Steel Spirals in Square and Round Columns

3,000-psi concrete

Column size, in.	With $1\frac{1}{2}$-in. cover outside spiral			With 2-in. cover outside spiral		
	Core diam, in.	Square	Round	Core diam, in.	Square	Round
16	13	No. 4 at $1\frac{7}{8}$ in.	No. 3 at $1\frac{7}{8}$ in.	12		No. 4 at 2 in.
18	15	No. 4 at $1\frac{7}{8}$ in.	No. 3 at $1\frac{7}{8}$ in.	14		No. 4 at $2\frac{1}{4}$ in.
20	17	No. 5 at $2\frac{3}{4}$ in.	No. 3 at 2 in.	16	No. 5 at $2\frac{1}{4}$ in.	No. 4 at $2\frac{5}{8}$ in.
22	19	No. 5 at $2\frac{5}{8}$ in.	No. 3 at 2 in.	18	No. 5 at $2\frac{1}{4}$ in.	No. 4 at $2\frac{5}{8}$ in.
24	21	No. 5 at $2\frac{5}{8}$ in.	No. 4 at $3\frac{3}{8}$ in.	20	No. 5 at $2\frac{1}{8}$ in.	No. 4 at $2\frac{5}{8}$ in.
26	23	No. 5 at $2\frac{1}{2}$ in.	No. 4 at 3 in.	22	No. 5 at $2\frac{1}{8}$ in.	No. 4 at $2\frac{5}{8}$ in.
28	25	No. 5 at $2\frac{3}{8}$ in.	No. 4 at $2\frac{3}{4}$ in.	24	No. 5 at 2 in.	No. 4 at $2\frac{5}{8}$ in.
30	27	No. 5 at $2\frac{3}{8}$ in.	No. 4 at $2\frac{5}{8}$ in.	26	No. 6 at $2\frac{7}{8}$ in.	No. 4 at $2\frac{3}{4}$ in.
32	29	No. 5 at $2\frac{1}{4}$ in.	No. 4 at $2\frac{1}{2}$ in.	28	No. 6 at $2\frac{3}{4}$ in.	No. 4 at $2\frac{1}{2}$ in.
34	31	No. 5 at $2\frac{1}{8}$ in.	No. 4 at $2\frac{1}{4}$ in.	30	No. 6 at $2\frac{5}{8}$ in.	No. 4 at $2\frac{3}{8}$ in.

Courtesy Portland Cement Association

existing spiral. Safe load is determined from Formula (7.2), substituting A_g' for A_g.

7. *Tied columns.* In determining the reinforcement required in tied columns designed in accordance with Formula (7.1), the procedure recommended is (1) record column load P; (2) select value of $0.180f_c'A_g$ from Table 7.5 and subtract it from P; (3) with the balance, select from Table 7.6 number and size of longitudinal bars required, and (4) record tie reinforcement.

As an example, we are given:

Column load $P = 283{,}000$ lb

Concrete strength $f_c' = 3{,}000$ psi

Reinforcing steel is intermediate grade

Determine size of tied column; number and size of vertical bars; and ties.

For illustration of the use of Tables 7.5 and 7.6, three cases will be calculated:

(*a*) $P = 283$ kips
Use 16 × 18 column: $\underline{155 \text{ kips}}$ (Table 7.5)
Balance = 128 kips

This value lies between the minimum load (37) and the maximum load (147) on reinforcement given for a 16 × 18-in. column. Use ten No. 9

bars (see Table 7.6: 128 kips). Note that the maximum load permitted on a 16 × 16-in. tied column in Table 7.5 is 131 + 138 = 269 kips, which is too small for the load given.

(b) Let 20 × 24 in. be the size desired for reasons other than load-carrying capacity:

$$P = 283 \text{ kips}$$
Use 20 × 24 column: <u>259 kips</u> (Table 7.5)
Balance = 24 kips

Four No. 7 bars can carry 31 kips (see Table 7.6); but the minimum reinforcement permitted in a 20 × 24-in. tied column is that corresponding to 61 kips (given in Table 7.5). Use eight No. 7 bars (see Table 7.6: 61 kips). For ties, see Fig. 7.14.

(c) Let the column size be limited to 12 in. in one direction:

$$P = 283 \text{ kips}$$
Use 12 × 24: 2 × 78 = 156 kips
(two 12 × 12-in. columns
in Table 7.5)

Balance = <u>127 kips</u>
Use ten No. 9 bars (see Table 7.6): 128 kips.

8. *Columns reinforced with spirals.* In designing spirally reinforced columns in accordance with Formula (7.2), the procedure recommended is (1) record column load P; (2) select value of $0.225f_c'A_g$ from Table 7.7 and subtract it from P; (3) with the balance, select from Table 7.8 number and size of longitudinal bars required; (4) check bars for proper spacing at lapped splices using the data in Table 7.9; and (5) select spiral reinforcement from Table 7.10.

As an example, we are given:
Column load $P = 283,000$ lb.
Concrete strength $f_c' = 3,000$ psi
Reinforcing steel is intermediate grade
Spiral is cold-drawn wire, $1\frac{1}{2}$-in. concrete protection.
Determine size of square column with spiral; number and size of vertical bars; and spiral dimensions.

For illustration of the use of Tables 7.7 to 7.10, three cases will be calculated:

(a) $P = 283$ kips

Use 16 × 16 column: <u>173 kips</u> (Table 7.7)
Balance = <u>110 kips</u>

This value lies between the minimum load (41) and the maximum load (150) on reinforcement given for a 16 × 16-in. column. Use nine No. 8 bars (see Table 7.8: 114 kips).
Note: Table 7.9 shows that nine is the maximum number of No. 8 bars that can be accommodated at splices in a 16 × 16-in. column. The spiral (Table 7.10) is No. 4 at $2\frac{1}{8}$-in. pitch, 13-in. core diameter.

(b) Let 20 × 20 in. be the size desired for reasons other than load-carrying capacity:

$$P = 283 \text{ kips}$$
Use 20 × 20 column: <u>270 kips</u> (Table 7.7)
Balance = 13 kips

The minimum reinforcement permitted in a 20 × 20-in. square column with spiral is that corresponding to 64 kips (given in Table 7.7). Use seven No. 7 bars (see Table 7.8: 67 kips). The spiral (Table 7.10) is No. 4 at $2\frac{3}{4}$-in. pitch, 17-in. core diameter.

(c) Redesign the 20 × 20-in. column in (b) in accordance with the code provision according to which it is permissible to design a circular column and to build it as a square column.

$$P = 283 \text{ kips}$$
20-in. circular column: <u>211 kips</u> (Table 7.7)
Balance = 72 kips

Use six No. 8 bars (see Table 7.8: 76 kips). The spiral (Table 7.10) is No. 3 at $2\frac{3}{4}$-in. pitch, 17-in. core diameter.
Note that design (c) is more economical than design (b).

c   Some of the older codes which are still in use are based on the assumption that the steel does not work to its full capacity, but rather in accordance with the rules for nonhomogeneous members as set forth in Art. 2.21. Under these conditions, the steel stress $A_s = nA_c$.

Typical of this type of code is the 1928 ACI Code and several variations of it as adopted by various cities. Under this code, for a reinforced-concrete column with lateral ties whose length between supports does not exceed eleven times the least lateral dimension, the permissible concentric load is

$$P = 0.225f_c'A_g[1 + (n-1)p] \qquad (7.5)$$

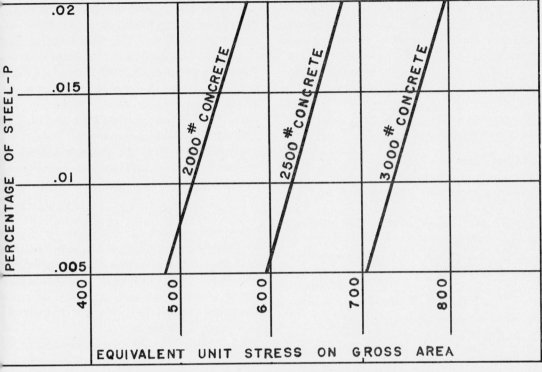

Fig. 7.18   **Unit Stresses, Tied Columns—1928 Code**

where f_c' is the ultimate strength for which concrete is designed—2,000, 2,500, or 3,000 psi—and A_g is the gross area of the section. $0.225f_c'$ becomes 450, 563, or 675 psi respectively for the three grades of concrete. Concrete columns of this type must have a minimum $p = 0.005$ and maximum $= 0.02$, or limits of $\frac{1}{2}$ and 2 percent. Probably the simplest method of solving concrete columns of this type is to assume the gross area and compute the quality of concrete and the steel area required. It may be advantageous to use a diagram similar to Fig. 7.18 to select this percentage of steel, the unit stresses having been computed.

Problems   What is the safe load on a short concrete column with effective section 12 in. square containing 1.5 percent of longitudinal reinforcing? (From a state license examination.)

Assume that 2,000-psi concrete is intended. From Formula (7.5)

$$P = 450 \times 144 \,[1 + (15 - 1) \times 0.015]$$
$$= 450 \times 144 \times 1.21 = 78{,}500 \text{ lb}$$

Or read directly from Fig. 7.18 for percentage 0.015; 545 psi. Then $P = 144 \times 545 = 78{,}500$ lb.

Problem (From a state license examination): Design a concrete column 10 ft high to support a central load of 135,000 lb, using $f_c = 500$, $n = 15$, $p = 0.025$. This problem is not in accordance with Fig. 7.18, either as to f_c or as to maximum p. The unit stress on the gross area may be

$$500\,[1 + (15 - 1)\,0.025] = 675 \text{ psi}$$

Then $A_g = 135{,}000/675 = 200$ sq in.

In order to satisfy exactly the requirements of the problem, it is impossible to use commercial sizes. Use $12\frac{1}{2} \times 16$ in. (or 16 in. round); 0.025 of 200 sq in. $= 5$ sq in. Use four No. 11 bars. The area of steel furnished is 5.625 sq in., which is in excess of the

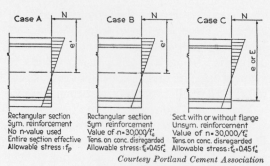

**Fig. 7.19   Bending and Direct Stress
in Columns**

required area and will carry 3,930 lb more than the problem calls for, a total load of 138,930 lb.

7.21   Bending and direct stress

a   The material included in this article is taken from Bulletin ST 62 of the Portland Cement Association.

Proportioning of sections for combined bending and axial load is treated in many textbooks as a subject apart from design of columns and beams. In accordance with such a distinction, formulae for columns are considered applicable to sections with concentric load alone, while data for beam design are confined to use for sections with bending moment alone.

A different and more practical treatment is presented in some publications, especially in the "Reinforced Concrete Design Handbook" of the American Concrete Institute, but further discussion is desirable in order to illustrate the design procedures pertaining to various cases of combined bending and axial load.

For formulae and derivations, reference is made to the Handbook and to the "Building Regulations for Reinforced Concrete," edition of 1951, published by the American Concrete Institute. The nomenclature from the Handbook is repeated here in part in paragraph *e* following.

In a section subject to concentric load only, the axial load N has an eccentricity e' which is equal to zero. If a moment M is added, the combined effect of M and N is the same as that of a load N with an eccentricity of $e' = 12M/N$ in., M being in foot-kips and N in kips. When the ratio of M/N increases, e' also increases until it finally approaches infinity. The limit of $e' = \infty$ represents the case of simple bending in which there is no axial load but only moment. Combined bending and axial load may be said to be the general case, concentric load being the special case for the limit of $e' = 0$, and simple bending being the special case for the limit of $e' = \infty$.

Under certain conditions some of the tables used for design of concentrically loaded columns may be used to design eccentrically loaded columns also. In accordance with the ACI Code, eccentrically loaded column sections may be designed as if they were subjected to a concentric load computed by the formula

$$P = N\,(1 + CDe'/t) \qquad (7.6)$$

The equivalent concentric load P will give a maximum fiber stress equal to the stress produced by M and N combined, assuming the section is uncracked. Values of C and D may be selected from Tables 7.11 and 7.12. This type of design will be denoted as Case A.

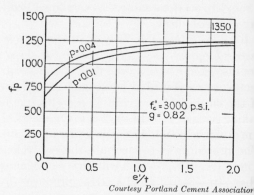

Fig. 7.20   Bending and Direct Stress in Columns

The design procedures for combined bending and axial load are so arranged that they apply also to bending alone. The main feature introduced in the procedure is that the area of tensile reinforcement A_s always appears in formulas involving i, in which $i = e/(e - jd)$. The eccentricity e (without prime) is meas-red from the tensile steel. Simple bending is the special case obtained by setting $e = \infty$, which gives $i = 1$, and $A_S i - A_S$. This type of design will be denoted as Case C.

When the eccentric load N moves in toward the position of the resultant of the compressive stresses in the section, the quantity $e - jd$) becomes smaller and $i = e/(e - jd)$ becomes larger. If e is nearly equal to jd, the procedure of Case C cannot be used. For such small eccentricities a third design procedure, Case B, is available. Case B is based upon the same assumptions as Case C, the regular beam design, but is here used only for rectangular sections with symmetrical reinforcement. For Case B, use design charts in Fig. 7.21. Figure 7.19 shows the conditions of the three design cases, A, B, and C.

The smaller the eccentricities in Case C, the less economical it is to design for the maximum tensile steel stress allowed in the Code. The approximate tensile steel stress that gives the minimum area of reinforcement, $A_S' + A_S$, may be determined from Fig. 7.25, which is developed from analytical work done by P. Massarik. The application of Fig. 7.25 is illustrated in paragraph c.

Paragraph d deals with investigation of stresses in sections subject to combined bending and axial load.

b *Tied columns, rectangular sections, symmetrical reinforcement.* Two types of design are discussed in connection with columns subjected to combined bending and axial load. If the entire section is considered effective in taking stresses and the section is symmetrical, the design is denoted as case A (see Fig. 7.19). The procedure is to compute the equivalent concentric load P which will give a maximum fiber stress equal to the stress produced by the actual concentric load N combined with the bending moment M. The section may be designed by means of the regular column data, using P as a concentric load.

The other type of design available for columns, Case B, applies to symmetrical sections in which tension on concrete is disregarded. It is based on the assumptions used in regular beam design, Case C, in which stress is taken as n times the stress in the surrounding concrete and tensile stress in concrete is disregarded. From the standpoint of basic assumptions, Cases B and C are alike, the main distinction being that Case B is confined to symmetrical, rectangular sections and is applicable to smaller eccentricities than Case C.

The ACI Code specifies two allowable stresses for concrete in compression, one for flexure, $f_c = 0.45f_c'$, and another for eccentrically loaded columns, which according to Section 1110 in the Code equals

$$f_p = f_a \frac{1 + De'/t}{1 + CDe'/t}$$

For the columns with ties, the following formulae apply:

$$f_a = \frac{0.18f_c' + 0.8f_s p}{1 + (n-1)p}$$

$$C = \frac{f_a}{0.45f_c'}$$

$$D = \frac{1 + (n-1)p}{\frac{1}{6} + \frac{1}{2}(n-1)pg^2}$$

Values of f_a, C, and D are given in Tables 7.11 and 7.12 for columns both with ties and with spirals. Table 7.13 contains values of f_p for tied columns with intermediate-grade steel and $g^2 = \frac{2}{3}$, or $g = 0.82$, corresponding to

$$d'/d = \frac{1.00 - 0.82}{2} = 0.09.$$

Variations in g within practical limits have negligible effect upon f_p.

The values in Table 7.13 for $f_c' = 3,000$ psi are plotted in Fig. 7.20, which shows how f_p varies from 613 and 774 psi for concentric load to $0.45f_c' = 1,350$ psi for bending alone. It is seen that the allowable stress f_p for a given concrete strength varies with p and especially with e'/t.

The f_p stress specified in the ACI Code for eccentrically loaded columns becomes equal to $0.45f_c'$ when $e'/t = \infty$, that is, for simple bending. While this seems proper so far as the allowable stress is concerned, an inconsistency arises at $e'/t = 1.0$, at which point a transition from cracked to uncracked section design procedure is to be made according to the Code. This question is discussed in examples that follow.

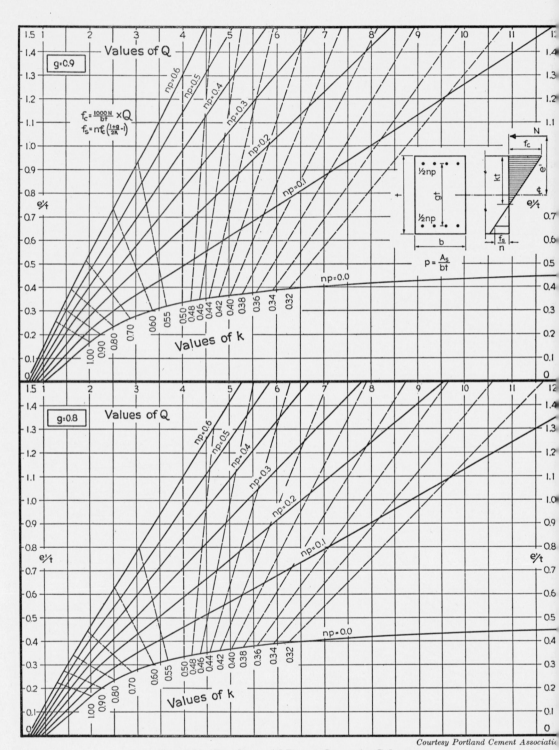

Fig. 7.21   Bending and Direct Stress in Columns

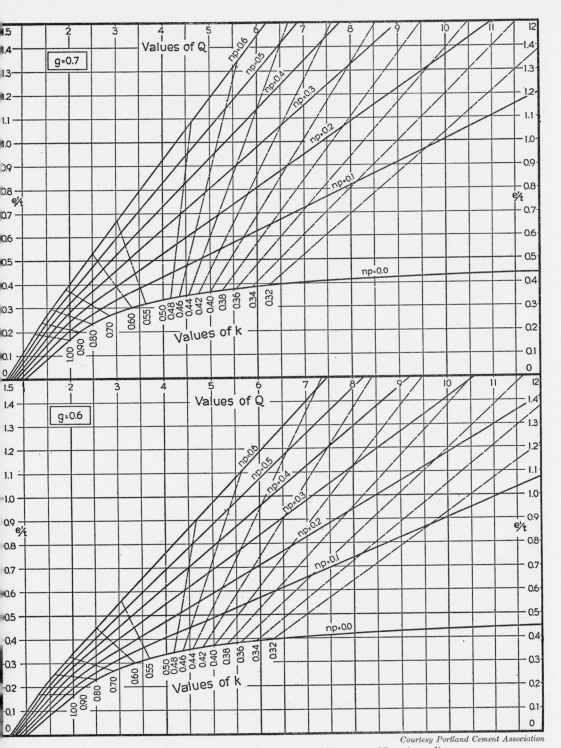

Fig. 7.21   Bending and Direct Stress in Columns (Continued)

Table 7.11   Coefficients for Design of Columns, Bending and Direct Stress

Values of $f_a = \dfrac{0.225f'_c + f_s p}{1 + (n-1)p}$ for Spiral Columns

0.8 times this value for Tied Columns

f'_c	n	Tied Columns						Spiral Columns									
		Values of p						Values of p									
		0.010	0.015	0.020	0.025	0.030	0.040	0.010	0.015	0.020	0.025	0.030	0.040	0.050	0.060	0.070	0.080
								$f_s = 16,000$									
2000	15	428	456	481	504	524	559	535	570	602	630	655	699	735	766	793	816
2500	12	521	551	579	604	627	668	651	689	723	755	784	835	879	917	950	980
3000	10	613	645	675	702	728	774	766	806	843	878	909	967	1017	1062	1101	1137
3750	8	750	785	817	847	875	927	938	981	1021	1059	1094	1159	1218	1270	1318	1361
5000	6	979	1016	1051	1084	1117	1177	1224	1270	1314	1356	1396	1471	1540	1604	1663	1718
								$f_s = 20,000$									
2000	15	456	496	531	563	592	641	570	620	664	704	739	801	853	897	934	967
2500	12	550	592	631	667	699	757	687	740	789	833	874	946	1008	1062	1109	1150
3000	10	642	687	729	767	803	868	803	859	911	959	1004	1085	1155	1218	1273	1323
3750	8	780	828	873	915	955	1027	975	1035	1091	1144	1193	1284	1366	1439	1506	1567
5000	6	1010	1060	1109	1156	1200	1283	1262	1326	1386	1444	1500	1604	1700	1788	1870	1946

Values of $C = \dfrac{f_a}{0.45f'_c}$

f'_c	n	Tied Columns						Spiral Columns									
		Values of p						Values of p									
		0.010	0.015	0.020	0.025	0.030	0.040	0.010	0.015	0.020	0.025	0.030	0.040	0.050	0.060	0.070	0.080
								$f_s = 16,000$									
2000	15	0.48	0.51	0.53	0.56	0.58	0.62	0.59	0.63	0.67	0.70	0.73	0.78	0.82	0.85	0.88	0.91
2500	12	0.46	0.49	0.51	0.54	0.56	0.59	0.58	0.61	0.64	0.67	0.70	0.74	0.78	0.82	0.84	0.87
3000	10	0.45	0.48	0.50	0.52	0.54	0.57	0.57	0.60	0.62	0.65	0.67	0.72	0.75	0.79	0.82	0.84
3750	8	0.44	0.46	0.48	0.50	0.52	0.55	0.56	0.58	0.61	0.63	0.65	0.69	0.72	0.75	0.78	0.81
5000	6	0.44	0.45	0.47	0.48	0.50	0.52	0.54	0.56	0.58	0.60	0.62	0.65	0.68	0.71	0.74	0.76
								$f_s = 20,000$									
2000	15	0.51	0.55	0.59	0.63	0.66	0.71	0.63	0.69	0.74	0.78	0.82	0.89	0.95	1.00	1.04	1.07
2500	12	0.49	0.53	0.56	0.59	0.62	0.67	0.61	0.66	0.70	0.74	0.78	0.84	0.90	0.94	0.99	1.02
3000	10	0.48	0.51	0.54	0.57	0.59	0.64	0.59	0.64	0.67	0.71	0.74	0.80	0.86	0.90	0.94	0.98
3750	8	0.46	0.49	0.52	0.54	0.57	0.61	0.58	0.61	0.65	0.68	0.71	0.76	0.81	0.85	0.89	0.93
5000	6	0.45	0.47	0.49	0.51	0.53	0.57	0.56	0.59	0.62	0.64	0.67	0.71	0.76	0.79	0.83	0.86

Courtesy Portland Cement Association

Three design conditions are considered and analyzed in connection with a rectangular section with symmetrical tied reinforcement: (1) concrete uncracked, allowable stress f_p; (2) concrete cracked, allowable stress f_c; and (3) concrete cracked, allowable stress f_p.

The data for the section are: $b = t = 20$ in., $f_c' = 3,000$ psi, $g = 0.8$, $p = 0.01$, and the reinforcement is assumed to be of intermediate-grade steel. Determine the axial load N which the section can support when $e'/t = 1.0$.

1. When the concrete is uncracked and the allowable stress is f_p, use Eq. (28) of the ACI Code:

$$P = N(1 + CDe'/t) \qquad (7.6)$$

P is the concentric load capacity of the section and equals $(0.18f_c' + 0.8f_s p)bt = (0.18 \times 3,000 + 0.8 \times 16,000 \times 0.01)20 \times 20 = 267$ kips.

CD from Tables 7.11 and 7.12 equals $0.45 \times 5.54 = 2.5$.

$$N = \frac{P}{1 + CDe'/t} = \frac{267}{1 + 2.5 \times 1.0} = 76 \text{ kips}$$

2. When the concrete is assumed cracked but the allowable stress is taken equal to $f_c = 0.45 \times 3,000 = 1,350$ psi, use Fig. 7.21. Select $Q = 8.9$. Then

$$N = \frac{f_c bt}{1,000Q} = \frac{1,350 \times 20 \times 20}{1,000 \times 8.9} = 61 \text{ kips}$$

3. If the allowable stress is taken as f_p and the section is considered cracked, select $f_p = 1,140$ psi from Table 7.13. The axial load permitted on the section is

$$N = \frac{f_c bt}{1,000Q} = \frac{1,140 \times 20 \times 20}{1,000 \times 8.9} = 51 \text{ kips}$$

Table 7.12   Coefficients for Design of Columns, Bending and Direct Stress

$$D = \frac{1+(n-1)p}{\frac{1}{6}+\frac{1}{2}(n-1)pg^2}$$

$$D = \frac{1+(n-1)p}{\frac{1}{6}+\frac{1}{4}(n-1)pg^2}$$

$$D = \frac{1+(n-1)p}{\frac{1}{8}+\frac{1}{4}(n-1)pg^2}$$

Values of $D = \dfrac{t^2}{2R^2}$

in which R = radius of gyration

$p = \dfrac{A_s}{A_g}$, in which A_g = gross area of concrete section

All reinforcement is arranged symmetrically

D is used for determination of f_p in eccentrically loaded columns*

g	$(n-1)p$																
	0.0	0.05	0.10	0.15	0.20	0.25	0.30	0.35	0.40	0.45	0.50	0.55	0.60	0.65	0.70	0.75	0.80
Rectangular Sections with Ties																	
1.00	6.0	5.5	5.1	4.8	4.5	4.3	4.1	4.0	3.8	3.7	3.6	3.5	3.4	3.4	3.3	3.2	3.2
0.95	6.0	5.5	5.2	4.9	4.7	4.5	4.3	4.2	4.0	3.9	3.8	3.7	3.7	3.6	3.5	3.5	3.4
0.90	6.0	5.6	5.3	5.1	4.8	4.7	4.5	4.4	4.3	4.2	4.1	4.0	3.9	3.8	3.8	3.7	3.7
0.85	6.0	5.7	5.4	5.2	5.0	4.9	4.7	4.6	4.5	4.4	4.3	4.2	4.2	4.1	4.1	4.0	4.0
0.80	6.0	5.7	5.5	5.4	5.2	5.1	4.9	4.8	4.7	4.7	4.6	4.5	4.5	4.4	4.3	4.3	4.3
0.75	6.0	5.8	5.6	5.5	5.4	5.3	5.2	5.1	5.0	4.9	4.9	4.8	4.8	4.7	4.7	4.6	4.6
0.70	6.0	5.9	5.7	5.6	5.6	5.5	5.4	5.3	5.3	5.2	5.2	5.1	5.1	5.1	5.0	5.0	5.0
0.65	6.0	5.9	5.9	5.8	5.7	5.7	5.6	5.6	5.6	5.5	5.5	5.5	5.4	5.4	5.4	5.4	5.4
0.60	6.0	6.0	6.0	5.9	5.9	5.9	5.9	5.9	5.9	5.9	5.8	5.8	5.8	5.8	5.8	5.8	5.8
Square Sections with Spirals																	
1.00	6.0	5.9	5.7	5.6	5.5	5.5	5.4	5.3	5.3	5.2	5.1	5.1	5.1	5.0	5.0	4.9	4.9
0.95	6.0	5.9	5.8	5.7	5.7	5.6	5.5	5.5	5.4	5.4	5.3	5.3	5.3	5.2	5.2	5.2	5.2
0.90	6.0	5.9	5.9	5.8	5.8	5.7	5.7	5.7	5.7	5.6	5.6	5.6	5.5	5.5	5.5	5.5	5.5
0.85	6.0	6.0	5.9	5.9	5.9	5.9	5.9	5.9	5.9	5.8	5.8	5.8	5.8	5.8	5.8	5.8	5.8
0.80	6.0	6.0	6.0	6.0	6.0	6.0	6.1	6.1	6.1	6.1	6.1	6.1	6.1	6.1	6.1	6.1	6.1
0.75	6.0	6.0	6.1	6.1	6.2	6.2	6.2	6.3	6.3	6.3	6.3	6.4	6.4	6.4	6.4	6.4	6.4
0.70	6.0	6.1	6.1	6.2	6.3	6.3	6.4	6.4	6.5	6.5	6.6	6.6	6.7	6.7	6.7	6.8	6.8
0.65	6.0	6.1	6.2	6.3	6.4	6.5	6.5	6.6	6.7	6.8	6.8	6.9	7.0	7.0	7.1	7.1	7.2
0.60	6.0	6.1	6.3	6.4	6.5	6.6	6.7	6.8	6.9	7.0	7.1	7.2	7.2	7.3	7.4	7.5	7.5
Round Sections with Spirals																	
1.00	8.0	7.6	7.3	7.1	6.9	6.7	6.5	6.4	6.2	6.1	6.0	5.9	5.8	5.7	5.7	5.6	5.5
0.95	8.0	7.7	7.5	7.2	7.1	6.9	6.7	6.6	6.5	6.4	6.3	6.2	6.1	6.1	6.0	6.0	5.9
0.90	8.0	7.8	7.6	7.4	7.3	7.1	7.0	6.9	6.7	6.6	6.6	6.5	6.5	6.4	6.4	6.3	6.3
0.85	8.0	7.8	7.7	7.6	7.4	7.3	7.3	7.2	7.1	7.0	7.0	6.9	6.9	6.8	6.8	6.7	6.7
0.80	8.0	7.9	7.8	7.7	7.6	7.6	7.5	7.5	7.4	7.4	7.3	7.3	7.2	7.2	7.2	7.1	7.1
0.75	8.0	7.9	7.9	7.9	7.8	7.8	7.8	7.7	7.7	7.7	7.7	7.7	7.6	7.6	7.6	7.6	7.6
0.70	8.0	8.0	8.0	8.0	8.0	8.0	8.0	8.0	8.0	8.0	8.1	8.1	8.1	8.1	8.1	8.1	8.1
0.65	8.0	8.1	8.1	8.2	8.2	8.3	8.3	8.3	8.4	8.4	8.4	8.5	8.5	8.5	8.5	8.6	8.6
0.60	8.0	8.1	8.2	8.3	8.4	8.5	8.6	8.6	8.7	8.8	8.8	8.9	8.9	9.0	9.0	9.1	9.1

Courtesy Portland Cement Association

The three values computed for N are plotted in Fig. 7.22 together with other N values determined for various ratios of e'/t up to 2.0. The ACI Code specifies for columns that curve a should be used from $e'/t = 0$ to $e'/t = 1.0$, and that curve c be used beyond $e'/t = 1.0$, but makes no reference to the use of the b curve.

In accordance with the Code provisions, the reinforced-concrete section is capable of sustaining $N = 76$ kips immediately to the left of $e'/t = 1.0$, but to the right of this point it is capable of supporting only 51 kips, or one-third less. Such a drop or discontinuity in the load curve is undesirable. If a transition is to be made from one to another design procedure, it should be made where two load curves intersect in Fig. 7.22. Curves a and c intersect at point 1, curves a and b at point 2.

The transition should be made at one or the other of these two points.

At first sight, point 1 in Fig. 7.22 might seem to be the proper place to discontinue using case A since this is approximately where tension begins to show up in the section. However, the Code states, in Section 1109, that column sections may be considered uncracked up to an eccentricity ratio of $e'/t = 1.0$, at which point there may be quite large tensile stresses in the concrete.

There is considerable justification for allowing some tensile stresses on concrete in columns designed for combined bending and axial load. In the first place, the tensile resistance of concrete is far from negligible. Concrete tensile stresses are utilized in many structures such as pavement slabs and concrete tanks. Another important point is that

Table 7.13 Allowable Stresses for Eccentrically Loaded Columns

f'_c	p	Values of f_p for $g = 0.82$			
		e'/t			
		¼	½	1	2
2000	0.01	610	690	770	820
	0.02	650	720	790	830
	0.03	680	740	800	840
	0.04	700	760	810	850
2500	0.01	760	860	960	1030
	0.02	800	890	980	1040
	0.03	830	910	990	1050
	0.04	860	930	1000	1060
3000	0.01	900	1030	1140	1230
	0.02	950	1060	1160	1240
	0.03	980	1080	1180	1250
	0.04	1010	1110	1200	1260
3750	0.01	1110	1270	1420	1530
	0.02	1160	1310	1440	1550
	0.03	1200	1340	1470	1560
	0.04	1230	1360	1480	1570
5000	0.01	1470	1680	1890	2040
	0.02	1520	1730	1920	2060
	0.03	1580	1760	1940	2070
	0.04	1610	1790	1960	2080

Courtesy Portland Cement Association

if the concrete cracks in the type of column discussed, the formation of the crack will automatically reduce the bending moment that caused the tensile stress. Also, the longitudinal reinforcement in columns has been shown to be far more effective than indicated by the value of $n = 30,000/f'_c$ used for beam design. Finally, it is impossible in most columns to obtain maximum moment and maximum axial load simultaneously since they are created by two different loadings.

Using beam design and disregarding concrete tensile stresses results in overdesign of the column section. As mentioned, (1) concrete can take a good deal of tension, (2) if it cracks the bending moment is reduced, and (3) the reinforcement is several times more effective than anticipated in beam design. Since it is difficult to express these facts in mathematical terminology, the Code substitutes the procedure of allowing tensile stresses on concrete for values of e'/t up to 1.0, which is far beyond point 1 in Fig. 7.22.

When point 1 is disregarded, the transition from curve a can be made only at point 2. Adopting this as the point of transition carries with it the necessity of changing to curve b, which represents beam design in conjunction with an allowable stress of $f_c = 0.45f'_c$ as used for bending alone.

Curves similar to those in Fig. 7.22 are plotted in Fig. 7.23 for various conditions as noted, and may be used for rectangular column sections with one-half of the total reinforcement at opposite faces. Points of intersection corresponding to point 2 in Fig. 7.22 are marked with circles, and the curves to the left of these points are for case A with f_{p}, whereas the curves to the right are for Case B with f_c.

Points marked with triangles on the curves in Fig. 7.23 correspond to $f_s = 20,000$ psi. When this is the steel stress allowed, the parts of the curves below these points are not to be used.

For ratios of e'/t larger than 2 and for cases in which the tensile steel stress exceeds 20,000 psi, use the regular beam design procedure denoted as Case C. For N/bt larger than 1.0, the column design procedure, case A, may be used; that is, the section may be designed as

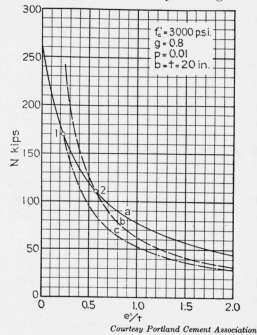

Courtesy Portland Cement Association

Fig. 7.22 Bending and Direct Stress in Columns

a column subject to a concentric load of $P = N(1 + CDe'/t)$.

In case A—that is, to the left of the points of intersection marked in Fig. 7.23—the Code makes a distinction between hard-grade and intermediate-grade steels. The curves are drawn for intermediate-grade steel, and for hard-grade steel the percentages selected from the chart must be multiplied by 0.8. This correction for the use of hard-grade steel applies to case A only.

Problem 1   Given $b = 20$ in., $t = 24$ in., $g = 0.8$, $f_c' = 2,500$ psi. The bars are assumed to be of intermediate grade, $N = 120$ kips, $M = 180$ ft-kips. Determine the reinforcement by use of Fig. 7.23.

Compute

$$\frac{N}{bt} = \frac{120}{20 \times 24} = 0.250$$

and

$$\frac{e'}{t} = \frac{12M}{tN} = \frac{12 \times 180}{24 \times 120} = 0.75$$

From Fig. 7.23 for $N/bt = 0.250$ and $e'/t = 0.75$, select $p = 0.024$. The total steel area equals $0.024 \times 20 \times 24 = 11.5$ sq in.

Problem 2   Determine how much moment the section in Problem 1 can carry with $p = 0.04$.

Compute

$$\frac{N}{bt} = \frac{120}{20 \times 24} = 0.250$$

From Fig. 7.23 for $N/bt = 0.250$ and $p = 0.04$, select $e'/t = 1.03$.

$$M = \frac{tN}{12} \times \frac{e'}{t} = \frac{24 \times 120}{12} \times 1.03 = 247 \text{ ft-kips}$$

Problem 3   Change M to 270 ft-kips in Problem 1 and determine the smallest width b required with $p = 0.04$.

Compute

$$\frac{e'}{t} = \frac{12M}{tN} = \frac{12 \times 270}{24 \times 120} = 1.13$$

From Fig. 7.23, for $e'/t = 1.13$ and $p = 0.04$, select $N/bt = 0.232$. Then

$$b = \frac{N}{0.232t} = \frac{120}{0.232 \times 24} = 21.6 \text{ (say 22 in.)}$$

c   Rectangular sections, unsymmetrical reinforcement. The design procedure considered in this section is denoted as Case C, which is the regular procedure for beam design. The problem of determining the tensile steel stress that gives the least total reinforcement will be discussed for rectangular sections.

The design is illustrated by means of numerical examples, and the general data applying to all the examples are as follows. As shown in Fig. 7.24, the section width is $b = 12$ in., the over-all depth is $t = 20$ in., and the depth to the bars is $d' = 2$ in., so that the distance between the bars at opposite faces is $gt = 16 = 0.8 \times 20$ in. The concrete has a 3,000-psi strength with $n = 10$, and the allowable extreme fiber stress in compression is $f_c = 0.45f_c' = 0.45 \times 3,000 = 1,350$ psi.

The combined effect of the concentric load N and the moment M is identical with that of a load N placed at a distance from the section center line equal to M/N, which is in feet when M is foot-kips and N is kips. The following letters denote eccentricities as shown in Fig. 7.24: e', distance from center line in inches; e, distance from tensile steel in inches; E, distance from tensile steel in feet.

The problem is to determine the reinforcement A_s and A_s' in a given rectangular section subject to eccentric loading, the load and its eccentricity being known quantities. First of all, investigate whether the design can be made without any compressive steel. This can be done when the external moment NE is equal to or smaller than the resisting moment of the compressive concrete stresses Rbd^2. N and E are known quantities. Therefore, $A_s' = 0$ gives $R = Ne/bd^2$. The first step is to ascertain from Art. 5.11 whether there is any reasonable steel stress which with the given values of f_c and n has an R quantity equal to Ne/bd^2.

It should not cause any concern that an f_s value thus determined often is smaller than the maximum steel stress allowed. It will be shown subsequently that it is not always economical to design for the maximum allowable steel stress.

Using the stress of f_s selected for $A_s' = 0$ and $R = Ne/bd^2$, the tensile steel area may be computed from the formula

$$A_s = \frac{1,000N}{f_s}\left(\frac{e}{jd} - 1\right)$$

Problem 4   The data are given in Fig. 7.24; N is taken as 30 kips. Determine the reinforcement A_s' and A_s.

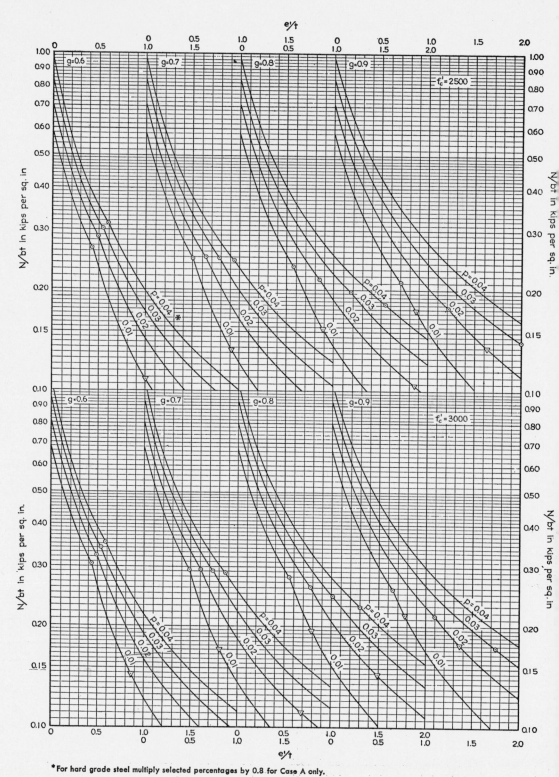

*For hard grade steel multiply selected percentages by 0.8 for Case A only.

Courtesy Portland Cement Association

Fig. 7.23 Bending and Direct Stress in Columns

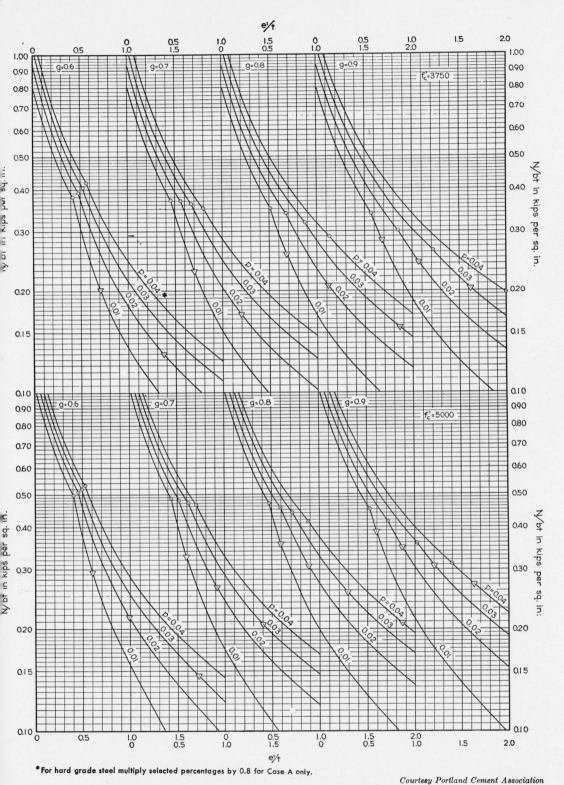

*For hard grade steel multiply selected percentages by 0.8 for Case A only.

Courtesy Portland Cement Association

Fig. 7.23   Bending and Direct Stress in Columns (Continued)

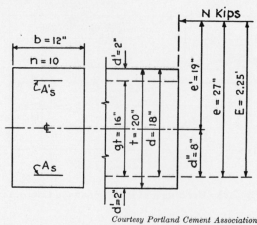

Courtesy Portland Cement Association

Fig. 7.24   Effect of Eccentric Load on Column

First investigate whether compressive steel is required. For $b = 12$ in. and $d = 18$ in., select $F = 0.324$. Compute

$$R = \frac{1,000N}{bd^2} = \frac{30,000 \times 27}{12 \times 324} = 208$$

From Table 5.1 for $f_s/n/f_c = 20,000/10/1,350$; $R = 236$. When the table value is larger than the computed R value, no compressive steel is required, so $A_s' = 0$. Entering the table with $f_s = 20,000$, $n = 10$, and the computed value of $R = 208$ gives $j = 0.872$. Incidentally, the concrete stress is $f_c = 1,240$ psi. Compute

$$A_s = \frac{1,000N}{f_s}\left(\frac{e}{jd} - 1\right) =$$
$$\frac{30,000}{20,000}\left(\frac{27}{0.872 \times 18} - 1\right) = 1.1 \text{ sq in.}$$

This completes the solution, but for further illustration, assume that N is increased.

Problem 5   The data are given in Fig. 7.24, but N is increased from 30 to 38 kips. Determine A_s' and A_s. Compute

$$R = \frac{1,000Ne}{bd^2} = \frac{38,000 \times 27}{12 \times 324} = 264$$

Since this is larger than $R = 236$ (see Problem 4), compressive steel must be used if a steel stress of $f_s = 20,000$ psi is to be maintained. However, decreasing f_s to 16,000 psi gives $R = 262$ and $j = 0.847$ (see Art. 5.11). Compressive steel may therefore be omitted when the tensile steel stress is decreased to $f_s = 16,000$ psi. Compute

$$A_s = \frac{1,000N}{f_s}\left(\frac{e}{jd} - 1\right) =$$
$$\frac{38,000}{16,000}\left(\frac{27}{0.847 \times 18} - 1\right) = 1.8 \text{ sq in.}$$

The design with steel stress decreased so $A_s' = 0$ gives a satisfactory solution. If f_s has to be decreased more than, say, 20 percent to avoid using compressive steel, it is advisable to determine the most economical steel stress—that is, the value of f_s which will give the minimum total steel area $A_s' + A_s$. This may be done by use of the curves in Fig. 7.25.

Problem 6   The data are given in Fig. 7.24; N is taken as 46 kips. Determine A_s' and A_s. From Fig. 7.25 for $e'/t = \frac{19}{20} = 0.95$ and $d'/d = \frac{2}{18} = 0.11$, select the coefficient of 1.10. Compute the most economical steel stress $f_s = 1.10nf_c = 1.10 \times 10 \times 1,350 = 15,000$ psi. For convenience in using tables, use 16,000 psi.

From Table 5.1 for $f_s/n/f_c = 16,000/10/1,350$, select $R = 262$ and $j = 0.847$. From Table 5.1 for $d'/d = 0.11$, select by interpolation $c = 0.685$. Compute

$$A_s' = \frac{Ne - Rbd^2}{cd} =$$
$$\frac{46,000 \times 27 - 262 \times 12 \times 324}{0.685 \times 18} = 1.5 \text{ sq in.}$$

$$A_s = \frac{1,000N}{f_s}\left(\frac{e}{jd} - 1\right) =$$
$$\frac{46,000}{16,000}\left(\frac{27}{0.847 \times 18} - 1\right) = \underline{2.2 \text{ sq in.}}$$
$$A_s' + A_s = 3.7 \text{ sq in.}$$

Problem 7   The data are the same as in Problem 6, except that the design is made for $f_s = 20,000$ psi.

From Table 5.1 and Art. 5.22, $R = 236$, $j = 0.866$, and $c = 0.66$.

$$A_s' = \frac{Ne - Rbd^2}{cd} =$$
$$\frac{46,000 \times 27 - 236 \times 12 \times 324}{0.66 \times 18} = 2.3 \text{ sq in.}$$

$$A_s = \frac{1,000 N}{f_s}\left(\frac{e}{jd} - 1\right) =$$
$$\frac{46,000}{20,000}\left(\frac{27}{0.866 \times 18} - 1\right) = \underline{1.7 \text{ sq in.}}$$
$$A_s' + A_s = 4.0 \text{ sq in.}$$

The 25 percent higher tensile steel stress requires 8 percent more steel area, which is a trend often encountered in problems of the type illustrated. For further illustration, if the design stress is chosen as $f_s = 12,000$ psi, $A_s' + A_s = 0.7 + 3.1 = 3.8$ sq in.; and if $f_s = 9,000$ psi, $A_s' + A_s = 0 + 4.5 = 4.5$ sq in. The steel areas computed for 9,000, 12,000, 16,000, and 20,000 psi are plotted in Fig. 7.26.

The curves in Fig. 7.26 show that when the design stress is increased from 9,000 to 20,000 psi, A_s decreases and A_s' increases, but the sum of $A_s + A_s'$ changes relatively little. The minimum steel area is obtained for $f_s = 15,000$ psi, but $A_s + A_s'$ is practically constant between 12,000 and 18,000 psi. This illustrates that the most economical stress need not be determined with any great degree of accuracy.

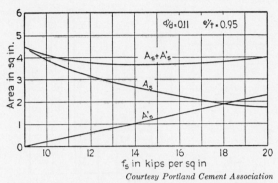

Courtesy Portland Cement Association

Fig. 7.26   Bending and Direct Stress in Columns

arrangement for the eccentricity ratio of $e'/t = 19/20 = 0.95$.

Problem 8   The section is as shown in Fig. 7.24 except that $e' = 10$ in., $e'/t = 10/20 = 0.50$, $e = e' + d$ in. $= 10 + 8 = 18$ in., and $E = e/12 = 18/12 = 1.50$ ft. $N = 80$ kips. Determine the reinforcement.

First ascertain whether to use Case A with f_p or Case C with $0.45f_c$. Compute $e'/t = 0.50$ and

$$\frac{N}{bt} = \frac{80}{12 \times 24} = 0.333 \text{ ksi}$$

In Fig. 7.23 for $f_c' = 3,000$ psi and $g = 0.8$, locate the point corresponding to $N/bt = 0.333$ and $e'/t = 0.5$. This point falls to the left of the intersections marked with circles, which shows that the design procedure denoted as Case A applies. From Fig. 7.23 select $p = 0.0175$ and compute the total area of reinforcement.

$$A_s + A_s' = 0.0175 \times bt = 0.0175 \times 12 \times 20 = 4.2 \text{ sq in. (Case A)}$$

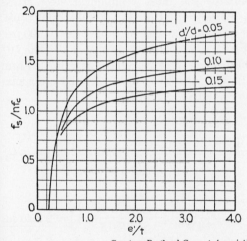

Courtesy Portland Cement Association

Fig. 7.25   Bending and Direct Stress in Columns

Within the range from 12,000 to 18,000 psi in Fig. 7.26, A_s' may be increased from 0.6 to 1.9 sq in. and A_s may be decreased from 3.2 to 1.9 sq in. without appreciably affecting the theoretical strength of the section as long as $A_s' + A_s$ remains equal to 3.8 sq in. Actually, the steel does more good in the tensile side than in the compressive side of the section, which means that the lower steel stress is preferable.

Symmetrical reinforcement is obtained in Fig. 7.26 for $f_s = 18,000$ psi, which gives $A_s' = A_s = 1.9$ sq in. This is an economical

Incidentally, the maximum concrete stress on this section may be determined from Table 7.13 for $f_c' = 3,000$ psi, $p = 0.0175$, and $e'/t = \frac{1}{2}$. This stress is 1,050 psi, which is 300 psi less than the allowable flexural stress for Case C. Note that the 1,050-lb stress is used with uncracked section, while the 1,350-lb stress is used with cracked section. It may be of interest for the comparison to design the section also as Case C.

Using $f_c = 1,350$ psi and considering the section cracked gives, from Fig. 7.21,

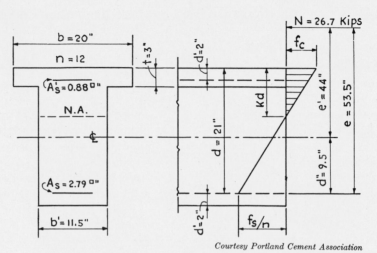

Courtesy Portland Cement Association

Fig. 7.27   T Section with Bending and Direct Stress

$$p = \frac{np}{n} = \frac{0.125}{10} = 0.0125$$

$$A_s + A_s' = 0.0125 \times bt = 0.0125 \times 12 \times 20 = 30 \text{ sq in. (case C)}$$

It is seen that Case A requires 40 percent more steel than Case C, indicating that it is more conservative in this example to consider the section uncracked. Either way, using Fig. 7.21 or 7.23, the steel should, strictly speaking, be arranged symmetrically, but actually a certain amount of variation is permissible in A_s and A_s' as long as $A_s + A_s'$ remains constant. For illustration, if seven No. 7 bars are provided, which gives $7 \times 0.6 = 4.2$ sq in., three bars may be placed in one side and four in the other. Such a small deviation from the symmetry assumed has little effect upon the extreme fiber stress.

d *Investigation of stresses—bending and direct stress.* Although it takes some minor liberties with the correct formula for this case, the value of j may be computed with sufficient accuracy from the following formula, and it is therefore used in the solution of the problem following.

$$j = 1 - \frac{\dfrac{k^2}{6} + np'\dfrac{d'}{d} + p''\dfrac{t}{2d}}{\dfrac{k}{2} + np' + p''}$$

Problem 9   In a given T section with compressive reinforcement subject to bending combined with axial load, determine f_s and f_c.

The data are shown in Fig. 7.27. Include compressive stresses below flange. Compute

$$\frac{e}{d} = \frac{53.5}{21.0} = 2.55$$

and estimate $j = 0.87$, which gives

$$i = \frac{\dfrac{e}{d}}{\dfrac{e}{d} - j} = \frac{2.55}{2.55 - 0.87} = 1.52$$

(See nomenclature, paragraph *e*.)

Compute (1) npi for tensile reinforcement; (2) np' and $\dfrac{np'd'}{d}$ for compressive reinforcement; and (3) p'' and $p''\dfrac{t}{2d}$ for the flange.

(1) $npi = 12 \times \dfrac{2.79}{11.5 \times 21.0} \times 1.52 = 0.211$

(2) $np' = 12 \times \dfrac{0.88}{11.5 \times 21.0} \qquad = 0.044$

(3) $p'' = \dfrac{(20.0 - 11.5) \times 3.0}{11.5 \times 21.0} \qquad = \underline{0.106}$

$$m = 0.361$$

(1) $\qquad\qquad\qquad npi = 0.211$

(2) $\qquad np'\dfrac{d'}{d} = 0.044 \times \dfrac{2.0}{21.0} = 0.004$

(3) $\qquad p''\dfrac{t}{2d} = 0.106 \times \dfrac{3.0}{42.0} = \underline{0.008}$

$$q = 0.223$$

$$k = \sqrt{m^2 + 2q} - m = \sqrt{0.130 + 0.446} - 0.361 = 0.760 - 0.361 = 0.399$$

$$j = 1 - \frac{\dfrac{k^2}{6} + np'\dfrac{d'}{d} + p''\dfrac{t}{2d}}{\dfrac{k}{2} + np' + p''} = 1 - \frac{0.027 + 0.004 + 0.008}{0.200 + 0.044 + 0.106} = 1 - \frac{0.039}{0.350} = 0.89$$

Substituting the computed value of $j = 0.89$ for $j = 0.87$ (estimated) gives the corrected quantities of $i = 2.55/1.66 = 1.54$, $npi = 0.214$, $k = 0.400$, and $j = 0.89$.

$$f_s = \frac{1,000N}{jA_s i} \times \frac{e}{d} = \frac{26,700 \times 2.55}{0.89 \times 2.79 \times 1.54}$$
$$= 17,800 \text{ psi}$$

$$f_c = \frac{f_s}{n} \times \frac{k}{1-k} = \frac{17,800}{12} \times \frac{0.400}{0.600} = 990 \text{ psi}$$

This example covers the general case and will serve as a guide for the simpler special cases. For rectangular sections, set $p'' = 0$. When there is no compressive steel, set $p' = 0$. When the beam is subject to bending only, set $i = 1$.

e *Nomenclature*

A_s area of tensile reinforcement or of column bars.

A_s' area of compressive reinforcement in flexural members.

b width of rectangular beam or width of flange of T beam.

b' width of web in T beam.

C $f_a/0.45f_c'$

c coefficient used in determination of A_s'.

D $t^2/2R^2$; used in investigation of eccentrically loaded columns.

d effective depth of flexural members.

d' distance from extreme fiber to compressive reinforcement.

d'' distance from center line of concrete section to tensile reinforcement.

E eccentricity measured from tensile-steel axis in feet.

e eccentricity measured from tensile-steel axis in inches.

e' eccentricity measured from gravity axis in inches.

F $bd^2/12,000$; used in determination of resisting moment of concrete sections.

f_a average stress in axially loaded columns.

f_c compressive stress in extreme fiber.

f_c' ultimate compressive strength of concrete.

f_p allowable stress in eccentrically loaded columns.

f_s stress in tensile reinforcement.

g ratio of distance (gt) between bars at opposite faces of section to over-all dimension (t).

i $e/(e - jd)$; used in sections subject to bending and axial load.

    ratio of distance (jd) between resultants of compressive and tensile stress to effective depth.

k ratio of distance (kd) between extreme fiber and neutral axis to effective depth.

M external moment in foot-kips.

N external force or load in kips.

n ratio of modulus of elasticity of steel (E_s) to that of concrete (E_c).

P external concentric load on columns.

p ratio of tensile reinforcement in beams; also ratio of longitudinal reinforcement in columns.

p' ratio of compressive reinforcement in beams.

Q $fbt/1,000N$.

R $\frac{1}{2}f_c jk$.

t over-all dimension of columns; also depth of flange.

7.30 WOOD COLUMNS

a In the modern design of wood columns, the formulae used are based on recommendations of the Forest Products Laboratory, which suggests the use of three distinct formulae based on the l/d ratio of the column as follows:

1. *Short columns*—length not to exceed $11d$, where compressive strength f_c is equal to the higher value tabulated in Table 1.1.

2. *Intermediate columns*—used from $11l/d$ to a length where the reduction in allowable stress equals $\frac{1}{3}f_c$, in which the formulae used are

$$f = f_c \left[1 - \frac{1}{3}\left(\frac{l}{Kd}\right)^4 \right]$$

and

$$K = \frac{\pi}{2}\sqrt{\frac{E}{5f_c}} = 0.702\sqrt{\frac{E}{f_c}}$$

3. *Long columns*—used for lengths beyond K as given above, up to $l = 50d$. For long columns, the formula is

$$f = \frac{0.329E}{(l/d)^2}$$

b Columns are frequently built up out of thinner material. In this case, however, they should be either bolted or connected with ring connectors, or if spiked, should be built in a boxlike manner instead of parallel planks. In any instance, even using spacer blocks, the allowable strength should be limited to 80 per cent of that of a solid column of equal net section.

The Forest Products Laboratory has set up a standard method of design of connector-jointed spaced columns based on the use of split-ring connectors as described in Art. 9.33. The regulations and formulae, with reference to Fig. 7.28, are as follows:

1. *Spacer-block position.* A single spacer block should be within 5 percent of center of column length.

If more than one spacer block is used, the distance between any two blocks should not exceed one-half the distance between centers of connectors in the end blocks. Connectors of the same size as used in the end blocks should be used for spacer blocks under those conditions.

Spacer blocks should be at least as thick as the thickness of the side members and not less in thickness than specified in "Manual of Timber Connector Construction."

The l/d value of individual members of spaced columns should not exceed 80.

For unstayed portion of individual members $l_2/d \times 1.25$ should not exceed 50.

2. *Check of unstayed portion* (l_2). With

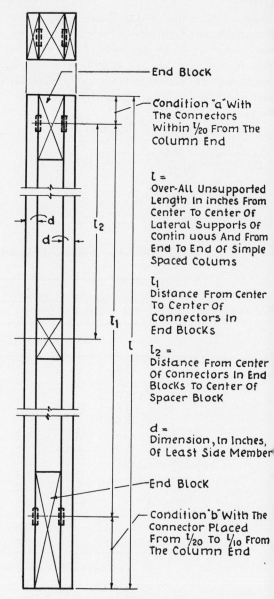

End Block

Condition "a" With The Connectors Within $\frac{1}{20}$ From The Column End

$l =$
Over-All Unsupported Length In inches From Center To Center Of Lateral Supports Of Continuous And From End To End Of Simple Spaced Columns

l_1
Distance From Center To Center Of Connectors In End Blocks

$l_2 =$
Distance From Center Of Connectors In End Blocks To Center Of Spacer Block

$d =$
Dimension, In Inches, Of Least Side Member

End Block

Condition "b" With The Connector Placed From $\frac{1}{20}$ To $\frac{1}{10}$ From The Column End

Fig. 7.28 Jointed Spaced Wood Columns

spacer blocks placed and calculations for permissible loads made as herein indicated, safe loads result and check of the unstayed portion is unnecessary. If a check is desired, use the appropriate simple column formula for unstayed portion, using $l = l_2 \times 1.25$.

3. *Fixity factor.* When the formulae for solid columns are applied to spaced columns, introduce a restraint or fixity factor as a multiplier of E in the formula for K for interme-

diate columns and in the Euler formula for long columns: condition a—when connectors are within $\frac{1}{20}$ from the ends of the column this factor may be $2\frac{1}{2}$; condition b—when connectors are placed from $\frac{1}{20}$ to $\frac{1}{10}$ from the end and long blocks are used this factor may be taken as 3.

4. *Intermediate.* For condition a,

$$K_2 = 0.702 \sqrt{\frac{2.5E}{f_c}} = K\sqrt{2.5} = K \times 1.5811$$

$$f = f_c \left[1 - \frac{1}{3} \left(\frac{1}{K_2 d} \right)^4 \right]$$

and for condition b,

$$K_3 = 0.702 \sqrt{\frac{3E}{f_c}} = K\sqrt{3} = K \times 1.7320$$

$$f = f_c \left[1 - \frac{1}{3} \left(\frac{1}{K_3 d} \right)^4 \right]$$

5. *Long.* For condition a,

$$f = \frac{0.329E \times 2.5}{(l/d)^2}$$

and for condition b,

$$f = \frac{0.329E \times 3}{(l/d)^2}$$

c Table 7.14, from the "Practical Builder," is a simple satisfactory table for the woods most commonly used.

Table 7.14 Allowable Load on Square Wood Columns*
kips

Length, feet	Side of square, in.						
	4	6	8	10	12	14	16
Longleaf pine, white oak, $1\,300 \left(1 - \frac{l}{60\,d} \right)$							
	15.6						
5	15.6						
6	14.6	35.1					
7	13.5	——					
8	12.5	34.3	62.4				
9	11.4	32.8	——				
10	10.4	31.2	62.4				
11		29.6	60.3	97.5			
12		28.1	58.2	——	140.4		
14		25.0	54.1	93.6	——	191.1	
16			49.9	88.4	137.3	——	249.6
18			45.8	83.2	131.0	189.3	——
20			41.6	78.0	124.8	182.0	249.6
Douglas fir, western hemlock $1{,}200 \left(1 - \frac{l}{60\,d} \right)$							
	14.4						
5	14.4						
6	13.4	32.4					
7	12.5	——					
8	11.5	31.7	57.6				
9	10.6	30.2	——				
10	9.6	28.8	57.6				
11		27.4	55.7	90.0			
12		25.9	53.8	——	129.6		
14		23.0	49.9	86.4	——	176.4	
16			46.1	81.6	126.7	——	230.4
18			42.2	76.8	121.0	174.7	——
20			38.4	72.0	115.2	168.0	230.4

*Loads above horizontal lines are the maximum allowable safe loads.

Table 7.15   Strength of Wood Stud Partitions

Nominal size	Actual size, in.	Distance on centers, in.	Height, ft	Per lineal foot of partitions		
				Safe load, lb	Weight, lb	Amount, fbm
2 × 4	$1\frac{5}{8} \times 3\frac{5}{8}$	12	8	3,675	16.30	6.66
2 × 4	$1\frac{5}{8} \times 3\frac{5}{8}$	12	10	2,374	19.56	8.00
2 × 4	$1\frac{5}{8} \times 3\frac{5}{8}$	12	12	1,637	22.82	9.33
2 × 4	$1\frac{5}{8} \times 3\frac{5}{8}$	16	8	2,756	13.04	5.33
2 × 4	$1\frac{5}{8} \times 3\frac{5}{8}$	16	10	1,780	15.50	6.33
2 × 4	$1\frac{5}{8} \times 3\frac{5}{8}$	16	12	1,228	18.00	7.33
2 × 6	$1\frac{5}{8} \times 5\frac{5}{8}$	12	8	8,546	25.30	10.00
2 × 6	$1\frac{5}{8} \times 5\frac{5}{8}$	12	10	7,677	30.56	12.00
2 × 6	$1\frac{5}{8} \times 5\frac{5}{8}$	12	12	6,096	35.42	14.00
2 × 6	$1\frac{5}{8} \times 5\frac{5}{8}$	16	8	6,409	20.24	8.00
2 × 6	$1\frac{5}{8} \times 5\frac{5}{8}$	16	10	5,758	24.03	9.50
2 × 6	$1\frac{5}{8} \times 5\frac{5}{8}$	16	12	4,572	27.83	11.00
3 × 6	$2\frac{5}{8} \times 5\frac{5}{8}$	12	8	13,810	41.00	15.00
3 × 6	$2\frac{5}{8} \times 5\frac{5}{8}$	12	10	12,406	49.20	18.00
3 × 6	$2\frac{5}{8} \times 5\frac{5}{8}$	12	12	9,851	57.20	21.00
3 × 6	$2\frac{5}{8} \times 5\frac{5}{8}$	16	8	10,357	32.80	12.00
3 × 6	$2\frac{5}{8} \times 5\frac{5}{8}$	16	10	9,304	38.95	14.25
3 × 6	$2\frac{5}{8} \times 5\frac{5}{8}$	16	12	7,388	45.10	16.50

Safe load based on studs being bridged at center
Weight and strength based on actual size.
Board measure based on nominal size.
Add weight of plaster or ceiling.
Single plate top and bottom included, same size as studs

7.31   Wood-stud partitions

Wood-stud partitions, bridged at the center of the height and otherwise braced by lath and plaster, are used to carry vertical loads in ordinary light-load structures. Most buildings in which wood-stud partitions are used as load-carrying walls have loads so light that it is not necessary to check the capacity of the studs. However, for the occasion when it is necessary to check this strength Table 7.15 is included. This table is taken from the "Manual of the Southern Pine Association."

7.40   CAST–IRON COLUMNS

Cast-iron columns are seldom used now because other, more efficient, materials are more economical. However, since the designer is frequently called upon to check the capacity of an existing cast-iron column, this article is included. The New York City Code covers the requirements for design of cast-iron columns as follows:

Cast iron columns shall have an outside diameter or side of at least 5 in. and their maximum length shall not exceed 70r. The allowable compression in pounds per square inch shall not exceed

$$f = 9,000 - 40\frac{l}{r}.$$

The thickness of metal shall be at least $\frac{1}{12}$ the diameter or least dimension of cross section with a minimum thickness of $\frac{3}{4}$ in. The core of columns above and below a joint shall be the same, but where one column is supported by another of larger diameter, the core of the latter shall be tapered down over a distance of at least 6 in. or a joint plate shall be inserted of sufficient strength to distribute the load. Wherever the core of a cast iron column has shifted more than $\frac{1}{4}$ the thickness of the shell, the thickness of the metal all around shall be assumed equal to the thinnest part.

Cast iron columns shall be machine faced at the end to a true surface perpendicular to the axis. They shall be bolted together with at least 4 bolts, $\frac{3}{4}$ in. or more in diameter, passing through the flanges, the bolts being of sufficient length to allow the nuts to be screwed up tightly; and as each column is placed in position, the bolts shall also be placed in position and the nuts shall be screwed up tightly.

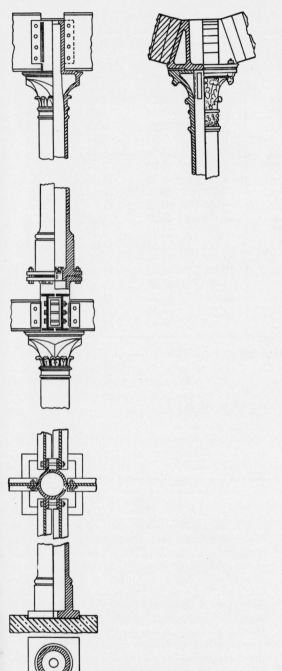

Fig. 7.29   Cast-Iron Column

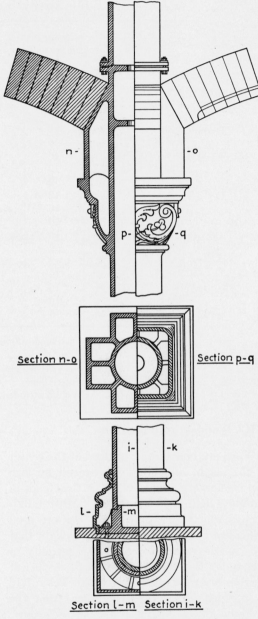

Fig. 7.29   Cast-Iron Column (Continued)

Where cast iron columns rest one on top of another, the top flange of the lower column shall project on all sides at least 3 in. from the outer surfaces of the column, and the shape and dimensions of the bottom flange of the upper column shall be the same as those of the top flange of the lower column, except that when a column is placed on a lot line, the flanges on the side toward such lot line may be omitted unless required for bolting. Flanges shall be at least one inch in thickness when finished, and shall be reinforced by fillets and brackets.

All holes in cast iron columns shall be drilled. The diameter of the holes shall be the diameter of the bolts plus $\frac{1}{16}$ in.

Cast iron columns may not be used in any case where the load is so eccentric as to cause tension in the cast iron or for such parts of the structural frame of structures as are required to resist stress due to wind.

All parts of a cast iron base or bearing plate shall be at least 1 in. thick.

Figure 7.29 shows typical round cast-iron columns and the various sections used in framing such columns. Frequently the columns are in the form of hollow squares or pilasters, but the type of detail is similar to the various details shown.

7.50 COMPOSITE OR COMBINATION COLUMNS

Composite columns are columns usually made up of steel and concrete, and recognized by the ACI Code under design conditions set up as follows:

(a) *Steel Columns Encased in Concrete.* The allowable load on a structural steel column which is encased in concrete at least $2\frac{1}{2}$ inches thick over all metal (except rivet heads) reinforced as hereinafter specified, shall be computed by the following formula:

$$P = A_r f_r' \left[1 + \frac{A_g}{100 A_r} \right]$$

Wherein A_r = cross-sectional area of steel column.
   f_r' = allowable stress for unencased steel column.
   A_g = total area of concrete section.

The concrete used shall develop a compressive strength f_c' of at least 2,000 p.s.i. at 28 days. The concrete shall be reinforced by the equivalent of welded wire mesh having wires of No. 10 W. and M. gage, the wires encircling the column being spaced not more than four inches apart and those parallel to the column axis not more than eight inches apart. This mesh shall extend entirely around the column at a distance of one inch inside the outer concrete surface and shall be lap-spliced at least forty wire diameters and wired at the splice. Special brackets shall be used to receive the entire floor load at each floor level. The steel column shall be designed to carry safely any construction or other loads to be placed upon it prior to its encasement in concrete.

(b) *Pipe Columns.* The allowable load on columns consisting of steel pipe filled with concrete shall be determined by this formula:

$$P = 0.225 f_c' A_c + f_r' A_r$$

The value of f_r' shall be given by this formula:

$$f_r' = \left[18,000 - 70\,\frac{l}{r} \right] F$$

wherein f_r' = allowable unit stress in metal pipe.
   l = unsupported length of column.
   r = least radius of gyration of metal pipe section.
   $$F = \frac{\text{yield point of pipe}}{45,000}$$

If the yield point of the pipe is not known, the factor F shall be taken as 0.5.

The first of these composite or combination columns is normally used to keep the size of columns within smaller overall area limits in high buildings, where the first floor space is normally the most valuable space in the building. An example of the second type of column is the Lally column, although this patented type has a number of special features which have been developed through the years.

7.60 COLUMN BASE PLATES

a Steel base plates, or billets, as they are frequently called, are generally used under columns for distributing the column loads over a sufficient area of the concrete foundations. The AISC Code allows for bearing on "Portland Cement Concrete unless otherwise specified, 600 pounds per square inch." This is the allowable bearing specified in most building codes and is the basis of design for the data in Table 8.2. The ACI Code, however, allows much higher values. Table 305(a) of the 1947 Code gives for bearing on full area, $0.25 f_c'$, and for bearing on one-third area or less, $0.375 f_c'$.

As we are usually interested in foundations which are considerably greater than three times the area of the base, this would allow 750 psi for a foundation of 2,000-psi concrete and 1,125 psi for 3,000-psi concrete.

b The following method of design based on an allowable bending stress of 20,000 psi is recommended in the AISC Handbook (see Fig. 7.30).

P = total column load in kips
$A = B \times C$ = area of plate in square inches
   t = thickness of plate in inches
   f = bearing pressure on foundation in kips per square inch

The column load P is assumed to be uniformly distributed within a rectangle whose dimensions are $0.95d$ and $0.80b$, and the base plate is assumed to have a uniform bearing pressure f on the foundation.

1. Determine the required area $A = P/f$.

2. Determine B and C so that dimensions m and n are approximately equal.

3. Determine m and n, the projections of the plate beyond the assumed dotted rectangle, and use the larger value to solve for t by one of the following formulas:

$$t^2 = 0.15fm^2 \qquad \text{or} \qquad t^2 = 0.15fn^2$$

Problem   A 14 WF 95 column has a reaction of 450 kips and rests on a concrete foundation with an allowable bearing pressure of 0.600 ksi. Design a steel base plate for this column.

$$A = \frac{450}{0.600} = 750 \text{ sq in.}$$

$$B = \frac{750}{28} = 26.8 \text{ in.}$$

Use $B = 27$ in. and assume $C = 28$ in.

$$0.80b = 0.80 \times 14.545 = 11.6 \text{ in.}$$
$$0.95d = 0.95 \times 14.12 = 13.4 \text{ in.}$$

$$f = \frac{450}{27 \times 28} = 0.595 \text{ ksi}$$

$$n = \frac{27 - 11.6}{2} = 7.7 \text{ in.}$$

$$m = \frac{28 - 13.4}{2} = 7.3 \text{ in.}$$

$$t^2 = 0.15 \times 0.595 \times 7.7 \times 7.7 = 5.29 \text{ in.}^2$$
$$t = 2.30 \text{ (use } 3 \text{ in.)}$$

Use a base plate 28 in. $\times$ 3 in. $\times$ 2 ft 3 in.

Standard rolled sizes for bearing plates are as follows and should be used wherever possible:

14 $\times$ $1\frac{1}{4}$ in., $1\frac{1}{2}$ in.   36 $\times$ 4 in., $4\frac{1}{2}$ in.
16 $\times$ $1\frac{1}{2}$ in., 2 in.   40 $\times$ $4\frac{1}{2}$ in., 5 in.
20 $\times$ 2 in., $2\frac{1}{2}$ in., 3 in.   44 $\times$ 5 in., $5\frac{1}{2}$ in.
24 $\times$ 2 in., $2\frac{1}{2}$ in., 3 in.   48 $\times$ $5\frac{1}{2}$ in., 6 in., $6\frac{1}{2}$ in.
28 $\times$ 3 in., $3\frac{1}{2}$ in.   52 $\times$ 6 in., $6\frac{1}{2}$ in.
32 $\times$ $3\frac{1}{2}$ in., 4 in.   56 $\times$ $6\frac{1}{2}$ in., 7 in., 8 in.

The base plate or billet should be cut or burned from one of the above sizes.

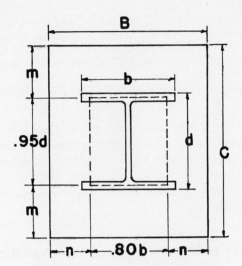

Fig. 7.30   Column Base Plate

c   Steel billets are normally bedded in grout on top of the concrete footings, and allowance for this should be made in setting the elevation of foundations. The minimum allowance for grout should be 1 in. and a greater depth should be allowed for bases or billets in excess of 12 in. square. Because of practical difficulties in placing grout under larger billets, and because of curl of the billet from shearing or burred edges from burning, it is well to allow approximately 1 in. depth of grout for each foot of side of billet, with a maximum of 3 in.

7.61   Grillages

a   For bearing of a column on a wall or along a footing at the lot line or for spreading a truss or girder load along a wall, the most economical method is the use of a single-tier grillage. It is preferable to use a pair of channels back to back instead of an I beam in order to obtain a greater web thickness and to reduce the width of necessary bearing. The general method of figuring a grillage is to compute the area required under the grillage in bearing, then cut and try until the economical beam or pair of channels is found to furnish the bearing area required without exceeding the allowable fiber stress of the beam. The following formula will give the length of

Table 7.16   Channel Grillages

Steel at 20,000 psi, $l = CK$

		C	150 psi, poor brick, $K = 34.15$	250 psi, good brick, $K = 25.3$	500 psi, 2,000-psi concrete wall, $K = 17.89$	750 psi, 3,000-psi concrete wall, $K = 14.6$	1,125 psi, 3,000-psi concrete footing, $K = 11.92$
6-in. channel	8.2	1.5	51.22 in. 14,751 lb	37.95 in. 18,216 lb	26.84 in. 25,766 lb	21.9 in. 31,546 lb	17.88 in. 38,608 lb
7-in. channel	9.8	1.7	58.05 in. 18,199 lb	43.01 in. 24,473 lb	30.41 in. 31,778 lb	24.82 in. 38,905 lb	20.26 in. 47,631 lb
8-in. channel	11.5	1.9	64.88 in. 21,995 lb	48.07 in. 27,150 lb	33.99 in. 38,410 lb	27.74 in. 47,018 lb	22.65 in. 57,589 lb
9-in. channel	13.4	2.08	71.03 in. 25,890 lb	52.62 in. 31,967 lb	37.21 in. 45,210 lb	30.37 in. 55,349 lb	24.80 in. 67,797 lb
10-in. channel	15.3	2.27	77.52 in. 30,232 lb	57.43 in. 37,329 lb	40.61 in. 52,793 lb	33.14 in. 64,623 lb	27.06 in. 79,151 lb
12-in. channel	20.7	2.7	92.21 in. 40,665 lb	68.31 in. 50,208 lb	48.30 in. 71,001 lb	39.42 in. 86,917 lb	32.18 in. 106,435 lb
12-in. channel	25	2.81	95.96 in. 43,902 lb	71.09 in. 54,206 lb	50.27 in. 76,662 lb	41.02 in. 93,833 lb	33.50 in. 114,946 lb
12-in. channel	30	2.91	99.38 in. 47,255 lb	73.62 in. 58,343 lb	52.06 in. 82,515 lb	42.49 in. 101,020 lb	34.69 in. 123,713 lb
15-in. channel	33.9	3.5	119.53 in. 60,960 lb	88.55 in. 75,268 lb	62.62 in. 106,454 lb	51.1 in. 130,305 lb	41.72 in. 159,579 lb
15-in. channel	40	3.62	123.62 in. 65,271 lb	91.59 in. 80,599 lb	64.76 in. 113,978 lb	52.85 in. 139,524 lb	43.15 in. 170,775 lb
15-in. channel	45	3.7	126.36 in. 68,614 lb	93.61 in. 84,718 lb	66.19 in. 119,804 lb	54.02 in. 146,664 lb	44.11 in. 179,638 lb
15-in. channel	50	3.78	129.19 in. 72,089 lb	95.63 in. 88,936 lb	67.62 in. 125,773 lb	55.19 in. 153,980 lb	45.06 in. 188,576 lb
15-in. channel	55	3.88	132.5 in. 76,923 lb	98.17 in. 93,752 lb	69.43 in. 132,611 lb	55.55 in. 159,151 lb	46.25 in. 198,758 lb
18-in. channel	42.7	3.94	134.55 in. 79,721 lb	99.68 in. 98,434 lb	70.49 in. 139,218 lb	56.53 in. 167,470 lb	46.96 in. 208,679 lb
18-in. channel	45.8	3.99	136.26 in. 81,756 lb	105.95 in. 105,950 lb	71.38 in. 142,760 lb	58.25 in. 174,750 lb	47.56 in. 214,020 lb
18-in. channel	51.9	4.11	140.36 in. 86,322 lb	103.98 in. 106,583 lb	73.53 in. 150,737 lb	60.01 in. 184,531 lb	48.99 in. 225,966 lb
18-in. channel	58	4.21	143.77 in. 90,575 lb	106.51 in. 111,836 lb	75.32 in. 158,172 lb	61.47 in. 193,628 lb	50.18 in. 237,105 lb

beam which is safe to use for any beam size selected.

$$l = \sqrt{\frac{160,000S}{f_1 b}}$$

In this case f_1 is the allowable bearing pressure, b the flange width, and S and l have their usual meanings. The length times the unit pressure times the width gives the capacity of this beam.

b   It will be noted that the above formula may be broken down into two parts, one which we shall call K, a function of allowable bearing pressure, the other which we shall call C, a function of the steel section used. Their values are

$$K = \sqrt{\frac{160,000}{f_1}}$$
$$C = \sqrt{S/b}$$
$$l = CK$$

Table 7.16 gives the constants for bearing conditions usually specified and for channel sections used, and the length and bearing for a single channel. The use of this table is shown by the following problem.

Problem A column carrying a load of 500 kips bears on a four-channel grillage on top of a concrete basement wall. The code under which we are working calls for a maximum allowable unit pressure of 750 psi. Design the grillage.

$$P = \frac{500}{4} = 125,000 \text{ lb on one channel}$$

One 15-in. channel, 33.9 lb, 51.1 in. long, will carry 130,305 lb. Therefore 125,000 will require a length of

$$\frac{125,000}{130,305} \times 51.1 = 49 \text{ in.}$$

The required grillage, therefore, is four 15-in. channels, 33.9 lb, 4 ft 1 in. long.

c It may be necessary to spread a beam or truss load into the top of a tile or concrete masonry wall where the allowable bearing is much less than that listed for poor brick. For example, let us design a beam grillage to carry a beam load of 30,000 lb on a tile wall with an allowable bearing stress of 80 psf. From the formulae in paragraph *b*,

$$K = \sqrt{\frac{160,000}{80}} = \sqrt{2,000} = 44.7$$

Try 8 WF 17 grillage.

$$C = \sqrt{\frac{14.1}{5.25}} = \sqrt{2.68} = 1.64$$

The allowable length = 44.7 × 1.64 = 73.3 in. The allowable load = 73.3 × 5.25 × 2 × 80 = 61,600 lb, which is greater than required. Try 6 I 12.5.

$$C = \sqrt{\frac{7.3}{3.33}} = \sqrt{2.2} = 1.47$$

The allowable length = 44.7 × 1.47 = 65.6 in. The allowable load = 65.6 × 3.33 × 2 × 80 = 34,800 lb. Therefore, use two 6 I 12.5, length $= \frac{30}{34.8} \times 65.6 = 56.6.$ Use 4 ft 9 in. long.

As a check for strength, a single cantilever carries 30,000/4 = 7,500 lb. The moment on the cantilever is 7,500 × 2.38/2 = 8,920 ft-lb.

$$f_s = \frac{8,920 \times 12}{7.3} = 14,660 \text{ psi}$$

Despite the fact that this is well under the allowable 20,000-psi stress, it will be found that the use of a 5 I will cause an overstress.

8

Foundations and Walls

8.10 FOUNDATIONS—GENERAL

a The type of foundation to be used depends on:

1. The type of soil and its bearing capacity
2. The amount of superimposed load
3. The location with regard to lot line, etc.
4. The depth to rock

b We may divide column foundations as to type as follows:

1. Spread footings, centrally loaded
   (*a*) Plain concrete
   (*b*) Reinforced concrete
   (*c*) Grillage

2. Combined footings
   (*a*) Simple combined
   (*b*) Cantilever
   (*c*) Mat

3. Piles
   (*a*) Wood
   (*b*) Concrete
   (*c*) Steel pipes or H sections

4. Caissons
   (*a*) Open
   (*b*) Pneumatic

c At the present time, building foundations are designed very largely by rule-of-thumb methods to spread the load on the subsoil within limits set by the code under which the engineer is working. In recent years, however, the science of soil mechanics has advanced rapidly, and some codes are modifying the old methods of design in accordance with our newly found knowledge. The proper application of the principles of soil mechanics depends on laboratory investigations and is a job for a specialist.

The determination of soil conditions, including water conditions and allowable pressures, should be made by the methods described in Art. 11.30 before proceeding with the design. Determination should also be made of all other conditions affecting the foundation layout, as described in Art. 11.20. This involves the determination of legal restrictions if footings are placed immediately adjacent to the lot line or the street line —both as to your own rights and the rights of support of the foundation on the adjacent lot.

If the class of subsoil is known and there is no information or code requirement that modifies the determination of bearing capacity, the values shown in Table 8.1 may be assumed for bearing values of the various soils.

In computing the vertical pressure of supporting materials, the weight of the excavated material permanently removed may be deducted from the weight of the structure provided the material does not heave or swell when the excavation is made. This may be compensated for by adding the weight of a column of the excavated material to the bearing value of the soil. Thus, if a loose coarse sand (classification 8 in Table 8.1), good for 3 tons per sq ft, weighing 100 lb per cu ft, is

Table 8.1 Allowable Bearing Value for Footings

Class and material	Tons per sq ft
1. Massive crystalline bedrocks, like granite, gneiss, or trap rock, in sound condition	100
2. Foliated rocks—schist, slate—in sound condition	40
3. Sedimentary rocks—sandstones, limestones, hard shales, conglomerates	15
4. Soft or broken bedrock except shale	10
5. Hardpan, partially cemented sands, and gravels	10
6. Compact gravel, or sand and gravel mixture	6
7. Loose gravel, compact coarse sand	4
8. Loose coarse sand, sand and gravel mixture, or compact fine sand	3
9. Loose fine sand	2
10. Stiff clay and soft shale	4
11. Medium stiff clay	$2\frac{1}{2}$
12. Medium soft clay and soft broken shale	$1\frac{1}{2}$

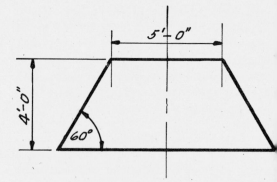

Fig. 8.1 Spread of Load under Footings

assumed, footings may be designed to carry 7,000 psf at a depth 10 ft below the surface.

When the bearing materials at a lower level are of lesser allowable bearing value than the bearing value selected, the weight on the footing should be recomputed at the lower level on the basis that the load spreads uniformly at an angle of 60 deg with the horizontal. Thus, if we assume a footing carrying 200 kips on a stiff clay (classification 10) good for 4 tons, or 8,000 lb, per sq ft, but resting 4 ft above a medium soft clay (classification 12) good for $1\frac{1}{2}$ tons, or 3,000 lb, per sq ft, both planes must be investigated for bearing (Fig. 8.1).

At the upper plane, the footing required is $\frac{200}{8}$, or 25 sq ft, which is 5 ft square. At the lower level, this load is spread over the area a^2, which is $[5 + 2(4 \cot 60°)]^2$ or $9.618^2 = 92.5$ sq ft. On this basis, the lower layer is loaded to $200/92.5 = 2,160$ psf, which is within the allowable limit.

Footings should be provided under all columns, piers, and walls to distribute the loads as uniformly as possible on level beds. Since dead load is on the footings continuously and live load may never be fully applied, it is be-

coming common practice to design footings on the basis of dead load rather than total load. This requires that loads in the footings be divided between live and dead loads. Then the footing having the largest percentage of live load is designed on the basis of the allowable soil pressure. From this the unit soil pressure due to dead load only is determined, and the area of each footing computed on this basis. The design of footing as to thickness and reinforcement, however, is made on the basis of total load.

As an example of the application of this method, let us assume five columns, each with a total load of 150 kips, as follows:

	Live load, kips	Dead load, kips	Dead load, percent	Design soil pressure, psf
Column 1	30	120	80	2,500
Column 2	45	105	70	2,857
Column 3	60	90	60	3,333
Column 4	75	75	50	4,000
Column 5	90	60	40	5,000

Assume 5,000-psf maximum soil pressure for total load for the footing with the lowest percentage dead load. Then column 5 footing will be 30 sq ft. The soil pressure for column 1 will be $\frac{40}{80}$ of 5,000, or 2,500 psf. The other footings are proportioned in the same manner, as tabulated above. Selection of footings should be made for 150 kips load from the proper table in Art. 8.11, or interpolated.

d Obviously, the amount of the superimposed load influences the type of foundation, particularly if the load is quite heavy. There is a point in the curve of costs beyond which it is cheaper to go even 50 or 100 ft to rock rather than attempt to support the load on spread footings. Most buildings higher than 15 or 20 stories are carried on rock, as are many buildings of lesser height, if rock is shallow.

e The location with regard to lot lines influences the type of footing required. On a footing carrying a single load, the load must be concentric on the footing. When the column is an interior column there is nothing difficult in this requirement, but when the column is a wall column adjacent to the lot line you cannot extend your footing under the adjacent property. The solution is to balance two or more columns on one footing so that the center of gravity of the computed loads coincides with the center of gravity of the footing area. This is accomplished by means of simple combined footings, cantilever footings, or mats.

f As stated in paragraph *d*, even with light loads it is frequently advisable to run the footing to rock if rock is not far below the level to which the footing would normally be carried.

If a structure rests partially on rock and partially on yielding soil, some codes require that the bearing capacity of the yielding soil be taken at not more than half the tabulated capacity. Experience indicates, however, that it is impossible to avoid settlement cracks if the building rests partially on rock and partially on yielding soil, or partially on piles and partially on spread footings, and such conditions should always be avoided.

g In all construction in a northern climate exterior walls or footings must run at least 4 ft below grade to get below the frost line. Otherwise upheaval and cracks due to frost pressure must be expected. In a building with a basement, of course, this requirement does not usually determine the depth. Ordinarily, interior footing depths are determined by placing the top of the footing under the basement floor, but if any part of the building is dropped to a lower grade, the line from the edge of one footing to the nearest bottom

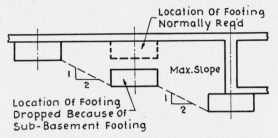

Fig. 8.2 Elevations of Footings as Controlled by Conditions

edge of any other footing cannot make an angle with the horizontal of over 1 vertical on 2 horizontal. If an angle exceeds this value, the adjacent footing must be lowered until the 1:2 condition is satisfied, unless sheet piling is introduced to support the soil. This condition is indicated in Fig. 8.2.

All footings must be carried below the depth of vegetation and organic matter in the soil. This usually requires depths of from 1 ft 6 in. to 2 ft into the undisturbed earth, although greater depths are required in fields which have been cultivated for a number of years.

h *Machinery foundations.* It is frequently desirable to isolate machinery foundations from the building structure. If the foundation of a machine is attached to the floor or walls of a building, the vibration of the machine may be transmitted to other machines and to other parts of the building and cause settlement. If necessary, floors adjacent to a foundation superstructure, such as a second-floor support for a motor-generator set, may be simply supported on a shelf on a foundation, provided that it is insulated in such a manner that no movement is transmitted.

The General Electric Company's recommendations for the design of foundations for motor-generator sets may be taken as good practice in design of foundations for most moving or vibrating machines. The company recommends that all parts be designed for the maximum stresses due to the worst possible combination of vertical loads, torque, longitudinal and transverse forces, stresses due to temperature variation, and foundation dead load. Where the foundation layout is partially built up of beam and column sections, the following unit stresses are recommended:

Concrete, compression = 350 psi
Concrete, bending = 400 psi
Steel, tension = 10,000 psi
Steel, compression ($n = 10$) = 4,000 psi

No reliance should be placed on concrete in shear. Suitably sized closed stirrups should be provided.

Use straight bars in both flanges of beams, and avoid bent-up bars. The subfoundation —that part of the foundation on which the superstructure rests—is usually a reinforced-concrete slab or mat. It should be of substantial thickness and reinforced top and bottom.

In computing soil loading, the center of gravity of the machine and foundation loads should coincide with the center of gravity of the footing. Although sometimes impossible to attain, it is the ideal condition.

Occasionally, if the subsoil is soft clay or other material that may flow, it is advisable to drive a row of steel sheet pilings around the entire perimeter to prevent the loss of subsoil and a resultant settlement of the foundation. In order to protect foundations immediately adjacent, it may be necessary also to enclose a machine footing in steel sheet piling.

Because machinery foundations depend largely on mass to dampen vibration, it is desirable to pour the foundation as nearly monolithic as possible. If this cannot be done, suitable keys and dowels should be provided between pours.

The General Electric Co. practice requires that anchor bolts be placed to an accuracy of $\frac{1}{16}$ in. without pipe sleeves, using built-up steel angle templates, well cross-braced. Some other manufacturers are satisfied to have anchor bolts placed with the upper third of the bolt in a pipe sleeve, then poured in after the machine has been placed over the anchor bolts.

i If any load applied to a footing is eccentric, the pressure is not uniform under the footing, but varies uniformly from a maximum at the edge nearest the point of load, to a minimum at the opposite edge. Graphically, we may represent the resultant pressures by a trapezoid as shown in Fig. 1.14. In the figure a unit length is represented by area A for the sake of simplifying the method. The pressure f increases and f_1 decreases very rapidly as the eccentricity of the load increases until the eccentricity is $\frac{1}{6}A$, at which point f becomes double the average pressure.

The unit pressure at the edge is obtained from the formula

$$f = \frac{P}{A}\left(1 \pm \frac{6e}{b}\right)$$

In the above formula, + is used to compute the f value and − to compute f_1. Although a slight eccentricity, while uneconomical, is permissible, an eccentricity in excess of $\frac{1}{10}$ may cause a dangerous unequal settlement. The best practice is to keep the load concentric.

8.11 Spread column footings centrally loaded

a For consideration of design methods, it is well to consider all centrally loaded spread footings either square or rectangular, under one heading. The most economical and most common type of footing is square, concentrically loaded.

Square footings may be divided into three classifications for design purposes:

1. Plain concrete—no reinforcement
2. Reinforced concrete
3. Steel grillages

Normally, plain-concrete footings are economical up to about 4 ft square, although the optimum size may vary depending on considerations of loads, available depths, or the like.

Table 8.2 is a table of footings used in the author's office. These tables are arranged so that when the load in kips and the allowable soil pressure are known, a steel billet size and footing designation (such as 5 ft 6 in. E) may be selected. Then from Table 8.3 the design of a footing using a 3,000-psi concrete may be selected and depth of footing and reinforcement determined. Table 8.2 advances by 10-kip intervals to 1,000 kips for soil pressures from 3,000 to 10,000 psf. In Table 8.2 note that the letters A through G refer to the same soil pressure throughout. The footings are arranged by 3-in. variations in side of square for simplicity of forming and reinforcement.

Table 8.2 Footing Table

Load, kips	Billets, in.	Footings (refer to Table 8.3) 3,000, A	4,000, B	5,000, C	6,000, D	7,000, E	8,000, F	10,000, G
10	$9 \times 8 \times \frac{1}{2}$	2'0''	1'9''	1'6''	1'6''	1'6''	1'6''	1'6''
20	$9 \times 8 \times \frac{1}{2}$	2'9''	2'6''	2'3''	2'0''	1'9''	1'9''	1'6''
30	$9 \times 8 \times \frac{1}{2}$	3'3''	3'0''	2'6''	2'6''	2'3''	2'0''	1'9''
40	$9 \times 8 \times \frac{3}{4}$	3'9''	3'3''	3'0''	2'9''	2'6''	2'6''	2'3''
50	$9 \times 8 \times \frac{3}{4}$	4'3''	3'9''	3'3''	3'0''	2'9''	2'9''	2'6''
60	$9 \times 8 \times \frac{3}{4}$	4'9''	4'0''	3'9''	3'3''	3'0''	3'0''	2'6''
70	$9 \times 8 \times \frac{3}{4}$	5'0''	4'6''	4'0''	3'6''	3'3''	3'0''	2'9''
80	$9 \times 8 \times \frac{3}{4}$	5'6''	4'9''	4'3''	3'9''	3'6''	3'3''	3'0''
90	$10 \times 8 \times \frac{3}{4}$	5'9''	5'0''	4'6''	4'0''	3'9''	3'6''	3'3''
100	$10 \times 9 \times 1$	6'0''	5'3''	4'9''	4'3''	4'0''	3'9''	3'3''
110	$10 \times 10 \times 1$	6'6''	5'6''	5'0''	4'6''	4'3''	3'9''	3'6''
120	$11 \times 10 \times 1$	6'9''	5'9''	5'0''	4'9''	4'3''	4'0''	3'6''
130	$12 \times 10 \times 1\frac{1}{4}$	7'0''	6'0''	5'3''	4'9''	4'6''	4'3''	3'9''
140	$12 \times 11 \times 1\frac{1}{4}$	7'3''	6'3''	5'6''	5'0''	4'9''	4'3''	4'0''
150	$12 \times 12 \times 1\frac{1}{2}$	7'6''	6'6''	5'9''	5'3''	4'9''	4'6''	4'0''
160	$12 \times 12 \times 1\frac{1}{2}$	7'9''	6'9''	6'0''	5'3''	5'0''	4'9''	4'3''
170	$13 \times 12 \times 1\frac{1}{2}$	8'0''	6'9''	6'0''	5'6''	5'0''	4'9''	4'3''
180	$14 \times 12 \times 1\frac{1}{2}$	8'3''	7'0''	6'3''	5'9''	5'3''	5'0''	4'6''
190	$14 \times 13 \times 1\frac{1}{2}$	8'6''	7'3''	6'6''	5'9''	5'6''	5'0''	4'6''
200	$14 \times 13 \times 1\frac{1}{2}$	8'6''	7'6''	6'6''	6'0''	5'6''	5'3''	4'9''
210	$14 \times 14 \times 2$	8'9''	7'6''	6'9''	6'3''	5'9''	5'3''	4'9''
220	$14 \times 14 \times 2$	9'0''	7'9''	7'0''	6'3''	5'9''	5'6''	4'9''
230	$15 \times 14 \times 2$	9'3''	8'0''	7'0''	6'6''	6'0''	5'6''	5'0''
240	$16 \times 14 \times 2$	9'6''	8'0''	7'3''	6'6''	6'0''	5'9''	5'0''
250	$16 \times 14 \times 2$	9'9''	8'3''	7'3''	6'9''	6'3''	5'9''	5'3''
260	$16 \times 15 \times 2$	9'9''	8'6''	7'6''	6'9''	6'3''	6'0''	5'3''
270	$16 \times 15 \times 2$	10'0''	8'6''	7'9''	7'0''	6'6''	6'0''	5'3''
280	$16 \times 15 \times 2$	10'3''	8'9''	7'9''	7'0''	6'6''	6'0''	5'6''
290	$17 \times 16 \times 2$	10'6''	9'0''	8'0''	7'3''	6'9''	6'3''	5'6''
300	$17 \times 16 \times 2$	10'6''	9'0''	8'0''	7'3''	6'9''	6'3''	5'9''
310	$18 \times 16 \times 2$	10'9''	9'3''	8'3''	7'6''	7'0''	6'6''	5'9''
320	$18 \times 16 \times 2$	11'0''	9'3''	8'3''	7'6''	7'0''	6'6''	5'9''
330	$19 \times 16 \times 2$	11'3''	9'6''	8'6''	7'9''	7'0''	6'9''	6'0''
340	$19 \times 16 \times 2$	11'3''	9'9''	8'6''	7'9''	7'3''	6'9''	6'0''
350	$20 \times 16 \times 2\frac{1}{2}$	11'6''	9'9''	8'9''	8'0''	7'3''	6'9''	6'0''
360	$20 \times 16 \times 2$	11'9''	10'0''	8'9''	8'0''	7'6''	7'0''	6'3''
370	$20 \times 17 \times 2$	11'9''	10'0''	9'0''	8'3''	7'6''	7'0''	6'3''
380	$20 \times 17 \times 2$	12'0''	10'3''	9'0''	8'3''	7'9''	7'0''	6'3''
390	$20 \times 18 \times 2$	12'3''	10'3''	9'3''	8'3''	7'9''	7'3''	6'6''
400	$20 \times 18 \times 2$	12'3''	10'6''	9'3''	8'6''	7'9''	7'3''	6'6''
410	$20 \times 19 \times 2\frac{1}{2}$	12'6''	10'9''	9'6''	8'6''	8'0''	7'6''	6'6''
420	$20 \times 19 \times 2\frac{1}{2}$	12'6''	10'9''	9'6''	8'9''	8'0''	7'6''	6'9''
430	$20 \times 20 \times 2\frac{1}{2}$	12'9''	11'0''	9'9''	8'9''	8'0''	7'6''	6'9''
440	$20 \times 20 \times 2\frac{1}{2}$	13'0''	11'0''	9'9''	9'0''	8'3''	7'9''	6'9''
450	$20 \times 20 \times 2\frac{1}{2}$	13'0''	11'3''	10'0''	9'0''	8'3''	7'9''	7'0''
460	$21 \times 20 \times 2\frac{1}{2}$	13'3''	11'3''	10'0''	9'0''	8'6''	7'9''	7'0''
470	$21 \times 20 \times 2\frac{1}{2}$	13'3''	11'6''	10'0''	9'3''	8'6''	8'0''	7'0''
480	$22 \times 20 \times 2\frac{1}{2}$	13'6''	11'6''	10'3''	9'3''	8'6''	8'0''	7'3''
490	$22 \times 20 \times 2\frac{1}{2}$	13'9''	11'9''	10'3''	9'6''	8'9''	8'0''	7'3''
500	$23 \times 20 \times 2\frac{1}{2}$	14'0''	11'9''	10'6''	9'6''	8'9''	8'3''	7'3''
510	$23 \times 20 \times 2\frac{1}{2}$	14'0''	12'0''	10'6''	9'6''	8'9''	8'3''	7'3''
520	$24 \times 20 \times 2\frac{1}{2}$	14'0''	12'0''	10'9''	9'9''	9'0''	8'3''	7'6''
530	$24 \times 20 \times 2\frac{1}{2}$	14'3''	12'3''	10'9''	9'9''	9'0''	8'6''	7'6''
540	$24 \times 20 \times 2\frac{1}{2}$	14'3''	12'3''	11'0''	9'9''	9'0''	8'6''	7'6''
550	$24 \times 21 \times 2\frac{1}{2}$	14'6''	12'3''	11'0''	10'0''	9'3''	8'6''	7'9''
560	$24 \times 21 \times 2\frac{1}{2}$	14'6''	12'6''	11'0''	10'0''	9'3''	8'9''	7'9''

Table 8.2 Footing Table (*Continued*)

Load, kips	Billets, in.	Footings (refer to Table 8.3)						
		3,000, A	4,000, B	5,000, C	6,000, D	7,000, E	8,000, F	10,000, G
570	24 × 22 × 2½	14′9″	12′6″	11′3″	10′3″	9′3″	8′9″	7′9″
580	24 × 22 × 2½	15′0″	12′9″	11′3″	10′3″	9′6″	8′9″	7′9″
590	24 × 22 × 2½	15′0″	12′9″	11′6″	10′3″	9′6″	9′0″	8′0″
600	24 × 23 × 2½		13′0″	11′6″	10′6″	9′6″	9′0″	8′0″
610	24 × 23 × 2½		13′0″	11′6″	10′6″	9′9″	9′0″	8′0″
620	24 × 23 × 3		13′3″	11′9″	10′6″	9′9″	9′0″	8′0″
630	24 × 24 × 3		13′3″	11′9″	10′9″	9′9″	9′3″	8′3″
640	24 × 24 × 3		13′3″	11′9″	10′9″	10′0″	9′3″	8′3″
650	25 × 24 × 3		13′6″	12′0″	10′9″	10′0″	9′3″	8′3″
660	25 × 24 × 3		13′9″	12′0″	11′0″	10′0″	9′6″	8′6″
670	25 × 24 × 3		13′9″	12′0″	11′0″	10′3″	9′6″	8′6″
680	26 × 24 × 3		13′9″	12′3″	11′0″	10′3″	9′6″	8′6″
690	26 × 24 × 3		14′0″	12′3″	11′3″	10′3″	9′9″	8′6″
700	26 × 24 × 3		14′0″	12′6″	11′3″	10′3″	9′9″	8′6″
710	27 × 24 × 3		14′3″	12′6″	11′3″	10′6″	9′9″	8′9″
720	27 × 24 × 3		14′3″	12′6″	11′6″	10′6″	9′9″	8′9″
730	28 × 24 × 3½		14′3″	12′9″	11′6″	10′6″	10′0″	8′9″
740	28 × 24 × 3½		14′6″	12′9″	11′6″	10′9″	10′0″	8′9″
750	28 × 24 × 3½		14′6″	12′9″	11′9″	10′9″	10′0″	9′0″
760	28 × 25 × 3½		14′6″	13′0″	11′9″	10′9″	10′0″	9′0″
770	28 × 25 × 3½		14′9″	13′0″	11′9″	11′0″	10′3″	9′0″
780	28 × 25 × 3½		14′9″	13′0″	12′0″	11′0″	10′3″	9′0″
790	28 × 26 × 3½		15′0″	13′3″	12′0′	11′0″	10′3″	9′3″
800	28 × 26 × 3½		15′0″	13′3″	12′0″	11′0″	10′3″	9′3″
810	28 × 26 × 3½		15′0″	13′3″	12′0″	11′3″	10′6″	9′3″
820	28 × 27 × 3½			13′6″	12′3″	11′3″	10′6″	9′3″
830	28 × 27 × 3½			13′6″	12′3″	11′3″	10′6″	9′6″
840	28 × 27 × 3½			13′6″	12′3″	11′6″	10′6″	9′6″
850	28 × 28 × 3½			13′9″	12′6″	11′6″	10′9″	9′6″
860	28 × 28 × 3½			13′9″	12′6″	11′6″	10′9″	9′6″
870	28 × 28 × 3½			13′9″	12′6″	11′6″	10′9″	9′6″
880	28 × 28 × 3½			14′0″	12′9″	11′9″	10′9″	9′9″
890	29 × 28 × 3½			14′0″	12′9″	11′9″	11′0″	9′9″
900	29 × 28 × 3½			14′0″	12′9″	11′9″	11′0″	9′9″
910	29 × 28 × 3½			14′3″	12′9″	11′9″	11′0″	9′9″
920	30 × 28 × 3½			14′3″	13′0″	12′0″	11′0″	10′0″
930	30 × 28 × 3½			14′3″	13′0″	12′0″	11′3″	10′0″
940	30 × 28 × 3½			14′6″	13′0″	12′0″	11′3″	10′0″
950	31 × 28 × 3½			14′6″	13′3″	12′3″	11′3″	10′0″
960	31 × 28 × 3½			14′6″	13′3″	12′3″	11′3″	10′0″
970	31 × 28 × 3½			14′9″	13′3″	12′3″	11′6″	10′3″
980	32 × 28 × 4			14′9″	13′3″	12′3″	11′6″	10′3″
990	32 × 28 × 4			14′9″	13′6″	12′3″	11′6″	10′3″
1,000	32 × 28 × 4			15′0″	13′6″	12′6″	11′6″	10′3″

b *Square reinforced-concrete footings.* The following sections quoted from the 1951 ACI Code may be taken as good practice in reinforced-concrete footing design:

[From Sec. 1204(*a*)] The external moment on any section shall be determined by passing through the section a vertical plane which extends completely across the footing, and computing the moment of the forces acting over the entire area of the footing on one side of said plane.

[From Sec. 1204(*b*)] The greatest bending moment to be used in the design of an isolated footing shall be the moment computed at sections located as follows:

1. At the face of the column or pedestal for footings supporting a concrete column or pedestal.

Table 8.3 Standard Footings

For use with Table 8.2

The upper figure is the total depth of the footing and the lower figure is the total reinforcement in each of the two directions.

	A	B	C	D	E	F	G
1'6"	1'0"	1'0"	1'0"	1'0"	1'0"	1'0"	1'0"
1'9"	1'0"	1'0"	1'0"	1'0"	1'0"	1'0"	1'0"
2'0"	1'0"	1'0"	1'0"	1'0"	1 0"	1'0"	
2'3"	1'0"	1'0"	1'0"	1'0"	1'0"		1'0"
							6 No. 4
2'6"	1'0"	1'0"	1'0"	1'0"	1'0"	1'0"	1'0"
					6 No. 4	6 No. 4	9 No. 4
2'9"	1'0"			1'0"	1'0"	1'0"	1'0"
				6 No. 4	8 No. 4	8 No. 4	11 No. 4
3'0"		1'0"	1'0"	1'0"	1'0"	1'0"	1'0"
		5 No. 4	6 No. 4	8 No. 4	9 No. 4	11 No. 4	12 No. 4
3'3"	1'0"	1'0"	1'0"	1'0"	1'0"	1'0"	1'0"
	5 No. 4	7 No. 4	8 No. 4	10 No. 4	11 No. 4	13 No. 4	15 No. 4
3'6"				1'0"	1'0"	1'0"	1'1"
				11 No. 4	13 No. 4	14 No. 4	16 No. 4
3'9"	1'0"	1'0"	1'0"	1'0"	1'1"	1'1"	1'1"
	6 No. 4	8 No. 4	10 No. 4	13 No. 4	13 No. 4	15 No. 4	18 No. 4
4'0"		1'0"	1'0"	1'1"	1'1"	1'1"	1'2"
		10 No. 4	11 No. 4	13 No. 4	14 No. 4	17 No. 4	18 No. 4
4'3"	1'0"		1'1"	1'1"	1'2"	1'2"	1'3"
	8 No. 4		12 No. 4	15 No. 4	15 No. 4	18 No. 4	19 No. 4
4'6"		1'0"	1'1"	1'2"	1'2"	1'3"	1'3"
		12 No. 4	14 No. 4	15 No. 4	17 No. 4	18 No. 4	21 No. 4
4'9"	1'0"	1'1"	1'2"	1'2"	1'3"	1'3"	1'4"
	10 No. 4	12 No. 4	14 No. 4	17 No. 4	17 No. 4	20 No. 4	21 No. 4
5'0"	1'0"	1'1"	1'2"	1'3"	1'3"	1'4"	1'4"
	12 No. 4	14 No. 4	16 No. 4	17 No. 4	20 No. 4	20 No. 4	24 No. 4
5'3"		1'2"	1'3"	1'3"	1'4"	1'4"	1'5"
		15 No. 4	17 No. 4	18 No. 4	20 No. 4	23 No. 4	26 No. 4
5'6"	1'1"	1'2"	1'3"	1'4"	1'4"	1'5"	1'6"
	13 No. 4	17 No. 4	19 No. 4	21 No. 4	24 No. 4	25 No. 4	27 No. 4
5'9"	1'1"	1'3"	1'4"	1'4"	1'5"	1'6"	1'6"
	11 No. 5	12 No. 5	21 No. 4	24 No. 4	25 No. 4	25 No. 4	31 No. 4
6'0"	1'2"	1'3"	1'4"	1'5"	1'6"	1'6"	1'7"
	11 No. 5	13 No. 5	15 No. 5	18 No. 5	26 No. 4	28 No. 4	33 No. 4
6'3"		1'4"	1'5"	1'5"	1'6"	1'7"	1'8"
		13 No. 5	15 No. 5	18 No. 5	19 No. 5	20 No. 5	23 No. 4
6'6"	1'3"	1'4"	1'5"	1'6"	1'7"	1'7"	1'8"
	12 No. 5	15 No. 5	18 No. 5	19 No. 5	20 No. 5	23 No. 5	25 No. 5
6'9"	1'3"	1'5"	1'6"	1'7"	1'7"	1'8"	1'9"
	14 No. 5	16 No. 5	18 No. 5	20 No. 5	23 No. 5	24 No. 5	27 No. 5
7'0"	1'4"	1'5"	1'6"	1'7"	1'8"	1'8"	1'9"
	10 No. 6	13 No. 6	15 No. 6	16 No. 6	24 No. 5	25 No. 5	29 No. 5
7'3"	1'4"	1'5"	1'7"	1'9"	1'8"	1'9"	1'10"
	11 No. 6	14 No. 6	15 No. 6	17 No. 6	19 No. 6	28 No. 5	31 No. 5
7'6"	1'4"	1'6"	1'7"	1'8"	1'9"	1'9"	1'11"
	13 No. 6	15 No. 6	16 No. 6	18 No. 6	19 No. 6	22 No. 6	23 No. 6
7'9"	1'5"	1'6"	1'8"	1'9"	1'9"	1'10"	1'11"
	13 No. 6	16 No. 6	17 No. 6	19 No. 6	21 No. 6	22 No. 6	25 No. 6
8'0"	1'5"	1'7"	1'8"	1'9"	1'10"	1'11"	2'0"
	14 No. 6	17 No. 6	19 No. 6	20 No. 6	22 No. 6	23 No. 6	25 No. 6

Table 8.3 Standard Footings (*Continued*)

	A	B	C	D	E	F	G
8'3"	1'5"	1'7"	1'9"	1'10"	1'11"	1'11"	2'0"
	12 No. 7	18 No. 6	19 No. 6	21 No. 6	26 No. 6	23 No. 6	29 No. 6
8'6"	1'6"	1'8"	1'9"	1'10"	2'0"	1'11"	2'1"
	12 No. 7	14 No. 7	No. 7 16	17 No. 7	26 No. 6	24 No. 6	31 No. 6
8'9"	1'6"	1'8"	1'10"	1'11"	2'0"	2'1"	2'1"
	13 No. 7	15 No. 7	17 No. 7	18 No. 7	19 No. 7	20 No. 7	25 No. 7
9'0"	1'7"	1'10"	1'10"	1'11"	2'0"	2'1"	2'2"
	14 No. 7	15 No. 7	17 No. 7	19 No. 7	21 No. 7	22 No. 7	26 No. 7
9'3"	1'7"	1'9"	1'11"	2'0"	2'1"	2'2"	2'3"
	14 No. 7	17 No. 7	17 No. 7	19 No. 7	21 No. 7	23 No. 7	26 No. 7
9'6"	1'7"	1'10"	1'11"	2'0"	2'1"	2'2"	2'3"
	15 No. 7	17 No. 7	19 No. 7	21 No. 7	23 No. 7	25 No. 7	28 No. 7
9'9"	1'8"	1'10"	2'0"	2'1"	2'2"	2'3"	2'4"
	16 No. 7	18 No. 7	20 No. 7	22 No. 7	24 No. 7	26 No. 7	30 No. 7
10'0"	1'8"	1'11"	2'0"	2'1"	2'2"	2'3"	2'5"
	17 No. 7	19 No. 7	21 No. 7	24 No. 7	26 No. 7	28 No. 7	31 No. 7
10'3"	1'9"	1'11"	2'1"	2'2"	2'3"	2'4"	2'6"
	17 No. 7	20 No. 7	22 No. 7	24 No. 7	27 No. 7	28 No. 7	32 No. 7
10'6"	1'9"	1'11"	2'1"	2'2"	2'3"	2'4"	
	18 No. 7	21 No. 7	23 No. 7	26 No. 7	29 No. 7	31 No. 7	
10'9"	1'10"	2'0"	2'1"	2'3"	2'4"	2'5"	
	18 No. 7	22 No. 7	25 No. 7	27 No. 7	29 No. 7	32 No. 7	
11'0"	1'10"	2'0"	2'2"	2'3"	2'5"	2'5"	
	19 No. 7	23 No. 7	26 No. 7	29 No. 7	31 No. 7	34 No. 7	
11'3"	1'10"	2'1"	2'2"	2'4"	2'5"	2'6"	
	21 No. 7	23 No. 7	27 No. 7	30 No. 7	33 No. 7	35 No. 7	
11'6"	1'11"	2'1"	2'3"	2'4"	2'6"	2'7"	
	21 No. 7	25 No. 7	28 No. 7	32 No. 7	33 No. 7	36 No. 7	
11'9"	1'11"	2'1"	2'3"	2'5"	2'6"		
	22 No. 7	26 No. 7	30 No. 7	32 No. 7	35 No. 7		
12'0"	1'11"	2'2"	2'4"	2'6"	2'7"		
	24 No. 7	27 No. 7	31 No. 7	33 No. 7	37 No. 7		
12'3"	2'0"	2'2"	2'4"	2'6"	2'7"		
	24 No. 7	29 No. 7	32 No. 7	35 No. 7	39 No. 7		
12'6"	2'0"	2'3"	2'5"	2'6"	2'8"		
	26 No. 7	29 No. 7	33 No. 7	37 No. 7	39 No. 7		
12'9"	2'1"	2'3"	2'5"	2'7"			
	26 No. 7	31 No. 7	35 No. 7	39 No. 7			
13'0"	2'1"	2'4"	2'6"	2'7"			
	28 No. 7	31 No. 7	36 No. 7	41 No. 7			
13'3"	2'2"	2'4"	2'6"	2'8"			
	28 No. 7	34 No. 7	38 No. 7	42 No. 7			
13'6"	2'2"	2'4"	2'7"	2'8"			
	28 No. 7	35 No. 7	39 No. 7	44 No. 7			
13'9"	2'2"	2'5"	2'7"				
	28 No. 7	36 No. 7	40 No. 7				
14'0"	2'3"	2'5"	2'8"				
	28 No. 7	37 No. 7	42 No. 7				
14'3"	2'3"	2'6"	2'8"				
	30 No. 7	38 No. 7	44 No. 7				
14'6"	2'3"	2'6"	2'9"				
	34 No. 7	40 No. 7	45 No. 7				
14'9"	2'4"	2'7"	2'9"				
	34 No. 7	41 No. 7	47 No. 7				
15'0"	2'4"	2'7"	2'9"				
	36 No. 7	43 No. 7	48 No. 7				

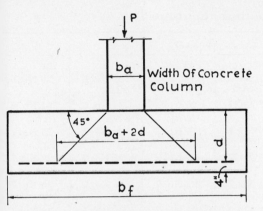

Fig. 8.3   Concrete Column on Reinforced-Concrete Footings

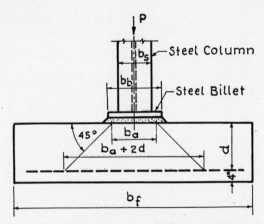

Fig. 8.4   Steel Column and Billet on Reinforced-Concrete Footing

2. Halfway between the face of the column and edge of the metallic base for footings under metallic bases. [In computing the depth for shear as required by the ACI Code, the allowance for grouting (see Art. 7.60c of this book) is used in computing the shear depth, but the net depth of footing is the depth listed in Table 8.3.]

[From Sec. 1204(c)]   The width resisting compression at any section shall be assumed as the entire width of the top of the footing at the section under consideration.

[From Sec. 1204(e and f)]   In two-way reinforced footings the total tensile reinforcement of any section shall provide a moment of resistance at least equal to 85% of the moment computed and the reinforcement thus determined shall be distributed uniformly across the full width of the section.

[From Sec. 1205(a)]   The critical section for shear to be used as a measure of diagonal tension shall be assumed as a vertical section obtained by passing a series of vertical planes through the footing each of which is parallel to a corresponding face of the column and at a distance equal to the depth d.

[From Sec. 1205(c)]   Critical sections for bond shall be assumed on the same planes as those prescribed for bending moment in Sec. 1204(b).

[From Sec. 1205(d)]   Computations for shear to be used as a measure of bond shall be based on the same section and loading as prescribed for bending moment in Sec. 1204(a).

[From Sec. 1205(e)]   The total tensile reinforcement at any section shall provide a bond resistance at least equal to 85% of the external shear at the section.

[From Sec. 1209(a)]   The thickness above the reinforcement at the edge shall be not less than 6 in.

[From Sec. 808(a)]   In isolated footings the shearing unit stress computed by the formula: $v = V/bjd$ shall not exceed $.03f_c{'}$ nor in any case shall it exceed 75 psi.

[From Sec. 507(a)]   The reinforcement of footings shall have not less than 3 in. of concrete between it and the ground contact surface.

Because shear rather than moment controls the depth of a reinforced-concrete footing, the sequence of design operations is as follows:

1. The determination of shear depth is a matter of cut and try. It is determined so that, using the nomenclature of Fig. 8.3 if concrete columns are used, or Fig. 8.4 for steel columns and billets,

$$P\left[\frac{b_f{}^2 - (b_a + 2d)^2}{b_f{}^2}\right] \equiv 4d(b_a + 2d)0.875f_v$$

or if we use 2,500- or 3,000-psi concrete ($f_v = 75$),

$$P\left[\frac{b_f{}^2 - (b_a + 2d)^2}{b_f{}^2}\right] \equiv 262.5d(b_a + 2d)$$

The first term is the footing load which produces shear, that is, that portion of the load falling outside the shear plane. The second term is the amount of shear carried by the shear planes around four vertical surfaces cut at $b_a + 2d$. As a start to cut and try for proper depth for shear, a depth d equal to b_a may be assumed and correction made on the basis of results obtained.

2. Determine the load which causes moment,

$$W = P\frac{b_f - b_a}{2b_f}$$

3. The total moment on a moment section is

$$M = \left(\frac{b_f - b_a}{4}\right) W$$

Compute the area of steel required to take this moment,

$$A_s = \frac{0.85M}{f_s j d}$$

Combining all the above equations, using 3,000-psi concrete and 20,000-psi stress in the steel, and using the load in kips,

$$A_s = \frac{P(b_f - b_a)^2}{164.5 d b_f}$$

4. The perimeter of bars required for bond resistance is

$$\Sigma_0 = \frac{0.85W}{u j d}$$

Using ACI stresses with 3,000-psi concrete, and combining the above equations,

$$\Sigma_0 = \frac{P(b_f - b_a)}{0.494 d b_f}$$

From the comparison of the formula for bond with the formula for area of steel, it will be found that

$$A_s = \frac{(b_f - b_a)}{333} \Sigma_0$$

5. The number and size of bars should be selected so that they satisfy the requirements of both area and bond as given above.

Problem 1 Assume a load of 300,000 lb with a soil pressure of 5,000 psf. The column is a 12 WF 72 and the billet is

$$\frac{300,000}{1,125} = 267 \text{ sq in.}$$

Use a 17 × 16-in. billet.

The average of base and column is 14.25. Use a trial depth of 17 in., plus $1\frac{1}{2}$-in. grout, or $18\frac{1}{2}$ in. in all. Then $b_a + 2d$ is 4.1 ft. On the basis of 17 in. to steel, or 21 in. total depth, the net soil pressure is $5,000 - 1.75(150) = 4,738$ psf and the area of footing required is

$$\frac{300,000}{4,738} = 63.3 \text{ sq ft}$$

Use 8 ft square.

The area producing shear is $8^2 - 4.28^2$, and the shear load is

$$300,000 \times \frac{64 - 18.32}{64} = 214,130 \text{ lb}$$

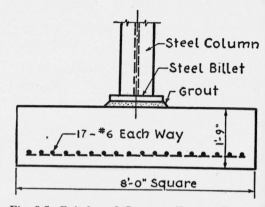

Steel Column

Steel Billet

Grout

17 - #6 Each Way

1'-9"

8'-0" Square

Fig. 8.5   Reinforced-Concrete Footing Problem

The shear capacity is $49.25 \times 17 \times 262.5 = 219,900$ lb. Therefore, the assumed depth is correct and the total depth of footing is 1 ft 9 in.

From the formula in paragraph 2 above, the load-producing moment is

$$W = 300 \times \frac{8 - 1.19}{16} = 127.6 \text{ kips}$$

The total moment on the moment section is

$$M = 127.6 \times \frac{8 - 1.19}{4} \times 12 = 2,607 \text{ in.-kips}$$

$$A_s = \frac{0.85 \times 2,607}{17.5 \times 17} = 7.45 \text{ sq in.} = 17 \text{ No. } 6$$

$$\Sigma_0 = \frac{0.85 \times 127.6}{0.240 \times 0.875 \times 17} = 30.4 \text{ in.} = 13 \text{ No. } 6$$

Use 17 No. 6 each direction (required for moment).

c   The design of plain-concrete footings may be based on the rules quoted in Art. 8.11 from Sec. 1204(*a*), Sec. 1204(*b*), and Sec. 1204(*c*) for computation of moment, and from Sec. 1205(*a*) for shear. After the moment has been determined, the design may be made by the section-modulus method as described in Art. 5.12*a*.

Problem 2 Assume an 8 WF 24 steel column on a steel billet, carrying a 75,000-lb load with an allowable soil pressure of 6,000 psf. Design a plain concrete footing, using 3,000-psi concrete.

Deducting 250 psf from the unit soil pressure for weight of footing, the required footing will be

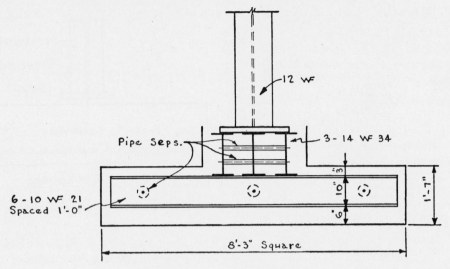

Fig. 8.6   Grillage Footing

$$\frac{75,000}{5,750} = 13.03 \text{ sq ft}$$

se 3 ft 9 in. square.

Using a pressure of 1,125 psi under the bil-
t, the required billet area will be

$$\frac{75,000}{1,125} = 67.6 \text{ sq in.}$$

However, in order to provide a billet under
n $8 \times 6\frac{1}{2}$-in. column, the minimum size of
illet should be 8×10 in. The fulcrum line
ould therefore be at a point $(6.5 + 8)/2 =$
.25 in. from the center of the column, and
he width of the cantilever producing mo-
nent is

$$\frac{45 \text{ in.} - 7.25 \text{ in.}}{2} = 18.82 \text{ in.}$$

This represents 0.42 of the width of the foot-
ng, or a load of $0.42 \times 75,000 = 31,500$ lb,
which will be the cantilever load.

The moment is therefore

$$M = 31,500 \times 9.41 = 296,400 \text{ in.-lb}$$

From Art. 5.12,

$$f = 150 \quad \text{and} \quad S = \frac{296,400}{150} = 1,976$$

Since

$$S = \frac{bd^2}{6} = \frac{45d^2}{6} = 7.5d^2$$

$$d = \sqrt{\frac{1,976}{7.5}} = \sqrt{263} = 16.3 \text{ in.}$$

Use 17 in.

To check this depth for shear, the area
within the shear planes is $7.25 + 34$ in. $=$
41.25 in. square, and in a footing which is
only 45 in. square, it is obvious that the load
producing shear is negligible.

d Steel-grillage footings, formerly very
popular for heavy loads, have given way
largely to the cheaper, simpler type of reinforced-concrete spread footing, described in
Art. 8.11*b*. The general rules covering the
use of steel-grillage footings are that they
should rest on a bed of at least 6 in. of concrete, with the grillages encased in a minimum
of 3 in. of concrete. The spaces between the
beams should be entirely filled with concrete.
The beams are held in place usually with
steel-pipe separators. The load is spread into
the soil by the lowest set of beams, which are
spaced uniformly across the footings. The
load from the column is taken by a steel billet
into the upper grillage which spreads the load
into the lower grillage. At all crossings, the
rules of Art. 4.10*i* relative to web shear and
buckling must be observed.

Problem 2   Assume the same column load
and soil conditions given in Art. 8.11*b*. The
column spreads a load of 300,000 lb upon an
8-ft-square footing. To obtain approximate
sizes, assume that the top billet will spread
the load upon a 20-in. square. Then the cantilever is

$$\frac{8\text{ ft} - 1\text{ ft 8 in.}}{2} = 3\text{ ft 2 in.} = 38\text{ in.}$$

and the load on the cantilever is

$$\frac{96 - 20}{2 \times 96} \quad \text{or} \quad 0.395 \text{ of the load}$$

The cantilever moment is

$$0.395 \times 300{,}000 \times 19 = 2251.5 \text{ in.-kips}$$

and the section modulus required in each layer is

$$\frac{2{,}251.5}{20} = 112.57$$

In the lower layer this can be either

Six 10 WF 21 = 126 lb per ft
Eight 8 WF 17 = 136 lb per ft
Eleven 7 I 15.3 = 168.3 lb per ft

In the upper layer this will be three 14 WF 34. Obviously the preferable design will use three 14 WF 34 in the upper layer and six 10 WF 21 in the lower layer if these check out for web shear and buckling.

The shearing load transmitted into each upper beam is

$$\frac{0.395 \times 300{,}000}{3} = 39{,}500 \text{ lb}$$

From Table 1.5 the allowable shear is 52 kips. The reaction for $3\frac{1}{2}$-in. bearing is 31, plus 6.9 for each additional inch of bearing. The total load of 100 kips on each of three beams would require

$$G = \frac{100 - 62}{6.9} = 5.5$$

and the minimum length of billet required is $7 + 5.5 = 12.5$ in. The beams should be placed about 8 in. o.c. to allow for flow of concrete, and the billet would therefore be 18×16 in.

Referring to Fig. 7.30 for the general method, we may assume that the lever arm for the outer beam is 8 in. $- (0.80 \times 6) = 3.2$ in., and

$$M = 100{,}000 \times 3.2 = 320{,}000 \text{ in.-lb}$$

S required for base plate $= \dfrac{320}{20} = 16$

Using 16-in. width,

$$S = \frac{16d^2}{6} = 2.67d^2$$

$$d = \sqrt{\frac{16}{2.67}} = \sqrt{6} = 2.45$$

Use $18 \times 16 \times 2\frac{1}{2}$ in.

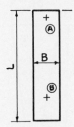

Fig. 8.7 Rectangular Footing

At each point where the 14-in. beam crosse the 10-in. beam, the load transmitted $\dfrac{300}{18} = 16.7$ kips, and the shear on the 10-in beam is

$$\frac{0.395 \times 300{,}000}{6} = 19.75 \text{ kips}$$

These are well within the limits of th 10 WF 21 as given in Table 1.5.

It will be noted that the correction of th actual cantilever load carried instead of th assumed 20×20-in. billet will not materiall change the grillage. The depth required fc the grillage is 6 in. of concrete + 10 in. lowe tier + 14 in. upper tier, or 30 in. under th billet as against 21 in. for the reinforced concrete footing.

8.12   Combined and cantilever footings

a   Combined footings and cantilever foot ings are used where one of the columns is to close to the lot line or adjacent building t permit the use of a concentric square or rec tangular footing. Aside from special corne conditions, etc., there are three types of com bined footings which may be used to carr two columns. If we call the wall column *A* and the interior column *B*, the selection c shape of footing will be made as follows:

Rectangular type, Fig. 8.7, is used if th load on column *B* is greater than on column *A*

Trapezoidal type, Fig. 8.8, is used if th load on column *A* is slightly greater than o column *B*.

T-shape type, Fig. 8.9, is used if the load o column *A* is considerably greater than on col umn *B*.

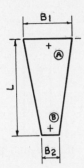

Fig. 8.8   Trapezoidal Footing

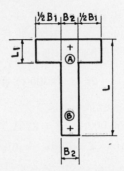

Fig. 8.9   T-Shape Footing

Starting from this basis, make an assumption of the type to be used and proceed with the design as follows:

b   For rectangular-type footing:

1. Compute the center of gravity y of column and wall loads, using the lot line as a base. For balanced foundations, the center of gravity of the loads should coincide with the center of gravity of the footing area.

2. Compute the required area of footing. Assume the allowable soil pressure based on the nature of the subsoil. Deduct an assumed weight per square foot of footing to obtain net allowable soil pressure. Thus, assuming ,000 psf or 4 tons, soil pressure, and footing at about 500 psf, the net allowable soil pressure is $8,000 - 500 = 7,500$ psf. The total required area is the sum of the column loads plus wall load, divided by net soil pressure, or

$$A = \frac{P_a + P_b + P_{\text{wall}}}{\text{net } f}$$

3. Compute the length of the footing. For a rectangular footing the length is twice the distance to the center of gravity obtained by step 1, or $L = 2y$.

4. Compute $B = A/L$ and check footing shape obtained against interference with other footings; compute width and length to carry billets.

5. From the information thus obtained, a shear diagram may be laid out treating the entire footing as a reinforced-concrete beam. From this shear diagram, compute maximum shear and maximum moment and design for depth and longitudinal steel.

6. Design cross steel if necessary to spread the load, and design stirrups. For stirrups, it is ordinarily necessary to use eight or more legs to each stirrup.

c   For trapezoidal footing:

1. Same as step 1 for rectangular-type footing.

2. Same as step 2 for rectangular-type footing.

3. Assume the length L of footing by allowing enough clearance past the end of column B to carry the billet satisfactorily.

4. Compute B_1 and B_2 from a solution of the following two simultaneous equations:

$(a)\quad B_1 + B_2 = \dfrac{2A}{L}$

$(b)\quad B_1 + 2B_2 = \dfrac{3y}{L}(B_1 + B_2)$

In equation (b) substitute the result of $B_1 + B_2$ found in equation (a) to obtain all the required figures except $B_1 + B_2$. Solve for B_1 and B_2.

5. Same as step 5 for rectangular-type footing.

6. Same as step 6 for rectangular-type footing.

d   For T-type footing:

1. Same as step 1 for rectangular-type footing.

2. Same as step 2 for rectangular-type footing.

3. Assume L as described in step 3 for trapezoidal footings. Assume B_2 similarly from the width to carry the billet for column B.

4. Compute L_1 from the formula

$$L_1 = \frac{2Ay - B_2L^2}{A - B_2L}$$

If the numerator in the formula is a negative quantity, a combined footing of this type will not be satisfactory, because the inner load is not heavy enough. Compute

$$B_1 = \frac{A - B_2 L}{L_1}$$
$$B = B_1 + B_2$$

5. Same as step 5 for rectangular-type footing.

6. Design cross steel in the T, and design stirrups.

e Combined-footing problem. Assume a column 1 ft 2 in. from the lot line, carrying a load of 250 kips. At a distance of 18 ft from it at right angles to the lot line the inner column carries a load of 200 kips, allowable soil pressure 6,000 psf. From Table 8.2 we find that the wall column will require a 16 × 14-in. billet, and the inner column a 14 × 13-in. billet. From Art. 8.12a it will be noted that this requires a trapezoidal footing.

To find the center of gravity of loads, from center of wall column,

P	x	Px
250 ×	0 =	0
200 ×	18 =	3,600
450		3,600

$$\bar{x} = \frac{3,600}{450} = 8 \text{ ft}$$

Distance from lot line = 1 ft 2 in.
Distance from lot line
to center of gravity = 9 ft 2 in.

Allow 1 ft beyond center of interior column. The total length is 20 ft 2 in.

Deducting 500 psf for weight of footing, the net soil pressure is 5,500, and the required area is 450/5.5 = 82.

$$B_1 + B_2 = \frac{2 \times 82}{20.17} = 8.12 \text{ (twice the average width)}$$

$$B_1 + 2B_2 = \frac{3 \times 9.17 \times 8.12}{20.17} = 11.1 \text{ (from Table 1.3, Trapezoid)}$$

Subtracting the first equation from the second,

$$B_1 + 2B_2 = 11.1$$
$$B_1 + B_2 = 8.12$$
$$B_2 = 2.98 \text{ ft} \qquad B_1 = 5.14 \text{ ft}$$

The increase in width per foot length 2.16/20.17 = 0.107.

At the wall end the footing is wide enoug to transmit shear along three sides, but th critical depth is across the footing on one lin· At the narrow end also, the critical depth in one line only across the footing.

Assume the net span of the footing for m ment at $13\frac{1}{2}$ in. less than the center-to-cent distance, or

$$18 - 1.12 = 16.88 \text{ ft.}$$

The trapezoidal load carried is
$$W = 16.88 \times 4.06 \times 5.5 = 376.4$$
The width of the narrow end of the net span 2.98 + (1.58 × 0.107) = 3.15 ft = 37.8 in.
At the wide end it is
3.15 + (16.88 × 0.107) = 4.95 ft = 59.5 in.

Although not strictly accurate, the result i close enough if the moments for rectangula and triangular load in Fig. 8.10 are added.

From Fig. 3.13, Case 1, $M = \dfrac{292 \times 16.88}{8} = 61$

From Fig. 3.13, Case 2, $M =$
$$84 \times 16.88 \times 0.1283 = 18$$
$$616 + 182 = 798 \text{ ft-kips or } 9,580 \text{ in.-kips}$$

Using 3,000-psi concrete ($K = 236$) with a average width of 4.06 ft (= 48.75 in.),

$$d = \sqrt{\frac{9,580,000}{236 \times 48.75}} = \sqrt{832.7} = 28.86$$

From Fig. 8.10, the unit shear at the narrow end of the beam for the above depth is

$$v = \frac{174,000}{0.875 \times 29 \times 37.8} = 182 \text{ psi}$$

A combined footing may be treated as a beam and the allowable shear if stirrups are used i 360 psi for 3,000-psi concrete. At the op posite end,

$$v = \frac{202,000}{0.875 \times 28.6 \times 59.5} = 134.5 \text{ psi}$$

Use 30 in. net depth, 34 in. gross depth.

$$A_s = \frac{9,580}{17.5 \times 30} = 18.25 \text{ sq in.} = 12 \text{ No. 11 bar}$$

Stirrups will be required at both ends of the beams. Using the method of Art. 5.30,

Shear at narrow end of beam = 174   kips
The concrete will take 30 × 37.8 × 90 = 89.3 kips
To be taken by stirrups: 84.7 kips

Referring to Table 5.11, in order to use ap-
roximately a 6-in. spacing a stirrup must be
elected for which the stirrup dividend is
× 84.7 = 508.

Use No. 5 four-leg
irrup for which the
irrup dividend is
× 325.5 = 651, $s_1 = \dfrac{651}{84.7} = 7.7$ in.   1 at 4 in.
                                              1 at 9 in.

llowing for increase
width,
ft × 0.107 =
$\dfrac{0.107}{2} = 0.05$

eduction in 1 ft
× 5.5 × 3.2   = 17.6
                    $s_2 = \dfrac{651}{67.1} = 9.75$ in.   1 at 10 in.

eduction in 10 in.
lowing for increase
width,
83 × 5.5 × 3.3   = 15.1
                    $s_3 = \dfrac{651}{52.0} = 12.5$ in.   1 at 12 in.

eduction in 12 in
llowing for increase
width.
× 5.5 × 3.4   = .8
                    $s_4 = \dfrac{651}{33.2} = 19.6$ in.   Maximum
                                                           spacing
                                                           15 in.

eduction,
25 × 5.5 × 3 52   = 24.2 in.   Use 15 in.
ne additional at
5 in. will reduce V_s
o zero.

t heavy end of foot-
ng, total shear,   = 202.0
hear carried by con-
rete,
0 × 0.875 × 59.5 × 90   = 140.6
                          61.4

sing No. 5 four-leg
tirrups, $s_1 = \dfrac{651}{61.4} = 10.6$ in.   1 at 5 in.
                                                           1 at 11 in.

eduction in
ft 4 in.,
33 × 5.5 × 4.89   = $\dfrac{35.8}{25.6}$
                   $s_2 = \dfrac{651}{25.6} = 25.4$ in.   Maximum
                                                           spacing
                                                           15 in.

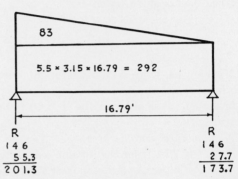

83

5.5 × 3.15 × 16.79 = 292

16.79'

R   R
1 4 6   1 4 6
5 5.3   2 7.7
2 0 1.3   1 7 3.7

Fig. 8.10   Load Diagram for Beam—Trapezoidal
Footing

The final design of the footing is given in
Fig. 8.11.

f   It is sometimes desirable to use a cantilever footing instead of combined footings.
There seems to be a great difference of opinion
between engineers on the relative desirability
of the two types.

For a cantilever footing, the wall-column
footing is made rectangular and offset so that
the column is eccentric on the footing. This
eccentricity is taken by means of a cantilever
girder, or strap, which carries the column on
the offset footing and uses the dead load of an
adjacent column to take the uplift. The
girder may be of steel or concrete, depending
on the amount to be carried, but it should not
bear on undisturbed earth.

The proportions shown in Fig. 8.12 are recommended by H. S. Woodward in an excellent
article in *Engineering News-Record*.

g   *Cantilever-footing problem.* Assume the
same conditions as in the combined-footing
problem in Art. 8.12e. Using the proportions
of Fig. 8.12,

$$B = \sqrt{\dfrac{1.15P}{2.5f}}$$

$$B = \sqrt{\dfrac{1.15 \times 250}{2.5 \times 5.5}} = \sqrt{20.9} = 4.58$$

Then

$$e = \dfrac{4.58}{2} - 1.17 = 1.12$$

$$M = 1.12 \times 250 = 280 \text{ ft-kips}$$

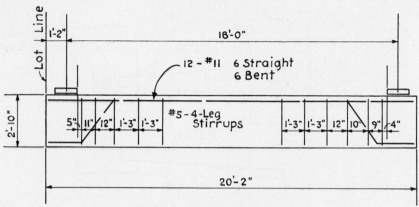

Fig. 8.11 Combined Footing

The uplift is

$$\frac{280}{18 - 1.12} = 16.5$$

On this basis, the factor 15 percent may be reduced to 7 percent, and

$$B = \sqrt{\frac{1.07 \times 250}{2.5 \times 5.5}} = \sqrt{19.5} = 4.42$$

Then

$$e = \frac{4.42}{2} - 1.17 = 1.04$$

$$M = 1.04 \times 250 = 260 \text{ ft-kips}$$

The uplift is

$$\frac{260}{18 - 1.04} = 15.3 \text{ kips}$$

The footing for the wall column is therefore 4 ft 5 in. by 11 ft. The footing for the interior column is not changed but remains a simple square footing for the full load as designed in Art. 8.10. The strap is designed as a simple cantilever beam for a moment of 260 ft-kips and a shear of 15.3 kips.

8.13 Pile foundations

a Foundations of bearing piles may be listed under the following classifications:

Wood piles

    Plain, untreated
    Treated

Concrete

    Cast in place
      With shells
        Tapered shells
        Cylindrical shells

        Providing sectional restraint
        Not providing sectional restraint
      Steel pipe
    Without shells
      Pedestal
      Straight shaft
    Precast
      Tapered
      Parallel-sided

Composite

    Wood piles with cast-in-place concrete
    Wood piles with precast concrete

Steel H Piles

No single type of pile answers every purpose, and each type has its advantages and disadvantages. The descriptive matter in paragraphs *b* through *e* following is taken from the article "Pile Foundations," by A. E. Cummings, Director of Research, Raymond Concrete Pile Co. The article is from the *Proceedings* of the Purdue Conference on Soil Mechanics and its Applications, sponsored by the Society for Promotion of Engineering Education.

b *Wood piles*

The plain wood pile is probably the oldest form of piling used by man. The principal advantage of the plain wood pile is its low cost. However, in spite of its low cost, it is not necessarily the cheapest type of foundation unit because of the restrictions that govern its use. In order that it will not decay, a plain wood pile must be cut off and capped below permanent ground water level. This requirement often involves deep excavation with

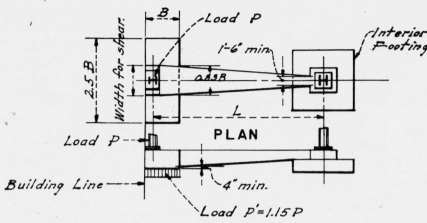

Fig. 8.12 Cantilever Footing

eeting and pumping. Another disadvantage of e wood pile is the fact that ordinarily it can sup-rt a considerably smaller load than some of the her types of pile. For a given load to be carried, is means a larger number of wood piles with rger footings and with a longer time required to ⸱ the job. Plain wood piles are subject to attack ⸱ fungi and bacteria as well as by insects and var-us marine animals.

In order to overcome some of the disadvantages plain wood piles, preservative processes have ⸱en developed in which the wood is treated with rious kinds of chemicals. The effectiveness of ese preservatives depends on two important fac-rs: (1) the thoroughness with which the treat-ent process is done and (2) the severity of the xposure conditions at the site where the treated le is to be used. It cannot be assumed that pre-rvative treatment will make the pile immune om attack by marine animals and insects espe-ally in localities where these animals are very active. either can it be assumed that preservative treat-ent will entirely prevent decay in places where e pile is exposed to the air and is alternately wet d dry. However, it may be taken for granted at, under similar conditions, a properly treated mber pile will last longer than an untreated pile. evertheless, the engineer who proposes to use eated timber piles as part of a permanent struc-re should always give some consideration to the uestion of replacement. Under a building founda-on the replacement of a pile is a very expensive rocess. In a railway trestle or similar structure placement is not so expensive. Because of the st of the treatment process, the treated pile loses me of the low cost advantage of the plain wood le.

c Concrete piles

Concrete piles came into general use during the ⸱st few years of the past century. There are two principal types of concrete pile; cast-in-place and pre-cast. The cast-in-place pile is formed in the ground in the position in which it is to be used in the foundation. The precast pile is cast above ground and, after it has been properly cured, it is driven or jetted just like a wood pile. The fields of usefulness of these two types of pile overlap to a large extent although there are conditions under which one or the other has a distinct advantage.

In ordinary building foundation work the cast-in-place pile is more commonly used than the pre-cast pile. The principal reasons for this are the following. The cast-in-place pile foundation can be installed more rapidly because there is no delay while test piles are being driven to predetermine pile lengths and there is no delay waiting for piles to cure sufficiently to withstand handling and driving stresses. Of particular importance in crowded locations is the fact that a cast-in-place pile job does not require a large open space for a pile-casting yard.

In marine installations either in salt or in fresh water, the precast pile is used almost exclusively. This is due to the difficulty involved in placing cast-in-place piles in open water. For docks and bulkheads, the cast-in-place pile is sometimes used in the anchorage system. On trestle type structures such as highway viaducts, the precast pile is more commonly used. A portion of the pile often extends above the ground and serves as a column for the superstructure.

Both precast and cast-in-place concrete piles have an advantage over other kinds of piles due to the fact that the concrete pile does not have to be cut off below permanent ground water level. When the concrete has been properly mixed and placed, the concrete pile can be exposed to air or to alternate wetting and drying without danger of corrosion or decay. Another advantage of the concrete pile in comparison with some of the other kinds of pile is the fact that concrete piles usually carry higher working loads.

Precast concrete piles are always reinforced internally so that they can resist stresses produced by handling and driving. When the pile is used as an ordinary foundation pile completely submerged in soil, the stresses in the pile under the usual working loads are relatively low. The carrying capacity of the pile depends primarily on the relation between the pile and the soil and not on the strength of the pile itself. In such cases it is the handling and driving stresses which determine the design of the pile and the amount of internal reinforcement. When the precast concrete pile serves as a column or when it is a sheet pile resisting horizontal forces, the amount of reinforcement is sometimes determined by the forces that will be exerted on the pile after it is in place in the ground. Even in such cases the design of the pile should be checked against the handling and driving stresses.

The concrete in a cast-in-place pile is not subject to handling and driving stresses since the pile is poured in place in the ground. Where they are used as columns or where they are subject to horizontal forces, cast-in-place concrete piles are reinforced internally. In ordinary foundation work where they are completely submerged in soil, cast-in-place piles are not reinforced internally. The stresses in the concrete are low and the carrying capacity of the pile is determined by the relation between the pile and the soil. Under these conditions the use of internal reinforcement in a cast-in-place pile represents an unnecessary expense.

Cast-in-place concrete piles may be divided into two kinds: (1) those in which a steel shell is left in the ground and (2) those in which no shell is left in the ground. The purpose of the shell is to prevent mud and water from mixing with the fresh concrete and to provide a form to protect the concrete while it is setting and to provide restraint to the cross section. With the shell-less pile, the fresh concrete is in direct contact with the surrounding soil.

Some kinds of shell piles are formed by driving a tapered steel shell into the ground and then filling the shell with concrete. With piles of this type, the full driving resistance is maintained since the shell remains in the position into which it is driven. The Raymond pile is one of this type. A thin steel restraining shell, closed at the bottom with a steel boot, is placed on the outside of a steel mandrel or core and the shell and the core are driven into the ground. When sufficient driving resistance has been developed, driving is stopped and the core is withdrawn from the shell which is then filled with concrete. Another kind of pile which is formed in a driven tapered shell is the Union Monotube Pile. These piles are driven without an interior core and the shell thickness must therefore be great enough to withstand the stresses developed during driving.

The McArthur Pile is another kind of cast-[in-]place concrete pile in which a steel shell rema[ins] in the ground. The driving tube is a piece of hea[vy] steel pipe open at both ends. A steel driving c[ore] is fitted inside this pipe and the two are driven [to]gether into the ground. When suitable driv[ing] resistance has been reached, driving is stopped a[nd] the core is removed from the tube. A thin me[tal] shell several inches smaller in diameter than t[he] driving tube is then dropped down inside the tu[be.] This thin shell is then filled with concrete and t[he] driving tube is withdrawn. With a pile of this ki[nd] the driving resistance is determined by means [of] the outer driving tube but the pile that rema[ins] in the ground is several inches smaller in diame[ter] than this tube. The carrying capacity of such [a] pile depends largely on the point resistance sin[ce] the surrounding soil may or may not come ba[ck] against the shell to provide frictional resistan[ce] along the side of the pile.

Steel pipe piles are formed by driving ordina[ry] steel pipe into the ground and filling it with co[n]crete. Sometimes a steel shoe or boot plate is us[ed] at the bottom of the pipe and the pile is then call[ed] a closed-end pipe pile. The uses of such piles a[re] about the same as those of other kinds of cast-i[n-]place concrete piles. When the bottom of the pi[pe] is left open during driving, the pile is called [an] open-end pipe pile. These open-end piles are us[u]ally driven to bearing on rock. The soil, which [is] in the pipe when driving is finished, is jetted a[nd] blown out with water and air jets and the pipe [is] then filled with concrete. Because of the cost [of] the pipe, a steel pipe pile usually costs more p[er] foot than other types of cast-in-place concrete pil[e.] However, when they are driven open-end to bea[r]ing on rock and then carefully cleaned out, pi[pe] piles are usually allowed greater loads than oth[er] kinds of concrete piles. Under such conditions t[he] high cost of the pipe is offset by the higher loadi[ng] and the consequent reduction in the number of pil[es] required to carry a given load.

The McArthur Pedestal Pile is a shell-less cas[t-]in-place concrete pile. The driving tube is a pie[ce] of heavy steel pipe which is open at both ends. [A] steel core is used inside the driving tube and t[he] two are driven together into the ground. Wh[en] sufficient driving resistance has been obtained, t[he] core is removed and a pedestal on the bottom [of] the pile is formed in the following manner. Aft[er] driving is finished and the core has been remove[d] enough concrete is dumped into the tube to fill t[he] bottom of it to a depth of five or six feet. The co[re] is then placed back in the tube on top of this co[n]crete and the tube is lifted about three feet. T[he] hammer is then operated on top of the core [in] order to drive the concrete out of the bottom of t[he] tube to form the pedestal. Sometimes several su[ch] charges of concrete are used in this manner to ma[ke] the pedestal. After the pedestal is completed, t[he] core is removed and the tube is filled with concre[te.]

to the ground surface. The shaft of the pile is en formed by the same method that is used for e straight-shaft pile.

The principal advantage of piles of this type lies the fact that they are usually the cheapest of the ncrete piles. This is due to the fact that, ordirily, the shell-less pile consists only of concrete, ereas the precast pile always has internal reinrcement and the shell types of cast-in-place pile ways have a steel shell which remains in the und. The principal criticisms of the shell-less e are based on the following facts. It is often ficult to prevent soil and water from getting xed with the fresh concrete and the finished piles e subject to distortion due to the soil stresses set by the driving of adjacent piles.

Precast concrete piles may be parallel-sided or ered. The cross-sections are usually round, ocgonal or square. Ordinarily, precast piles are signed for the particular job on which they are be used and they are then made at or near the site by the piling contractor. Sometimes they e made in pile manufacturing plants and are pped by rail or water to the job site. Railroads d State Highway Departments often have certain ndard designs for precast piles although they metimes design special piles for a particular b.

The tapered types of precast piles are usually ited in length to about 40 feet. For longer gths, the less flexible parallel-sided piles are used. ecast piles with diameters as great as 24 or even inches are sometimes used and the maximum gths that have been used up to the present time e well over 100 feet.

d   Composite piles

Composite piles came into general use about 25 30 years ago. Their development was due to an ort on the part of engineers to make use of the vantages of different types of piles in order to oduce a very long pile that was not too expensive. dinarily, a composite pile consists of a wood pile pped with a cast-in-place concrete pile. The conete section extends from the permanent ground ter level up to the pile cut-off elevation and the od pile is used below water level. Such a pile kes advantage of the low cost of a wood pile, and the same time it eliminates the necessity of the pensive sheeting, excavation and pumping that uld be required to cut off and cap the wood pile the water level. The upper end of the wood pile sometimes cut in the form of a tenon which procts up into the concrete section. All of the varis types of cast-in-place concrete piles are comned in this manner with wood piles to form mposite piles. It is necessary to fasten together e two sections of the pile so that they do not parate after they are in the ground. A number different kinds of fastenings have been devel-

oped for this purpose. Also it is necessary to provide a seal between the pile shell and the wood pile so as to exclude mud and water from the joint. Composite piles are also made with precast concrete piles superimposed on wood piles. The precast section is cast with a recess in its lower end to receive the tenon of the wood pile and various devices are used to fasten the two sections of the pile together.

e   Steel H piles

A comparatively recent development in the piling industry is the use of rolled structural shapes as bearing piles. The profile usually used for this purpose is that known as the H-beam. This type of pile has proved to be especially useful for trestle structures in which the pile extends above the ground line and serves not only as a pile but also as a column. Because of the small cross-sectional area of these piles, they can often be driven into river bottoms of dense gravel into which it would be very difficult to drive a displacement pile even with the aid of jetting. By displacement pile is meant any pile with a solid cross-section of considerable area. However, this ability of the H-beam pile to penetrate easily into dense materials works to its disadvantage in other kinds of soil conditions. In many cases bearing piles are used to support loads simply by friction between the pile and the surrounding soil. In other cases, piles are used primarily for compaction. Under such conditions, particularly when compaction is the principal purpose of the pile, a considerably longer H-beam pile is required to carry the same load that can be supported by a shorter displacement pile. Where the H-beam pile is exposed to air or where it is alternately wet and dry, it is subject to the same corrosive action that would occur to any other steel structure under the same conditions. In some installations the upper ends of H-beam piles have been encased in concrete from the permanent ground water level up to the pile cut-off.

f   The design of pile foundations may be divided into two parts—the determination of the number of piles and their grouping, and the design of the pile cap. The previous discussion has not touched upon the allowable loads on piles. Piles are usually driven to carry their load in accordance with one of the generally accepted formulae—usually the *Engineering News* formula. The maximum loading to which they are to be driven, however, must be assumed by the engineer in order to determine the number of piles to be used. For wood piles, the usual code limitation is 500 psi of the right section of the pile at mid length. This limitation, of course, requires the assumption of sizes within the usual code limitations, and common office practice limits wood piles to a capacity of 15 to 20 tons each.

For concrete piles of any type, the permissible load is governed by the code or agency under which the designer is working. Common practice, unless otherwise specified, is to design for either 30 or 40 tons per pile, although frequently codes permit greater loads.

Rolled structural steel H piles are usually limited to 9,000 psi of section.

The spacing of piles is limited by the compressibility of the material in which they are driven and to some extent by the displacement of the pile. Ordinarily it is impracticable to drive wood piles closer than 2 ft 6 in. on centers in each direction. Although steel H piles may be driven 2 ft 6 in. on centers, if the piles are heavily loaded the rock bearing at the tip may be the controlling factor, and it is advisable to use a 3-ft spacing for steel piles as well as concrete.

Although piles may be spotted accurately when they are started, the chances are that obstructions below grade will divert them so that they will often "creep" in driving as much as 6 in. It is therefore good practice to stagger piles under a wall, and to use not less than three piles under a column or pier. This will frequently control to some extent the number of piles required since, because of this limitation, some piles may be loaded to only a fraction of their capacity.

g   The general layout of pile caps is shown in Fig. 8.13. The design of pile caps is similar to the design of footings as described in Art. 8.11. The following requirements from the ACI Code apply:

[From Sec. 1202(*d*)]   In the case of footings on piles, computations for moments and shears may be based on the assumption that the reaction from any pile is concentrated at the center of the pile.

[From Sec. 1205(*a*)]   The critical section for shear to be used as a measure of diagonal tension shall be assumed as a vertical section obtained by passing a series of vertical planes through the footing, each of which is parallel to a corresponding

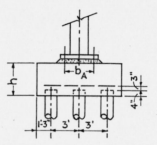

Fig. 8.13   Typical Pile Cap

face of the column, pedestal or wall, and located distance therefrom equal to one-half the depth for footings on piles.

[From Sec. 1205(*f*)]   In computing the exterr shear on any section through a footing support on piles, the entire reaction from any pile who center is located 6 in. or more outside the secti shall be assumed as producing shear on the sectio the reaction from any pile whose center is locat 6 in. or more inside the section shall be assumed producing no shear on the section. For interme ate positions of the pile center, the portion of t pile reaction to be assumed as producing she on the section shall be based on a straight l interpolation between full value at 6 in. outsi the section and zero value at 6 in. inside t section.

h   Standard pile-cap designs using up nine piles are shown in Table 8.4. The valu given are the values frequently used for wo piles (30 kips), concrete piles (60 kips), a steel H piles (100 kips). Other values may prorated and computed as illustrated in t following problem.

Problem   Design a pile foundation for column load of 450 kips, using concrete pil which may be driven to support 40 tons eac The average b_a of steel column and billet 17.22 in.

If we assume the net pile load at 90 perce of the pile value, it will be 72 kips, and will require

$$\frac{450}{72} = 6.25, \text{ or } 7 \text{ piles}$$

By comparison with Table 8.4, we will st with an assumed depth of 3 ft 2 in., or depth d of 31 in.

$$b_a + d = 48.22 \text{ in.}$$

In a seven-pile footing, the center distan

Table 8.4   Pile Caps

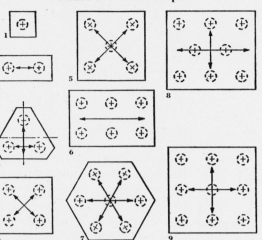

No. of piles	Pile value, kips	Column load, kips	b_a, in.	h	Reinforcement each way
1	30	28		1'7''	
	60	58		1'7''	
	100	98		1'7''	
2	30	56	$8\frac{1}{8}$	1'10''	5 No. 5
	60	115	$9\frac{1}{4}$	2'5''	5 No. 6
	100	194	$10\frac{3}{4}$	2'9''	5 No. 7
3	30	85	$8\frac{1}{8}$	1'10''	5 No. 6
	60	174	$10\frac{1}{4}$	2'3''	5 No. 7
	100	243	$12\frac{1}{2}$	2'4''	7 No. 7
4	30	111	9	2'0''	5 No. 6
	60	229	$12\frac{1}{4}$	2'6''	5 No. 7
	100	388	$15\frac{1}{4}$	2'6''	6 No. 7
5	30	135	$9\frac{1}{2}$	2'0''	5 No. 7
	60	282	13	2'7''	5 No. 8
	100	480	$17\frac{1}{2}$	3'1''	6 No. 8
6	30	164	$10\frac{1}{4}$	2'4''	5 No. 7
	60	340	$14\frac{3}{4}$	2'9''	6 No. 8
	100	570	$18\frac{1}{2}$	3'2''	6 No. 9
7	30	192	$10\frac{3}{4}$	2'5''	4 No. 7
	60	396	$15\frac{1}{2}$	3'2''	4 No. 8
	100	670	$19\frac{3}{4}$	3'9''	4 No. 9
8	30	215	11	2'7''	6 No. 6
	60	450	17	3'1''	6 No. 7
	100	760	$20\frac{1}{2}$	3'8''	6 No. 8
9	30	243	$12\frac{1}{2}$	2'8''	5 No. 7
	60	504	$17\frac{3}{4}$	3'5''	5 No. 8
	100	858	$21\frac{3}{4}$	4'2''	6 No. 8

Note: Reinforcement shown is amount required for each arrow in sketch. Pile spacing is 3 ft o.c. throughout. Edge distance is 1 ft 3 in.

between outside piles (in the plan of Table 8.4) is 6 ft. Therefore no part of the two outside piles is within the shear width of 48.22 in. The top and bottom piles in the diagram are centered 2 ft $7\frac{1}{2}$ in. from the center line, 5 ft $2\frac{1}{2}$ in., or $62\frac{1}{2}$ in., between outside piles. In accordance with Art. 8.13g the inner edge of piles is $62\frac{1}{2}$ in. minus 12 in., or $50\frac{1}{2}$ in. between outside piles. Therefore six piles are outside the shear lines. Use bars in three directions.

The load causing shear is

$$\tfrac{6}{7} \text{ of } 450,000 = 386 \text{ kips}$$

The shear capacity is

$$48.22 \times 4 \times 31 \times 0.875 \times 75 = 393 \text{ kips}$$

The moment arm is

$$\frac{72 \text{ in.} - 17.22 \text{ in.}}{2} = 27.39 \text{ in.}$$

The moment is

$$M = \tfrac{450}{7} \times 27.39 \text{ in.} = 1,760 \text{ in.-kips}$$
$$A_s = \frac{0.85 \times 1,760}{0.875 \times 20 \times 31} = 2.85 = 7 \text{ No. 6}$$
$$\Sigma_o = \frac{0.85 \times \tfrac{450}{7}}{0.875 \times 31 \times 240} = 8.4 \text{ in.} = 4 \text{ No. 6}$$

Therefore moment is the determining factor, and we will use 7 No. 6 in each of the three directions.

8.14   Caisson foundations

a   Article 8.10b refers to caisson foundations as a fourth type of column foundation. Formerly, pneumatic caissons were used for practically all caisson jobs where water was encountered during excavation to rock. Now many jobs which formerly would have been pneumatic-caisson jobs are open-caisson work instead, owing to improved methods.

b   In general, the pneumatic caisson is constructed as shown in Figs. 8.14 and 8.15. As the shaft is sunk, first the steel cylinder around the working chamber is filled with concrete, then the working chamber, and then the shaft; finally, the air lock is removed for use on another caisson. This question is from a state license examination: "Explain briefly the operation of a pneumatic caisson. Illus-

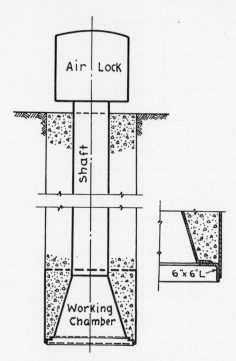

Fig. 8.14 Pneumatic Caisson

trate with a schematic diagram." The description and diagram given should be satisfactory as an answer for this problem.

c Open caissons are installed by several methods. In stiff to hard nonplastic clay, walls or pits may sometimes be excavated to rock with no support whatever. Often wood or steel sheet piling is used, being driven down as the excavating proceeds. Where the clay will stand to a depth of 4 or 5 ft, the poling-board method, or Chicago lagging method, is used. In this procedure a hole is dug about 5 ft deep and of the size required, then wood sheeting is placed and held in position by a steel internal ring or by wood supports. Then another 5-ft depth is excavated and the process repeated. This system is not workable if the soil is not stiff enough to stand.

There are several newer methods, all patented by the various foundation companies. One system—the Gow method—uses a series of telescoping cylinders in lengths of 8 ft or more, each successive cylinder being 2 in. less in diameter than the one above. The excavating is done by means of a large earth auger, and the excavation may be belled out at the

base. Steel cylinders are placed as the excavation proceeds. When the bearing material is reached, the caisson is sealed, driving the bottom cylinder in to stop any inflow of water. Concrete is placed, and the cylinders withdrawn. Occasionally, if pumps cannot control the inflow of water, the caisson bottoms must be cleaned by divers and sealed by concrete tremied into the water.

d The design of a caisson, either open or pneumatic, is a simple problem in compression. Building codes vary greatly on matters of caisson designs; the subject is frequently omitted completely. Without citing the codes from which the various clauses are taken, the following may be taken as governing good design of open caissons. For caissons or piers where the subsoil material furnishes proper lateral stability, use a maximum allowable axial compressive stress of $0.25f_c'$, but not over 850 psi. Where permanent lateral support is not provided, the allowable working stress should be reduced in accordance with the following formula, where H is the height and D the diameter.

$$f = f_c \left(1.3 - \frac{H}{20D} \right)$$

except that f may not exceed 850 psi.

Open caissons are normally limited to a minimum diameter of 2 ft, but if manual work is required, a practical minimum is 3 ft.

When constructed of reinforced concrete, and properly supported laterally, the caisson may be designed in accordance with the requirements of the ACI Code for columns as given in Art. 7.20.

Since the caisson ordinarily is cylindrical and the billet square, it is desirable to increase the bearing capacity at the top of the caisson to cut down the size of the billet and consequent overhang which requires an enlargement of the top of the caisson. This increase in bearing value is accomplished by putting spiral reinforcement in the upper 3 ft of the caisson in accordance with the design of spirally hooped columns. This procedure is shown in detail in Fig. 8.15, and may increase the bearing capacity at the top of the caisson to 1,000 psi. The billet must be designed for

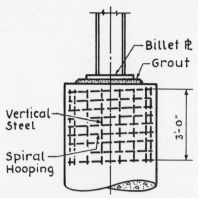

Fig. 8.15   Spiral Reinforcement—Top of Caisson

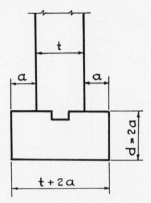

Fig. 8.16   Offset Footing

the special condition, however, and cannot be taken directly from the load table. The original design of a caisson does not offer any great problem, but frequently a redesign must be made in a hurry when obstacles such as boulders are encountered that cause eccentricity or a reduction in the size of the base. A common specification requires that if the stress in the caisson due to eccentricity of rock bearing increases the total design stress by over 10 percent, a like increase in strength must be provided.

Another common specification requirement is that: "The actual axis of any caisson shall not vary from its designed axis by more than 1/60th of the depth of any horizontal section. The center of any caisson at any horizontal section shall not deviate from its actual axis by more than 5 percent of the diameter. The full sectional area of any caisson must be maintained throughout." The actual stress due to eccentricity may be computed from Art. 1.60. From this formula it will be noted that the maximum eccentricity allowable without revision of design is 0.2 in. per foot of diameter. Allowable stress on a caisson may be increased by improving the quality of the mix or by putting in 1 percent or more of vertical steel, properly hooped in accordance with the column design given in Art. 7.20.

8.15   Concrete wall footings

a   Offset wall footings as shown in Fig. 8.16 are often used for practical reasons even though they may not be required to spread

the load. Frequently, the general excavation is carried to the elevation of the top of the footing and the wall-footing excavation made neat below this level without forming. Into this excavation the concrete is poured, providing a firm foundation on which to start the wall forming. The cheaper and surer wall forming thus provided usually will more than offset the cost of the small amount of extra concrete. For this purpose, the minimum offset *a* should be 4 in., and the depth 8 in. A 2×4 should be embedded in the top of the wet concrete to provide a key for the wall.

b   If a concrete wall footing is poured for the purpose of carrying wall load, it should, if possible, be concentric with the wall above. If the wall is on the lot line so that the footing offset must be omitted on one side, the wall footing should be checked for eccentricity. Under these conditions, an offset of over half the wall thickness is useless, because when the offset is half the wall thickness, the eccentricity is one-sixth the footing width, and the soil pressure varies from zero at the edge of the offset to double the average at the outside edge.

To check the maximum soil pressure, the formula for trapezoidal loading (Art. 8.10) should be used:

$$f = \frac{P}{A} \left(1 \pm \frac{6e}{b} \right)$$

An illustration of this method is given in the following problem.

Problem 1   Assume a bearing wall with a load of 8,000 lb per running foot from a wall

16 in. thick, with a 6-in. offset inside. Compute the maximum soil pressure.

$$f = \frac{8,000}{1.83}\left(1 + \frac{6 \times 3}{22}\right) = 7,950 \text{ psf}$$

c Plain concrete is preferable for most wall footings. The depth may be governed by any one of several factors. If the offset required is not over 6 in. on either side of the wall, the depth may be made twice the offset, and computation of stresses may be omitted. This assumes a uniform stress distribution over an area enclosed by the width indicated in Fig. 8.16. If the depth thus obtained is excessive, the proper depth should be obtained by assuming a uniform upward soil pressure on a strip of footing 1 ft wide on a cantilever span of a, and computing the depth to resist moment and shear in a plain-concrete beam as described in Art. 5.12.

Problem 2 Assume a 16-in. wall with a load of 12,000 lb per running foot, bearing on a soil with a capacity of 3,000 psf. Design the footing, using a 3,000-psi plain-concrete footing.

The footing width is 12,000/3,000 = 4 ft = 48 in., and the wall thickness is 16 in. The offset a is $\frac{48 - 16}{2} = 16$ in. The moment on the cantilever is

$$M = (3 \times 1.33) \times 8 = 32 \text{ in.-kips}$$

From Art. 5.12, $f_c = 150$ lb. Then the section modulus S of the footing is

$$S = \frac{32,000}{150} = 213.3$$

Since the section modulus of a rectangle $= bd^2/6$,

$$d_m = \sqrt{\frac{213.3 \times 6}{12}} = \sqrt{106.7} = 10.4 \text{ in.}$$

Use 12 in.

The area producing shear is 16 in. − 12 in. or 4 in. wide, which is negligible. Therefore the depth will be controlled by moment.

d If the load is such that a plain-concrete footing would be too deep for economy, reinforcement should be added in the lower face. An illustration of the calculations involved is shown in the following problem.

Problem 3 Assume a 16-in. wall with a load of 30,000 lb per foot of length, with a soil pressure of 5,000 psf. The width of footing required will be 30,000/5,000 = 6 ft. The offset a will be 28 in., and the moment on the cantilever will be

$$M = (2.33 \times 5) \times 14 = 163,300 \text{ in.-lb}$$

To check this first for a plain-concrete footing,

$$S = \frac{163,300}{150} = 1,088$$

$$d = \sqrt{544} = 23.3 \text{ in.}$$

Use 24 in.

For a reinforced-concrete footing, using 3,000-psi concrete, from Art. 5.11, for $f_s = 20,000$ lb and $f_c' = 3,000$, $f_c = 1,350$. Then K is 236 and $Kbd^2 = 163,300$, or

$$d = \sqrt{\frac{163,300}{12 \times 236}} = \sqrt{57.8} = 7.6 \text{ in. net}$$

To check this depth for shear:

$$\text{Width producing shear} = \frac{72 - [16(2 \times 7.6)]}{2} = 20.4 \text{ in.}$$

$$\text{Load outside the shear line} = \frac{20.4}{72} \times 30,000 = 8,500$$

This would produce a unit shear of

$$\frac{8,500}{0.875 \times 12 \times 7.6} = 106.5 \text{ psi}$$

against an allowable limit of 75 psi

Try 10 in. net depth:

$$\text{Width producing shear} = \frac{72 - (16 + 20)}{2} = 18 \text{ in.}$$

$$\text{Load in shear} \qquad = \tfrac{18}{72} \times 30,000 = 7,500$$

he unit shear is

$$\frac{7,500}{0.875 \times 12 \times 10} = 71.3 \text{ psi}$$

$$A_s = \frac{163.3}{17.5 \times 10} = 0.935 \text{ sq in. per lin ft}$$

Jse No. 6 bars, $5\frac{1}{2}$ in. o.c. Total depth of footing is 10 in. + 4 in. = 1 ft 2 in. (see Fig. 8.17).

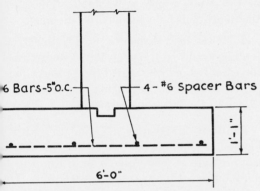

Fig. 8.17   Reinforced-Concrete Wall Footing

.20   MASONRY WALLS AND PIERS

a   Masonry walls and piers include bearng walls, piers, and buttresses constructed of tone, brick, structural clay tile, architectural erra cotta, and concrete masonry units oonded together with mortar.

Aside from resistance to fire (which is discussed in Art. 1.42) and weather, the principal structural requirement of a bearing wall s resistance to vertical loads. This, however, may be combined with resistance to bending, either through eccentricity of loading, which s almost always present, or to unbalanced

roof thrust or direct wind load. The discussion of this last factor—wind load—appears in Art. 10.21, since it is usually a factor which applies only to low steel buildings.

b   Building codes generally set up two sets of controls for bearing walls:

1. Maximum permissible bearing load per square inch for different materials.
2. Minimum wall thickness for walls of various heights within a single story and in different stories of multistory wall-bearing buildings.

Usually the latter is the only controlling requirement that matters. If you are working under a specific code, the limitations above should be ascertained before proceeding with the design. In the absence of any code requirements, the following requirements from the New York City Code may be accepted as good practice for permissible bearing loads.

The generally accepted code for the second controlling criterion given above is the building code recommended by the National Board of Fire Underwriters. These wall thicknesses and permissible heights are shown in Fig. 8.18. The maximum length of window and door

Table 8.5   Allowable Bearing on Masonry

Material	Using lime-cement mortar, psi	Using cement mortar, psi
Brick	250	325
Brick (with crushing strength over 4,500 psi)	$8\frac{1}{3}\%$ of crushing strength, not over 500	10% of crushing strength, not over 500
Clay tile, cells horizontal (on gross area)	60	70
Concrete-block masonry	$8\frac{1}{3}\%$ of crushing strength (usually 80)	10% of crushing strength (usually 80)
Granite	640	800
Limestone	400	500
Marble	400	500
Sandstone	250	300

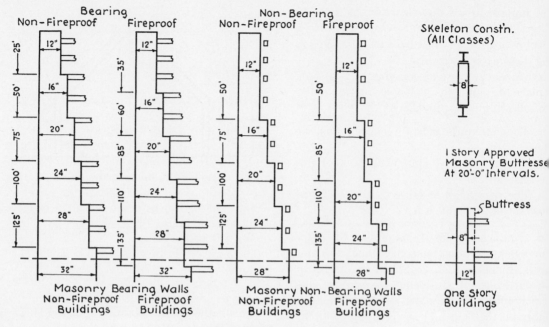

Fig. 8.18 Masonry Walls

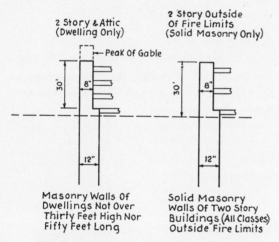

Fig. 8.18 Masonry Walls (Continued)

openings in any wall section must not exceed 50 percent of the length unless the wall thickness is increased 4 in. for each 15 percent of added openings, and the maximum percentage of openings must not exceed 75 percent. This, however, does not preclude the use of solid masonry piers in place of columns, as described in paragraph c following. Piers between windows must be checked on the basis of Table 8.5.

Most building departments require tha walls shall be bonded by means of heade courses every fifth or sixth course, or som other type of masonry bond, if the full thick ness of wall is to be considered as acting Metal wall anchors are only given considera tion as bonding facing to backup, but not fo the purpose of figuring the full wall thicknes in Fig. 8.18. Where metal wall anchors ar used, only the thickness of backup is used a wall thickness.

If brick facing is used with tile or concrete block backup, the bearing strength of the entire wall is taken at the lesser value rathe than at the bearing value of the brick. I steel beams bear on a wall of this kind, it i common practice to design the bearing plate for a load of 250 psi and to put in a brick bearing pad of the required width, toothec into the masonry to a depth below the bear ing plate equal to the width of the pad.

Solid masonry walls must be supported lat erally at intervals not exceeding 18 times the wall thickness in the top story and 20 time the wall thickness elsewhere. For walls o brick and tile, these intervals become 16 anc 18 times the thickness, respectively. This lat ral support may be by floors, if the distance is vertical, or by crosswalls, piers, buttresses, or columns, properly bonded when the controlling distance is horizontal.

c Masonry piers or columns may be used in place of columns in wall construction under the following code provisions:

1. The minimum side dimension must be 12 in.

2. The maximum height shall be 10 times the least side.

3. The maximum stresses shall not exceed those set up in Table 8.5.

d Nonbearing partitions of clay tile, gypsum block, or other masonry should be not less in thickness than 1/48th of the height of the partition. (Some codes require not less than 1/40th.) These partitions must be built solidly on the floor and wedged solidly to the underside of the slab above so that they obtain a lateral support from the slab.

e The design of masonry buttresses to resist lateral as well as vertical pressure is now seldom required, since the bending is normally taken by steel or reinforced concrete, the masonry being used for architectural purposes only. If a masonry buttress is used to resist thrust of a hammer-beam truss, a vaulted roof, or other lateral thrust, or a combined vertical and lateral load, it involves a graphical or analytical method of vector analysis combining the superimposed load with the weight of the top stone, and making the base of the top stone wide enough so that the resultant intersects the joint within the middle third of the top stone. The new resultant is used as the applied load, and is combined with the weight of the second stone in the same manner, etc., until the load is transferred to the foundation. Figure 8.19 indicates the method as applied to a buttress. The general method of each step corresponds to the method of solution of a retaining wall footing as given in Art. 8.30*b*.

Problem Assume a church roof with the cross section shown in Fig. 8.19. The rigid frames are spaced 14 ft apart and carry a total load of 50 lb per square foot of roof area.

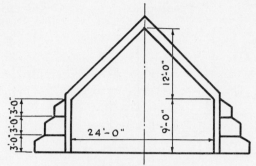

Fig. 8.19 Buttress Design

Design a stone buttress for this rigid frame, using stone weighing 160 lb per cu ft, and buttresses 2 ft wide.

The horizontal thrust H of this type of rigid frame is

$$H = \frac{5wL^2}{32h}$$

where h is the rise of the truss. The total load wL is $50 \times 14 \times 24 = 16.8$ kips, and the vertical reaction is 8.4.

$$H = \frac{5 \times 16.8 \times 24}{32 \times 12} = 5.25$$

The top 3-ft section of the buttress weighs

$$2 \text{ ft } 8 \text{ in. (avg ht.)} \times 3 \times 2 \times 160 = 2.56 \text{ kips}$$

The total load at the bottom of the section is $8.4 + 2.56 = 10.96$, and the diversion of stress line in this height is

$$\frac{5.25}{10.96} \times 3 = 1.44$$

Center of gravity of vertical loads from inner face:

$$
\begin{array}{l}
8.4 \ \times 0.33 = 2.8 \\
\underline{2.56 \times 1.5 \ = 3.84} \\
10.96 \qquad\qquad 6.64
\end{array}
$$

$$x = \frac{6.64}{10.96} = 0.605$$

$$\text{Diversion} = \underline{1.44}$$

$$\text{Intersection of base of section} = \overline{2.04}$$

$$\text{Outer edge of middle third} \ \ = 2.0$$

Therefore, the upper section is satisfactory if the pier is properly bonded to adjacent wall.

The middle 3-ft section weighs

$$
\begin{array}{l}
3 \times 4.5 \times 2 \times 160 = \ \ 4.32 \\
\text{Load from above} = \underline{10.96} \\
\qquad\qquad\qquad\qquad\quad 15.28
\end{array}
$$

$$\text{Diversion} = \frac{5.25}{15.28} \times 3.0 = 1.03$$

Point of application at top of section $= \dfrac{2.04}{3.07}$

Outer edge of middle third $= 3.0$

Therefore, the middle section is satisfactory if the pier is properly bonded to adjacent wall.

The bottom 3-ft section weighs

$$3 \times 6 \times 2 \times 160 = \quad 5.77$$
$$\text{Load from above} = \underline{15.28}$$
$$21.05$$

$$\text{Diversion} = \frac{5.25}{21.08} \times 3 = 0.75$$

Point of application at top of section $= \dfrac{3.07}{3.82}$

Outer edge of middle third $= 4.0$

Therefore, the buttress is satisfactory throughout.

f Reinforced-concrete building walls not subject to lateral stresses may also be classed as masonry walls. In the absence of other governing data, the following paragraphs taken from the ACI Code, Sec. 1112, may be considered as good design:

The allowable working stresses in reinforced concrete bearing walls with minimum reinforcement of .0025 times the cross sectional area of the wall, shall be $0.25f_c'$ for walls having a ratio of height to thickness of 10 or less, and shall be reduced proportionately to $15f_c'$ for walls having a ratio of height to thickness of 25.

Panel and enclosure walls of reinforced concrete shall have a thickness of not less than five inches, and not less than $\frac{1}{30}$ of the distance between the supporting or enclosing members.

Bearing walls of reinforced concrete shall be not less than six inches thick for the uppermost fifteen feet of their height, increasing one inch in thickness for every 25 feet or fraction thereof.

Reinforced concrete bearing walls shall have a thickness of at least $\frac{1}{25}$ of the unsupported height or width, whichever is the shorter, provided, however, that approved buttresses, built in columns, or piers designed to carry all the vertical loads may be used in lieu of increased thickness.

Reinforced concrete walls shall be anchored to floors, columns, pilasters, buttresses and intersecting walls with reinforcement at least equivalent to three-eighths inch round bars, twelve inches on centers for each layer of wall reinforcement.

Reinforced concrete walls shall be reinforced with an area of steel in each direction, both vertical and horizontal, at least equal to 0.0025 times the cross sectional area of the wall if of bars, and .0018 times the area if of electrically welded wire fabric, of not less than No. 10 ga. wires. Walls

more than 10 inches in thickness shall have the reinforcement for each direction placed in two layers, parallel with the faces of the wall. One layer consisting of not less than one-half nor more than two-thirds the total required, shall be placed not less than 2 in. nor more than one-third the thickness of the wall from the exterior surface. The other layer, comprising the balance of the required reinforcement shall be placed not less than $\frac{3}{4}$ in. nor more than one-third the thickness of the wall from the interior surface. Bars shall be not less than three-eighths inch round and shall be spaced not over 18 in. o.c.

In addition to the minimum steel prescribed above, there shall be not less than two five-eighths inch round bars around all window openings, extending at least 24 in. beyond the corner of the openings.

In accordance with the requirements stated above, the following reinforcement would be required in walls of various thickness.

For a 5-in. wall: one layer, No. 3, 9 in. o.c.

For a 6-in. wall: one layer, No. 3, $7\frac{1}{2}$ in. o.c.

For an 8-in. wall: one layer, No. 4, 10 in. o.c.

For a 10-in. wall: two layers, each No. 3, 9 in. o.c.

For a 12-in. wall: two layers, each No. 3, $7\frac{1}{2}$ in. o.c.

For a 14-in. wall: two layers, each No. 4, $11\frac{1}{2}$ in. o.c.

For a 16-in. wall: two layers, each No. 4, 10 in. o.c.

For an 18-in. wall: two layers, each No. 4, 9 in. o.c.

g It will be noted that these requirements are specifically for "reinforced-concrete walls," and must be followed when the authority under which the work is being done requires it. However, even walls which are normally classified as plain-concrete walls should be provided with at least two No. 6 bars, spaced about 2 in. below the top edge and two No. 6 bars 2 in. above the footing in any wall to arrest shrinkage cracking or to assist in spanning over soft spots in the footing. The small additional cost is amply paid for by the greater freedom from cracks.

8.30 RETAINING WALLS

a The design of a retaining wall requires that it be so constructed that

1. The wall will not overturn

2. The soil pressure under the toe will not exceed the allowable bearing value of the soil in question

3. The wall will not move outward bodily due to thrust

4. The wall or any of its component parts will not rupture

b The forces acting on any wall are the horizontal thrust P_H derived from the various formulae in Art. 8.30*c* and the vertical load V of the wall and all other vertical loads on the wall. In order to avoid the danger of overturning, the line of the resultant of these two forces should pass within the middle third of the base of the wall. Referring to Art. 8.10*i*, it will be seen that if the center of pressure comes within the middle third, the pressure diagram is a trapezoid. If it comes right at the edge of the middle third, the eccentricity is one-sixth and the pressure diagram becomes a triangle; the pressure at the toe is double the normal pressure and at the heel is zero. If the center of pressure falls outside the middle third, that is, if the eccentricity exceeds one-sixth, there is an uplift at the inner edge, and the structure may or may not be stable. Therefore, good practice requires that the line of intersection shall lie within the middle third of the base.

The maximum soil pressure under the toe of the wall should not exceed the maximum soil pressure allowed by the code, or as noted in Art. 8.10*c*. This maximum soil pressure is determined by means of the formula in Art. 8.10*i*.

Resistance to sliding is furnished in two ways: by friction on the base and by direct compressive resistance of the earth in front of the toe of the wall. Friction may be taken to furnish a resistance of $0.5V$. In other words, if the total horizontal thrust is not over half the weight of the wall, the friction alone is sufficient to prevent sliding without the compressive resistance. The lateral compressive resistance at the base is resisted by a counter pressure, or "passive pressure," which is discussed in Art. 8.30*f* following.

c The fundamental law of fluid pressure states that the lateral pressure from a fluid

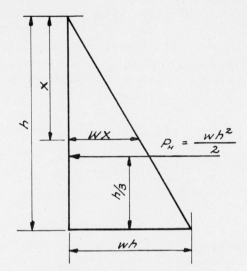

Fig. 8.20   Fluid Pressure Diagram

against the wall of any container is a unit pressure equal to the weight of the fluid times the depth to the level under consideration. In other words, at depth x the unit pressure is

$$w_x = wx$$

Based on triangular loading, therefore, the loading diagram is as indicated in Fig. 8.20, and the total pressure on a strip one foot wide is

$$P_H = \frac{wh^2}{2}$$

Water, or any other liquid, is a true fluid and exerts full pressure on the wall:

$$w_x = 62.5x$$

and

$$P_H = 31.25h^2$$

This law of fluid pressure is applicable also to the design of retaining walls carrying the lateral pressure from earth or other solids. The simplest method of retaining-wall computation is to convert the lateral pressure into an equivalent fluid pressure. For a level bank behind the wall, the equivalent fluid pressure may be found from the following formulae:

$$w_e = w \tan^2\left(45° - \frac{\phi}{2}\right)$$

and

$$P_H = \frac{w_e h^2}{2}$$

where w_e is the equivalent fluid pressure, w the weight of earth per cubic foot, and ϕ the

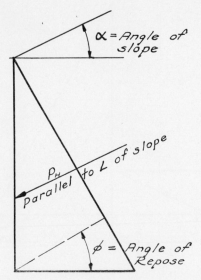

Fig. 8.21   Pressure Diagram for Sloping Surcharge

angle of repose of the material. Table 8.6 gives the weight and equivalent pressures of the various materials ordinarily encountered. For ordinary clay or sand and gravel, w_e may be taken as 25 psf, or as many engineers use it, 30 psf.

d   If the bank is inclined above the top of the wall, as shown in Fig. 8.21, the equivalent fluid pressure becomes,

$$w_e = \frac{w \cos^2 \phi}{\left[1 + \sqrt{\dfrac{\sin \phi \sin (\phi - \alpha)}{\cos \alpha}}\right]^2}$$

When α, the angle of slope, is equal to ϕ, the angle of repose, which is the limiting slope,

$$w_e = w \cos^2 \phi$$

For ordinary earth or clay on natural slope, w_e becomes 64 lb, and substituting the value in the formulae of Art. 8.30c,

$$w_e = 64h$$
$$P_H = 32h^2$$

The pressure for other materials under this type of loading is given in Table 8.6 as "Equivalent slope pressure."

e   Figure 8.22 indicates the pressure diagram of a wall which retains earth pressure and is loaded with a surcharge such as would result from street traffic, railway traffic, etc. The pressures w_e and P_H in the triangles are obtained from the formulae of Art. 8.30c. The

Table 8.6   Weight, Angle of Repose, and Equivalent Pressure of Various Materials

Material	Slope of repose	Angle of repose	Weight per cu ft., lb	Equivalent liquid pressure, psf	Equivalent slope pressure, psf	Passive pressure, psf
Dry ashes	1 on 1	45°	40	6.9	20.0	233
Cinders, bituminous dry	1 on 1	45°	45	7.7	22.5	262
Clay in lumps, dry	1 on 1⅓	36°52′	63	15.8	40.4	252
Clay, damp, plastic	1 on 3	18°26′	110	57.1	99.0	210
Clay, sand, and gravel, dry	1 on 1⅓	36°52′	100	25.0	64.0	400
Earth, dry, loose	1 on 1⅓	36°52′	76	19.0	48.8	304
Earth, dry, packed	1 on 1⅓	36°52′	95	23.8	61.0	380
Earth, moist, packed	1 on 1	45°	96	16.5	48.0	458
Earth, soft mud, packed	1 on 3	18°26′	115	59.7	103.5	220
Gravel, dry	1 on 1⅓	36°52′	104	26.0	66.5	416
Limestone, crushed, dry	1 on 1	45°	85	14.6	42.5	494
Sand, dry	1 on 1½	33°41′	106	30.4	73.5	370
Shale, crushed	1 on 1⅓	36°52′	105	26.3	67.2	420
Slag, crushed	1 on 1⅓	36°52′	72	18.0	46.1	288
Slag screenings	1 on 1⅓	36°52′	117	29.3	75.0	468
Coal, bituminous	1 on 1⅓	36°52′	50	12.5	32.0	200
Coal, anthracite	1 on 2	26°34′	60	23.0	48.0	157
Coke	1 on 1⅓	36°52′	30	7.5	19.2	120
Iron ore	1 on 1⅓	36°52′	300	75.0	192.0	1,200

unit pressure on the rectangle w_{se} is obtained from the formula,

$$w_{se} = w_s \tan^2\left(45° - \frac{\phi}{2}\right)$$

The rectangle of pressure causes a total thrust

$$P_H = w_{se}h$$

This pressure is applied at a height $h/2$. The total combined equivalent fluid horizontal pressure for ordinary earth pressure becomes

$$P_H = P_{H\triangle} + P_{H\square} = 12.5h(0.02w_s + h)$$

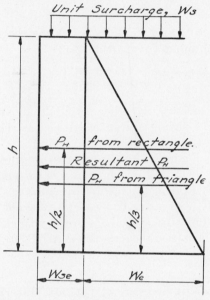

Fig. 8.22   Pressure Diagram for Ordinary Surcharge

The point of application of the combined pressure P is

$$h_1 = \frac{h}{3}\left(\frac{w_s + 300h}{w_s + 200h}\right)$$

It may be better understood if we state that the weight of surcharge is converted into equivalent fluid earth pressure of a height equal to w_s/w and the area and center of gravity of the rectangular and triangular load diagrams determined.

f In Art. 8.30*b* reference was made to the compressive resistance of the earth in front of the toe of the wall, or the passive pressure. The extent of the passive pressure at the maximum is

$$w = w \tan^2\left(45° + \frac{\phi}{2}\right)$$

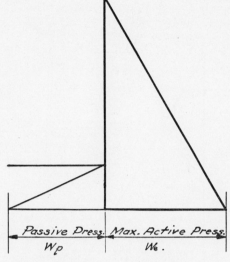

Fig. 8.23   Passive Pressure

Note the similarity to the formula for equivalent active pressure. The resistance due to passive pressure is used as indicated in Fig. 8.23.

g The simplest type of retaining wall is the plain-concrete wall or masonry wall shown in Fig. 8.24. For the wall with no surcharge, the design consists of five steps:

1. Compute the thrust P_H from the formulae in Art. 8.30*c* and its point of application.

2. Assume a wall on the basis that b, the base width, is $0.415h$ and the top width is $b/6$. Compute the weight and center of gravity of the wall.

3. Locate either graphically or analytically the point at which the resultant of the horizontal and vertical forces cuts the base. If

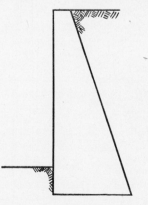

Fig. 8.24   Gravity-Type Retaining Wall

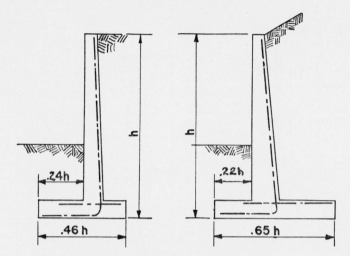

Fig. 8.25   T-Shaped Retaining Wall

it falls outside the middle third, vary the assumed width and revise until it comes within the middle third.

4. Check the assumed section for sliding due to thrust. In a footing of this type, it will ordinarily check satisfactorily. The frictional resistance on the base may be taken as 0.50, or in other words, if the thrust P_H is not greater than half the downward weight, the frictional resistance alone will resist sliding. In addition to this factor, the toe of the wall should be set below frost line, and when the earth has been tamped and settled against the face of the wall, it will resist a pressure equal to the passive pressure.

5. Compute the maximum soil pressure under the toe of the wall. If it exceeds the allowable soil pressure, revise the wall accordingly.

If the wall is surcharged, the width of the base will be about 0.52h instead of 0.415h as given above. If the vertical surface is on the face of the wall and the sloped surface on the back, the downward load is made up of the trapezoid of masonry acting through its center of gravity and a triangle of earth acting through its center of gravity, and the resultant weight and center of gravity must be computed. This wall is not so efficient as a wall with a sloped face, and the width of base

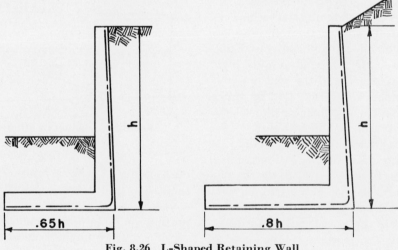

Fig. 8.26   L-Shaped Retaining Wall

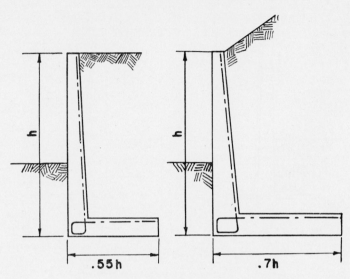

Fig. 8.27 Reversed-L Retaining Wall

should be about 0.55*h*, or for sloping surcharge, *b* is 0.7*h*.

Tables 8.7 and 8.8 are taken from the pubcations of the Portland Cement Association nd give recommended sizes for gravity-type walls of lower heights.

h For most retaining walls, the so-called einforced-concrete cantilever retaining wall s usually less costly than the mass-type wall escribed in Art. 8.30*g*. In general, there are hree types in use. The most economical is n inverted T shape (Fig. 8.25) in which the ooting projects beyond the face of the wall n both directions. If the wall retains earth ressure from a neighboring lot which is igher, so that all parts of the wall must be within the lower lot, an L shape (Fig. 8.26) hould be used. If the wall retains high ground, so that all parts of the wall must be on the higher lot, a reversed L (Fig. 8.27) should be used. The approximate dimensions of walls are given in the illustrations.

Tables 8.9 and 8.10 (from the Portland Cement Association) give details of design for a wall of the reversed L shape. Since the design of the wall itself has nothing to do with the design of the base, this wall design may be used for any of the three types of cantilever wall selected. The moment in the base of either the L-shaped or reversed L-shaped wall

is the same as the moment in the wall. Therefore the base thickness and the steel are identical with that of the wall, except that in the L-shaped wall the base steel is in the bottom slab, and in the reversed L it is looped around and lies in the top of the slab.

The base of the T-shaped retaining wall is designed as a pair of cantilever beams loaded as indicated in Fig. 8.28. The toe of the base is loaded upward with the load on *AB* so that

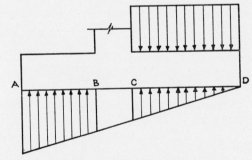

Fig. 8.28 Load on Cantilever Base

the tensile steel is in the bottom. The heel of the base is loaded downward with the weight of the earth and upward with the triangular pressure on *CD*, the net load being a downward load which produces tension in the top of the footing.

Table 8.7   Vertical-faced Gravity Retaining Walls Without Surcharge

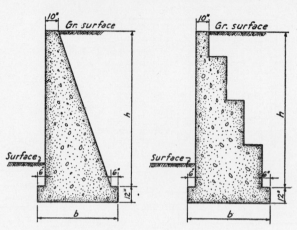

h, ft	b	Concrete, volume, cu yd per ft
3	2'3''	0.20
4	2'7''	0.27
5	3'0''	0.37
6	3'4''	0.48
7	3'9''	0.60
8	4'3''	0.76
9	4'9''	0.94
10	5'3''	1.14

Courtesy Portland Cement Association

Table 8.8   Vertical-faced Gravity Retaining Walls, Sloping Surcharge

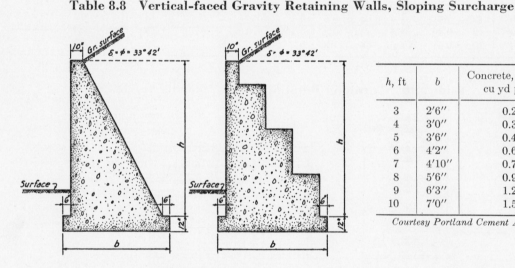

h, ft	b	Concrete, volume, cu yd per ft
3	2'6''	0.22
4	3'0''	0.32
5	3'6''	0.44
6	4'2''	0.60
7	4'10''	0.78
8	5'6''	0.99
9	6'3''	1.25
10	7'0''	1.52

Courtesy Portland Cement Association

8.31   Basement retaining walls

a   Basement walls are usually called upon to resist earth pressure. Sometimes—for example, a store with the first floor level at grade—this earth pressure is on the full height of the wall, but usually—in residences, schools, and the like—it is on the lower portion only. If the wall is against a driveway, or otherwise placed so that a superimposed load of trucks, railroad tracks, or the like may cause a surcharge, the walls must be designed to resist it.

b   If the walls are properly supported at the basement and first-floor lines, they may be designed as a vertical slab. The moment resulting from earth thrust causes compression on the outer face of the wall and tension on the inner surface. The dead load of the structure on top of the wall causes compression on the entire wall. If the result of this combined bending and direct stress causes only compression, the wall is ordinarily strong enough. If the result is a net tension, the wall must be checked to determine whether reinforcement must be placed to resist this tension.

c   Article 5.12*b* and Figs. 5.2 and 5.3 give a problem in the solution of a basement retaining wall of plain concrete. This problem does not allow for the effect of direct stress on the wall, and therefore has an additional

Table 8.9 Cantilever Retaining Walls Without Surcharge

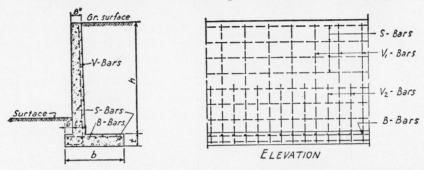

h, ft	b	t, in.	Concrete, cu yd per ft	V bars				B bars			S bars			Reinforcement, lb per ft
				Size	Spacing, in.	V₁ length	V₂ length	Size	Spacing, in.	Length	Number	Size	Spacing, in.	
5	2′9″	10	0.22	No. 2	12	6′6″		No. 2	12	2′4″	8	No. 3	12	4.5
6	3′4″	10	0.27	No. 2	7	7′6″		No. 2	7	3′0″	10	No. 3	12	6.8
7	3′10″	10	0.31	No. 3	9	8′4″		No. 3	9	3′6″	12	No. 3	12	10.4
8	4′6″	12	0.41	No. 4	12	9′8″	5′4″	No. 4	12	4′2″	13	No. 3	12	12.6
9	5′0″	12	0.46	No. 4	9	10′8″	5′4″	No. 4	9	4′8″	15	No. 3	12	16.9
10	5′6″	12	0.51	No. 5	11	11′8″	6′2″	No. 5	11	5′2″	16	No. 3	12	22.1

Courtesy Portland Cement Association

Table 8.10 Cantilever Retaining Walls, Sloping Surcharge

Note: Spacing of S-Bars is approximate. Use tabular number of bars and space evenly with 2″ cover.

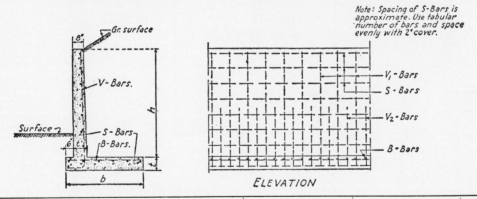

h, ft	b	t, in.	Concrete, cu yd per ft	V bars				B bars			S bars			Reinforcement, lb per ft
				Size	Spacing, in.	V₁ length	V₂ length	Size	Spacing, in.	Length	Number	Size	Spacing, in.	
5	3′6″	10	0.25	No. 3	10	6′4″		No. 3	10	3′2″	9	No. 3	12	7.7
6	4′3″	10	0.30	No. 4	10	7′4″		No. 4	10	3′10″	11	No. 3	12	13.1
7	5′0″	10	0.35	No. 4	7	8′4″		No. 4	7	4′8″	13	No. 3	12	19.8
8	6′0″	12	0.47	No. 5	9	9′8″	6′0″	No. 5	9	5′8″	15	No. 3	12	24.4
9	7′0″	13½	0.59	No. 5	7	11′0″	6′8″	No. 5	7	6′8″	17	No. 3	12	34.1
10	7′9″	15	0.71	No. 6	9	12′2″	6′10″	No. 6	9	7′4″	19	No. 3	12	40.9

Courtesy Portland Cement Association

factor of safety. Let us assume that we have a dead load of 1,000 lb per running foot of wall. This will distribute over the full wall thickness, and cause a uniform compression stress of $1,000/(12 \times 12.5) = 6\frac{2}{3}$ psi. The maximum tensile fiber stress on the wall is therefore $150 - 6\frac{2}{3} = 143\frac{1}{3}$ psi. If the wall above were a 12-in. brick wall, a $12\frac{1}{2}$-in. thick-

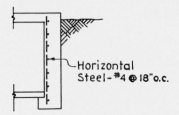

Horizontal
Steel-#4 @ 18"o.c.

Fig. 8.29 Basement Retaining Wall

ness would be required for the foundation. However, if we wish to try a 12-in. thickness for the retaining wall,

$$f_m = \frac{46,600}{288} = 162$$

$$f_d = \frac{1,000}{144} = \underline{6.95}$$

Net $f = 155.05$, which is excessive for 12 in.

Therefore a $12\frac{1}{2}$-in. retaining wall is necessary.

d Earth pressure against the full height of the wall requires reinforcement as indicated in Table 8.11 for ordinary earth pressure. The values for curb or driveway wall provide for a 300 psf surcharge, the load normally to be expected from an H-20 loading on the adjacent pavement. No reduction is made for direct compression load on the wall, since the reduction is comparatively small, as was shown in Art. 8.31c.

e The problem is more complex if the wall is concrete through part of the height, with brick above grade, as in Fig. 8.30. This wall is laid out as a beam in Fig. 8.31. The steps in the computation of this beam are as follows.

1. Compute W, total earth pressure $= 15A^2$, where A is in feet.

2. Compute reactions R_A and R_B, remembering that the center of the load is $\frac{1}{3}A$ from R_A.

3. Compute x, the point of maximum moment,

$$x = \sqrt{\frac{R_B}{15}}$$

4. Design $M_{\max}$,

$$M_{\max} = R_B\left(L + \frac{2x}{3} - A\right)$$

Reduce $M_{\max}$ to inch-pounds.

5. Design for M at top of concrete, $M_B = R_B B$, and reduce to inch-pounds.

6. Compute f_d, the total direct load carried at top of concrete, and reduce to pounds per square inch.

7. Compute the section modulus of the brick wall and the concrete wall for a strip 12 in. wide, using the relation $S = 2d^2$, where d is the thickness of the wall in inches.

8. Compute f_a and f_b, the bending stress at points a and b,

$$f_a = \frac{M_{\max}}{S_A}$$

$$f_b = \frac{M_B}{S_B}$$

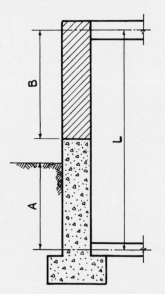

Fig. 8.30 Basement-Wall Design

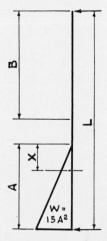

Fig. 8.31 Load Diagram—Basement Wall

Table 8.11 Basement Retaining Walls

Floor-to-floor distance, ft	Ordinary earth pressure			Curb or driveway walls		
	12-in. wall	16-in. wall	20-in. wall	12-in. wall	16-in. wall	20-in. wall
11				No. 4 at 8 in.		
12				No. 4 at 7 in.		
13	No. 4 at 8 in.			No. 5 at 8¾ in.	No. 5 at 9 in.	
14	No. 4 at 6½ in.			No. 5 at 7 in.	No. 5 at 9 in.	
15	No. 5 at 8 in.	No. 5 at 9 in.		No. 6 at 8½ in.	No. 5 at 8 in.	
16	No. 6 at 9½ in.	No. 5 at 9 in.		No. 6 at 7 in.	No. 5 at 7 in.	No. 5 at 7 in.
17	No. 6 at 8½ in.	No. 5 at 8½ in.		No. 7 at 8½ in.	No. 6 at 9 in.	No. 5 at 7 in.
18	No. 7 at 9 in.	No. 6 at 9½ in.	No. 5 at 7 in.	No. 7 at 7 in.	No. 6 at 7 in.	No. 5 at 6½ in.
19	No. 7 at 7½ in.	No. 6 at 8 in.	No. 5 at 7 in.	No. 7 at 6 in.	No. 7 at 8¼ in.	No. 6 at 7¾ in.
20	No. 7 at 6½ in.	No. 7 at 9½ in.	No. 6 at 9 in.	No. 7 at 5¼ in.	No. 7 at 7¼ in.	No. 7 at 9½ in.
Spacer bars	No. 5 at 12 in.	No. 6 at 12 in.	No. 7 at 13 in.	No. 5 at 12 in.	No. 6 at 12 in.	No. 7 at 13 in.

Curb or driveway walls are designed for surcharge of 300 psf.
(Walls up to 10 ft high do not need reinforcement.)

The net tension in the concrete is $f_a - f_d$, and this is limited to 150 psi in 3,000-psi concrete (see Art. 5.12). The net tension at the top of the concrete is $f_b - f_d$, and this is limited to 10 psi (see Art. 10.33b).

8.32 Tunnel design

a The building designer is often called upon to design an underground passageway or tunnel between several buildings, either as a pedestrian walkway or as a pipe tunnel. This article is not intended to cover subways or underwater tunnels, which present major problems of specialized design.

Since the ordinary tunnel of the type described here is a rectangular reinforced-concrete box section, for simplicity of forming, it may be designed as a continuous beam by the method of Art. 3.21, the method of moment distribution. A tunnel of this type is shown in Fig. 8.32.

b If we assume a tunnel of the type mentioned above, and with the dimensions shown in Fig. 8.32, overlaid with a 2-ft-thick earth fill, the applied loads and center lines will be as shown in Fig. 8.33. The tunnel shown could probably be built with an 8-in. wall instead of a 12-in. wall, but it is difficult to set two layers of reinforcement and pour an 8-in. wall of this height satisfactorily. Almost invari-

ably a honeycombed concrete will result, and possibly a leaky wall.

In the development of Fig. 8.33, the center-line distances are used. The load on the roof of the tunnel consists of

$$2 \text{ ft of earth at } 100 \quad = 200 \text{ psf}$$
$$\tfrac{2}{3} \text{ ft of concrete at } 150 = \underline{100} \text{ psf}$$
$$\text{Total} = 300 \text{ psf}$$

The load upward on the floor of the tunnel is

$$2 \text{ ft of earth} \times 8 \text{ ft wide} \qquad = 1{,}600 \text{ lb}$$
$$2 \text{ side walls, at 10 cu ft concrete} = 3{,}000 \text{ lb}$$
$$\text{Roof and floor, 12 sq ft concrete} = \underline{1{,}200} \text{ lb}$$
$$\text{Total} = 5{,}800 \text{ lb}$$

The equivalent fluid pressure of the earth against the side walls at 30 lb per ft depth causes a trapezoidal load made up of the triangle and rectangle shown on each side of Fig. 8.33.

The stiffness factor $K = I/L$ gives the following for the roof and floor and the side walls. The moment of inertia varies as the cube of the thickness.

$$K_{\text{roof}} = K_{\text{floor}} = \frac{8^3}{7} = \frac{512}{7} = 73$$
$$K_{\text{side wall}} = \frac{12^3}{9.33} = \frac{1{,}728}{9.33} = \underline{185}$$
$$\text{Total} = 258$$

The distribution would be, for floor and roof,

$$\frac{73}{258} = 0.28$$

For side walls, it would be

$$\frac{185}{258} = 0.72$$

The fixed-end moments will be as follows:

$$\text{Roof fem} = \frac{(0.300 \times 7) \times 7 \times 12}{12}$$
$$= 14.7 \text{ in.-kips}$$

$$\text{Floor fem} = \frac{5.8 \times 7 \times 12}{12}$$
$$= 40.6 \text{ in.-kips}$$

$$\begin{aligned}\text{Side walls,}\\ \text{top, fem}\end{aligned} = \frac{0.653 \times 9.33 \times 12}{12} = 6.1$$

$$+ \frac{1.3 \times 9.33 \times 12}{15} = \frac{9.8}{\text{Total} = 15.9} \text{ in.-kips}$$

$$\begin{aligned}\text{Side walls,}\\ \text{bottom,}\\ \text{fem}\end{aligned} = \frac{0.653 \times 9.33 \times 12}{12} = 6.1$$

$$+ \frac{1.3 \times 9.33 \times 12}{10} = \frac{14.6}{\text{Total} = 20.7} \text{ in.-kips}$$

Since the design is symmetrical, it may be cut down the middle vertically, and a carry-over factor of opposite sign used in balancing the moment, as in the following problem.

Top		Right	Bottom
0.28	0.72	0.72	0.28
−14.7	+15.9	−20.7	+40.6
+1.8	−7.2	−14.4	−5.5
	+4.2		
		+2.1	+2.8
−0.9	−1.8	−3.5	−1.4
+0.7	+2.0		
		+1.0	+0.7
−0.4	−0.6	−1.2	−0.5
+0.3	+0.7		
		+0.4	+0.3
−0.2	−0.3	−0.5	−0.2
+0.2	+0.3		
		+0.1	+0.1
−13.2		−0.1	−0.1
in.-kips			
		−36.8	
		in.-kips	

The positive moment is the simple span moment minus the final negative end moment. The simple-span-moment coefficient for the floor and roof slabs, $\frac{1}{8}$, is 1.5 times the original

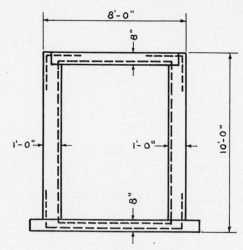

Fig. 8.32   Tunnel Section

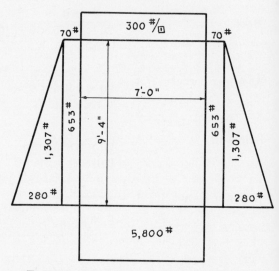

Fig. 8.33   Load Diagram—Tunnel Section

fem, $\frac{1}{12}$, or $+M = 1.5 \times 14.7 = 22.1$. The positive moment for the side walls is a combination of Cases 1 and 2 of Fig. 3.13. For the uniform load the coefficient is 0.125, and for the triangular load it is 0.128; but since they do not occur at the same point, it is a safe approximation to use $\frac{1}{8}$ here also. Likewise, the average original fem ($\frac{1}{15}$ at the top and $\frac{1}{10}$ at the bottom) is $\frac{1}{12}$; so for the side walls we may approximate the positive moment at

$$\frac{15.9 + 20.7}{2} \times 1.5 = 27.5 \text{ in.-kips}$$

Top Positive M	Right Approximate Positive M	Bottom Approximate Positive M
$+22.1$ -13.2 $\overline{+\ 8.9}$ in.-kips	$+27.5$ $-\left(\dfrac{36.8+13.2}{2}\right)=\dfrac{-25.0}{+2.5}$ in.-kips	$+60.9$ -36.8 $\overline{+24.1}$ in.-kips

From the resultant figures, it is evident that if the equivalent fluid pressure is less than the assumed pressure, the resultant positive moment and fixed-end moments will both decrease, probably to the extent that the net positive moment in the side wall will become a negative moment. The area of steel required for computed moments is:

Roof: $\quad +A_s = \dfrac{8.9}{20 \times 0.875 \times 6}$
$= 0.085$ sq in./ft

At upper corner: $-A_s = \dfrac{13.2}{20 \times 0.875 \times 6}$
$= 0.125$ sq in./ft

Side wall: $\quad +A_s = \dfrac{3.2}{20 \times 0.875 \times 10}$
$= 0.018$ sq in./ft

At lower corner: $-A_s = \dfrac{36.8}{20 \times 0.875 \times 6}$
$= 0.35$ sq in./ft

Floor: $\quad +A_s = \dfrac{24.1}{20 \times 0.875 \times 6}$
$= 0.23$ sq in./ft

In accordance with the minimum steel requirements for reinforced-concrete walls as given in the ACI Code and quoted in Art. 8.20 the minimum steel in the 8-in. floor and roof is 0.264 sq in. and in a 12-in. wall is 0.38 sq in., or 0.19 in. each face. To comply with minimum steel requirements and moment requirements, we will use:

In the roof: No. 3 rods 10 in. o.c. straight in the bottom of the slab and No. 3 rods 10 in. o.c. lapped to the corner bars in the top of the slab.

In the side wall: No. 4 rods $12\frac{1}{2}$ in. o.c. in both faces, the outer bars bent around the corner to take the negative moment.

In the floor: No. 4 rods 10-in. o.c. in the top of the slab, with corner bars No. 4 at $12\frac{1}{2}$ in. o.c. in the outer face to develop the negative moment.

Connections

9.10 RIVETING AND BOLTING (STEEL)

a Although they differ in their application, the structural problems in riveting and in bolting of steel are alike, and may be treated in one article. They are the common means of attaching steel to steel, and their design is a problem usually in simple shear and occasionally in direct tension.

Formerly the design of connections was based on the theory that the stress was carried entirely in shear through the bolts or rivets, with no allowance for friction. More recently it has been found that the main purpose served by the rivets or bolts is to clamp the members together and that the greater portion of the stress is transferred through friction. This fact—that stress is transferred through friction—has not been recognized by the Code except to permit special high-tension bolts tightened to a predetermined torque to be used for the full allowable stress permitted for rivets, as are also ribbed bolts and fitted turned bolts in reamed holes. These stresses are listed in Table 9.1. Stresses for unfinished bolts are those listed in Table 9.2.

From Sec. 15 of the AISC Specification, the allowable stress in tension for rivets, on an area based on the nominal diameter, and for bolts, on a nominal area at the root of the thread, is 20,000 psi. The allowable shear for rivets and turned bolts in reamed or drilled holes is 15,000 psi, and for unfinished bolts it is 10,000 psi on the full cross section of rivets or bolts. Bearing of the rivet against the side

of the hole through which it is driven is dependent on whether the rivet is in enclosed bearing—(in double shear) or in unenclosed bearing—(in single shear).

Thus in Fig. 9.1 the rivet is in "enclosed bearing," or "double-shear bearing," on plate *B*, and in "unenclosed bearing," or "single-shear bearing," on plates *A* and *C*. In Fig. 9.2 the rivet is in "unenclosed bearing" on plates *D* and *E*. The allowable bearing stress for rivets and turned bolts in reamed holes is 40,000 psi for double shear and 32,000

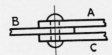

Fig. 9.1   Enclosed Bearing

psi for single shear. The allowable bearing stress for unfinished bolts in double shear is 25,000 psi and in single shear 20,000 psi.

Rivets are normally used for all shop connections, and for field connections where special rigidity is required, as listed in Sec. 7 of

Fig. 9.2   Unenclosed Bearing

the AISC Code (see Art. 1.21). Ordinarily all shop connections, trusses, wind-bracing connections, and connections to or within 18 in. of a column should be riveted. Turned bolts in reamed or drilled holes, high-tension

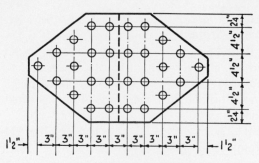

Fig. 9.3   Problem in Riveting

bolts, or structural ribbed bolts driven into place, may be substituted for rivets.

Rivets and unfinished bolts are used in holes $\frac{1}{16}$ in. greater in diameter than the nominal rivet or bolt diameter, and in computing the plate areas, an additional $\frac{1}{16}$ in. is deducted to obtain the net area. Thus a $\frac{3}{4}$-in. rivet is driven in a $\frac{13}{16}$-in. hole and the width deducted from the plate is $\frac{7}{8}$ in. For compression members the area of the rivet hole is not deducted; in other words, gross area is used in compression members.

There are a number of other rules pertaining to rivet design given in Secs. 20 to 23 of the AISC Code with which the designer should be familiar. These rules are quoted in the various problems which are given. The older codes gave different stresses for shop and field rivets. Later this was changed so as to give different stresses for machine-driven and hand-driven rivets. Nowadays all rivets are considered to be machine-driven; so the single set of rivet values as given in Table 9.1 is used.

b There are more problems on rivets and riveted joints on the various license examinations than on any other single subject except beams. Most of the problems are quite simple, requiring only a knowledge of the tables and the general principles of joint design. Although it is common practice to use the stresses listed in the tables referred to, these stresses may be modified by the problem in hand, which should therefore be read carefully.

Problem   Two plates, $18 \times \frac{3}{4}$ in. in section, are to be spliced for tension by two plates, $18 \times \frac{7}{16}$ in. Using $\frac{7}{8}$-in. rivets, design and sketch a splice for maximum efficiency, using these stresses (in psi): tension 16,000, shear 12,000, bearing 24,000. (From a state license examination.)

This brings in stresses which are not given in the tables and must be computed. The value of a $\frac{7}{8}$-in. rivet in double shear, referring to Table 9.2 for unfinished bolts, is $1.2 \times 12,030 = 14,440$ psi.

The value of a $\frac{7}{8}$-in. rivet in bearing on a $\frac{3}{4}$-in. plate at 24,000, from Table 9.1, is $0.875 \times 0.75 \times 24,000 = 15,760$ psi. Therefore double shear controls and the rivet value is 14,440 psi.

The AISC Code, Sec. 23(a), states,

The minimum distance between centers of rivet holes shall preferably be not less than three times the diameter of the rivet

and Sec. 23(e) gives the minimum edge distance for a $\frac{7}{8}$-in. rivet in a sheared plate as $1\frac{1}{2}$ in.

In an 18-in. plate, the maximum number of rivets will be $\frac{18}{3} = 6$ rivets. Net width then is 18 in. $-$ 6 in. $= 12$ in. We will try this design. The net tensile value of two plates $18 \times \frac{7}{16}$ (12 in. net width) $= 2 \times 12 \times \frac{7}{16}$ in. $\times 16,000 = 168,000$ lb.: Then:

$$\frac{168,000}{14,400} = 11.65$$

Use 12 $\frac{7}{8}$-in. rivets.

Gross area of plate $= \frac{3}{4}$ in. $\times 18$

$\qquad = 13.5 \times 16,000 = 216,000$

$$\frac{168,000}{216,000} = 77.8\% \text{ efficiency}$$

We will next try four rivets across in the first row next to the joint. The net tensile value of the splice plates is $2 \times 14 \times \frac{7}{16}$ in. $\times 16,000 = 196,000$

$$\frac{196,000}{14,400} = 14 \text{ rivets}$$

Net in $\frac{3}{4}$-in. plate at 1st rivet $= 17 \times 0.75$
$\qquad\qquad\qquad\qquad \times 16,000 = 204,000$
Net in $\frac{3}{4}$-in. plate at 2d line $= 16 \times 0.75$
$\qquad\qquad\qquad\qquad \times 16,000 = 192,000$
Efficiency of joint $\frac{196}{216} = 90.6\%$ [Fig. 9.3]

c   *Eccentric rivet connections.* The design of riveted joints given in Art. 9.10a and b, as vell as the design of connection angle riveting given in the handbooks, is based on concentric loading, and the full value of the rivet is used to carry the load in direct shear. When the load becomes eccentric, however, the rivet group is called upon to resist bending as well as direct load and the rivets in the group are not equally stressed. In this article and in Table 9.3, which is the standard table taken from the AISC Manual, the following nomenclature will be used:

n = total number of rivets in one vertical row

m = total number of vertical rows

N = total number of rivets in the group, or $N = mn$

P = total load on the connection

S = maximum load on one rivet*

C = coefficient tabulated in Table 9.3

d = distance from the center of gravity of the group to the individual rivet

b = uniform vertical rivet spacing

D = spacing of outside rows of rivets (see Table 9.3)

a = spacing between individual rows in the case of uniform spacing

l = lever arm of the applied load

All distances are measured in inches.

Using the above nomenclature, it may be stated that each rivet in the group carries an equal share of the vertical load, or P/N, but in addition, each carries a stress resisting the tendency of the entire group to rotate about the center of gravity of the group. The theoretical stress on any one rivet is the resultant of the direct and eccentric stress components, and is greatest for the rivet on the side toward the load at the distance greatest from the center of the group. The stress due to eccentricity is equal to the moment in inch-pounds divided by the polar section modulus of the group of rivets, or M/S_ρ.

In actual practice, an added factor of safety applies due to: (a) the fact, only recently recognized, that friction between the connected surfaces, rather than rivet shear, is the con-

trolling factor and (b) the fact that, through the theory of limit design, the stress is redistributed before failure occurs. Building codes do not give recognition to these two factors, however, and it is therefore proper to make computations in accordance with accepted theory.

The polar section modulus may be obtained from the formula

$$S_\rho = \frac{N_1 d_1{}^2 + N_2 d_2{}^2 + N_3 d_3{}^2 + \cdots + N_n d_n{}^2}{d_{\max}}$$

Normally d is the hypotenuse of a right triangle and the two legs of the triangle are more easily obtained than the hypotenuse. We therefore substitute the squares of the two right distances for the square of the hypotenuse in the problem that follows.

Problem Assume the riveted connection shown in Fig. 9.4, which is carrying a load of 20,000 lb on a lever arm of 5 in., or 100,000 in.-lb moment. Which rivet has the maximum stress and what is the amount of the stress? Substituting the right distances for the diagonals, we may tabulate our computations as follows.

$$
\begin{aligned}
8 \text{ at } 5.5^2 &= 242 \\
8 \text{ at } 2.75^2 &= 60.5 \\
8 \text{ at } 1.5^2 &= 18 \\
8 \text{ at } 4.5^2 &= \underline{162} \\
I_\rho &= 482.5
\end{aligned}
$$

To obtain $d_{\max}$,

$$
\begin{aligned}
5.5^2 &= 30.25 \\
4.5^2 &= \underline{20.25} \\
&\; 50.5
\end{aligned}
$$

$$\sqrt{50.5} = 7.11$$

$$S_\rho = \frac{482.5}{7.11} = 67.86$$

The direct stress per rivet is

$$\frac{20,000}{16} = 1,250 \text{ lb},$$

which is a vertical stress. The stress in the corner rivet due to moment is

$$100,000/67.86 = 1,474 \text{ lb}$$

at right angles to the radial line to the corner rivets. In Fig. 9.5, the resultant forces on the outside rivets are shown.

*This use of S is for Table 9.3 only. (Elsewhere S_ρ is the polar section modulus of the rivet group.)

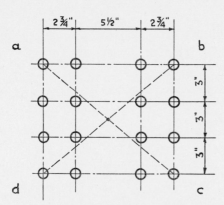

Fig. 9.4 Problem in Eccentric Riveting

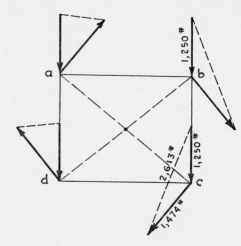

Fig. 9.5 Stresses on Extreme Rivets

There is a simple formula for obtaining the section modulus of a group of rivets with uniform spacing as follows:

1. For a single line of rivets,

$$S_1 = \frac{\text{spacing} \times N(N+1)}{6}$$

2. For several lines, the polar moment of the entire group M rows wide and N rows high is

$$S_\rho = \sqrt{S_x{}^2 + S_y{}^2}$$

where

$$S_x = M\left[\frac{\text{spacing} \times N(N+1)}{6}\right]$$

$$S_y = N\left[\frac{\text{spacing} \times M(M+1)}{6}\right]$$

Thus for the problem above

$$S_x = S_y = 4\left(\frac{3 \times 4 \times 5}{6}\right) = 40$$

$$S_\rho = \sqrt{1,600 + 1,600} = \sqrt{3,200} = 56.6$$

d The table of rivet groups under eccentric application of load given in Table 9.3 is taken from the AISC handbook. For any rivet group and any given lever arm of applied load, a coefficient C may be found such that C times the allowable value of one rivet equals the total load P permissible on the connection. Thus

$$P = CS$$

Or knowing P, and dividing by the allowable rivet value S, the necessary coefficient is of that magnitude or greater.

General expressions for the coefficient C are very complex, and for all except simple sym-metrical cases the joint must be detailed by a cut-and-try process based on the foregoing principles and without deriving coefficients. Table 9.3 gives the coefficients C for the simplest cases occurring repeatedly in practice. Figure 9.6 shows an example of the use of the table.

In the case of eccentric brackets of the type shown in Fig. 9.7 in which the moment pro-

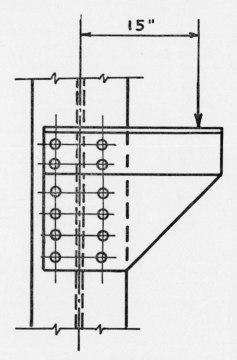

Fig. 9.6 Load on Column Bracket

Table 9.1   Power-driven Rivets

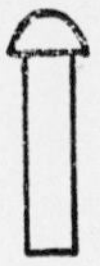

POWER DRIVEN RIVETS
(SHOP AND FIELD)
AND
TURNED BOLTS IN REAMED HOLES

ALLOWABLE LOADS IN KIPS

Shear ....15,000 lbs. per square inch
Bearing: S. S.............32,000 " " " "
         "   D. S.............40,000 " " " "

Rivet Dia.	½		⅝		¾		⅞		1		1⅛		1¼	
Area	.1963		.3068		.4418		.6013		.7854		.9940		1.2272	
Single Shear	2.95		4.60		6.63		9.02		11.78		14.91		18.41	
Double Shear	5.89		9.20		13.25		18.04		23.56		29.82		36.82	
Thickness of Plate	Bearing		Bearing		Bearing		Bearing		Bearing		Bearing		Bearing	
	32.0	40.0	32.0	40.0	32.0	40.0	32.0	40.0	32.0	40.0	32.0	40.0	32.0	40.0
.125 ⅛	2.00	2.50	2.50	3.12	3.00	3.75								
.140	2.24	2.80	2.80	3.50	3.36	4.20	3.92	4.90						
.160	2.56	3.20	3.20	4.00	3.84	4.80	4.48	5.60						
.180	2.88	3.60	3.60	4.50	4.32	5.40	5.04	6.30						
.1875 3⁄16	3.00	3.75	3.75	4.69	4.50	5.62	5.25	6.56						
.200		4.00	4.00	5.00	4.80	6.00	5.60	7.00	6.40	8.00				
.220		4.40	4.40	5.50	5.28	6.60	6.16	7.70	7.04	8.80				
.240		4.80	4.80	6.00	5.76	7.20	6.72	8.40	7.68	9.60				
.250 ¼		5.00		6.25	6.00	7.50	7.00	8.75	8.00	10.0				
.260		5.20		6.50	6.24	7.80	7.28	9.10	8.32	10.4	9.36	11.7		
.280		5.60		7.00	6.72	8.40	7.84	9.80	8.96	11.2	10.1	12.6		
.300		6.00		7.50		9.00	8.40	10.5	9.60	12.0	10.8	13.5		
.3125 5⁄16				7.81		9.38	8.75	10.9	10.0	12.5	11.3	14.1		
.320				8.00		9.60	8.96	11.2	10.2	12.8	11.5	14.4	12.8	16.0
.340				8.50		10.2		11.9	10.9	13.6	12.2	15.3	13.6	17.0
.360				9.00		10.8		12.6	11.5	14.4	13.0	16.2	14.4	18.0
.375 ⅜				9.38		11.3		13.1	12.0	15.0	13.5	16.9	15.0	18.8
.380						11.4		13.3		15.2	13.7	17.1	15.2	19.0
.400						12.0		14.0		16.0	14.4	18.0	16.0	20.0
.420						12.6		14.7		16.8	15.1	18.9	16.8	21.0
.4375 7⁄16						13.1		15.3		17.5		19.7	17.5	21.9
.440								15.4		17.6		19.8	17.6	22.0
.460								16.1		18.4		20.7	18.4	23.0
.480								16.8		19.2		21.6		24.0
.500 ½								17.5		20.0		22.5		25.0
.520								18.2		20.8		23.4		26.0
.540										21.6		24.3		27.0
.560										22.4		25.2		28.0
.5625 9⁄16										22.5		25.3		28.1
.580										23.2		26.1		29.0
.600										24.0		27.0		30.0
.620												27.9		31.0
.625 ⅝												28.1		31.3
.6875 11⁄16												30.9		34.4
.750 ¾														37.5

Table 9.2 Unfinished Bolts

UNFINISHED BOLTS

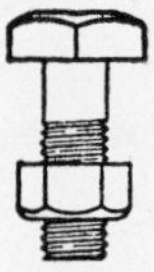

ALLOWABLE LOADS IN KIPS

Shear..........................10,000 lbs. per square inch
Bearing: S. S..............20,000 " " " "
             D. S..............25,000 " " " "

(See A.I.S.C. Specification Section 22(e) for conditional increase of ⅓)

Bolt Dia.	½		⅝		¾		⅞		1		1⅛		1¼	
Area	.1963		.3068		.4418		.6013		.7854		.9940		1.2272	
Single Shear	1.96		3.07		4.42		6.01		7.85		9.94		12.27	
Double Shear	3.93		6.14		8.84		12.03		15.71		19.88		24.54	
Thickness of Plate	Bearing		Bearing		Bearing		Bearing		Bearing		Bearing		Bearing	
	20.0	25.0	20.0	25.0	20.0	25.0	20.0	25.0	20.0	25.0	20.0	25.0	20.0	25.0
.125 ⅛	1.25	1.56	1.56	1.95	1.88	2.35								
.140	1.40	1.75	1.75	2.19	2.10	2.63	2.45	3.06						
.160	1.60	2.00	2.00	2.50	2.40	3.00	2.80	3.50						
.180	1.80	2.25	2.25	2.81	2.70	3.38	3.15	3.94						
.1875 3/16	1.88	2.38	2.34	2.93	2.81	3.52	3.28	4.10						
.200	2.00	2.50	2.50	3.13	3.00	3.75	3.50	4.38	4.00	5.00				
.220	....	2.75	2.75	3.44	3.30	4.13	3.85	4.81	4.40	5.50				
.240	....	3.00	3.00	3.75	3.60	4.50	4.20	5.25	4.80	6.00				
.250 ¼	....	3.13	3.13	3.91	3.75	4.69	4.38	5.47	5.00	6.25				
.260	....	3.25	....	4.06	3.90	4.88	4.55	5.69	5.20	6.50	5.85	7.31		
.280	....	3.50	....	4.38	4.20	5.25	4.90	6.13	5.60	7.00	6.30	7.88		
.300	....	3.75	....	4.69	4.50	5.63	5.25	6.56	6.00	7.50	6.75	8.44		
.3125 5/16	....	3.91	....	4.88	....	5.86	5.47	6.84	6.25	7.81	7.03	8.79		
.320	....	4.00	....	5.00	....	6.00	5.60	7.00	6.40	8.00	7.20	9.00	8.00	10.0
.340			....	5.31	....	6.38	5.95	7.44	6.80	8.50	7.65	9.56	8.50	10.6
.360			....	5.63	....	6.75	....	7.88	7.20	9.00	8.10	10.1	9.00	11.3
.375 ⅜			....	5.86	....	7.03	....	8.20	7.50	9.38	8.44	10.6	9.38	11.7
.380					....	5.94	....	7.13	....	8.31	7.60	9.50	8.55	10.7	9.50	11.9
.400					....	6.25	....	7.50	....	8.75	8.00	10.0	9.00	11.3	10.0	12.5
.420							....	7.88	....	9.19	....	10.5	9.45	11.8	10.5	13.1
.4375 7/16							....	8.20	....	9.57	....	10.9	9.84	12.3	10.9	13.7
.440							....	8.25	....	9.63	....	11.0	9.90	12.4	11.0	13.8
.460							....	8.63	....	10.1	....	11.5	....	12.9	11.5	14.4
.480							....	9.00	....	10.5	....	12.0	....	13.5	12.0	15.0
.500 ½									....	10.9	....	12.5	....	14.1	12.5	15.6
.520									....	11.4	....	13.0	....	14.6	....	16.3
.540									....	11.8	....	13.5	....	15.2	....	16.9
.560									....	12.3	....	14.0	....	15.7	....	17.5
.5625 9/16											....	14.1	....	15.8	....	17.6
.580											....	14.5	....	16.3	....	18.1
.600											....	15.0	....	16.9	....	18.8
.620											....	15.5	....	17.4	....	19.4
.625 ⅝											....	15.6	....	17.6	....	19.5
.6875 11/16											....	17.2	....	19.3	....	21.5
.750 ¾													....	21.1	....	23.4
.8125 13/16															....	25.4

Table 9.3 Rivet Groups under Eccentric Load

RIVET GROUPS UNDER ECCENTRIC APPLICATION OF LOAD

Nomenclature:
- n = total number of rivets in any one vertical row.
- P = permissible load, acting with lever arm l.
- S = permissible load on one rivet by Specification.
- C = coefficient as tabulated below.
- P = C × S; or, knowing P, required minimum $C = \frac{P}{S}$

Case I

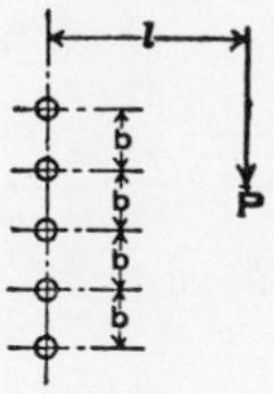

In Table, b = 3″

n \ l	1″	2″	3″	6″	9″	12″	15″	18″	21″	24″
2	1.7	1.2	.89	.49	.33	.25	.20	.17	.14	.12
3	2.7	2.1	1.7	.95	.65	.49	.40	.33	.28	.25
4	3.7	3.1	2.6	1.5	1.1	.82	.66	.55	.47	.41
5	4.7	4.2	3.5	2.2	1.6	1.2	.98	.82	.71	.62
6	5.8	5.2	4.6	3.0	2.2	1.7	1.4	1.1	.99	.87
7	6.8	6.3	5.6	3.9	2.8	2.2	1.8	1.5	1.3	1.2
8	7.8	7.3	6.7	4.8	3.6	2.8	2.3	1.9	1.7	1.5
9	8.8	8.4	7.7	5.8	4.4	3.5	2.8	2.4	2.1	1.8
10	9.8	9.4	8.8	6.8	5.2	4.2	3.4	2.9	2.5	2.2
11	10.9	10.4	9.8	7.8	6.1	4.9	4.1	3.5	3.0	2.7
12	11.9	11.5	10.9	8.8	7.0	5.7	4.8	4.1	3.5	3.1

In general, $$C = \frac{n}{\sqrt{\left[\frac{6l}{(n+1)\,b}\right]^2 + 1}}$$

Case II

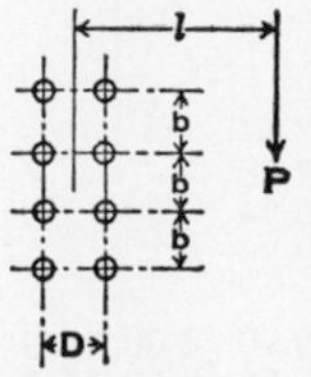

In Table, b = 3″ and D = 5½″ or 9½″

l	1″		2″		3″		6″		9″		12″		15″		18″		21″		24″	
n \ D	5½	9½	5½	9½	5½	9½	5½	9½	5½	9½	5½	9½	5½	9½	5½	9½	5½	9½	5½	9½
2	3.1	3.4	2.5	2.9	2.1	2.5	1.4	1.8	1.1	1.4	0.8	1.2	0.7	1.0	0.6	0.9	0.5	0.8	0.5	0.7
3	4.9	5.1	4.1	4.4	3.4	3.9	2.3	2.9	1.7	2.2	1.4	1.8	1.1	1.6	1.0	1.4	0.9	1.2	0.8	1.1
4	6.8	7.0	5.8	6.1	5.0	5.4	3.4	4.0	2.5	3.1	2.0	2.6	1.7	2.2	1.4	1.9	1.2	1.7	1.1	1.5
5	8.8	8.9	7.7	7.9	6.7	7.0	4.6	5.2	3.5	4.1	2.8	3.3	2.3	2.8	1.9	2.4	1.7	2.1	1.5	1.9
6	10.9	10.8	9.6	9.7	8.5	8.7	6.0	6.5	4.5	5.1	3.6	4.2	3.0	3.6	2.6	3.1	2.2	2.7	2.0	2.4
7	12.9	12.8	11.7	11.6	10.4	10.6	7.5	8.0	5.8	6.3	4.6	5.2	3.8	4.4	3.3	3.8	2.8	3.3	2.5	3.0
8	15.0	14.8	13.7	13.6	12.4	12.4	9.2	9.6	7.1	7.6	5.7	6.2	4.8	5.3	4.1	4.6	3.5	4.0	3.1	3.6
9	17.0	16.9	15.8	15.6	14.5	14.4	11.0	11.2	8.6	9.0	6.9	7.4	5.8	6.3	4.9	5.4	4.3	4.8	3.8	4.3
10	19.1	18.9	17.9	17.7	16.6	16.4	12.8	13.0	10.1	10.5	8.2	8.7	6.9	7.4	5.9	6.4	5.2	5.6	4.6	5.0
11	21.2	20.9	20.0	19.7	18.7	18.4	14.8	14.8	11.8	12.1	9.7	10.0	8.1	8.5	7.0	7.4	6.1	6.5	5.4	5.8
12	23.2	23.0	22.1	21.8	20.8	20.5	16.8	16.7	13.5	13.7	11.2	11.4	9.4	9.8	8.1	8.5	7.1	7.5	6.3	6.7

In general, $$C = \frac{n}{\sqrt{\left[\frac{l\,(n-1)\,b}{D^2 + \frac{1}{3}(n^2-1)\,b^2}\right]^2 + \left[\frac{l\,D}{D^2 + \frac{1}{3}(n^2-1)\,b^2} + \frac{1}{2}\right]^2}}$$

Case III

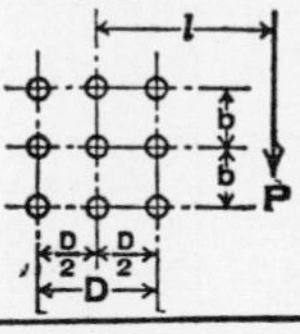

Case III, not tabulated.

In general, $$C = \frac{n}{\sqrt{\left[\frac{l\,(n-1)\,b}{D^2 + \frac{1}{2}(n^2-1)\,b^2}\right]^2 + \left[\frac{l\,D}{D^2 + \frac{1}{3}(n^2-1)\,b^2} + \frac{1}{3}\right]^2}}$$

Case IV

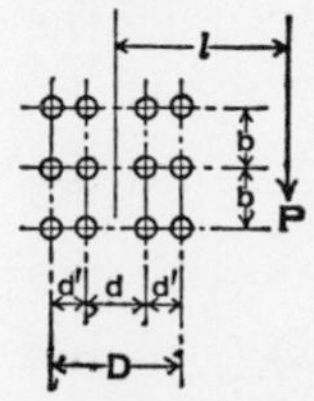

In Table, b = 3″
d′ = 2½″ d′ = 3″
d = 4½″ d = 5½″
d′ = 2½″ d′ = 3″
D = 9½″ D = 11½″

l	1″		2″		3″		6″		9″		12″		15″		18″		21″		24″	
n \ D	9½	11½	9½	11½	9½	11½	9½	11½	9½	11½	9½	11½	9½	11½	9½	11½	9½	11½	9½	11½
2	6.2	6.4	5.0	5.3	4.2	4.5	2.8	3.1	2.1	2.4	1.7	1.9	1.4	1.6	1.2	1.4	1.1	1.2	1.0	1.1
3	9.6	9.8	8.0	8.2	6.7	7.1	4.6	5.0	3.5	3.8	2.8	3.1	2.3	2.6	2.0	2.2	1.8	2.0	1.6	1.8
4	13.3	13.4	11.2	11.5	9.7	10.0	6.7	7.1	5.1	5.4	4.1	4.4	3.4	3.7	2.9	3.2	2.6	2.8	2.3	2.5
5	17.2	17.2	14.8	15.0	12.9	13.1	9.1	9.4	6.9	7.3	5.6	5.9	4.7	5.0	4.0	4.3	3.5	3.8	3.1	3.4
6	21.2	21.1	18.6	18.6	16.4	16.5	11.7	12.1	9.0	9.4	7.3	7.6	6.1	6.4	5.2	5.5	4.6	4.9	4.1	4.3
7	25.2	25.1	22.5	22.5	20.1	20.1	14.7	14.9	11.3	11.7	9.2	9.5	7.7	8.0	6.6	6.9	5.8	6.1	5.1	5.4
8	29.3	29.2	26.5	26.4	23.9	23.9	17.8	18.0	13.9	14.2	11.3	11.6	9.5	9.8	8.2	8.5	7.2	7.5	6.4	6.6
9	33.4	33.3	30.6	30.5	27.9	27.8	21.2	21.3	16.7	16.9	13.7	13.9	11.5	11.8	9.9	10.2	8.7	9.0	7.7	8.0
10	37.6	37.4	34.8	34.6	32.0	31.8	24.8	24.8	19.7	19.9	16.2	16.4	13.7	13.9	11.8	12.1	10.4	10.6	9.2	9.5
11	41.7	41.5	39.0	38.7	36.2	35.9	28.5	28.5	22.9	23.0	18.9	19.1	16.0	16.2	13.9	14.1	12.2	12.4	10.9	11.1
12	45.8	45.6	43.2	42.8	40.3	40.0	32.4	32.2	26.3	26.3	21.8	21.9	18.5	18.7	16.0	16.3	14.1	14.4	12.6	12.8

In general, $$C = \frac{n}{\sqrt{\left[\frac{l\,(n-1)\,b}{d^2 + D^2 + \frac{2}{3}(n^2-1)\,b^2}\right]^2 + \left[\frac{l\,D}{d^2 + D^2 + \frac{2}{3}(n^2-1)\,b^2} + \frac{1}{4}\right]^2}}$$

Table 9.4 Net Section Modulus of Plates

NET SECTION MODULI OF PLATES

Diameter of holes assumed ⅛″ larger than nominal diameter of rivet

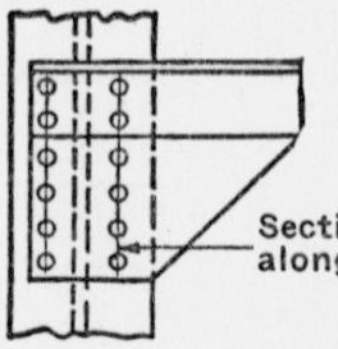

Section Moduli taken along this line

Rivets spaced 3″ vertically

No. of Rivets in One Vertical Line	Depth of Plate in Inches	¾″ RIVETS — Thickness of Plate, In.					⅞″ RIVETS — Thickness of Plate, In.					1″ RIVETS — Thickness of Plate, In.				
		¼	⅜	½	⅝	¾	⅜	½	⅝	¾	⅞	½	⅝	¾	⅞	1
2	6	1.2	1.8	2.3	2.9	3.5	1.7	2.3	2.9	3.4	4.0	2.2	2.7	3.2	3.8	4.3
3	9	2.5	3.8	5.0	6.3	7.5	3.6	4.8	5.9	7.1	8.3	4.5	5.6	6.8	7.9	9.0
4	12	4.4	6.3	8.7	11	13	6.2	8.2	10	12	14	7.8	9.7	12	14	16
5	15	6.8	10	14	17	20	10	13	16	19	22	12	15	18	21	24
6	18	9.6	15	19	24	29	14	18	23	27	32	17	21	26	30	34
7	21	13	20	26	33	39	19	25	31	37	43	23	29	35	41	47
8	24	17	26	34	43	51	24	32	40	48	56	30	38	45	53	61
9	27	22	32	43	54	65	31	41	51	61	71	38	48	57	67	77
10	30	27	40	53	67	80	38	50	63	75	88	47	59	71	83	94
12	36	38	58	77	96	115	54	72	90	108	126	68	85	102	119	136
14	42	52	78	104	130	157	74	98	123	147	172	92	115	138	161	184
16	48	68	102	136	170	204	96	128	160	192	224	120	150	180	211	241
18	54	86	129	172	215	259	122	162	203	243	284	152	190	228	266	304
20	60	106	160	213	266	319	150	200	250	300	350	188	235	282	329	376
22	66	129	193	257	322	386	182	242	303	363	424	227	284	341	398	454
24	72	153	230	306	383	459	216	288	360	432	504	270	338	406	473	541
26	78	180	270	359	449	539	254	338	423	507	592	317	397	476	555	634
28	84	208	313	417	521	625	294	392	490	588	686	368	460	552	644	736
30	90	240	359	478	598	718	338	450	563	675	788	422	528	633	739	845
32	96	272	408	544	680	816	384	512	640	768	896	480	600	721	841	961
34	102	308	461	614	768	922	434	578	723	867	1012	542	678	813	949	1085
36	108	344	517	689	861	1033	486	648	810	972	1134	608	760	912	1064	1216

Interpolate for intermediate thicknesses of plates.

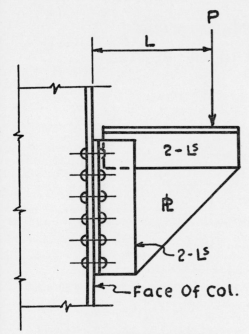

Fig. 9.7　Load on Column Bracket

duces tension on the rivets, there is no exact knowledge as to the location of the neutral axis; it probably lies somewhere below the center line of the connection. Nor is there exact knowledge of the permissible combination of tension with vertical shear on the uppermost rivets. A safe and accepted method of design for brackets of the type shown is to consider the rivets to be under an eccentric loading similar to that exemplified in Table 9.3. The coefficient C for such cases will be twice the values tabulated in the table to conform with the two vertical rows of rivets. The resultant stress on one extreme rivet should not exceed the AISC Specification allowance of 15.0 kips per sq in.

For example, assume the following conditions: $P = 22$ kips, $l = 12$ in., $\frac{3}{4}$-in. rivets, 3-in. pitch.

Allowable stress on one rivet =
$$15.0 \times 0.4418 = 6.63 \text{ kips}$$
$$C = \frac{P}{2 \times S} - \frac{22}{2 \times 6.63} = 1.66$$

From Table 9.3 for $l = 12$ in., six rivets are required in each of two vertical rows.

e　Further problems in riveting and bolt-

ing are found in developing horizontal shear, as in riveting the flanges to plate girders or cover-plated beams, and in riveting together compound steel beams as in Art. 4.23.

The horizontal shear at any point in the web or flange may be computed from the formula given in Art. 4.23,

$$v_h = \frac{V M_s}{I}$$

where v_h is the horizontal unit shear at the point considered, V is the total shear at this point, M_s is the static moment of the area beyond the point under consideration, and I the moment of inertia of the section. This unit horizontal shear is ordinarily computed at intervals and the spacing obtained by dividing the value of one rivet by the unit shear. For example, determine the rivet spacing required to fasten a $16 \times \frac{7}{8}$-in. plate to a 27 WF 145 at a point where the total shear is 100 kips (see Art. 4.22c), using $\frac{7}{8}$-in. rivets in pairs:

$$I \text{ of 27-in. beam, net} = 4{,}761$$
$$I \text{ of two } 16 \times \tfrac{7}{8}\text{-in. plates, net}$$
$$= 2 \times 14 \times 0.875 \times 13.88^2 = \frac{4{,}730}{9{,}491}$$
$$M_s = 12.25 \times 13.88 = 170.2$$
$$v_h = \frac{100{,}000 \times 170.2}{9{,}491} = 1{,}790 \text{ lb per in.}$$

Using two $\frac{7}{8}$-in. rivets, the spacing may be

$$S = \frac{9{,}020 \times 2}{1{,}790} = 10.1$$

Use 10-in. spacing.

9.20　WELDING

a　The subject of welding warrants much more space than may be devoted to it here. Although this article does not discuss the merits, methods, or economics of welding, it may be well to call attention to the advantage of welding in two situations: (1) where the noise of riveting is undesirable, such as in the neighborhood of a hospital, or in alterations and additions to a school, office building, or apartment house, and (2) in connecting to an existing structure, where welding elimi-

Each rivet works three times in
shear, four times in bearing

Each weld works but once. One stress must be
carried three times

Fig. 9.8 Comparison of Welding and Riveting

nates field drilling, bucking rivets, or cutting through to permit bolting.

While riveted construction is cheaper for some structures, welded construction is more economical for others, and many of the minor details of a riveted structure may be shop-welded to advantage. Although combinations of welding and riveting are sometimes economical, generally shop-riveted–field-welded or shop-welded–field-riveted structures are uneconomical since neither process is used to full advantage. Shop riveting and shop welding may be combined to advantage, but it is usually uneconomical to combine field welding and field riveting.

A welded detail may be cheaper than a riveted detail under certain conditions, while the reverse may be true if the conditions are varied slightly. For example, it is cheaper to weld clip angles to thick sections when doing so eliminates drilling, but if holes must be drilled or punched in the piece for some other purpose it may be more economical to rivet.

When a riveted detail would require countersunk holes, such as in a beam-and-plate lintel, lower cost and better appearance will result if the parts are welded together.

The primary consideration in selecting the details for a welded structure is the elimination of shop operations. Wherever possible, eliminate holes in main material, but if holes must be used in a member avoid welding on that piece. It should be possible to arrange the details so that some pieces are plain for field welding, some punched for field bolting or for temporary erection bolts prior to welding, and some welded with holes in detail material only; there should be very few pieces upon which more than one operation is required.

For a tier building where field bolting is permitted, it is usually possible to shop-weld the details to the columns, with no holes in main material, and to punch the girders for erection bolts and for the permanent bolts of the secondary beam connections. The secondary beams have welded clip angles and there are no holes in main material. The field welding would be a minimum, involving only nominal welds on the top and seat angles and the welding of the column splices. Should specifications require field welding of beams, a single angle butt-welded detail would result in similar shop classifications, reduce shop welding slightly, and add a minimum amount of field welding.

For a light mill building, columns, trusses, and crane girders could be welded, with no holes in main material, purlins, girts, and bracing being bolted. Truss splices, if required, could be welded on the ground before raising, and the welding after erection reduced to truss-to-column connections only. If rod bracing is used, clip angles may be used to avoid holes in main material, but if some holes are necessary, flame-cutting while on the welded skids will save the cost of handling to the punches.

While it is desirable to eliminate all the holes in a welded structure, economical erection requires some cheap and positive temporary fastening to facilitate plumbing and the correction of center-to-center and overall dimensions. The use of two erection bolts at each primary connection is the most satisfactory method so far devised. Secondary members require no erection bolts if the details are such that the piece may be readily located and there is little likelihood of displacement between the erection and final welding.

Since the cost of removing erection bolts usually exceeds the value of the bolts, they should be permitted to remain in the structure, nd the details should be designed so that the rection bolts will not interfere with the acion of the joint. Note the location of erection olts in Fig. 9.13.

b The fundamental principles of design of velded structures vary little from those of iveted structures. The AISC Specification, ec. 16(*a*) and (*f*), refers to stresses on welded onstruction, and Secs. 24 and 25 are devoted o welding and the design of welding.

The welds most commonly used in strucural welding are butt welds and fillet welds. Vhile plug-and-slot welds are not generally ccepted and the filling of such holes is not avored by the American Welding Society odes, such welds are occasionally used. Butt velds are stressed in tension or compression. he size is designated by the thickness of the hinner part of the sections joined. Fillet velds are stressed in shear for any direction f the applied load. A fillet weld is approxinately an isosceles triangle of weld metal used to the parent metal along two legs. The ize is designated by the length of the shorter f these legs and the strength determined by he throat dimension, which is 0.707 times the heoretical weld size.

In a *butt weld* a long thin weld is more effiient than a short thick one of equal strength.

Fig. 9.9   Butt Weld

'or example, a butt weld in a $4 \times \frac{3}{8}$ plate is qual in strength to one in $\frac{3}{4}$a $2 \times$ plate but ises less weld metal. The volume of weld netal in a butt weld, neglecting reinforcement nd shoulders and assuming 90-deg bevel, is qual to the width times the square of the lepth. Since the strength varies as the prodict of width and depth, it is apparent that in-reasing the depth decreases the efficiency.

In a *fillet weld*, since the strength varies diectly as the weld size, smaller welds are more fficient than larger ones as long as the cost per unit of volume is constant. However, velds less than $\frac{3}{16}$ in. and welds requiring

more than one pass cost more per unit of volume. Since welds larger than $\frac{3}{8}$ in. are usually made in two or more passes, the most efficient welds are $\frac{3}{16}$, $\frac{1}{4}$, $\frac{5}{16}$, and $\frac{3}{8}$ in., respectively. While this is true of the weld itself, it may not be true of the joint, since a greater length of weld is needed for the same stress. For example a $\frac{1}{4}$-in. weld must be half again

Fig. 9.10   Fillet Weld

as long as a $\frac{3}{8}$-in. weld to carry the same stress. If the extra length of weld does not require additional detail or main material, the smaller weld is more efficient. Otherwise the cost of additional material must be considered in determining the most efficient weld size.

While it is uneconomical in welded construction to transfer a stress through fillers, or across two or more joints, since each transfer requires a new weld, in riveted construction the same rivet will work at each plane of stress. For example, in a cover-plated girder the same rivets work successively through each joint from the outer cover to the flange, whereas in welded construction new welds would be required at each joint.

Where a filler is required in riveted construction, the rivets will transmit the stress across a thin filler with very little loss in efficiency. In welded construction, however, the stress must be transmitted by the filler, requiring the stress to be carried twice. Furthermore, the thickness of the filler limits the weld size; so it may be impossible to obtain sufficient welding to transmit the stress.

Welds are cheapest when made in the flat position (down-welding) and most expensive in the overhead position. Therefore, field welds should be down-welded whenever possible and shop welds should be arranged for a maximum of down-welding with a minimum of handling.

Sometimes welds are required in places where no appreciable stress occurs, or where the stress is purely nominal in comparison

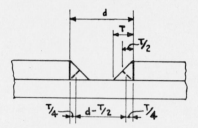

Fig. 9.11 Depth of Weld

with the thickness of the material joined. Examples are seal welds or a beam bearing on a slab or another beam. If such welds are made too small, they may crack because of the quench effect of the larger adjacent masses of metal.

The minimum fillet-weld size used should be as follows for various thicknesses of metal:

$\frac{3}{16}$-in. fillet weld up to $\frac{1}{2}$-in. metal
$\frac{1}{4}$-in. fillet weld up to $\frac{3}{4}$-in. metal
$\frac{5}{16}$-in. fillet weld up to $1\frac{1}{4}$-in. metal
$\frac{3}{8}$-in. fillet weld up to 2-in. metal
$\frac{1}{2}$-in. fillet weld up to 4-in. metal

The minimum length of a weld should be four times the weld size.

  c In a *butt weld* the allowable stress is equal to the product of the throat thickness times the unit stress and the width of weld.

For tension: $P = T \times 15{,}600 \text{ psi} \times W$
For compression: $P = T \times 18{,}000 \text{ psi} \times W$

In a *fillet weld* the allowable stress is equal to the product of the weld size in eighths times 1,200 lb and the length of the weld.

$$P = \frac{T}{1/8} \times 1{,}200 \times L$$

The use of *slots* or *holes* filled with weld metal and designed for the full shear value of the weld area is not permitted by the Building Code of the American Welding Society. Such welds are designed as fillet welds.

The length of a fillet weld in a slot or hole is the average length of the throat of the fillet. For a round hole this length $L = \pi(d - T/2)$.

The *length of a weld* is the effective length as described in the Code. No allowance need be made for the difference between the actual and effective length. The welder will produce the effective length shown on the drawings by lengthening the weld, turning the corner of the connected piece, or by some other device of welding technique.

Adequate provision must be made for any stresses due to eccentricity of the parts or welds. A butt weld under pure tension or shear will have no eccentricity, and under combinations of direct and bending stresses may be treated as a similar section of base material.

In a fillet weld, however, since the plane of rupture is at 45 deg to the applied force, eccentricity is always present. The computation of stresses in fillet welds becomes quite involved if any attempt is made to resolve the forces into the plane of rupture. Present practice assumes all the forces to be resolved into the planes of the legs of the fillet. Since the allowable fiber stresses have been determined by tests of fillet-welded assemblies rather than from tests of weld metal, this assumption is reasonable. Figures 9.18 to 9.2_ give values for eccentrically loaded fillet welds. In the development of these tables and formulae the weld is assumed to be a plane of unit width ($\frac{1}{8}$-in. fillet at 1,200 lb per linear inch) and the strength of other welds is in direct ratio to their relative weld sizes.

  d In the design of beams it is common practice to assume that they are simply supported. This presumes a connection that is sufficiently flexible to permit the ends of the beam to revolve so the beam may assume the slope of a free-ended beam.

In riveted work this free-end condition is partially attained by the use of a light top angle. In some early welded designs, types of top connections were used that permitted practically no flexibility and localized the strain in the weld. Since there was insufficient welding to take care of a fixed-end condition, some welds failed. This caused some engineers to attempt to produce a fully flexible connection—one that would permit sufficient deformation in the joint, within the elastic limit of the material, to permit free-end deflection in the beam. While not impossible, it is impracticable to produce this ideal con

TYPICAL COLUMN BASES

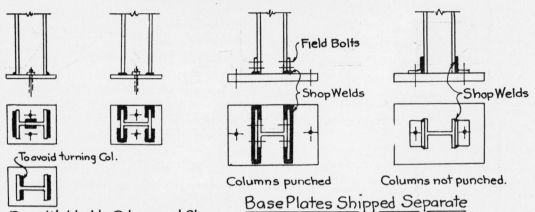

To avoid turning Col.

Base Welded to Column at Shop

Field Bolts
Shop Welds
Shop Welds

Columns punched   Columns not punched.

Base Plates Shipped Separate

CRANE COLUMN BASES

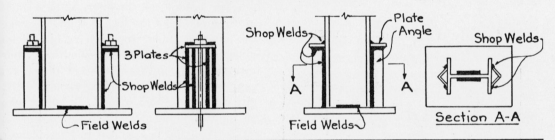

3 Plates
Shop Welds
Field Welds

Shop Welds
Plate Angle
Field Welds

Shop Welds
Section A-A

TYPICAL COLUMN SPLICES

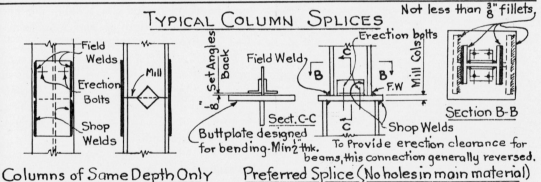

Field Welds
Erection Bolts
Shop Welds
Mill

Columns of Same Depth Only

Set Angles Back
Field Weld
Buttplate designed for bending-Min 2" thk.
Sect. C-C

Not less than 3/8" fillets.
Erection bolts
Mill Cols.
F.W.
Shop Welds
Section B-B

To Provide erection clearance for beams, this connection generally reversed.

Preferred Splice (No holes in main material)

CRANE COLUMN SPLICE

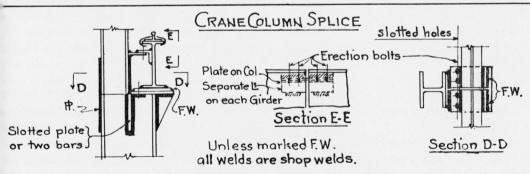

Slotted plate or two bars

Plate on Col.
Separate L on each Girder
Section E-E

Unless marked F.W. all welds are shop welds.

slotted holes
Erection bolts
F.W.
Section D-D

Fig. 9.12 Typical Welded-Column Details

TYPICAL BEAM DETAILS

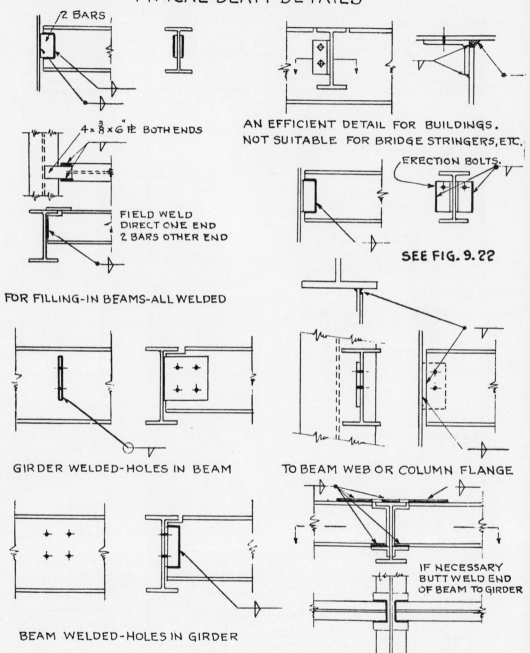

2 BARS

4 × ⅜ × 6" ℄ BOTH ENDS

FIELD WELD
DIRECT ONE END
2 BARS OTHER END

FOR FILLING-IN BEAMS-ALL WELDED

AN EFFICIENT DETAIL FOR BUILDINGS.
NOT SUITABLE FOR BRIDGE STRINGERS, ETC.

ERECTION BOLTS.

SEE FIG. 9.22

GIRDER WELDED-HOLES IN BEAM

TO BEAM WEB OR COLUMN FLANGE

BEAM WELDED-HOLES IN GIRDER

IF NECESSARY
BUTT WELD END
OF BEAM TO GIRDER

WHEN SPECIFICATIONS PERMIT,
BOLT FILLING-IN BEAMS

BEAM CONTINUOUS OVER GIRDER

Fig. 9.13   Typical Welded-Beam Details

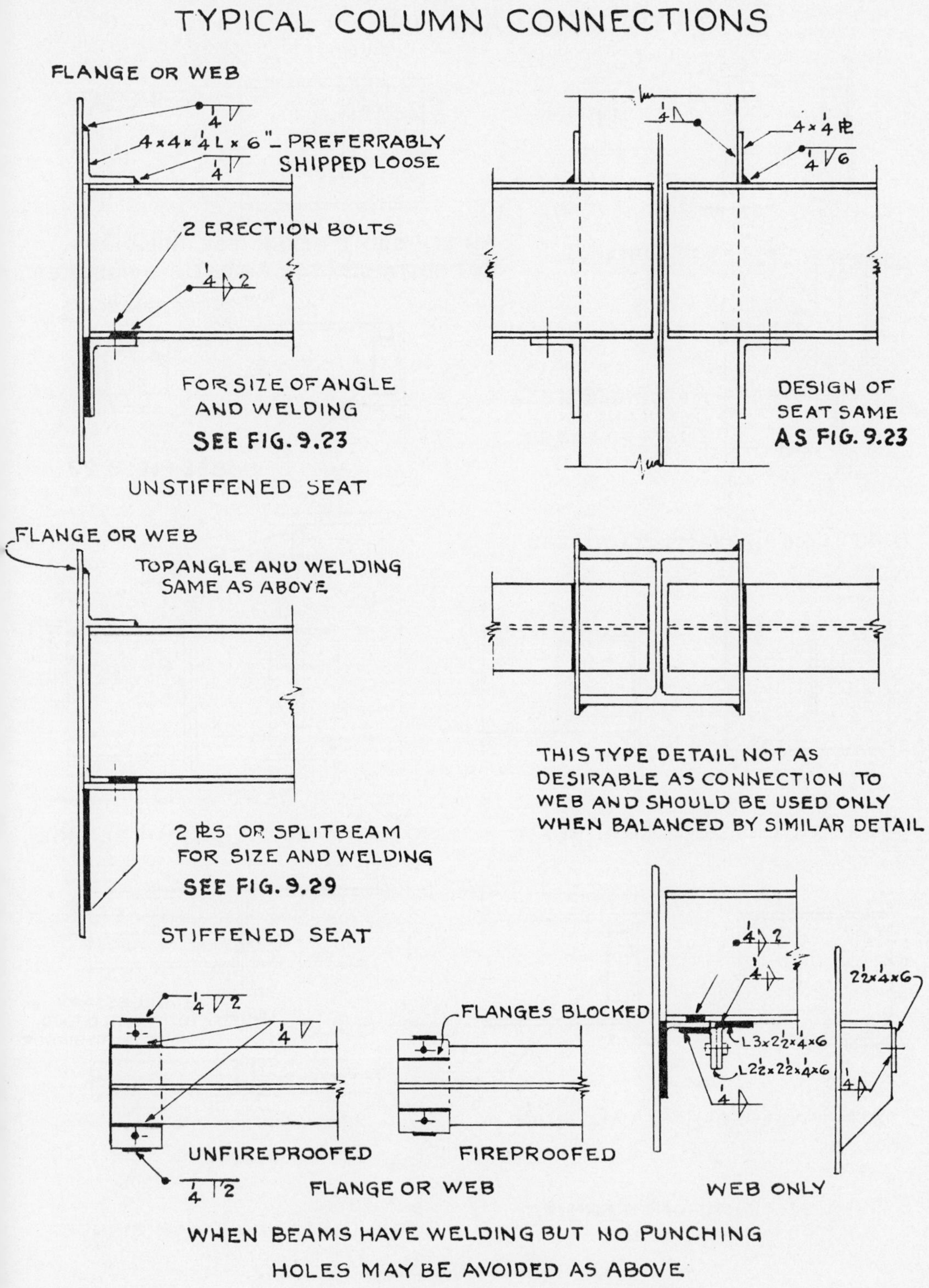
TYPICAL COLUMN CONNECTIONS
FLANGE OR WEB
1/4
4×4×1/4 L × 6" – PREFERRABLY SHIPPED LOOSE
1/4
2 ERECTION BOLTS
1/4 2
FOR SIZE OF ANGLE AND WELDING
SEE FIG. 9.23
UNSTIFFENED SEAT
1/4
4×1/4 PL
1/4 6
DESIGN OF SEAT SAME AS FIG. 9.23
FLANGE OR WEB
TOP ANGLE AND WELDING SAME AS ABOVE
2 PLS OR SPLIT BEAM FOR SIZE AND WELDING
SEE FIG. 9.29
STIFFENED SEAT
THIS TYPE DETAIL NOT AS DESIRABLE AS CONNECTION TO WEB AND SHOULD BE USED ONLY WHEN BALANCED BY SIMILAR DETAIL
1/4 2
1/4
1/4
FLANGES BLOCKED
1/4 2
2 1/2×1/4×6
L3×2 1/2×1/4×6
L2 1/2×2 1/2×1/4×6
1/4
1/4
1/4 2
UNFIREPROOFED
FIREPROOFED
FLANGE OR WEB
WEB ONLY
WHEN BEAMS HAVE WELDING BUT NO PUNCHING
HOLES MAY BE AVOIDED AS ABOVE

Fig. 9.14 Typical Welded-Column Connections

PLATE GIRDERS

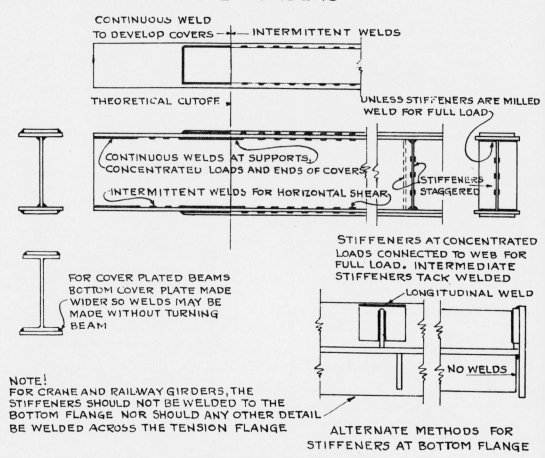

CONTINUOUS WELD
TO DEVELOP COVERS —— INTERMITTENT WELDS

THEORETICAL CUTOFF   UNLESS STIFFENERS ARE MILLED
                            WELD FOR FULL LOAD

CONTINUOUS WELDS AT SUPPORTS,
CONCENTRATED LOADS AND ENDS OF COVERS
INTERMITTENT WELDS FOR HORIZONTAL SHEAR   STIFFENERS STAGGERED

STIFFENERS AT CONCENTRATED
LOADS CONNECTED TO WEB FOR
FULL LOAD. INTERMEDIATE
STIFFENERS TACK WELDED

FOR COVER PLATED BEAMS
BOTTOM COVER PLATE MADE
WIDER SO WELDS MAY BE
MADE WITHOUT TURNING
BEAM

LONGITUDINAL WELD

NO WELDS

NOTE!
FOR CRANE AND RAILWAY GIRDERS, THE
STIFFENERS SHOULD NOT BE WELDED TO THE
BOTTOM FLANGE NOR SHOULD ANY OTHER DETAIL
BE WELDED ACROSS THE TENSION FLANGE

ALTERNATE METHODS FOR
STIFFENERS AT BOTTOM FLANGE

ALTERNATE CONSTRUCTION

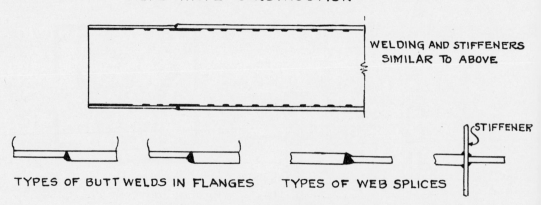

WELDING AND STIFFENERS
SIMILAR TO ABOVE

STIFFENER

TYPES OF BUTT WELDS IN FLANGES   TYPES OF WEB SPLICES

Fig. 9.15 Typical Welded-Plate Girder

TRUSS DETAILS

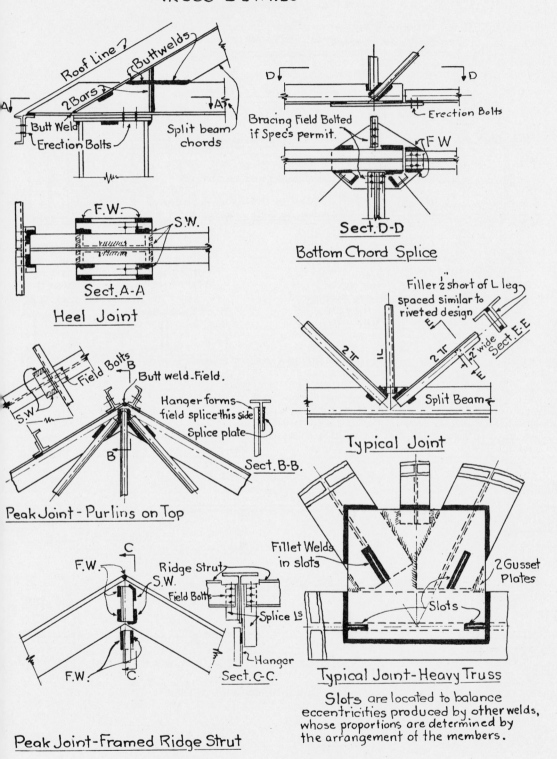

Fig. 9.16   Typical Welded-Truss Details

FOR CONTINUITY

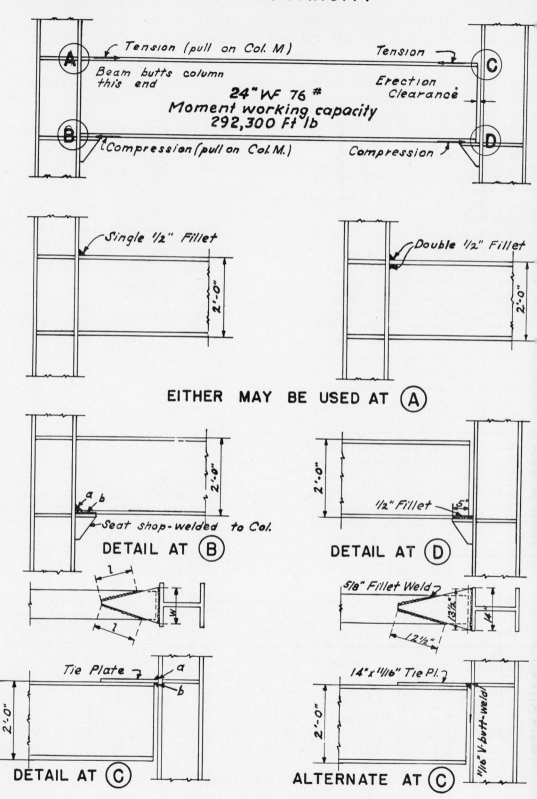

Fig. 9.17 Typical Welded Details for Continuity

ALLOWABLE ECCENTRIC LONGITUDINAL LOADS ON FILLET WELDS

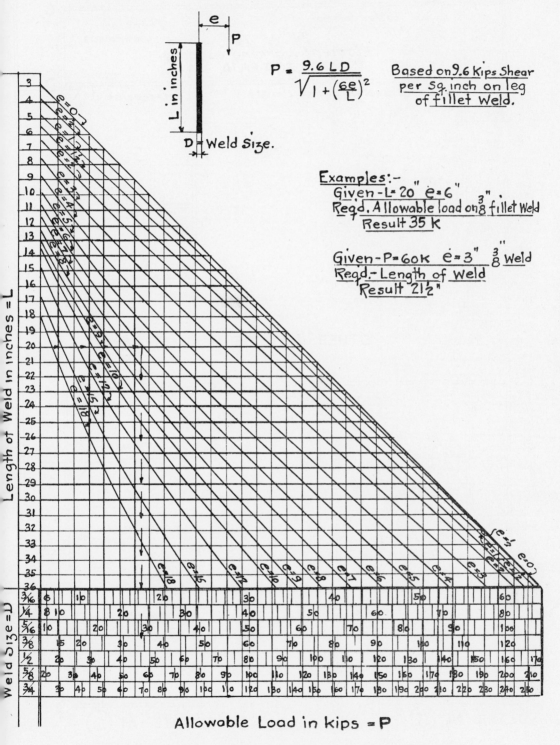

$$P = \frac{9.6 \, LD}{\sqrt{1 + \left(\frac{6e}{L}\right)^2}}$$

Based on 9.6 Kips Shear per Sq. inch on leg of fillet weld.

Examples:-
Given - L = 20" e = 6"
Reqd. Allowable load on $\frac{3}{8}$" fillet weld
Result 35 K

Given - P = 60 K e = 3" $\frac{3}{8}$" Weld
Reqd. - Length of weld
Result 21½"

Fig. 9.18   Allowable Eccentric Longitudinal Loads on Fillet Welds

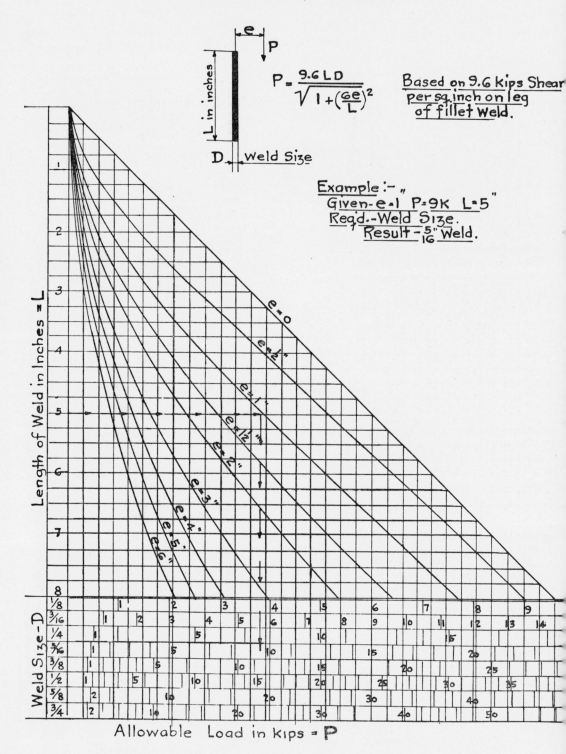

Fig. 9.19 Allowable Eccentric Longitudinal Loads on Short Welds

ALLOWABLE ECCENTRIC TRANSVERSE LOADS
ON FILLET WELDS.

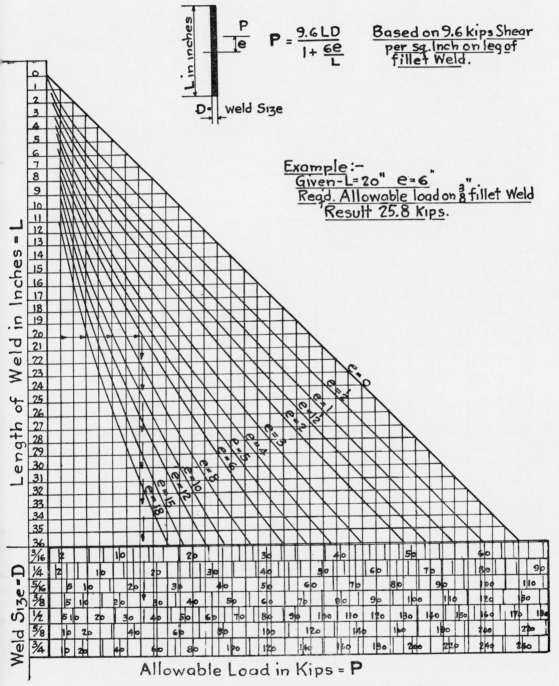

$$P = \frac{9.6\,LD}{1 + \frac{6e}{L}}$$

Based on 9.6 kips Shear per sq. Inch on leg of fillet Weld.

Example:–
Given–L=20" e=6"
Reqd. Allowable load on ⅜" fillet Weld
Result 25.8 Kips.

Fig. 9.20   Allowable Eccentric Transverse Loads on Fillet Welds

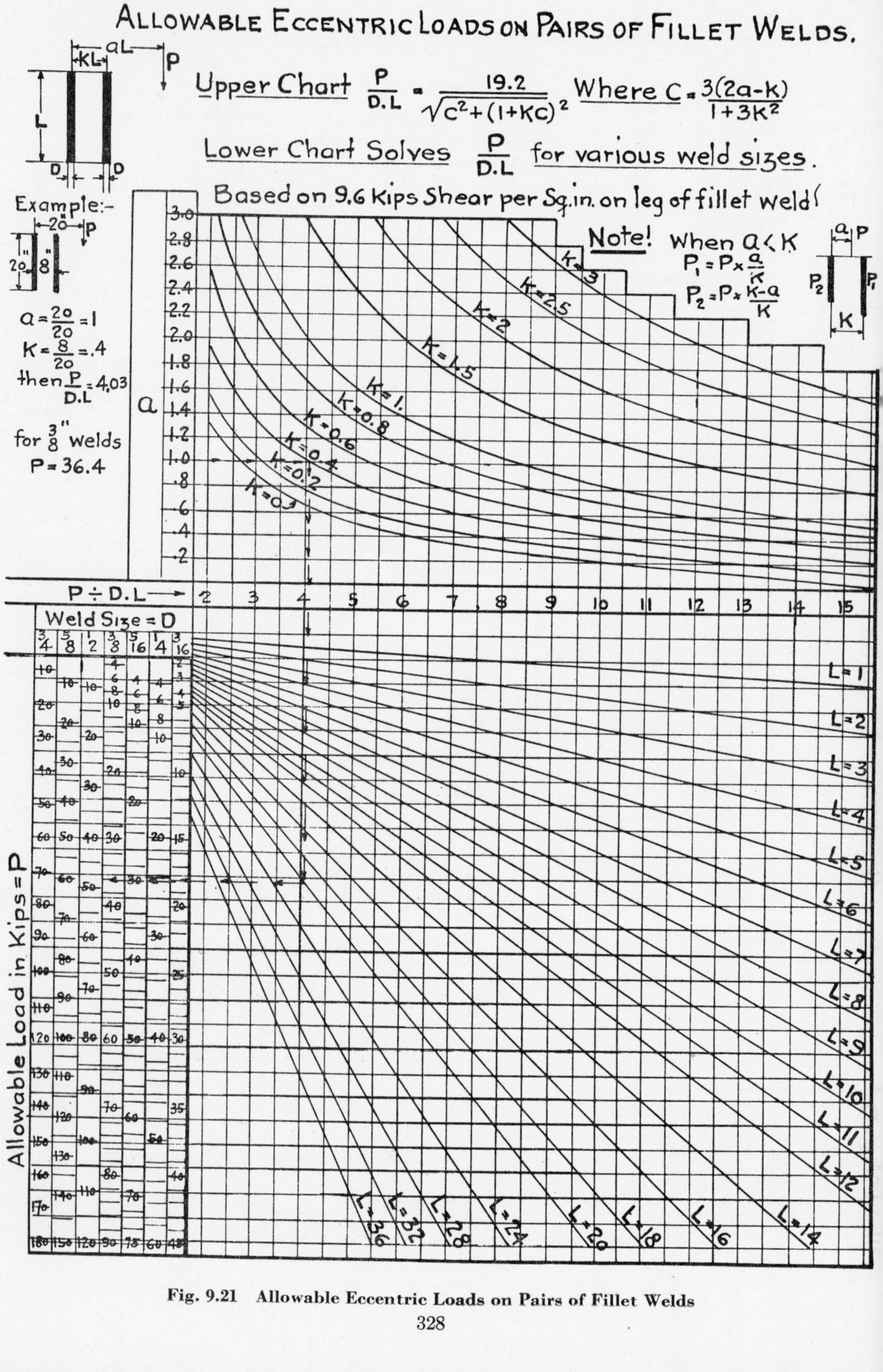

Fig. 9.21   Allowable Eccentric Loads on Pairs of Fillet Welds

328

ALLOWABLE LOADS ON FRAMED CONNECTIONS

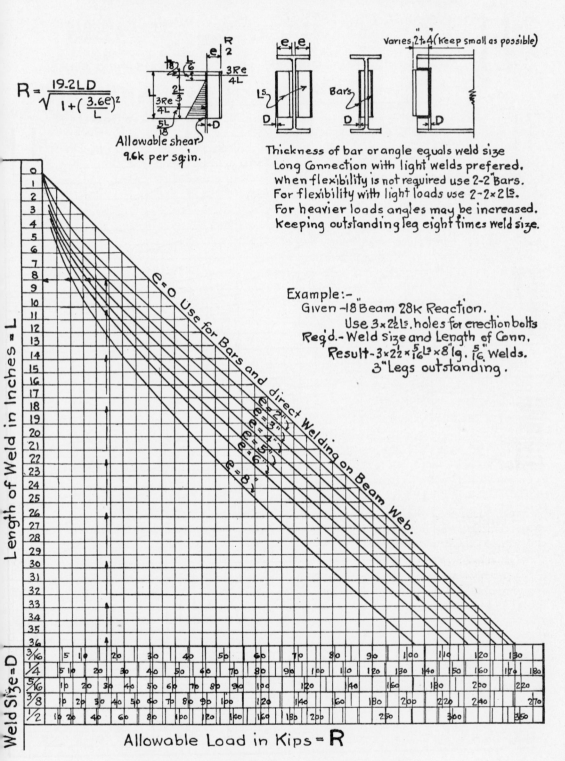

$$R = \frac{19.2 LD}{\sqrt{1 + \left(\frac{3.6e}{L}\right)^2}}$$

Allowable shear 9.6k per sq. in.

Varies 2 to 4 (keep small as possible)

Thickness of bar or angle equals weld size
Long Connection with light welds prefered.
When flexibility is not required use 2-2" Bars.
For flexibility with light loads use 2-2×2 Ls.
For heavier loads angles may be increased.
keeping outstanding leg eight times weld size.

Example:-
Given -18" Beam 28k Reaction.
Use 3×2½ Ls. holes for erection bolts
Req'd.- Weld size and Length of Conn.
Result-3×2½×5/16 Ls×8" lg. 5/16" Welds.
3" Legs outstanding.

e=0 Use for Bars and direct Welding on Beam Web.

Length of Weld in Inches = L

Weld Size= D

Allowable Load in Kips = R

Fig. 9.22   Allowable Loads on Framed Connections

dition, and it is no more necessary in a welded building than in a riveted one.

In Figs. 9.14 and 9.23 a top angle is shown that is about six times as flexible as the standard riveted top angle. It is connected with welds exceeding in strength the rivets in the standard riveted connection. This connection is strong enough to hold the top flange of the beam laterally to prevent rolling and to maintain the top flange in a horizontal plane to reduce the buckling stresses in the beam web.

The beam seat should also be sufficiently flexible to permit the beam to assume the desired end slope. The seat shown in Figs. 9.14 and 9.23 is designed to accomplish this purpose. It is assumed that as the beam deflects it will tend to rotate about the toe of the seat angle. The seat angle is too flexible to support the beam on this lever arm and deflects until the beam and beam seat come to equilibrium with the slope of the seat angle approximately that of a simple beam. At that point the stress in the seat angle is assumed to be 20,000 psi in bending, and the crippling stress in the beam web is 24,000 psi. The length of bearing is determined by the 1946 AISC formula, $a = (R/24,000t) - K$ (see Fig. 9.22).

It has been suggested that the permissible stress in the seat angle be 33,000 psi under these conditions. Since the stress in the beam seat and the buckling stress in the beam web are interdependent, however, equilibrium can only occur when these parts are stressed to the same degree. Any attempt to make the seat more flexible will tend to shorten the length of bearing and produce crushing of the beam web at the end of the beam.

When side connections are used, flexibility may be achieved by using a light angle similar to riveted construction. For economy, the leg against the beam web is made as short as possible, while the width of the outstanding leg is selected to produce the desired flexibility.

When connecting to a comparatively rigid support, such as a column, or a girder with beams framing opposite, all the flexibility must be in the connection.

If the girder web rotates or is so thin that it produces angular motion at the end of the beam, a more rigid type of connection may be necessary. For connection material and welding for side connections see Fig. 9.22.

The design of stiffened seats involves no unusual theory. The moment on the group of welds is obtained by multiplying the beam reaction by its lever arm obtained from Fig. 9.25. The calculation of the moment of inertia of the group of welds is based on the assumption that the neutral axis coincides with the center of gravity of the group (see Fig. 9.24). In order to simplify the calculations and use of the figure, the horizontal welds are fixed at 20 percent of the vertical welds, on the assumption that such proportions are most practical.

Since the lever arm for a stiffened seat is always greater than for a flexible seat for usual loading conditions, a stiffened seat is less economical and should not be used where a flexible seat will fulfill the requirements.

e Welded plate girders are usually made of three plates. The web and flange plates are designed for shear and moment in the same way as riveted girders. The flange should be so proportioned that not more than one pair of cover plates is required.

The welding required between the flange plates and the web is determined by the horizontal shear per linear inch, which equals VM_s/I, where V is the vertical shear at the section, M_s is the statical moment of that portion beyond the plane of the weld, and I is the moment of inertia of the entire section. Multiplying this shear by 12 and dividing by the allowable weld stress per linear inch gives the total inches of weld per foot.

If the factors V, M_s, or I vary throughout the length of the girder, separate calculations will be required for as many variations in the welding as the judgment of the designer dictates.

Cover plates are extended beyond the theoretical length a sufficient distance to permit continuous welding to connect for the proportion of stress in the covers. It is assumed that the stress in the girder flange without covers is the full permissible stress and that

ALLOWABLE LOADS ON UNSTIFFENED SEATS

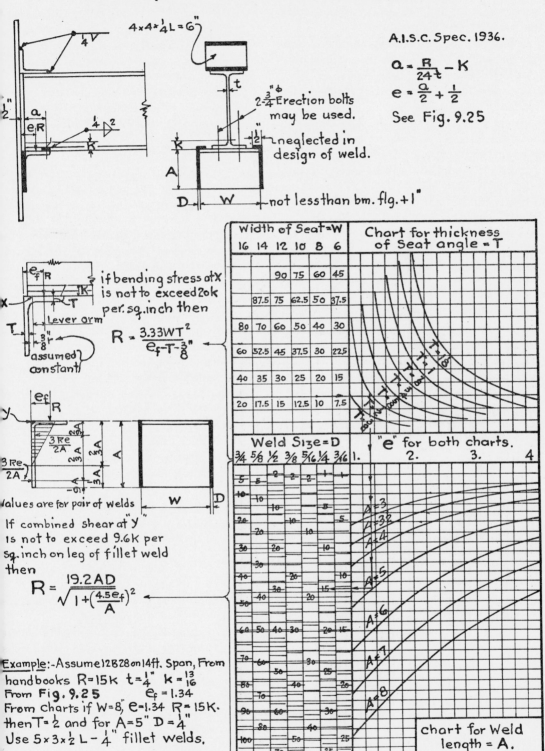

$4 \times 4 \times \frac{1}{4} L = 6"$

A.I.S.C. Spec. 1936.

$a = \frac{R}{24t} - K$

$e = \frac{a}{2} + \frac{1}{2}$

See Fig. 9.25

$2-\frac{3}{4}"\phi$ Erection bolts may be used.

$\frac{1}{2}"$ neglected in design of weld.

not less than bm. flg. + 1"

if bending stress at X is not to exceed 20k per sq. inch then

$R = \frac{3.33 W T^2}{e_f - T - \frac{3}{8}"}$

(assumed constant)

Lever arm

$T - \frac{3}{8}"$

Values are for pair of welds

If combined shear at "y" is not to exceed 9.6k per sq. inch on leg of fillet weld then

$R = \frac{19.2 AD}{\sqrt{1 + \left(\frac{4.5 e_f}{A}\right)^2}}$

Example:- Assume 12B28 on 14ft. Span, From handbooks R=15k $t=\frac{1}{4}"$ $k=\frac{13}{16}$
From **Fig. 9.25** $e_f = 1.34$
From charts if W=8", e=1.34 R=15K.
then T=½ and for A=5" D=¼"
Use 5×3×½ L – ¼" fillet welds.

Width of Seat = W

16	14	12	10	8	6
	90	75	60	45	
	87.5	75	62.5	50	37.5
80	70	60	50	40	30
60	52.5	45	37.5	30	22.5
40	35	30	25	20	15
20	17.5	15	12.5	10	7.5

Chart for thickness of Seat angle = T

Weld Size = D

| ¾ | ⅝ | ½ | ⅜ | 5/16 | ¼ | 3/16 |

"e" for both charts.   1.   2.   3.   4

chart for Weld length = A.

Fig. 9.23   Allowable Loads on Unstiffened Seats

331

ALLOWABLE LOADS ON STIFFENED SEATS

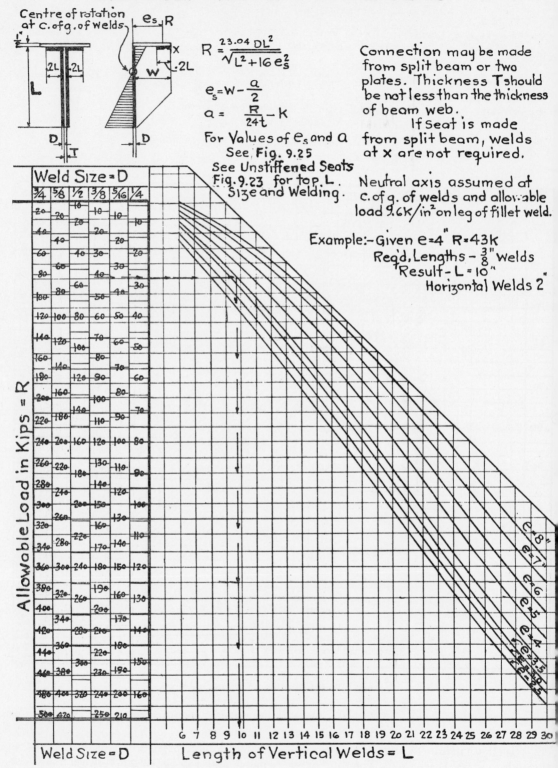

Centre of rotation at c. of g. of welds.

$$R = \frac{23.04\, DL^2}{\sqrt{L^2 + 16\, e_s^2}}$$

$$e_s = W - \frac{a}{2}$$

$$a = \frac{R}{24t} - k$$

For Values of e_s and a See Fig. 9.25
See Unstiffened Seats Fig. 9.23 for top L. Size and Welding.

Connection may be made from split beam or two plates. Thickness T should be not less than the thickness of beam web.
If seat is made from split beam, welds at x are not required.

Neutral axis assumed at c. of g. of welds and allowable load 9.6 k/in² on leg of fillet weld.

Example:- Given e=4" R=43k
Req'd. Lengths - ⅜" welds
Result- L = 10"
Horizontal Welds 2"

Fig. 9.24 Allowable Loads on Stiffened Seats

332

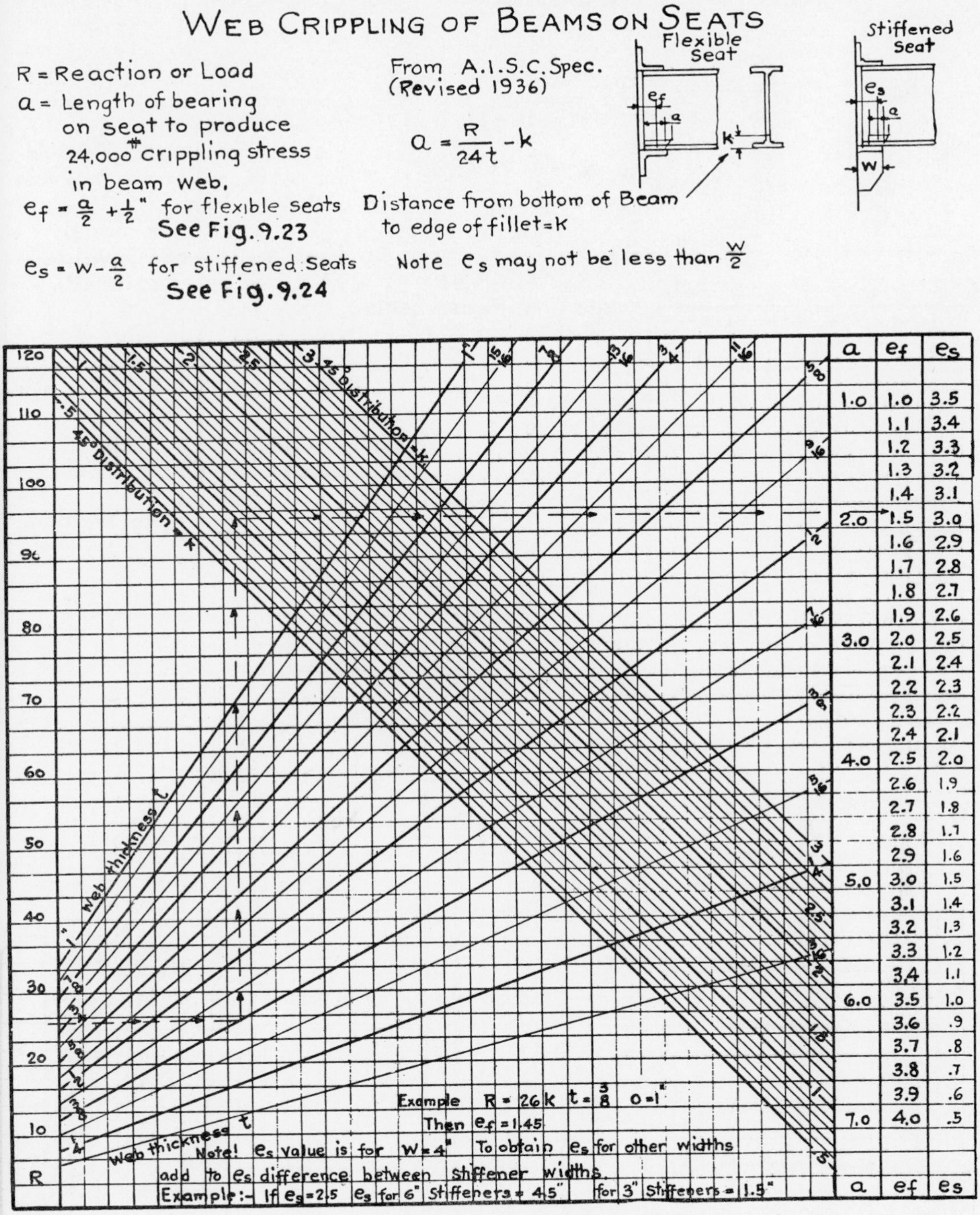

WEB CRIPPLING OF BEAMS ON SEATS

R = Reaction or Load

a = Length of bearing on seat to produce 24,000# crippling stress in beam web.

$e_f = \frac{a}{2} + \frac{1}{2}"$ for flexible seats
See Fig. 9.23

$e_s = w - \frac{a}{2}$ for stiffened seats
See Fig. 9.24

From A.I.S.C. Spec. (Revised 1936)

$$a = \frac{R}{24t} - k$$

Distance from bottom of Beam to edge of fillet = k

Note e_s may not be less than $\frac{w}{2}$

Flexible Seat

Stiffened Seat

			a	ef	es
			1.0	1.0	3.5
				1.1	3.4
				1.2	3.3
				1.3	3.2
				1.4	3.1
			2.0	1.5	3.0
				1.6	2.9
				1.7	2.8
				1.8	2.7
				1.9	2.6
			3.0	2.0	2.5
				2.1	2.4
				2.2	2.3
				2.3	2.2
				2.4	2.1
			4.0	2.5	2.0
				2.6	1.9
				2.7	1.8
				2.8	1.7
				2.9	1.6
			5.0	3.0	1.5
				3.1	1.4
				3.2	1.3
				3.3	1.2
				3.4	1.1
			6.0	3.5	1.0
				3.6	.9
				3.7	.8
				3.8	.7
				3.9	.6
			7.0	4.0	.5

Example R = 26k   t = $\frac{3}{8}$ o = 1
Then $e_f = 1.45$
Note! e_s value is for w = 4" To obtain e_s for other widths add to e_s difference between stiffener widths.
Example:- If $e_s = 2.5$ e_s for 6" stiffeners = 4.5" for 3" stiffeners = 1.5"

Fig. 9.25   Web Crippling of Beams on Seats

the covers will take a share of the stress based on the ratio of section modulus without covers to section modulus with covers. Between the ends tack welds are used. The total of all the welding between the end of the cover and any point should develop all the stress at that point.

The minimum size of tack weld between flange and web plates and between flange and cover plates should not be less than indicated

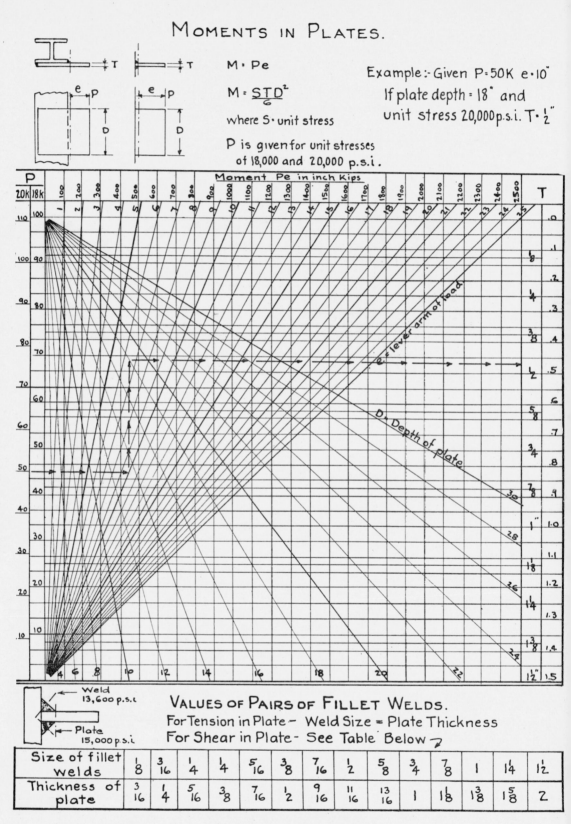

Fig. 9.26 Moments in Plates

334

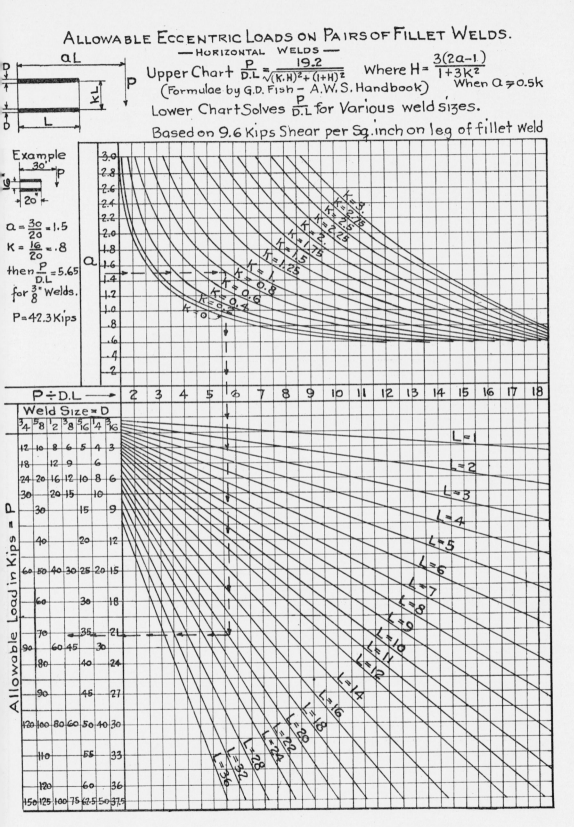

Fig. 9.27 Allowable Eccentric Loads on Pairs of Horizontal Fillet Welds

335

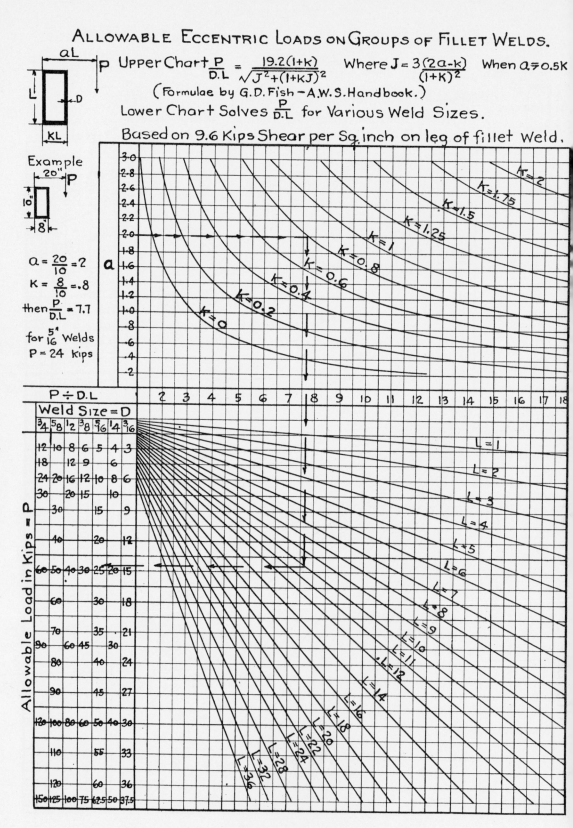

Fig. 9.28 Allowable Eccentric Load on Groups of Fillet Welds

336

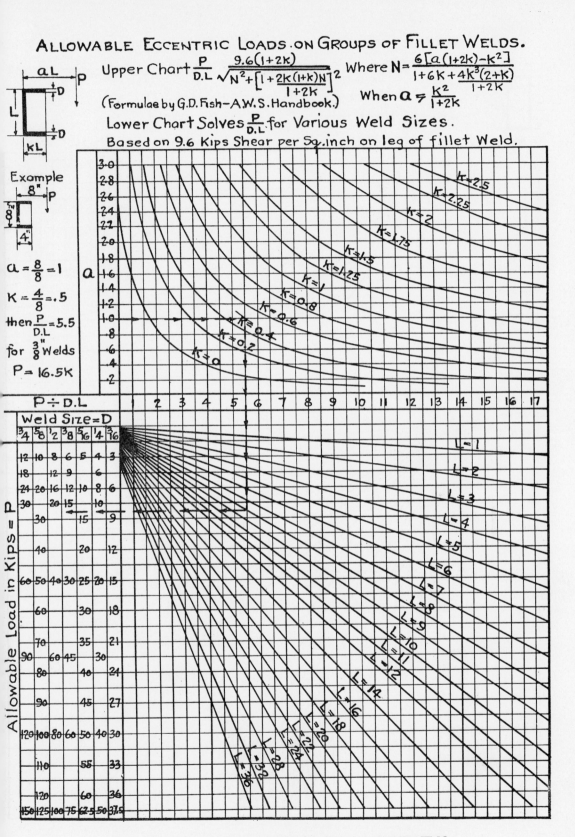

Fig. 9.29 Allowable Eccentric Load on Groups of Fillet Welds

337

ALLOWABLE ECCENTRIC LOADS ON GROUPS OF FILLET WELDS

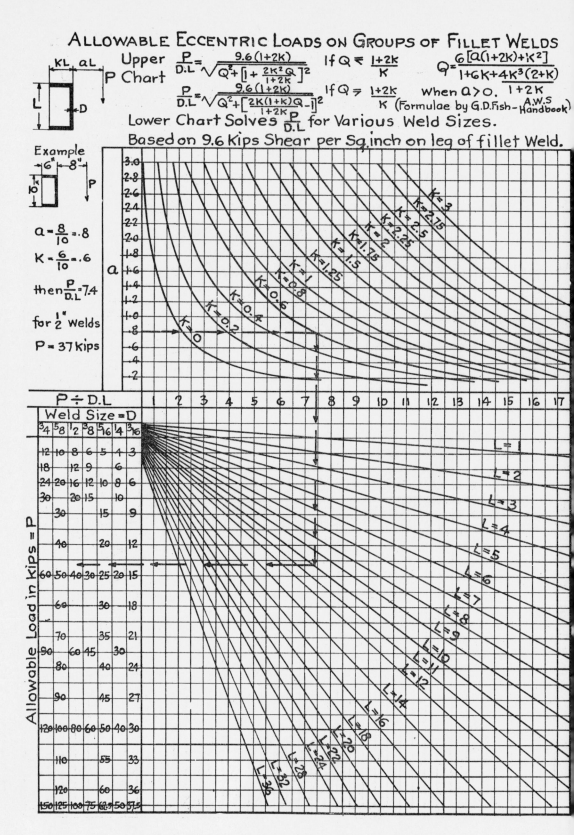

Fig. 9.30   Allowable Eccentric Load on Groups of Fillet Welds

338

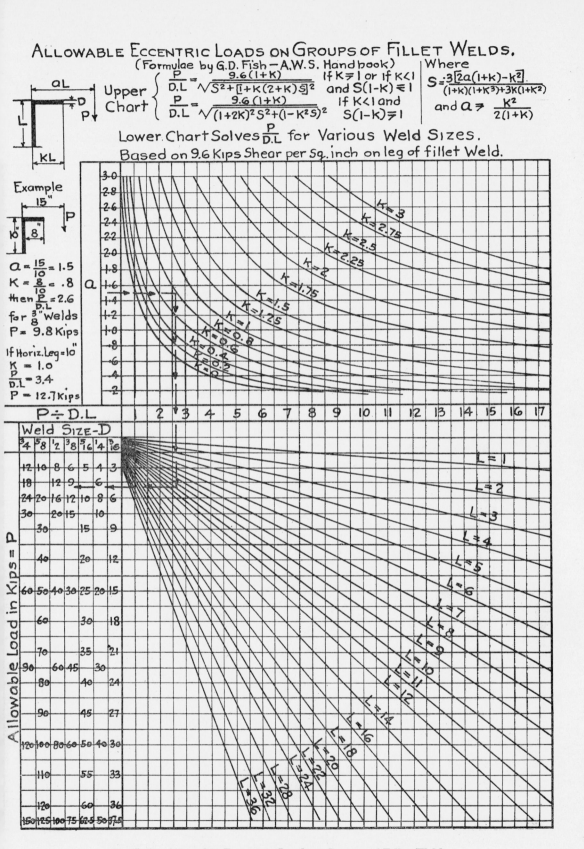

Fig. 9.31 Allowable Eccentric Load on Groups of Fillet Welds

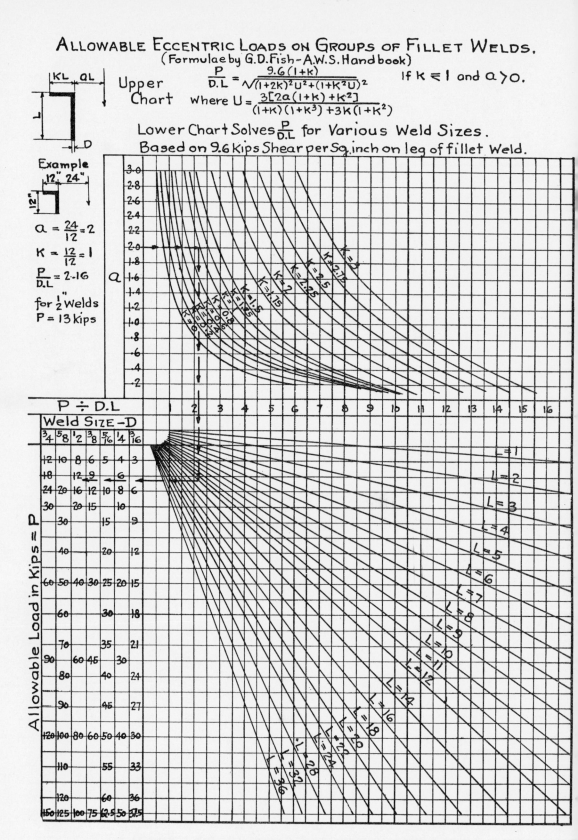

Fig. 9.32 Allowable Eccentric Load on Groups of Fillet Welds

Table 9.5 Allowable Loads on Fillet Welds

$P = 9.6DL$, where D = weld size, inches; L = weld length, inches; P = allowable load, kips
Based on 13,600 psi shear on throat = 9.6 kips per sq in. on leg

L	\multicolumn{11}{c}{D, in.}										
	$\frac{1}{8}$	$\frac{3}{16}$	$\frac{1}{4}$	$\frac{5}{16}$	$\frac{3}{8}$	$\frac{7}{16}$	$\frac{1}{2}$	$\frac{5}{8}$	$\frac{3}{4}$	$\frac{7}{8}$	1
.5	.6	.9	1.2	1.5	1.8	2.1	2.4	3	3.6	4.2	4.8
1.0	1.2	1.8	2.4	3.0	3.6	4.2	4.8	6	7.2	8.4	9.6
1.5	1.8	2.7	3.6	4.5	5.4	6.3	7.2	9	10.8	12.6	14.4
2.0	2.4	3.6	4.8	6.0	7.2	8.4	9.6	12	14.4	16.8	19.2
2.5	3.0	4.5	6.0	7.5	9.0	10.5	12.0	15	18.0	21.0	24.0
3.0	3.6	5.4	7.2	9.0	10.8	12.6	14.4	18	21.6	25.2	28.8
3.5	4.2	6.3	8.4	10.5	12.6	14.7	16.8	21	25.2	29.4	33.6
4.0	4.8	7.2	9.6	12.0	14.4	16.8	19.2	24	28.8	33.6	38.4
4.5	5.4	8.1	10.8	13.5	16.2	18.9	21.6	27	32.4	37.8	43.2
5.0	6.0	9.0	12.0	15.0	18.0	21.0	24.0	30	36.0	42.0	48.0
5.5	6.6	9.9	13.2	16.5	19.8	23.1	26.4	33	39.6	46.2	52.8
6.0	7.2	10.8	14.4	18.0	21.6	25.2	28.8	36	43.2	50.4	57.6
6.5	7.8	11.7	15.6	19.5	23.4	27.3	31.2	39	46.8	54.6	62.4
7.0	8.4	12.6	16.8	21.0	25.2	29.4	33.6	42	50.4	58.8	67.2
7.5	9.0	13.5	18.0	22.5	27.0	31.5	36.0	45	54.0	63.0	72.0
8.0	9.6	14.4	19.2	24.0	28.8	33.6	38.4	48	57.6	67.2	76.8
8.5	10.2	15.3	20.4	25.5	30.6	35.7	40.8	51	61.2	71.4	81.6
9.0	10.8	16.2	21.6	27.0	32.4	37.8	43.2	54	64.8	75.6	86.4
9.5	11.4	17.1	22.8	28.5	34.2	39.9	45.6	57	68.4	79.8	91.2
10.0	12.0	18.0	24.0	30.0	36.0	42.0	48.0	60	72.0	84.0	96.0
10.5	12.6	18.9	25.2	31.5	37.8	44.1	50.4	63	75.6	88.2	100.8
11.0	13.2	19.8	26.4	33.0	39.6	46.2	52.8	66	79.2	92.4	105.6
11.5	13.8	20.7	27.6	34.5	41.4	48.3	55.2	69	82.8	96.6	110.4
12	14.4	21.6	28.8	36	43.2	50.4	57.6	72	86.4	100.8	115.2
13	15.6	23.4	31.2	39	46.8	54.6	62.4	78	93.6	109.2	124.8
14	16.8	25.2	33.6	42	50.4	58.8	67.2	84	100.8	117.6	134.4
15	18.0	27.0	36.0	45	54.0	63.0	72.0	90	108.0	126.0	144.0
16	19.2	28.8	38.4	48	57.6	67.2	76.8	96	115.2	134.4	153.6
17	20.4	30.6	40.8	51	61.2	71.4	81.6	102	122.4	142.8	163.2
18	21.6	32.4	43.2	54	64.8	75.6	86.4	108	129.6	151.2	172.8
19	22.8	34.2	45.6	57	68.4	79.8	91.2	114	136.8	159.6	182.4
20	24.0	36.0	48.0	60	72.0	84.0	96.0	120	144.0	168.0	192.0
21	25.2	37.8	50.4	63	75.6	88.2	100.8	126	151.2	176.4	201.6
22	26.4	39.6	52.8	66	79.2	92.4	105.6	132	158.4	184.8	211.2
23	27.6	41.4	55.2	69	82.8	96.6	110.4	138	165.6	193.2	220.8
24	28.8	43.2	57.6	72	86.4	100.8	115.2	144	172.8	201.6	230.4
25	30.0	45.0	60.0	75	90.0	105.0	120.0	150	180.0	210.0	240.0
26	31.2	46.8	62.4	78	93.6	109.2	124.8	156	187.2	218.4	249.6
27	32.4	48.6	64.8	81	97.2	113.4	129.6	162	194.4	226.8	259.2
28	33.6	50.4	67.2	84	100.8	117.6	134.4	168	201.6	235.2	268.8
29	34.8	52.2	69.6	87	104.4	121.8	139.2	174	208.8	243.6	278.4
30	36.0	54.0	72.0	90	108.0	126.0	144.0	180	216.0	252.0	288.0

Table 9.6   Welds for Attaching Angles

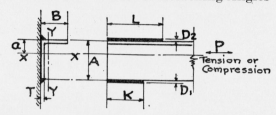

Size of angle, k/sq. in.	20k/ sq in.		19k/ sq in.		18k/ sq in.		17k/ sq in.		16k/ sq in.		15k/ sq in.		14k/ sq in.		13k/ sq in.		12k/ sq in.		11k/ sq in.		10k/ sq in.	
	K	L	K	L	K	L	K	L	K	L	K	L	K	L	K	L	K	L	K	L	K	L
8 × 8	9.0	23.5	8.5	22.0	8.0	21.0	7.5	20.0	7.0	18.5	7.0	17.5	6.0	16.5	5.0	15.0	5.5	14.0	5.0	13.0	4.5	12.0
8 × 6	9.0	20.0	8.0	19.0	8.0	17.5	7.5	16.5	7.0	15.5	6.5	15.0	6.0	14.0	5.5	13.0	5.0	12.0	5.0	10.5	4.0	10.0
8 × 4	8.5	15.5	8.0	15.0	7.5	14.0	7.5	13.0	7.0	12.5	6.5	11.5	6.0	11.0	5.5	10.0	5.0	9.5	4.5	8.5	4.0	8.0
7 × 4	7.5	14.5	7.0	14.0	7.0	13.0	6.5	12.5	6.0	12.0	6.0	11.0	5.5	10.0	5.0	10.0	4.5	9.0	4.5	8.0	4.0	7.0
6 × 6	6.5	17.5	6.5	17.0	6.0	16.0	6.0	15.0	5.5	14.0	5.5	13.0	5.0	12.0	4.5	11.5	4.0	11.0	4.0	10.5	3.5	8.5
6 × 4	6.5	14.0	6.5	13.0	6.0	12.5	5.5	11.5	5.0	11.0	5.0	10.0	4.5	9.5	4.5	8.5	4.0	8.0	3.5	7.5	3.0	7.0
6 × 3½*	6.5	12.5	6.0	12.0	6.0	11.0	5.5	10.5	5.0	10.5	5.0	9.5	4.5	9.0	4.5	8.0	4.0	7.5	3.5	7.0	3.0	6.5
5 × 5	5.5	14.5	5.0	14.0	5.0	13.0	5.0	12.5	4.5	11.5	4.0	11.0	4.0	10.0	3.5	9.5	3.5	9.5	3.0	8.0	3.0	7.0
5 × 3½	5.5	11.5	5.0	11.0	5.0	10.5	4.5	10.0	4.5	9.0	4.0	9.0	4.0	8.0	3.5	7.5	3.5	7.0	3.0	6.5	3.0	5.5
5 × 3*	5.5	10.5	5.0	10.0	5.0	9.5	4.5	9.0	4.5	8.5	4.0	8.0	4.0	7.5	3.5	7.0	3.0	6.5	3.0	6.0	3.0	5.5
4 × 4	4.5	12.0	4.5	11.0	4.0	10.5	4.0	10.0	3.5	9.5	3.5	8.5	3.5	8.0	3.0	7.5	3.0	7.0	2.5	6.5	2.5	5.5
4 × 3½	4.5	10.5	4.5	10.0	4.0	9.5	4.0	9.0	3.5	8.5	3.5	8.0	3.0	7.5	3.0	6.5	3.0	6.0	2.5	6.0	2.5	5.0
4 × 3	4.5	9.5	4.5	9.0	4.0	8.5	4.0	8.0	3.5	8.0	3.5	7.0	3.0	7.0	3.0	6.5	3.0	5.5	2.5	5.5	2.5	4.5
3½ × 3½	4.0	10.0	4.0	9.5	3.5	9.5	3.5	8.5	3.0	8.5	3.0	7.5	3.0	7.0	2.5	6.5	2.5	6.0	2.5	5.5	2.0	5.0
3½ × 3	4.0	9.0	4.0	8.5	3.5	8.5	3.5	7.5	3.0	7.5	3.0	7.0	3.0	6.5	2.5	6.0	2.5	5.5	2.0	5.0	2.0	4.5
3½ × 2½*	4.0	8.0	4.0	7.5	3.5	7.5	3.0	7.0	3.0	7.0	3.0	6.0	3.0	5.5	2.5	5.5	2.5	5.0	2.0	4.5	2.0	4.0
3 × 3	3.5	8.5	3.5	8.0	3.0	8.0	3.0	7.0	3.0	7.0	2.5	6.5	2.5	6.0	2.0	6.0	2.0	5.5	2.0	4.5	1.5	4.5
3 × 2½	3.5	7.5	3.5	7.0	3.0	7.0	3.0	6.5	3.0	6.0	2.5	6.0	2.5	5.0	2.0	5.0	2.0	4.5	2.0	4.0	1.5	4.0
3 × 2*	3.5	6.5	3.0	7.0	3.0	6.0	3.0	5.5	2.5	5.5	2.5	5.0	2.0	5.0	2.0	4.5	2.0	4.0	2.0	3.5	1.5	3.5
2½ × 2½	3.0	7.5	3.0	7.0	2.5	6.5	2.5	6.0	2.5	5.5	2.0	5.5	2.0	5.0	2.0	4.5	1.5	4.5	1.5	4.0	1.5	3.5
2½ × 2	3.0	6.5	3.0	6.0	2.5	6.0	2.5	5.0	2.5	5.0	2.0	5.0	2.0	4.5	2.0	4.0	1.5	4.0	1.5	3.5	1.5	3.0
2 × 2	2.5	5.5	2.5	5.5	2.0	5.5	2.0	5.0	2.0	4.5	1.5	4.5	2.0	4.0	1.5	4.0	1.5	3.5	1.5	3.0	1.0	3.0
2 × 1½	2.5	4.5	2.5	4.5	2.0	4.5	2.0	4.0	2.0	4.0	2.0	3.5	1.5	3.5	1.5	3.0	1.5	3.0	1.5	2.5	1.0	2.5
1¾ × 1¾	2.0	4.0	2.0	4.0	1.5	4.0	1.5	3.5	1.5	3.5	1.5	3.0	1.5	3.0	1.5	2.5	1.5	2.5	1.0	2.5	1.0	2.0
1¾ × 1¼	1.5	3.5	1.5	3.5	1.5	3.5	1.5	3.0	1.5	3.0	1.5	2.5	1.5	2.0	1.5	2.0	1.0	2.0	1.0	2.0	1.0	2.0
1½ × 1½	1.5	3.0	1.5	3.0	1.5	2.5	1.5	2.5	1.0	2.5	1.0	2.5	1.0	2.0	1.0	2.0	1.0	2.0	1.0	1.5	1.0	1.5
1¼ × 1¼	1.0	2.0	1.0	2.0	1.0	2.0	1.0	2.0	1.0	1.5	1.0	1.5	1.0	1.5	1.0	1.5	0.5	1.5	0.5	1.5	0.5	1.5
1 × 1	1.0	1.0	1.0	1.0	1.0	1.0	0.5	1.0	0.5	1.0	0.5	1.0	0.5	1.0	0.5	1.0	0.5	1.0	0.5	1.0	0.5	0.5

*Special sizes.

Assume $D_1 = D_2 = D$

Weld size D = angle thickness T

Allowable shear on leg of fillet weld = 9.6 kips per sq in.

Then $K = \dfrac{Pa}{9.6AD}$, $L = \dfrac{P(A-a)}{9.6AD}$

Eccentricity about Y-Y axis has been neglected. If leg $B \lessgtr A$ and $D_2 \lessgtr 2T$, the additional stress induced in the weld will not exceed 25 percent of the computed stress.

Lengths of welds are adjusted to nearest $\frac{1}{2}$ in. Since no weld should be shorter than four times the weld size, it may be necessary to increase the lengths of short welds.

Since for any particular case length of weld times size of weld is a constant, either may be varied by proportion.

$$\frac{\text{New length}}{\text{Tabular length}} = \frac{\text{Tabular size}}{\text{New size}}$$

K and L for any other unit stresses may be obtained by proportion or interpolation.

in Art. 9.20b. The minimum length of weld should be about eight times the weld size and the maximum clear distance between welds not more than twenty-four times the thinnest plate for the tension flange or sixteen times the thinnest plate for the compression flange.

At supports, ends of cover plates, and other points having large concentrations of stress, continuous welds should be used even when not required by static load stresses (see Fig. 9.15).

Continuous welds of smaller size may be used instead of intermittent welds when in the judgment of the designer it is advisable to al the joint to prevent corrosion, or when the girder is subjected to dynamic loading.

The design of web stiffeners is similar to riveted construction, except that bars are used instead of angles. The full area of the stiffener is considered effective to carry load. The ends are not usually milled, but fillet welds are used to carry the load from flange to stiffener and from stiffener to web. It may sometimes be cheaper to mill the stiffeners and tack-weld them to the flanges; for example, where the loads involved would require a large amount of welding and there is sufficient duplication to permit cheap milling.

Intermediate stiffeners are so proportioned that the width is approximately 90 percent of the flange projection and the thickness one-sixteenth of the width. Welds must develop the shear but should not be less than the minimum size (see Art. 9.20b). The minimum length of weld should be eight times the weld size, and clear distance between welds not more than sixteen times the thickness of stiffener.

The plates are usually varied in thickness only, although they may also be varied in width.

Where large shears occur near the end of long girders it may be advantageous to vary the web thickness and butt-weld the web plates.

9.30   TIMBER JOINTS

a   The use of wood and timber is to a large extent limited by the type of joint used, and these joints very largely determine the size of the members.

In the subject matter of timber joints may be included simple beam hangers and joist hangers; nails and screws; bolts and splitting timber connectors; and heel plates, fish plates, and other truss details.

Beam hangers and joist hangers are usually not designed by the engineer, but are specified and bought by the contractor from a builders' hardware dealer.

b   In the design of wood or timber joints, it is necessary to make a complete analysis of all the different stresses entering into the design. Compression or bearing joints are comparatively simple, although they require an understanding of the various compressive stresses in timber. The bearing stress parallel with the grain (end-grain bearing) and the bearing stress perpendicular to the grain (side-grain bearing) are given in Table 1.1.

c   However, a compression problem may include also a diagonal bearing which must be obtained by means of the Hankinson formula for inclined bearing:

$$N = \frac{PQ}{P \sin^2 \theta + Q \cos^2 \theta}$$

in which P is the allowable unit stress in compression parallel with the grain, Q is the allowable unit stress in compression perpendicular to the grain, θ is the angle between the direction of grain and direction of load normal to face considered (usually the angle between grain of the two members of the joint), and N is the unit compressive stress at angle θ with the grain.

The Sholten Nomograph of the Hankinson formula as taken from charts of the West Coast Lumbermen's Association is shown in Fig. 9.33. The two triangular diagrams shown differ only in scale, the values in the larger triangle (in 1,000-psi units) being used for larger bolt values and those in the smaller triangle for lag screws and timber joints.

The following problem explains the use of the nomograph.

Problem   Given a select Douglas fir, with $P = 1,200$ psi, $Q = 345$ psi, and $\theta = 40°$, determine the value of N. In the smaller diagram, connect point x ($= 345$) on line AC with point y ($= 1,200$) on line AB. Where this line intersects the ray for 40°, the value of $N = 593$ may be read on the diagram.

A similar problem to determine the value of a bolt in inclined bearing is shown in the small sketch of Fig. 9.33, using a 1-in. bolt through two 6 × 12-in. outer members and a 12 × 12-in. inner member. The values of P and Q as taken from a table similar to Table 9.10 are 4,193 and 2,233, respectively. The intersection of line mn with the ray for 35° gives a value of 3,250, which is the bolt value for N bearing.

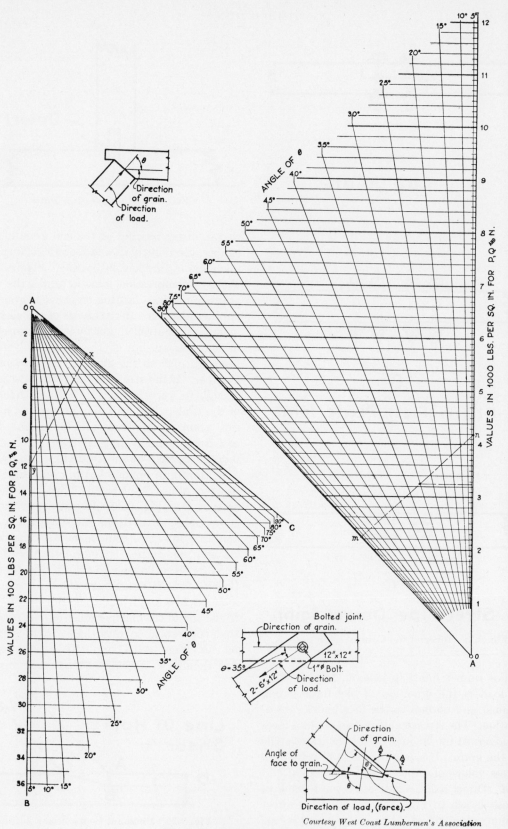

Courtesy West Coast Lumbermen's Association

Fig. 9.33   Hankinson Formula

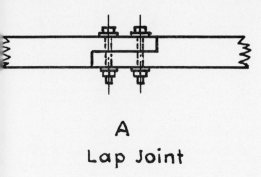

A
Lap Joint

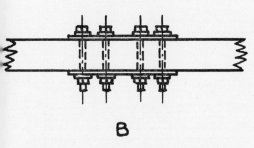

B
Plain Fish Plate Joint

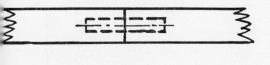

C
Steel Pipe Dowel Joint

Fig. 9.34   Direct-Line Compression Splices

For timber joints in general, the direction f load is the direction of the force acting gainst and normal to the face under consideration. The stress value of two contact faces s governed by the face cut at the lesser angle o the grain. If a joint angle is bisected, the tress values of adjacent faces are equal.

d Direct axial compression joints such as hose shown in Fig. 9.34 are used for direct ompression splices. The entire stress is car-

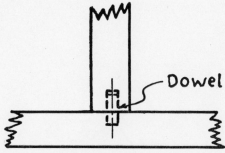

Fig. 9.35   Compression Joint

ried in direct bearing on the end grain of the timber, the bolts of dowels merely holding the members in line and in bearing. Figure 9.35 shows a compression joint in which the end grain comes into bearing on the side grain of another member. Here the size of the vertical member is controlled, not by its own capacity in compression, but by the allowable bearing perpendicular to the grain of the horizontal member. If the stress on the vertical is great enough to warrant utilizing the full capacity of the timber, the load may be spread on the side grain of the horizontal by means of a cast-iron or built-up steel shoe. A housed tenon joint may be substituted for a dowel.

e Joints in oblique bearing introduce the problem of providing against horizontal shear, as shown in Fig. 9.36. It is obvious that a compressive stress down the diagonal may be analyzed into two components, one horizontal and one vertical. The depth of cut AB must be deep enough to take the horizontal thrust, and BC must take the stress on the inclined fibers. In addition, the length DB to the end of the member must be long enough to develop shear to resist the horizontal thrust on AB. Figures 9.37 and 9.38 show two similar details to accomplish the same result.

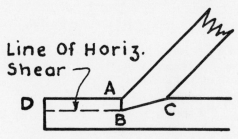

Fig. 9.36   Diagonal Compression Joint

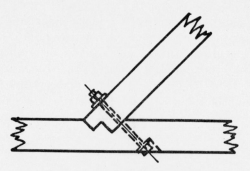

Fig. 9.37   Diagonal Compression Joint

The possible details are almost unlimited, particularly if steel sections be used for the detail connections.

f By far the best tension joints in wood trusses are obtained by using split-ring connectors as described in Arts. 9.33 and 10.12. However, if connectors cannot be used, the methods herein described are used.

Direct tension joists in trusses are used principally for bottom-chord splices, and the simplest is the plain fish-plate joint, with either steel or wood splice plates. The design of the bolt is described in Art. 9.32.

A type of tension joint which requires the bolts only for the purpose of holding the members in tight contact is the tabled fish-plate joint shown in Fig. 9.39. In this joint the tables are deep enough, both in the member and in the splice plate, to transmit the stress in end compression and long enough between

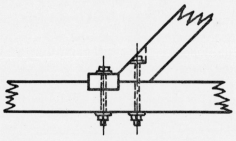

Fig. 9.38   Diagonal Compression Joint

cuts to transmit the same stress in horizontal shear. In order to keep the cuts from being too deep, the stress may be divided and two or three tables used instead of one.

g For tension members carrying comparatively light stresses, such as diagonal members of a truss, typical details are shown in

Fig. 9.40. Detail *A* indicates a diagonal framing between the two parts of a double chord member. In this case, the bolts are designed to carry the full stress. Detail *B* a more common detail: a rod with beveled washers, completely replacing any wood member at this point. Detail *C* shows a method of using a steel strap bent around the horizontal member and bolted to the diagonal.

h Of all the joints in a wood truss, the end joint usually carries the heaviest stress to be transferred between a tension and compression member. In Fig. 9.41 the bolts are only for the purpose of holding the members in contact. The stress is transmitted in detail *A* directly through the cuts as in Fig. 9.34.   Detail

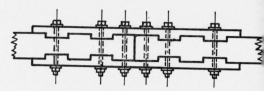

Fig. 9.39   Tabled Fish-Plate Joint

B of Fig. 9.41 shows a steel shoe, a detail frequently used for this joint—the advantage being that the lug transmits the stress into the member and can be set up at any point desired to obtain horizontal shear area along the chord. In detail *A*, the length required beyond the end of the top chord may be so great as to make this detail objectionable.

9.31   Nails and screws

a Tests by the Forest Products Laboratory of the U.S. Department of Agriculture provide the best information on the holding power of nails and screws. The resistance to withdrawal of common wire nails is given by the formula $P = 1.150G^2d$, where P is the safe load per linear inch of penetration, G the specific gravity of the wood, and d the diameter of the nail in inches. Table 9.7 gives the value per inch derived from the above formula for various sizes of nails driven into the commoner kinds of seasoned wood. Nails driven into bored holes of slightly less than their own diameter have a somewhat higher holding power than nails without lead holes.

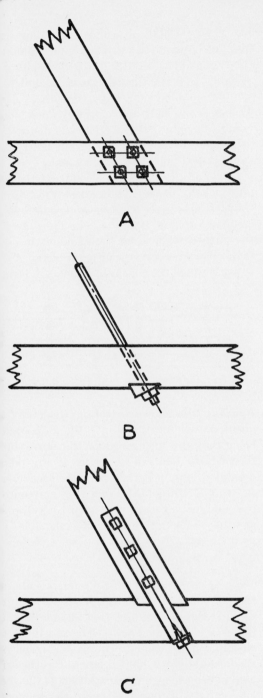

Fig. 9.40   Tension-Member Joints

in shear instead of in direct tension. For this condition, the allowable load per common wire nail in lateral resistance when driven into the side grain of seasoned wood is determined from the formula $P = Kd^{1.5}$.

Table 9.8 gives the value of the constant K and the value per nail for various sizes of nails used in different varieties of wood. These

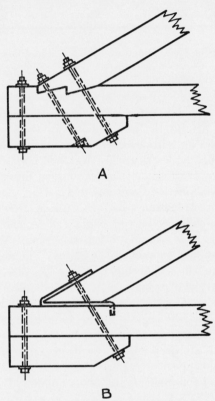

Fig. 9.41   Wood Truss Heel Joints

loads apply when woods of approximately the same density are used, and where the nail penetrates the main member two-thirds of its length for softwood, or one-half for hardwood. Where metal side plates are used, the above values may be increased 25 percent. When driven into the end grain, two-thirds of the values given in Table 9.8 may be used. Nails must be so spaced and staggered as to avoid splitting the wood. It is advantageous to bore lead holes for the nails slightly smaller than the diameter of the nail.

Problem Yellow-pine roof rafters on a 45-deg slope, spanning 20 ft, spaced 16 in. o.c.,

b Although the above formula and Table 9.7 have been developed for the safe resistance to withdrawal for nails, it is not good policy to use nails in this manner. They should be used so that the stresses are resisted

Table 9.7   Resistance to Withdrawal of Common Wire Nails

Driven perpendicular to the grain in seasoned wood

Wood	Specific gravity	Resistance, lb						
		8d	10d	12d	16d	20d	30d	40d
Birch or oak	0.69	60	67	67	74	87	94	102
Douglas fir	0.51	28	32	32	35	41	44	48
Maple	0.68	57	65	65	71	84	91	99
Longleaf yellow pine	0.64	39	45	45	47	50	55	59
Shortleaf yellow pine	0.59	32	36	36	38	41	44	48
Northern white pine	0.37	15	17	17	19	22	24	26
Ponderosa pine, redwood	0.42	17	19	19	21	25	27	30

Table 9.8   Safe Lateral Resistance of Common Wire Nails

Size nail		8d	10d	12d	16d	20d	30d	40d
Length, in.		$2\frac{1}{2}$	3	$3\frac{1}{4}$	$3\frac{1}{2}$	4	$4\frac{1}{2}$	5
Diam d, in.		0.131	0.148	0.148	0.162	0.192	0.207	0.225
$d^{1.5}$		0.0474	0.0570	0.0570	0.0652	0.0841	0.0942	0.1068

Wood	Constant K	Resistance, lb						
Eastern hemlock, white pine	1,080	51	61	61	70	91	101	115
Norway pine, redwood	1,350	64	77	77	88	113	127	144
Douglas fir, yellow pine	1,650	78	94	94	107	136	155	177
Maple, oak	2,040	96	116	116	133	171	191	219

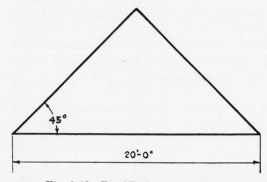

Fig. 9.42   Roof Rafters as a Truss

and carrying a load of 50 psf are tied to prevent spreading by being nailed to the attic floor joists. What nailing is required? (Fig. 9.42).

The load causing thrust is $10 \times 1.33 \times 50 = 666$ lb. Since the slope is 45 deg, the thrust is equal to one-half of this, or 333 lb. This will require three 20d nails. Since both rafters and floor joists will probably be nominal 2-in. material ($1\frac{5}{8}$ in. actual thickness), the nail cannot have two-thirds of its length in the main member, but it can be clinched to serve the same purpose (Fig. 9.43).

c For wood screws, the total safe lateral resistance is given by the formula $P = Kd^2$ where K is a constant as follows:

For eastern hemlock or white pine: 2,100
For Norway pine or redwood: 2,700
For Douglas fir or yellow pine: 3,300
For maple or oak: 4,000

The values for converting screw gage to d^2 are as follows:

Ga	d^2	Ga	d^2
0	0.0036	9	0.0313
1	0.0053	10	0.0361
2	0.0074	11	0.0412
3	0.0098	12	0.0467
4	0.0125	14	0.0586
5	0.0156	16	0.0718
6	0.0190	18	0.0864
7	0.0228	20	0.1024
8	0.0269	24	0.1384

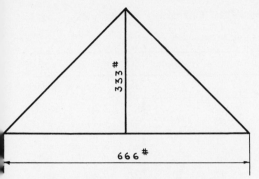

Fig. 9.43   Stresses in Roof-Rafter Truss

The above formula is based on a length of screw in the holding block equal to seven times the shank diameter.

9.32   Bolted wood joints

a The design of bolted wood joints does not involve simple compression on the grain, but rather complex bearing and bending, and is most easily done by the use of Table 9.9, which was compiled by the National Lumber Manufacturers Association.

In this table, P and Q are unit stresses in compression parallel and perpendicular to the grain, respectively. The safe loads given are for one bolt, acting singly or in combination, with snug-fitting bolt holes. The table is designed for side members half the thickness of the center member. If side members are thinner than one-half the main member, the safe load is decreased proportionately. Where steel plates are used for side members, the tabulated values may be increased by 25 per cent for loads parallel to the grain, with no increase being allowed for loads perpendicular to the grain.

The woods that may be used in each group in Table 9.9 are:

Group 1. Tidewater red cypress, coast and inland Douglas fir, western larch, southern yellow pine, redwood, tamarack.

Group 2. Western red cedar, Port Orford cedar, Rocky Mountain Douglas fir, western hemlock, Norway pine.

Group 3. White cedar, balsam fir, commercial white fir, eastern hemlock, white pine, Idaho white pine, Ponderosa pine, spruce.

Group 4. Commercial white ash, beech, birch, pecan, hard maple, commercial red and white oak.

For two-member joints, use one-half the value for the thinner member. For joints of over three members of equal thickness, the load varies as the number of shear planes involved, the load for each shear plane being equal to one-half the tabulated load for a piece the thickness of the member involved.

For loads neither parallel nor perpendicular to the grain, the value should be selected for each direction, and the true value obtained by Hankinson's formula as described in Art. 9.30 c.

The spacing between two rows of bolts in a line parallel to the direction of the load should be not less than $2\frac{1}{2}$ times the bolt diameter for an l/d ratio of 2, and 5 times the bolt diameter for an l/d ratio of 6 or more, where l is the length of the bolt in the main member and d the diameter of the bolt. For intermediate values, the spacing should be determined by direct interpolation. The edge margin should be at least $1\frac{1}{2}$ times the bolt diameter.

In a row of bolts, the spacing must be at least four times the bolt diameter, and the end margin in tension seven times the bolt diameter for softwood and five times for hardwood; in compression the end margin should be four times the bolt diameter.

9.33   Split-ring timber connectors

a Probably the most efficient method of transmitting stresses in timber structures such as trusses is by means of Teco split-ring connectors. The Timber Engineering Co., whose initials give the connectors their name, makes several different types of timber-to-timber and steel-to-timber connectors, including split rings, toothed rings, claw plates, shear plates, spike grids, and clamping plates. The split-ring connectors are probably the most common and efficient, and a discussion of this type will indicate the method of computation to be used for other types. Further information on the use of timber connectors may be obtained from the publications of the Timber Engineering Co., Washington, D.C.

Table 9.9   Bolted Wood Joints

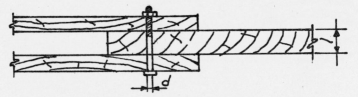

Safe loads with common bolts

Length, l, in.	Diam d, in.	l/d	Area $A = ld$	Group 1		Group 2		Group 3		Group 4	
				P	Q	P	Q	P	Q	P	Q
$1\frac{5}{8}$	$\frac{1}{2}$	3.3	0.81	1,000	460	780	320	620	240	1,140	660
	$\frac{5}{8}$	2.6	1.02	1,260	500	970	370	780	280	1,460	740
	$\frac{3}{4}$	2.2	1.22	1,520	560	1,180	410	940	310	1,750	830
	$\frac{7}{8}$	1.9	1.42	1,780	620	1,370	460	1,090	340	2,050	910
	1	1.6	1.63	2,030	680	1,560	490	1,260	370	2,340	1,000
$2\frac{5}{8}$	$\frac{1}{2}$	5.3	1.31	1,250	720	1,070	530	940	400	1,440	1,060
	$\frac{5}{8}$	4.2	1.64	1,850	830	1,510	600	1,250	440	2,140	1,200
	$\frac{3}{4}$	3.5	1.97	2,380	910	1,870	670	1,510	500	2,740	1,330
	$\frac{7}{8}$	3.0	2.30	2,830	1,010	2,210	730	1,760	550	3,280	1,460
	1	2.6	2.63	3,260	1,100	2,520	800	2,020	600	3,770	1,600
$3\frac{5}{8}$	$\frac{1}{2}$	7.3	1.81	1,260	960	1,090	720	980	550	1,450	1,220
	$\frac{5}{8}$	5.8	2.27	1,970	1,140	1,700	830	1,540	620	2,270	1,610
	$\frac{3}{4}$	4.8	2.72	2,810	1,260	2,360	940	2,020	700	3,240	1,840
	$\frac{7}{8}$	4.1	3.17	3,620	1,390	2,950	1,010	2,420	760	4,180	2,030
	1	3.6	3.63	4,340	1,520	3,440	1,100	2,780	830	5,020	2,210
$5\frac{1}{2}$	$\frac{5}{8}$	8.8	3.44	1,970	1,360	1,700	1,120	1,540	900	2,270	1,670
	$\frac{3}{4}$	7.3	4.13	2,830	1,810	2,460	1,390	2,220	1,040	3,260	2,340
	$\frac{7}{8}$	6.3	4.81	3,850	2,110	3,350	1,540	3,010	1,150	4,450	2,890
	1	5.5	5.50	5,020	2,300	4,340	1,680	3,860	1,260	5,780	3,320
	$1\frac{1}{8}$	4.9	6.19	6,290	2,510	5,320	1,820	4,560	1,370	7,250	3,650
$7\frac{1}{2}$	$\frac{5}{8}$	12.0	4.69	1,970	1,220	1,700	1,040	1,540	880	2,270	1,460
	$\frac{3}{4}$	10.0	5.63	2,830	1,760	2,460	1,440	2,220	1,210	3,260	2,110
	$\frac{7}{8}$	8.6	6.56	3,850	2,340	3,350	1,910	3,010	1,540	4,450	2,900
	1	7.5	7.50	5,030	2,920	4,370	2,270	3,950	1,720	5,810	3,710
	$1\frac{1}{8}$	6.7	8.44	6,400	3,400	5,560	2,500	5,000	1,870	7,340	4,500
$9\frac{1}{2}$	$\frac{3}{4}$	12.7	7.13	2,830	1,570	2,460	1,370	2,220	1,150	3,260	1,880
	$\frac{7}{8}$	10.9	8.31	3,850	2,200	3,350	1,810	3,010	1,520	4,450	2,590
	1	9.5	9.50	5,030	2,860	4,370	2,350	3,950	1,940	5,810	3,470
	$1\frac{1}{8}$	8.4	10.69	6,400	3,640	5,560	2,930	5,000	2,330	7,340	4,460
	$1\frac{1}{4}$	7.6	11.88	7,860	4,310	6,840	3,340	6,170	2,540	9,070	5,410
$11\frac{1}{2}$	1	11.5	11.50	5,030	2,690	4,370	2,230	3,950	1,910	5,810	3,200
	$1\frac{1}{8}$	10.2	12.94	6,400	3,460	5,560	2,830	5,000	2,380	7,340	4,100
	$1\frac{1}{4}$	9.2	14.38	7,860	4,220	6,840	3,460	6,170	2,840	9,070	5,170

The split rings are ring-type dowels as shown in Fig. 9.44 set into grooves cut into the contact faces of the timber. The $2\frac{1}{2}$-in. split ring is desirable for trussed rafters or for lumber construction involving only lumber of 2 in. nominal dimension. The 4-in. split ring, the most widely used connector, may be used efficiently for truss spans of from 30 to 150 ft Both $2\frac{1}{2}$-in. and 4-in. split rings work wel when used for column corbels, wind braces and beam and girder seats. In addition, ther are numerous uses for them in exterior con

Fig. 9.44 Split-Ring Connector

struction, such as towers and bridges of all types.

b Load charts. The load charts shown in Figs. 9.50 and 9.51 give the allowable permanent loads for one split ring and bolt in single shear. The charts are broken vertically into three species groups as specified in Table 9.10. Within each group there are curves representing the actual thickness of lumber and the number of loaded faces. Use the curve conforming to the condition existing in the joint. Each curve is plotted according to the Hankinson formula, with load in pounds and angle of load to grain as the variables. Select the proper angle at the bottom or top of the chart, proceed vertically to the selected curve, and then horizontally to read the allowable permanent load. Lumber thicknesses less than those shown on the load data charts for the corresponding number of loaded faces are not recommended. For more than one connector unit, multiply the connector load by the number of units.

Connector data. The data given in Figs. 9.50 and 9.51 cover dimensions of the connectors, minimum lumber sizes, recommended bolt and bolt-hole diameters, recommended washer sizes, and similar self-explanatory information.

Permissible increases for load duration. Wood is stronger under short-time loading than under permanent loading, and increased connector loads are permissible in such circumstances. With the data on each connector are given the permissible increases applicable thereto.

Loading of three months' duration is loading continuously applied for not over three months. Such loading in combination with permanent loading should not exceed 25 percent of the total load.

Snow loading refers to the maximum snow load intermittently but not permanently applied.

Wind or earthquake loading refers to maximum wind or earthquake loading, or any other loading, not exceeding 5-min duration.

Impact loading refers only to that portion of the load producing impact.

Under no conditions should any combination of loading exceed twice the load-chart values, nor should increases be taken if the permanent loading alone exceeds the load-chart values.

Decreases for moisture-content condition. The expected moisture condition of lumber when fabricated and used should be determined, and the required decreases if necessary made in accordance with the tabulated data with each connector.

Load limitations for multiple connectors in a single piece. When applying these limitations, certain conditions must be met before application. First, the angle of load to grain must be more than 45 deg. Second, consider only those connectors whose loads, or components thereof, on one or both faces of the piece act in the same direction perpendicular to the grain. When these conditions exist, the maximum allowable load should be the summation of the allowable loads for each connector used. However, the total allowable load should not exceed the load permitted for a single connector multiplied by the percentages given with the data for each connector. The spacing should not be less than that for parallel-to-grain spacing at the appropriate angle of load to grain (see Figs. 9.45 to 9.47).

Spacing charts. Spacing is the distance between centers of connectors measured along a line joining their centers. *R* in Fig. 9.47 is the spacing between the rings shown.

On the first page of the data for each connector is the spacing chart. Each chart has five parabolic curves representing recommended spacing for full load at the particular angle of load to grain noted on the curve. For intermediate angles of load, straight-line interpolation may be used. If the spacing for full load is desired, select the proper angle of load-to-grain curve and find where it intersects the radial lines representing angle of

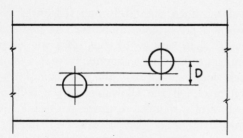

Fig. 9.45   Maximum Offset

axis to grain; the distance from that point to the lower left-hand corner is the spacing. In laying out this spacing, however, it is probably more convenient to use the parallel-to-grain and perpendicular-to-grain components for measurements of the spacing. The parallel-to-grain component may be read at the bottom of the chart by projecting downward from the point on the curve. The perpendicular-to-grain component of the spacing may be read at the left-hand side of the chart by projecting horizontally from the point on the curve.

The fifth curve on the chart is a quarter circle. This curve represents the spacing for 75 percent of full load for any angle of load to grain and also the minimum spacing permissible. Between 75 and 100 percent of full load, for an angle of load to grain interpolate radially on a straight line between the 75-percent curve and the curve corresponding to the proper angle of load to grain.

Reductions in load for edge distance and end distance are not additive to spacing reductions but are coincident.

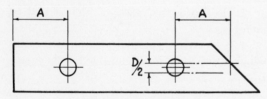

Fig. 9.46   End Distance A

End-distance charts. End distance is the distance measured parallel to grain from the center of a connector to the square-cut end of the member. If the end of the member is not square cut, the end distance should be measured parallel to the grain from any point on the center half of the connector diameter (drawn perpendicular to the center line of the piece) to the nearest point on the end of the member. The length of a perpendicular from the center of the connector to the end cut should never be less than the required edge distance. Figure 9.46 demonstrates end-distance measurement A.

End-distance charts are shown in Figs. 9.50 and 9.51. These charts are divided into two sections, depending on whether the member is in tension or compression. If in tension, project vertically on the chart from the end distance to the curve, then horizontally to get the percentage of load allowable. This process can be reversed, of course, by going from per-

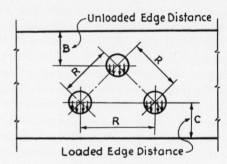

Fig. 9.47   Edge Distances

cent of full load required to spacing required. In compression, there is an additional variable: the angle of load to grain. The operation is the same except that the curve for the proper angle of load to grain should be used. For intermediate angles, interpolate between the curves on a straight line. On some of the charts the curves are cut off at the right-hand side of the chart. The end-distance dimension marking this cutoff is the minimum permissible and gives full load for an angle of load to grain of 0 deg.

Reductions in load for edge distance or spacing are not additive to end-distance reductions but are coincident.

Edge-distance charts. Edge distance is the distance from the edge of the member to the center of the connector closest to the edge of the member measured perpendicular to the edge. The loaded edge distance is the edge distance measured from the edge toward

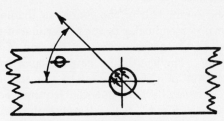

Fig. 9.48   Angle of Load to Grain

which the load induced by the connector acts. The unloaded edge distance is the edge distance measured from the edge away from which the load induced by the connector acts. Figure 9.47 shows a typical measurement of edge distance, where B is the unloaded edge distance and C the loaded edge distance. For unloaded edge distance the standard and minimum edge distance is the dimension at the right-hand edge of the chart. For the loaded edge distance there is a variation according to the angle of load to grain. First, select the proper curve for the desired angle. Then a given edge distance projected vertically to the curve and then horizontally to the side will give the percentage of full load allowable. The upper right-hand corner represents the standard and minimum loaded edge distance for angle of load to grain of 0 deg. For intermediate angles, interpolate on a straight line.

Interrelationship of thickness, distance, and spacing. Loads reduced because of thickness (see tabulated loads, Figs. 9.50 and 9.51) do not permit any reduction of edge distance. Reduced edge distance or spacing without further reduction of load, and, conversely, loads reduced for edge distance or spacing, do not permit reduction of thickness.

When allowable load is reduced because of reduced edge distance, end distance, or spacing, the reduced allowable load for each shall be determined separately and the lowest allowable load so determined for any one connector shall apply to this and all other connectors resisting a common force in a joint. Such load reductions are not cumulative. Conversely, if the allowable load is reduced because of a reduced distance or spacing, the other distances or spacings may be reduced to those resulting in the same reduced allowable load.

c   Angle of load to grain. The angle of load to grain is the angle between the resultant load exerted by the connector acting on the member and the longitudinal axis of the member (see Fig. 9.48).

Angle of axis to grain. The angle of axis to grain is the angle of the connector axis formed by a line joining the centers of two adjacent connectors located in the same face of a member in a joint and the longitudinal axis of the member (see Fig. 9.49).

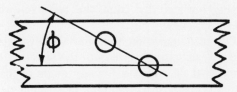

Fig. 9.49   Angle of Axis to Grain

d   Procedure for the design of connector joints

1. Determine stresses for structural members.

2. Form a tentative plan for framing the structure and select the lumber species to be used.

3. Compute the sizes of the structural members.

4. Select the type and size of connectors which seem to be most suitable for the structure.

Table 9.10   Connector Load Grouping of Species When Structurally Graded

Group A	Group B	Group C
Douglas fir (dense)	Douglas fir (coast region)	Cypress, southern and tidewater red
Oak, red and white	Larch, western	Hemlock, west coast
Pine, southern (dense)	Pine, southern	Pine, Norway
		Redwood

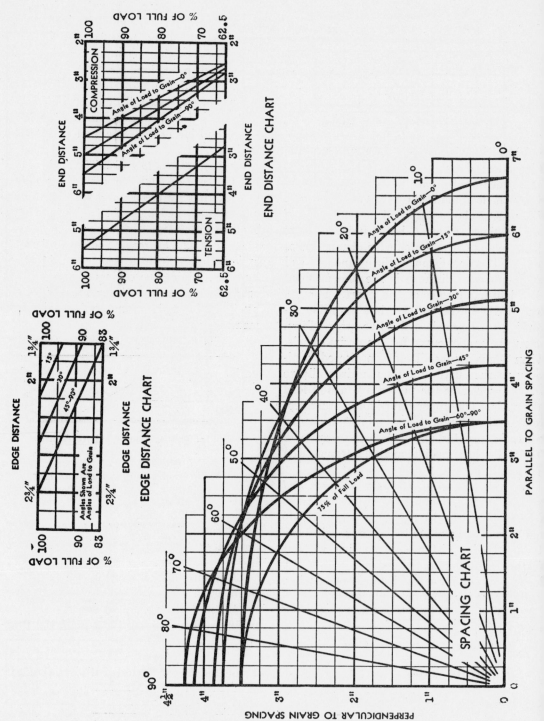

Fig. 9.50 2½-in. Split-Ring Data

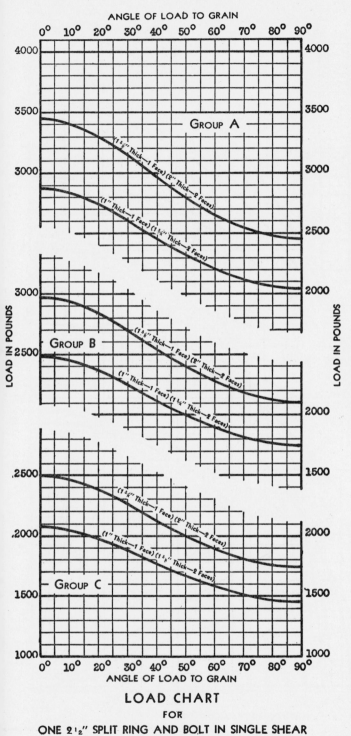

LOAD CHART

FOR

ONE 2½" SPLIT RING AND BOLT IN SINGLE SHEAR

2½" SPLIT RING DATA

Split Ring—Dimensions	
Inside Diameter at center when closed......................	2½"
Depth......................	¾"
Weight, per 100 rings, lbs........	28
Lumber, Minimum dimensions allowed	
Width......................	3⅝"
Thickness, rings in one face.....	1"
Thickness, rings opposite in both faces......................	1⅝"
Bolt, diameter, minimum..........	½"
(With rings of different size, use minimum for larger ring.)	
Bolt hole, maximum diameter....	9/16"
Projected Area for portion of one ring within a member, square inches......................	1.10
Washers, minimum	
Round, Cast or Malleable Iron, diameter......................	2⅛"
Square Plate	
Length of Side...............	2"
Thickness...................	⅛"
(For trussed rafters and similar light construction standard wrought washers may be used.)	

SPLIT RING SPECIFICATIONS

Split rings shall be TECO split rings as manufactured by the Timber Engineering Company. Split rings shall be manufactured from hot rolled S. A. E.—1010 carbon steel. Each ring shall form a closed true circle with the principal axis of the cross section of the ring metal parallel to the geometric axis of the ring. The ring shall fit snugly in the prepared groove. The metal section of each ring shall be beveled from the central portion toward the edges to a thickness less than that at mid-section. It shall be cut through in one place in its circumference to form a tongue and slot.

PERMISSIBLE INCREASES FOR LOAD DURATION

	Permanent Loading	Three Months Loading	Snow Loading	Wind or Earthquake Loading	Impact Loading
Split Rings..	0%	15%	15%	50%	100%

DECREASES FOR MOISTURE CONTENT CONDITIONS

Condition when Fabricated....	Seasoned	Unseasoned	Unseasoned
Condition when Used.........	Seasoned	Seasoned	Unseasoned or Wet
Split Rings......	0%	20%	33%

MAXIMUM RECOMMENDED VALUES FOR A GROUP OF CONNECTORS ACTING 45°-90° WITH THE GRAIN

Load Limitations for Multiple Connectors in a Single Piece.) (% of Allowable Loads on One Connector.)

Type & Size of Connector	Thickness of Loaded Member, Inches			
	1½"	2"	2½"	3" and Thicker
2½" Split Ring..	300%	300%	300%	300%

For each additional connector exceeding 4, add 33 per cent of the allowable load for one connector.

Fig. 9.50   2½-in. Split-Ring Data (Continued)

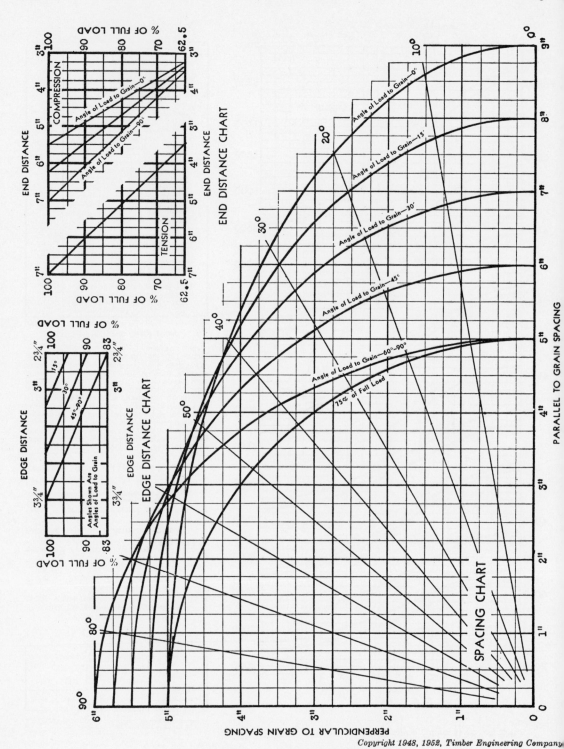

Fig. 9.51   4-in. Split-Ring Data

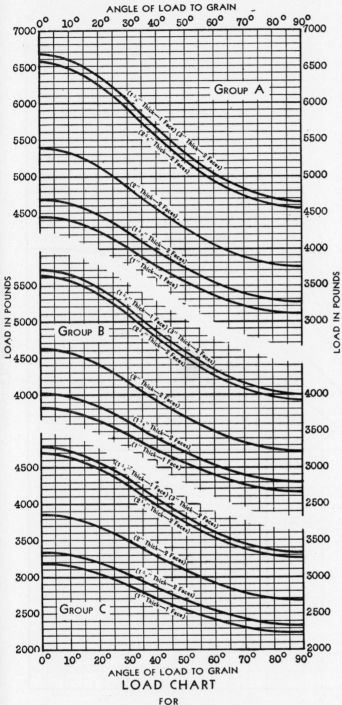

ANGLE OF LOAD TO GRAIN

LOAD IN POUNDS

GROUP A

GROUP B

GROUP C

ANGLE OF LOAD TO GRAIN

LOAD CHART

FOR

ONE 4″ SPLIT RING AND BOLT IN SINGLE SHEAR

4″ SPLIT RING DATA

Split Ring—Dimensions	
Inside Diameter at center when closed......................	4″
Depth..........................	1″
Weight, per 100 rings, lbs........	70
Lumber, Minimum dimensions allowed	
Width...........................	5½″
Thickness, rings in one face......	1″
Thickness, rings opposite in both faces.........................	1⅝″
Bolt, diameter, minimum..........	¾″
(With rings of different size, use minimum for larger ring.)	
Bolt hole, maximum diameter....	13/16″
Projected Area for portion of one ring within a member, square inches...........................	2.25
Washers, minimum	
Round, Cast or Malleable Iron, diameter...................	3″
Square Plate	
Length of Side..............	3″
Thickness..................	3/16″
(For trussed rafters and similar light construction standard wrought washers may be used.)	

SPLIT RING SPECIFICATIONS

Split rings shall be TECO split rings as manufactured by the Timber Engineering Company. Split rings shall be manufactured from hot rolled S. A. E.—1010 carbon steel. Each ring shall form a closed true circle with the principal axis of the cross section of the ring metal parallel to the geometric axis of the ring. The ring shall fit snugly in the prepared groove. The metal section of each ring shall be beveled from the central portion toward the edges to a thickness less than that at mid-section. It shall be cut through in one place in its circumference to form a tongue and slot.

PERMISSIBLE INCREASES FOR LOAD DURATION

	Permanent Loading	Three Months Loading	Snow Loading	Wind or Earthquake Loading	Impact Loading
Split Rings..	0%	15%	15%	50%	100%

DECREASES FOR MOISTURE CONTENT CONDITIONS

Condition when Fabricated....	Seasoned	Unseasoned	Unseasoned
Condition when Used.........	Seasoned	Seasoned	Unseasoned or Wet
Split Rings......	0%	20%	33%

MAXIMUM RECOMMENDED VALUES FOR A GROUP OF CONNECTORS ACTING 45°–90° WITH THE GRAIN

(Load Limitations for Multiple Connectors in a Single Piece.) (% of Allowable Loads on One Connector.)

Type & Size of Connector	Thickness of Loaded Member, Inches			
	1½″	2″	2¾″	3″ and Thicker
4″ Split Ring....	233%	248%	269%	300%

For each additional connector exceeding 4, add 33 per cent of the allowable load for one connector.

Fig. 9.51   4-in. Split-Ring Data (Continued)

5. Determine the angle of load to grain for each member in the joint to get ring capacity, required edge and end distances, and spacings for connectors.

6. Design those joints first which carry the greatest loads, since the sizes of the members required to space the connectors in these joints will be a determining factor in arriving at final member sizes.

7. Determine the amount of load in the joint which must be transferred between each two members to be joined, and design for the largest load first. The positioning of the connectors for the smaller loads will usually not be a problem; they should, however, be checked.

8. Calculate the number of connectors required to carry the loads and proceed to locate them on gage lines drawn with reference to the edges of the overlapped members. The spacings between connectors must also be checked.

9. If gage lines do not permit full spacings, and full capacities of connectors must be developed, the face widths of certain members must then be increased to provide the spacings required, or it may be that other sizes of connectors can be used without increasing the lumber sizes.

10. Check end distances and spacings for connectors in each member.

Inasmuch as the use of timber connectors is largely confined to truss design, no problem is given in this article. For the use of these charts and tables, refer to Art. 10.12.

e The net section of a timber in a connector joint is usually adequate to transmit the full strength of the timber in tension, but it is advisable to check this critical or net section. The critical section usually will pass through the center line of a bolt and connector at the plane of maximum stress; it is equal to the full cross section of the timber minus the projected area of the portion of connectors and bolt within the member.

The net cross section required may be determined by multiplying the total load in pounds by the proper constant selected from Table 9.11. The projected area to be deducted in determining the actual net section is obtained from Table 9.12.

Table 9.11   Constants for Determining Required Net Section in Tension

Product in square inches

Type of loading	Thickness of wood member, in.	Constants for each connector load group		
		Group A	Group B	Group C
Standard	4 or less	0.00041	0.00046	0.00048
	over 4	0.00051	0.00058	0.00060
Wind or earthquake	4 or less	0.00031	0.00036	0.00037
	over 4	0.00039	0.00044	0.00046
Impact	4 or less	0.00023	0.00027	0.00028
	over 4	0.00029	0.00033	0.00035
Dead load	4 or less	0.00047	0.00053	0.00055
	over 4	0.00058	0.00067	0.00069

Table 9.12   Projected Area of Connectors and Bolts

Square inches

Split ring and bolt	Number of faces	Thickness of lumber, in.				
		$1\frac{5}{8}$	$2\frac{5}{8}$	$3\frac{5}{8}$	$5\frac{1}{2}$	$7\frac{1}{2}$
$2\frac{1}{2}$-in. ring on $\frac{1}{2}$-in. bolt	1	1.73	2.23	2.73	3.67	4.67
	2	2.64	3.14	3.64	4.58	5.58
4-in. ring on $\frac{3}{4}$-in. bolt	1	3.09	3.84	4.59	6.00	7.50
	2	4.97	5.72	6.47	7.16	9.38

9.40　CONCRETE CONNECTIONS

a　When concrete beams, girders, and columns are poured at the same time they are monolithic and present no problem of connections or joints. There are, however, several conditions under which some form of connection must be designed to carry concrete construction, as follows:

1. Where concrete beams are carried by a steel column or steel beam.

2. Where concrete beams or columns are designed to carry a future extension, requiring provision for carrying future concrete beams and slabs.

3. Where concrete columns are designed to carry additional stories to be added in the future.

b　Probably the most satisfactory way of carrying a concrete-beam load on a steel column or steel beam is by means of multiple seat angles as shown in Fig. 9.52, preferably welded to the face of the column. This detail, using $3 \times 3 \times \frac{1}{4}$-in. angles the full width of the concrete beam, spaced 4 in. vertically, will provide for all the stresses to be carried into the steel column. A similar detail could be used on the face of a channel or the web of a beam.

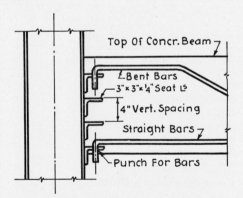

Fig. 9.52　Multiple Seat Connections

c　If concrete beams are designed to carry a future slab, a recess is usually provided in the top of the beam, as indicated in Fig. 9.53.

d　If concrete beams are designed to carry a future beam, the method used depends upon the size of beam to be added and the required

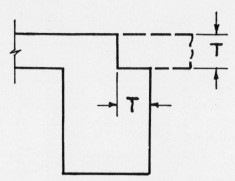

Fig. 9.53　Concrete Beam Seat for Future Slab

shear capacity. If the original beam is twice the depth of the beam to be framed in later, a pocket can be left in the original beam for the later beam, similar to the system shown in Fig. 9.53. Another method sometimes used is to install concrete inserts in the original cast-iron or steel beam, into which at a later date bolts can be installed to carry a multiple seat connection similar to that of Fig. 9.52. If concrete inserts are used, they should be filled with grease to keep them from plugging up with concrete or from rusting. The bolts which go into the concrete inserts are in single shear, and this fact is ordinarily the governing factor in the design of such details.

e　There are several details used for providing for future extension of columns. The simpler but more costly detail is to put dowels for the future bars into the original column, projecting the required length above the roof line, then pour lean concrete around them (for later removal) and flash around the column stub. As an alternate, if the bars are not too heavy, they may be bent flat against the roof so that later they may be bent back into their proper place when the addition is made. This method, although it takes less material and is easier to keep watertight, requires difficult bar bending when the addition is made.

The method preferred by the author is to use a dowel bar threaded on one end, to which is attached a sleeve nut. The open end of the sleeve nut is filled with grease to prevent concrete from filling it, and the sleeve nut is placed flush with the top of the concrete. The roofing is then level. When the addition is

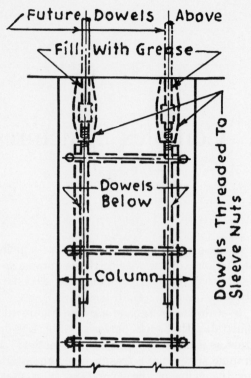

Fig. 9.54   **Provision for Future Extension—Concrete Column**

made, the grease is cleaned from the sleeve nut and another threaded dowel inserted to provide the dowel for future connection (see Fig. 9.54).

f   Sometimes it is necessary to connect a new concrete beam or slab to an existing beam or column where no provision has been made for the connection. Provided that the existing member can be used without overstressing it, the connection may be made by installing a single seat angle for a slab or multiple seat angles for a beam, connecting them by the use of Rawl anchors or other similar lead sleeves. These sleeves are installed in holes drilled in the concrete in such a manner that when the bolt is inserted and tightened up, it is held by the lead which has been wedged into the irregularities and interstices of the concrete.

g   Occasionally it is necessary to carry a concrete slab on the bottom flange of a steel beam in such a manner that the slab can be tied to the beam by dowels. These dowels are usually threaded and put through holes in the web of the steel beams with nuts on both sides of the web to lock the dowels, as shown in Fig. 9.55.

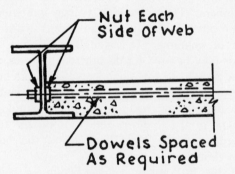

Fig. 9.55   **Anchorage of Slab to Bottom Flange of Steel Beam**

10

Complex Structures

10.10 TRUSSES

a A truss is a framework of steel, timber, or both, arranged to form a series of triangles, the bending stresses being translated into direct stresses applied concentrically to the members. The purpose of trusses is obvious —to carry loads over large rooms without use of columns. Occasionally, however, a truss may be used for decorative purposes, as in a church, or for economy where a pitched roof is required, as in some industrial plants. The ordinary pitched roof on a home employs a type of truss, the rafters forming the top chords and the attic floor joists the bottom chords.

Table 10.1 gives coefficients for the commoner type of symmetrical roof trusses, and this method of solution is perfectly satisfactory. If the truss does not come within the scope of these tables, the problem may be solved either analytically or graphically. The graphical method is faster and can be used to check results. If the diagram scale is not accurate enough, it will at least serve as a geometric representation from which to compute actual stress in members.

Usually it is uneconomical to carry bending and direct stress in a truss member. It is preferable to bring the loads into the truss at panel points only, even at the cost of some slight additional framing. This arrangement is called for more with steel than with wood trusses, and will be further discussed later. Direct stresses are always assumed to be applied on the center of gravity of the member,

and these stress lines must meet at a point at the joint. Otherwise eccentric stresses will result that may set up dangerous secondary stresses.

b *Graphic analysis of a truss.* Figure 10.1 illustrates the truss analysis for a scissors truss as a means of showing this method. A graphic analysis of a truss is based on obtaining the value of the component of a stress when the value of the stress and the direction of the member along which the stress component will act are known. A graphic analysis of a truss must be accurately laid out, since a small error in angle will be magnified in proceeding through the truss.

The first step is to compute analytically the reactions on the truss and lay out the truss diagram, applying the loads at the panel points and the reactions at the end. The loads on a truss should be applied on the panel points. Loads occurring between panel points cause bending in the member, and then the member must be figured as a beam, the reactions taken to the panel points, and the truss member figured for bending and direct stress combined. In laying out a truss diagram, assign capital letters to the spaces between loads or reactions, but not to panel points. A truss is made up of a series of triangles, so letter each internal triangle and each space between two external loads.

For the stress diagram, lay out at a convenient scale the applied load on the load line, going clockwise from the left end top of the truss. Use lower-case letters corresponding to the capitals on the truss diagram, but a

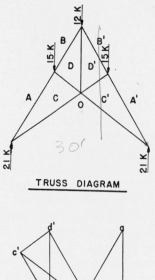

TRUSS DIAGRAM

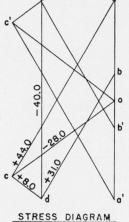

STRESS DIAGRAM

Fig. 10.1   Scissors Truss

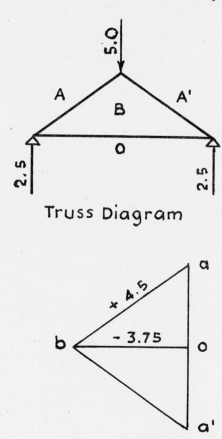

Fig. 10.2   King-Post Truss

space between loads on the truss diagram becomes a point of intersection on the stress diagram. Thus in the scissors truss, go from A to B and use lower-case letters in putting these loads on the stress diagram; then from B to B', B' to A', then back up the reaction line from A' to O, and from O back to A, closing the load line. Some texts show the load applied at the outer panel points of the truss immediately over the reaction, but this may be confusing rather than helpful. The load comes into the support, not into the truss. It has no effect whatever on the truss stresses, and is therefore omitted in the trusses that are shown.

Starting from the reaction stresses OA, we know the amount of the stress and the line of the two components AC and OC. From point a we may draw on our stress diagram, parallel with the top chord AC, a line of indef-

inite length. From point o, parallel with the lower chord OC, we may draw another line of indefinite length. Where these lines intersect will determine point c, and the length of the lines oc and ac will tell us the amount of stress in these two members. Having point c on our stress diagram, we look for other truss triangles where the adjacent letters in the stress diagram have been located. We have point c and the direction of the member CD and point b and the top chord direction. From point c draw an indefinite line parallel to CD, and from point b draw an indefinite line parallel to BD; the intersection of these two lines locates point d. From this we have the direction of line DD' and $B'D'$ and points b' and d' on the stress diagram; point d' may be located, then c', and if the layout was accurately made, it will check back at the point a' and close the truss.

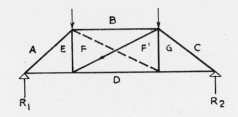

Complete the layout of the stress diagram using the same scale as for the load line. Scale off the amount of the stresses and put them on the diagram. The next step is to determine the nature of the stresses, tension or compression. This may be done by reading from the truss diagram around any joint in a clockwise direction. Using the lower-chord center joint $OCDD'C'O$ as an example, read from the stress diagram in the same order. Reading from o to c, we read diagonally down or away from the joint, indicating that the stress is away from the joint or tensile stress. From C to D we read diagonally down against the joint—a compressive stress; from d to d' we read up or away from the joint—tensile stress; from d' to c' diagonally down—a compressive stress; and finally from c' to

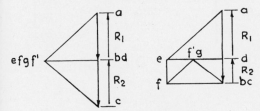

Fig. 10.3   Queen-Post Truss

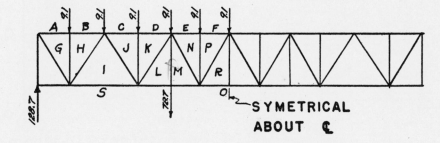

TRUSS   DIAGRAM

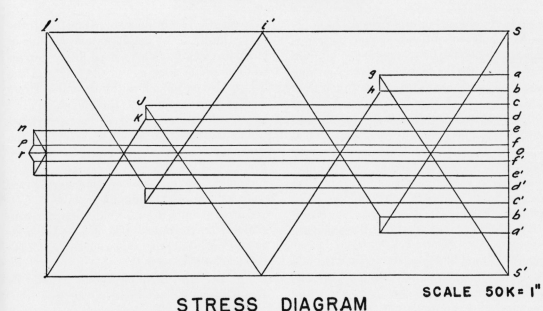

STRESS   DIAGRAM   SCALE 50K = 1"

Fig. 10.4   Irregular Warren Truss with Columns Hung

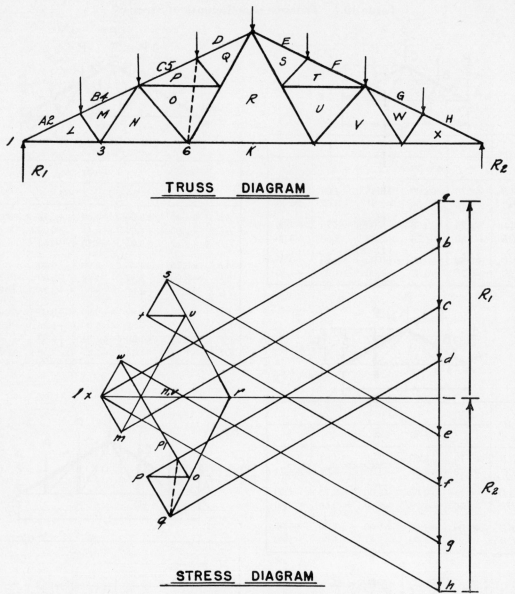

TRUSS   DIAGRAM

STRESS   DIAGRAM

Fig. 10.5 Fink Truss

o diagonally down—a tensile stress. This simple method may be applied to any truss, no matter how complicated it may be. Although other engineers may differ in this convention, + to indicate compressive stresses and − to indicate tensile stresses are used here.

A number of the commoner forms of roof trusses and their respective stress diagrams are given in Figs. 10.2 to 10.4.

c *The Fink truss*, a common type of factory roof truss, particularly applicable to use as a steel truss because of its short compres-

sion members, requires a slight variation of procedure from that described above. In following the method described, it will be noted that after reaching point *n* on the stress diagram, the designer can no longer follow the normal procedure (see Fig. 10.5). Members *PO* and *PQ* are temporarily omitted here and an imaginary member *OQ* is installed as shown in dotted lines. This enables the designer to find point *q* on the stress diagram, with which the stress in members *PQ* and *OP* may be found.

Table 10.1   Trusses—Coefficients of Stresses

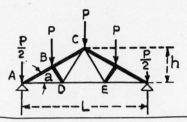

M	Pitch				
	$\frac{1}{3}$	$a = 30°$	$\frac{1}{4}$	$\frac{1}{5}$	$\frac{1}{6}$
AB	+2.70	+3.00	+3.35	+4.04	+4.74
BC	+2.15	+2.50	+2.91	+3.67	+4.43
AD	−2.25	−2.60	−3.00	−3.75	−4.50
DE	−1.50	−1.73	−2.00	−2.50	−3.00
BD	+0.83	+0.87	+0.90	+0.93	+0.95
CD	−0.75	−0.87	−1.00	−1.25	−1.50

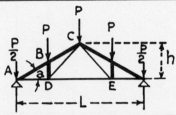

M	Pitch				
	$\frac{1}{3}$	$a = 30°$	$\frac{1}{4}$	$\frac{1}{5}$	$\frac{1}{6}$
AB	+2.70	+3.00	+3.35	+4.04	+4.74
BC	+2.70	+3.00	+3.35	+4.04	+4.74
AD	−2.25	−2.60	−3.00	−3.75	−4.50
DE	−1.50	−1.73	−2.00	−2.50	−3.00
BD	+1.00	+1.00	+1.00	+1.00	+1.00
CD	−1.25	−1.32	−1.41	−1.60	−1.80

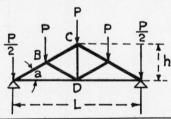

M	Pitch				
	$\frac{1}{3}$	$a = 30°$	$\frac{1}{4}$	$\frac{1}{5}$	$\frac{1}{6}$
AB	+2.70	+3.00	+3.35	+4.04	+4.74
BC	+1.80	+2.00	+2.24	+2.69	+3.16
AD	−2.25	−2.60	−3.00	−3.75	−4.50
BD	+0.90	+1.00	+1.12	+1.35	+1.58
CD	−1.00	−1.00	−1.00	−1.00	−1.00

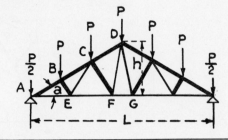

M	Pitch				
	$\frac{1}{3}$	$a = 30°$	$\frac{1}{4}$	$\frac{1}{5}$	$\frac{1}{6}$
AB	+4.51	+5.00	+5.59	+6.73	+8.00
BC	+3.95	+4.50	+5.14	+6.36	+7.70
CD	+2.77	+3.25	+3.80	+4.83	+6.00
AE	−3.75	−4.33	−5.00	−6.25	−7.50
EF	−3.00	−3.47	−4.00	−5.00	−6.20
FG	−2.25	−2.60	−3.00	−3.75	−4.70
BE	+0.83	+0.87	+0.90	+0.93	+1.00
CE	−0.75	−0.87	−1.00	−1.25	−1.50
CF	+1.25	+1.30	+1.34	+1.39	+1.50
DF	−1.04	−1.14	−1.27	−1.49	−1.70

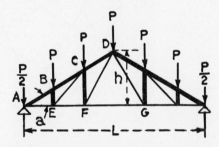

M	Pitch				
	$\frac{1}{3}$	$a = 30°$	$\frac{1}{4}$	$\frac{1}{5}$	$\frac{1}{6}$
AB	+4.51	+5.00	+5.59	+6.73	+7.91
BC	+4.51	+5.00	+5.59	+6.73	+7.91
CD	+3.61	+4.00	+4.47	+5.39	+6.32
AE	−3.75	−4.33	−5.00	−6.25	−7.50
EF	−3.00	−3.46	−4.00	−5.00	−6.00
FG	−2.25	−2.60	−3.00	−3.75	−4.50
BE	+1.00	+1.00	+1.00	+1.00	+1.00
CE	−1.25	−1.32	−1.41	−1.60	−1.80
CF	+1.50	+1.50	+1.50	+1.50	+1.50
DF	−1.68	−1.73	−1.80	−1.95	−2.12

M = Member of truss   + Indicates compression
Pitch = h/L − Indicates tension
Stress in any member = coefficient multiplied by W

Table 10.1 Trusses—Coefficients of Stresses (*Continued*)

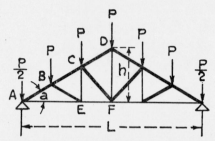

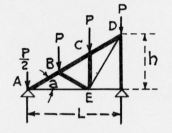

M	Pitch				
	$\frac{1}{3}$	$a = 30°$	$\frac{1}{4}$	$\frac{1}{5}$	$\frac{1}{6}$
AB	+4.51	+5.00	+5.59	+6.73	+7.91
BC	+3.61	+4.00	+4.50	+5.39	+6.32
CD	+2.70	+3.00	+3.30	+4.04	+4.74
AE	−3.75	−4.33	−5.00	−6.25	−7.50
EF	−3.00	−3.46	−4.00	−5.00	−6.00
BE	+0.90	+1.00	+1.10	+1.35	+1.58
CE	−0.50	−0.50	−0.50	−0.50	−0.50
CF	+1.25	+1.32	+1.40	+1.60	+1.80
DF	−2.00	−2.00	−2.00	−2.00	−2.00

M	Pitch				
	$\frac{1}{3}$	$a = 30°$	$\frac{1}{4}$	$\frac{1}{5}$	$\frac{1}{6}$
AB	+1.80	+2.00	+2.24	+2.69	+3.16
BC	+0.90	+1.00	+1.12	+1.35	+1.58
CD	+0.90	+1.00	+1.12	+1.35	+1.58
AE	−1.50	−1.73	−2.00	−2.50	−3.00
EF	0	0	0	0	0
BE	+0.90	+1.00	+1.12	+1.35	+1.58
CE	+1.00	+1.00	+1.00	+1.00	+1.00
DE	−1.68	−1.73	−1.80	−1.95	−2.12

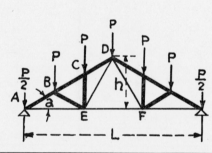

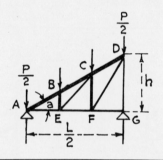

M	Pitch				
	$\frac{1}{3}$	$a = 30°$	$\frac{1}{4}$	$\frac{1}{5}$	$\frac{1}{6}$
AB	+4.51	+5.00	+5.59	+6.72	+7.91
BC	+3.54	+4.00	+4.55	+5.57	+6.64
CD	+3.40	+4.00	+4.71	+5.98	+7.27
AE	−3.75	−4.33	−5.00	−6.25	−7.50
EF	−2.25	−2.60	−3.00	−3.75	−4.50
BE	+0.93	+1.00	+1.08	+1.21	+1.34
CE	+0.93	+1.00	+1.08	+1.21	+1.34
DE	−1.50	−1.73	−2.00	−2.50	−3.00

M	Pitch				
	$\frac{1}{3}$	$a = 30°$	$\frac{1}{4}$	$\frac{1}{5}$	$\frac{1}{6}$
AB	+1.80	+2.00	+2.24	+2.69	+3.16
BC	+1.80	+2.00	+2.24	+2.69	+3.16
CD	+0.90	+1.00	+1.12	+1.35	+1.58
AE	−1.50	−1.73	−2.00	−2.50	−3.00
EF	−0.75	−0.87	−1.00	−1.25	−1.50
FG	0	0	0	0	0
BE	+1.00	+1.00	+1.00	+1.00	+1.00
CE	−1.25	−1.32	−1.41	−1.60	−1.80
CF	+1.50	+1.50	+1.50	+1.50	+1.50
DF	−1.68	−1.73	−1.80	−1.95	−2.12

M = Member of truss   + Indicates compression
Pitch = h/L − Indicates tension
Stress in any member = coefficient multiplied by W

Table 10.1   Trusses—Coefficients of Stresses (*Continued*)

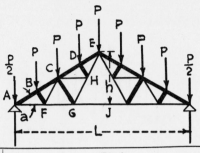

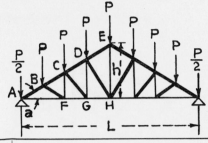

M	Pitch $\frac{1}{3}$	$a = 30°$	$\frac{1}{4}$	$\frac{1}{5}$	$\frac{1}{6}$
AB	+6.31	+7.00	+7.83	+9.42	+11.07
BC	+5.76	+6.50	+7.38	+9.05	+10.75
CD	+5.30	+6.00	+6.93	+8.68	+10.44
DE	+4.65	+5.50	+6.48	+8.31	+10.12
AF	−5.25	−6.06	−7.00	−8 75	−10.50
FG	−4.50	−5.20	−6.00	−7.50	−9.00
GJ	−3.00	−3.46	−4.00	−5.00	−6.00
BF	+0.83	+0.87	+0.89	+0.93	+0.95
CF	−0.75	−0.87	−1.00	−1.25	−1.50
CG	+1.66	+1.73	+1.79	+1.86	+1.90
CH	−0.75	−0.87	−1.00	−1.25	−1.50
DH	+0.83	+0.87	+0.89	+0.93	+0.95
EH	−2.25	−2.60	−3.00	−3.75	−4.50
HG	−1.50	−1.73	−2.00	−2.50	−3.00

M	Pitch $\frac{1}{3}$	$a = 30°$	$\frac{1}{4}$	$\frac{1}{5}$	$\frac{1}{6}$
AB	+6.31	+7.00	+7.83	+9.42	+11.07
BC	+5.41	+6.00	+6.71	+8.08	+9.49
CD	+4.51	+5.00	+5.59	+6.73	+7.91
DE	+3.61	+4.00	+4.47	+5.39	+6.32
AF	−5.25	−6.06	−7.00	−8.75	−10.50
FG	−4.50	−5.20	−6.00	−7.50	−9.00
GH	−3.75	−4.33	−5.00	−6.25	−7.50
BF	+0.90	+1.00	+1.12	+1.35	+1.58
CF	−0.50	−0.50	−0.50	−0.50	−0.50
CG	+1.25	+1.32	+1.41	+1.60	+1.80
DG	−1.00	−1.00	−1.00	−1.00	−1.00
DH	+1.68	+1.73	+1.80	+1.95	+2.12
EH	−3.00	−3.00	−3.00	−3.00	−3.00

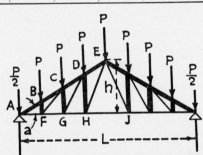

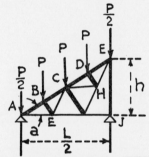

M	Pitch $\frac{1}{3}$	$a = 30°$	$\frac{1}{4}$	$\frac{1}{5}$	$\frac{1}{6}$
AB	+6.31	+7.00	+7.83	+9.42	+11.07
BC	+6.31	+7.00	+7.83	+9.42	+11.07
CD	+5.41	+6.00	+6.71	+8.08	+9.49
DE	+4.51	+5.00	+5.59	+6.73	+7.91
AF	−5.25	−6.06	−7.00	−8.75	−10.50
FG	−4.50	−5.20	−6.00	−7.50	−9.00
GH	−3.75	−4.33	−5.00	−6.25	−7.50
HJ	−3.00	−3.46	−4.00	−5.00	−6.00
BF	+1.00	+1.00	+1.00	+1.00	+1.00
CF	−1.25	−1.32	−1.41	−1.60	−1.80
CG	+1.50	+1.50	+1.50	+1.50	+1.50
DG	−1.68	−1.73	−1.80	−1.95	−2.12
DH	+2.00	+2.00	+2.00	+2.00	+2.00
EH	−2.14	−2.18	−2.24	−2.36	−2.50

M	Pitch $\frac{1}{3}$	$a = 30°$	$\frac{1}{4}$	$\frac{1}{5}$	$\frac{1}{6}$
AB	+2.70	+3.00	+3.35	+4.04	+4.74
BC	+2.15	+2.50	+2.91	+3.67	+4.43
CD	+1.59	+2.00	+2.46	+3.30	+4.11
DE	+1.04	+1.50	+2.01	+2.92	+3.79
AF	−2.25	−2.60	−3.00	−3.75	−4.50
FG	−1.50	−1.73	−2.00	−2.50	−3.00
GJ	0	0	0	0	0
BF	+0.83	+0.87	+0.89	+0.93	+0.95
CF	−0.75	−0.87	−1.00	−1.25	−1.50
CG	+1.66	+1.72	+1.79	+1.86	+1.90
CH	−0.75	−0.87	−1.00	−1.25	−1.50
DH	+0.83	+0.87	+0.89	+0.93	+0.95
EH	−2.25	−2.60	−3.00	−3.75	−4.50
HG	−1.50	−1.73	−2.00	−2.50	−3.00

M = Member of truss   Pitch = h/L + Indicates compression   − Indicates tension

Stress in any member = coefficient multiplied by W

Table 10.1 Trusses—Coefficients of Stresses (*Continued*)

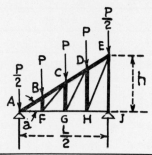

M	Pitch				
	$\frac{1}{3}$	$a = 30°$	$\frac{1}{4}$	$\frac{1}{5}$	$\frac{1}{6}$
AB	+2.70	+3.00	+3.35	+4.04	+4.74
BC	+2.70	+3.00	+3.35	+4.04	+4.74
CD	+1.80	+2.00	+2.24	+2.69	+3.16
DE	+0.90	+1.00	+1.12	+1.35	+1.58
AF	−2.25	−2.60	−3.00	−3.75	−4.50
FG	−1.50	−1.73	−2.00	−2.50	−3.00
GH	−0.75	−0.87	−1.00	−1.25	−1.50
HJ	0	0	0	0	0
BF	+1.00	+1.00	+1.00	+1.00	+1.00
CF	−1.25	−1.32	−1.41	−1.60	−1.80
CG	+1.50	+1.50	+1.50	+1.50	+1.50
DG	−1.68	−1.73	−1.80	−1.95	−2.12
DH	+2.00	+2.00	+2.00	+2.00	+2.00
EH	−2.14	−2.18	−2.24	−2.36	−2.50

M	Pitch				
	$\frac{1}{3}$	$a = 30°$	$\frac{1}{4}$	$\frac{1}{5}$	$\frac{1}{6}$
AB	+8.11	+9.00	+10.06	+12.12	+14.23
BC	+7.56	+8.50	+9.62	+11.75	+13.91
CD	+6.38	+7.25	+8.27	+10.21	+12.17
DE	+5.62	+6.50	+7.53	+9.46	+11.38
EF	+5.06	+6.00	+7.08	+9.08	+11.07
AG	−6.75	−7.79	−9.00	−11.25	−13.50
GH	−6.00	−6.93	−8.00	−10.00	−12.00
HK	−5.25	−6.06	−7.00	−8.75	−10.50
KM	−3.75	−4.33	−5.00	−6.25	−7.50
BG	+0.83	+0.87	+0.89	+0.93	+0.95
CG	−0.75	−0.87	−1.00	−1.25	−1.50
CH	+1.25	+1.30	+1.34	+1.39	+1.42
DH	−1.04	−1.15	−1.26	−1.49	−1.71
DK	+2.08	+2.17	+2.24	+2.32	+2.37
DN	−0.59	−0.66	−0.75	−0.90	−1.06
EN	+0.83	+0.87	+0.89	+0.93	+0.95
KN	−1.77	−1.98	−2.24	−2.71	−3.18
NF	−2.35	−2.65	−2.98	−3.61	−4.24

M	Pitch				
	$\frac{1}{3}$	$a = 30°$	$\frac{1}{4}$	$\frac{1}{5}$	$\frac{1}{6}$
AB	+2.70	+3.00	+3.36	+4.04	+4.74
BC	+1.80	+2.00	+2.24	+2.69	+3.16
CD	+0.90	+1.00	+1.12	+1.35	+1.58
DE	0	0	0	0	0
AF	−2.25	−2.60	−3.00	−3.75	−4.50
FG	−1.50	−1.73	−2.00	−2.50	−3.00
GH	−0.75	−0.87	−1.00	−1.25	−1.50
BF	+0.90	+1.00	+1.12	+1.35	+1.58
CF	−0.50	−0.50	−0.50	−0.50	−0.50
CG	+1.25	+1.32	+1.41	+1.60	+1.80
DG	−1.00	−1.00	−1.00	−1.00	−1.00
DH	+1.68	+1.73	+1.80	+1.95	+2.12
EH	0	0	0	0	0

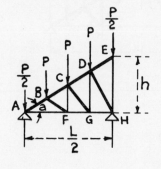

M = Member of truss   + Indicates compression
Pitch = h/L − Indicates tension
Stress in any member = coefficient multiplied by W

Table 10.1　Trusses—Coefficients of Stresses (*Continued*)

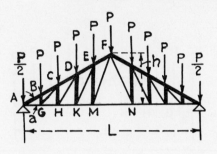

M	Pitch				
	$\frac{1}{3}$	$a = 30°$	$\frac{1}{4}$	$\frac{1}{5}$	$\frac{1}{6}$
AB	+8.11	+9.00	+10.06	+12.12	+14.23
BC	+8.11	+9.00	+10.06	+12.12	+14.23
CD	+7.21	+8.00	+8.94	+10.77	+12.65
DE	+6.31	+7.00	+7.83	+9.42	+11.07
EF	+5.41	+6.00	+6.71	+8.08	+9.49
AG	−6.75	−7.79	−9.00	−11.25	−13.50
GH	−6.00	−6.93	−8.00	−10.00	−12.00
HK	−5.25	−6.06	−7.00	−8.75	−10.50
KM	−4.50	−5.20	−6.00	−7.50	−9.00
MN	−3.75	−4.33	−5.00	−6.25	−7.50
BG	+1.00	+1.00	+1.00	+1.00	+1.00
CG	−1.25	−1.32	−1.41	−1.60	−1.80
CH	+1.50	+1.50	+1.50	+1.50	+1.50
DH	−1.68	−1.73	−1.80	−1.95	−2.12
DK	+2.00	+2.00	+2.00	+2.00	+2.00
EK	−2.14	−2.18	−2.24	−2.36	−2.50
EM	+2.50	+2.50	+2.50	+2.50	+2.50
FM	−2.61	−2.65	−2.69	−2.80	−2.92

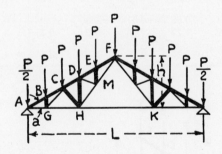

M	Pitch				
	$\frac{1}{3}$	$a = 30°$	$\frac{1}{4}$	$\frac{1}{5}$	$\frac{1}{6}$
AB	+8.11	+9.00	+10.06	+12.12	+14.23
BC	+8.11	+9.00	+10.06	+12.12	+14.23
CD	+6.31	+7.00	+7.83	+9.42	+11.07
DE	+6.91	+7.67	+8.57	+10.32	+12.12
EF	+6.91	+7.67	+8.57	+10.32	+12.12
AG	−6.75	−7.79	−9.00	−11.25	−13.50
GH	−6.00	−6.93	−8.00	−10.00	−12.00
HK	−3.75	−4.33	−5.00	−6.25	−7.50
BG	+1.00	+1.00	+1.00	+1.00	+1.00
CG	−1.25	−1.32	−1.41	−1.60	−1.80
CH	+1.25	+1.32	+1.41	+1.60	+1.80
DH	+1.50	+1.50	+1.50	+1.50	+1.50
DM	−0.53	−0.60	−0.69	−0.85	−1.01
EM	+1.00	+1.00	+1.00	+1.00	+1.00
HM	−2.92	−3.04	−3.20	−3.54	−3.91
MF	−3.89	−4.06	−4.27	−4.71	−5.21

M = Member of truss　　　+ Indicates compression
Pitch = *h/L*　　　　　　　− Indicates tension
Stress in any member = coefficient multiplied by *W*

Table 10.1   Trusses—Coefficients of Stresses (*Continued*)

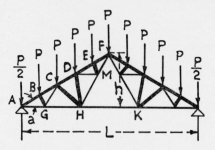

M	Pitch				
	$\frac{1}{3}$	$a = 30°$	$\frac{1}{4}$	$\frac{1}{5}$	$\frac{1}{6}$
AB	+8.11	+9.00	+10.06	+12.12	+14.23
BC	+7.56	+8.50	+9.62	+11.75	+13.91
CD	+6.00	+6.80	+7.74	+9.52	+11.32
DE	+6.45	+7.50	+8.72	+11.00	+13.28
EF	+5.89	+7.00	+8.28	+10.63	+12.97
AG	−6.75	−7.79	−9.00	−11.25	−13.50
GH	−6.00	−6.91	−8.00	−10.00	−12.00
HK	−3.75	−4.33	−5.00	−6.25	−7.50
BG	+0.83	+0.87	+0.89	+0.93	+0.95
CG	−0.75	−0.87	−1.00	−1.25	−1.50
CH	+1.31	+1.37	+1.44	+1.56	+1.66
DH	+1.31	+1.37	+1.44	+1.56	+1.66
DM	−0.75	−0.87	−1.00	−1.25	−1.50
EM	+0.83	+0.87	+0.89	+0.93	+0.95
HM	−2.25	−2.60	−3.00	−3.75	−4.50
MF	−3.00	−3.46	−4.00	−5.00	−6.00

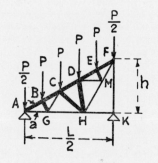

M	Pitch				
	$\frac{1}{3}$	$a = 30°$	$\frac{1}{4}$	$\frac{1}{5}$	$\frac{1}{6}$
AB	+3.61	+4.00	+4.47	+5.39	+6.32
BC	+3.05	+3.50	+4.02	+5.01	+6.01
CD	+1.50	+1.80	+2.15	+2.79	+3.42
DE	+1.94	+2.50	+3.13	+4.27	+5.38
EF	+1.39	+2.00	+2.68	+3.90	+5.06
AG	−3.00	−3.46	−4.00	−5.00	−6.00
GH	−2.25	−2.60	−3.00	−3.75	−4.50
HK	0	0	0	0	0
BG	+0.83	+0.87	+0.89	+0.93	+0.95
CG	−0.75	−0.87	−1.00	−1.25	−1.50
CH	+1.30	+1.37	+1.44	+1.56	+1.66
DH	+1.30	+1.37	+1.44	+1.56	+1.66
DM	−0.75	−0.87	−1.00	−1.25	−1.50
EM	+0.83	+0.87	+0.89	+0.93	+0.95
HM	−2.25	−2.60	−3.00	−3.75	−4.50
MF	−3.00	−3.46	−4.00	−5.00	−6.00

M = Member of truss   + Indicates compression
Pitch = h/L   − Indicates tension
Srtess in any member = coefficient multiplied by W

Table 10.1   Trusses—Coefficients of Stresses (*Continued*)

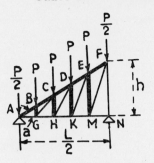

M	Pitch				
	$\frac{1}{3}$	$a = 30°$	$\frac{1}{4}$	$\frac{1}{5}$	$\frac{1}{6}$
AB	+3.61	+4.00	+4.47	+5.39	+6.32
BC	+3.61	+4.00	+4.47	+5.39	+6.32
CD	+2.70	+3.00	+3.35	+4.04	+4.74
DE	+1.80	+2.00	+2.24	+2.69	+3.16
EF	+0.90	+1.00	+1.12	+1.35	+1.58
AG	−3.00	−3.46	−4.00	−5.00	−6.00
GH	−2.25	−2.60	−3.00	−3.75	−4.50
HK	−1.50	−1.73	−2.00	−2.50	−3.00
KM	−0.75	−0.87	−1.00	−1.25	−1.50
MN	0	0	0	0	0
BG	+1.00	+1.00	+1.00	+1.00	+1.00
CG	−1.25	−1.32	−1.41	−1.60	−1.80
CH	+1.50	+1.50	+1.50	+1.50	+1.50
DH	−1.68	−1.73	−1.80	−1.95	−2.12
DK	+2.00	+2.00	+2.00	+2.00	+2.00
EK	−2.14	−2.18	−2.24	−2.36	−2.50
EM	+2.50	+2.50	+2.50	+2.50	+2.50
FM	−2.61	−2.65	−2.69	−2.80	−2.92

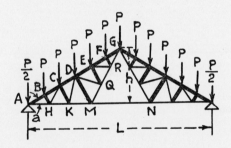

M	Pitch				
	$\frac{1}{3}$	$a = 30°$	$\frac{1}{4}$	$\frac{1}{5}$	$\frac{1}{6}$
AB	+9.92	+11.00	+12.30	+14.81	+17.39
BC	+9.36	+10.50	+11.85	+14.44	+17.08
CD	+8.18	+9.25	+10.51	+12.91	+15.34
DE	+7.63	+8.75	+10.06	+12.53	+15.02
EF	+7.70	+9.00	+10.51	+13.32	+16.13
FG	+7.14	+8.50	+10.06	+12.95	+15.81
AH	−8.25	−9.53	−11.00	−13.75	−16.50
HK	−7.50	−8.66	−10.00	−12.50	−15.00
KM	−6.75	−7.79	−9.00	−11.25	−13.50
MN	−4.50	−5.20	−6.00	−7.50	−9.00
BH	+0.83	+0.87	+0.89	+0.93	+0.95
CH	−0.75	−0.87	−1.00	−1.25	−1.50
CK	+1.25	+1.30	+1.34	+1.39	+1.42
DK	−1.04	−1.15	−1.26	−1.49	−1.71
DM	+2.50	+2.60	+2.68	+2.79	+2.85
DQ	−1.04	−1.15	−1.26	−1.49	−1.71
EQ	+1.25	+1.30	+1.34	+1.39	+1.42
ER	−0.75	−0.87	−1.00	−1.25	−1.50
FR	+0.83	+0.87	+0.89	+0.93	+0.95
MQ	−2.25	−2.60	−3.00	−3.75	−4.50
QR	−3.00	−3.46	−4.00	−5.00	−6.00
RG	−3.75	−4.33	−5.00	−6.25	−7.50

M = Member of truss   + Indicates compression
Pitch = h/L − Indicates tension
Stress in any member = coefficient multiplied by W

Table 10.1 Trusses—Coefficients of Stresses (*Continued*)

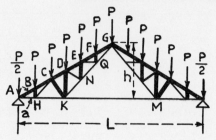

M	Pitch				
	$\frac{1}{3}$	$a = 30°$	$\frac{1}{4}$	$\frac{1}{5}$	$\frac{1}{6}$
AB	+9.92	+11.00	+12.30	+14.81	+17.39
BC	+9.92	+11.00	+12.30	+14.81	+17.39
CD	+8.11	+9.00	+10.06	+12.12	+14.23
DE	+9.01	+10.00	+11.18	+13.46	+15.81
EF	+9.92	+11.00	+12.30	+14.81	+17.39
FG	+9.92	+11.00	+12.30	+14.81	+17.39
AH	−8.25	−9.53	−11.00	−13.75	−16.50
HK	−7.50	−8.66	−10.00	−12.50	−15.00
KM	−4.50	−5.20	−6.00	−7.50	−9.00
BH	+1.00	+1.00	+1.00	+1.00	+1.00
CH	−1.25	−1.32	−1.41	−1.60	−1.80
CK	+1.25	+1.32	+1.41	+1.60	+1.80
DK	+2.00	+2.00	+2.00	+2.00	+2.00
DN	−0.90	−1.00	−1.12	−1.35	−1.58
EN	+1.50	+1.50	+1.50	+1.50	+1.50
EQ	−0.75	−0.87	−1.00	−1.25	−1.50
FQ	+1.00	+1.00	+1.00	+1.00	+1.00
KN	−3.75	−3.97	−4.24	−4.80	−5.41
NQ	−5.00	−5.29	−5.66	−6.40	−7.21
QG	−6.25	−6.61	−7.07	−8.00	−9.01

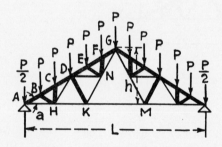

M	Pitch				
	$\frac{1}{3}$	$a = 30°$	$\frac{1}{4}$	$\frac{1}{5}$	$\frac{1}{6}$
AB	+9.92	+11.00	+12.30	+14.81	+17.39
BC	+8.95	+10.00	+11.25	+13.66	+16.13
CD	+8.81	+10.00	+11.40	+14.07	+16.76
DE	+8.25	+9.50	+10.96	+13.70	+16.44
EF	+7.28	+8.50	+9.91	+12.55	+15.18
FG	+7.14	+8.50	+10.06	+12.95	+15.93
AH	−8.25	−9.53	−11.00	−13.75	−16.50
HK	−6.75	−7.79	−9.00	−11.25	−13.50
KM	−4.50	−5.20	−6.00	−7.50	−9.00
BH	+0.93	+1.00	+1.07	+1.21	+1.34
CH	+0.93	+1.00	+1.07	+1.21	+1.34
DH	−1.50	−1.73	−2.00	−2.50	−3.00
DK	+2.50	+2.60	+2.68	+2.79	+2.85
DN	−1.50	−1.73	−2.00	−2.50	−3.00
EN	+0.93	+1.00	+1.07	+1.21	+1.34
FN	+0.93	+1.00	+1.07	+1.21	+1.34
KN	−2.25	−2.60	−3.00	−3.75	−4.50
NG	−3.75	−4.33	−5.00	−6.25	−7.50

M = Member of truss   + Indicates compression
Pitch = h/L − Indicates tension
Stress in any member = coefficient multiplied by W

Table 10.1 Trusses—Coefficients of Stresses (*Continued*)

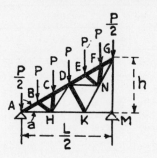

M	Pitch				
	$\frac{1}{3}$	$a = 30°$	$\frac{1}{4}$	$\frac{1}{5}$	$\frac{1}{6}$
AB	+4.51	+5.00	+5.59	+6.73	+7.91
BC	+3.54	+4.00	+4.55	+5.59	+6.64
CD	+3.40	+4.00	+4.70	+5.99	+7.27
DE	+2.84	+3.50	+4.25	+5.62	+6.96
EF	+1.87	+2.50	+3.21	+4.47	+5.69
FG	+1.73	+2.50	+3.35	+4.87	+6.32
AH	−3.75	−4.33	−5.00	−6.25	−7.50
HK	−2.25	−2.60	−3.00	−3.75	−4.50
KM	0	0	0	0	0
BH	+0.93	+1.00	+1.07	+1.21	+1.34
CH	+0.93	+1.00	+1.07	+1.21	+1.34
DH	−1.50	−1.73	−2.00	−2.50	−3.00
DK	+2.50	+2.60	+2.68	+2.79	+2.85
DN	−1.50	−1.73	−2.00	−2.50	−3.00
EN	+0.93	+1.00	+1.07	+1.21	+1.34
FN	+0.93	+1.00	+1.07	+1.21	+1.34
KN	−2.25	−2.60	−3.00	−3.75	−4.50
NG	−3.75	−4.33	−5.00	−6.25	−7.50

M = Member of truss   + Indicates compression
Pitch = h/L − Indicates tension
Stress in any member = coefficient multiplied by W

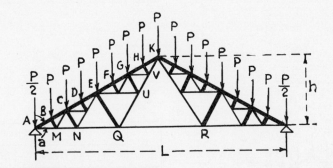

M	Pitch				
	$\frac{1}{3}$	$a = 30°$	$\frac{1}{4}$	$\frac{1}{5}$	$\frac{1}{6}$
AB	+13.52	+15.00	+16.77	+20.19	+23.72
BC	+12.97	+14.50	+16.32	+19.82	+23.40
CD	+12.41	+14.00	+15.88	+19.45	+23.08
DE	+11.86	+13.50	+15.43	+19.08	+22.77
EF	+11.30	+13.00	+14.98	+18.71	+22.45
FG	+10.75	+12.50	+14.53	+18.34	+22.14
GH	+10.19	+12.00	+14.09	+17.97	+21.82
HK	+9.64	+11.50	+13.64	+17.60	+21.50
AM	−11.25	−12.99	−15.00	−18.75	−22.50
MN	−11.50	−12.12	−14.00	−17.50	−21.00
NQ	−9.00	−10.39	−12.00	−15.00	−18.00
QR	−6.00	−6.93	−8.00	−10.00	−12.00
BM	+0.83	+0.87	+0.89	+0.93	+0.95
CM	−0.75	−0.87	−1.00	−1.25	−1.50
CN	+1.66	+1.73	+1.79	+1.86	+1.90

M	Pitch				
	$\frac{1}{3}$	$a = 30°$	$\frac{1}{4}$	$\frac{1}{5}$	$\frac{1}{6}$
CS	−0.75	−0.87	−1.00	−1.25	−1.50
DS	+0.83	+0.87	+0.89	+0.93	+0.95
ES	−2.25	−2.60	−3.00	−3.75	−4.50
SN	−1.50	−1.73	−2.00	−2.50	−3.00
EQ	+3.33	+3.46	+3.58	+3.71	+3.79
ET	−2.25	−2.60	−3.00	−3.75	−4.50
TU	−1.50	−1.73	−2.00	−2.50	−3.00
FT	+0.83	+0.87	+0.89	+0.93	+0.95
GT	−0.75	−0.87	−1.00	−1.25	−1.50
GU	+1.66	+1.73	+1.79	+1.86	+1.90
GV	−0.75	−0.87	−1.00	−1.25	−1.50
HV	+0.83	+0.87	+0.89	+0.93	+0.95
QU	−3.00	−3.46	−4.00	−5.00	−6.00
UV	−4.50	−5.20	−6.00	−7.50	−9.00
VK	−5.25	−6.06	−7.00	−8.75	−10.50

Table 10.2 Double Angle Members—Equal Legs in Compression

Size, in.	t, in.	area, sq in.	r x-x axis	r y-y axis	Axis x-x 4	5	6	8	10	12	Max. L	Axis y-y 6	7	8	10	12	Max L
8×8	1⅛	33.46	2.42	3.55	562	559	554	543	529	512	24.2	563	560	557	550	542	35.5
	1	30.00	2.44	3.53	505	501	497	488	475	459	24.4	504	502	499	493	486	35.3
	⅞	26.46	2.45	3.51	445	443	438	430	420	407	24.5	445	443	440	434	428	35.1
	¾	22.88	2.47	3.49	385	382	380	373	363	352	24.7	384	382	380	376	370	34.9
	⅝	19.22	2.49	3.47	323	321	319	312	305	296	24.9	323	322	320	316	310	34.7
	½	15.50	2.50	3.45	261	258	257	252	247	239	25.0	260	259	258	254	251	34.5
6×6	1	22.00	1.80	2.72	366	362	357	344	327	306	18.0	367	364	361	353	344	27.2
	⅞	19.46	1.81	2.70	324	320	316	304	289	271	18.1	324	322	319	312	304	27.0
	¾	16.88	1.83	2.68	281	278	274	265	252	236	18.3	282	279	276	271	263	26.8
	⅝	14.22	1.84	2.66	237	234	231	223	213	200	18.4	237	235	233	228	221	26.6
	½	11.50	1.86	2.64	192	190	187	181	172	162	18.6	192	190	188	184	179	26.4
	⅜	8.72	1.88	2.62	146	143	141	137	131	123	18.8	145	144	142	139	135	26.2
5×5	1	18.00	1.48	2.33	297	292	286	270	249	224	14.8	297	295	291	283	273	23.3
	⅞	15.96	1.49	2.31	263	259	254	240	221	200	14.9	264	261	258	250	241	23.1
	¾	13.88	1.51	2.28	230	226	221	219	194	175	15.1	230	227	224	218	210	22.8
	⅝	11.72	1.52	2.26	194	191	187	177	164	148	15.2	194	192	189	183	176	22.6
	½	9.50	1.54	2.23	157	154	151	144	133	121	15.4	156	155	153	148	142	22.3
	⅜	7.22	1.56	2.22	119	117	115	109	102	93	15.6	119	117	116	112	107	22.2
4×4	¾	10.88	1.19	1.88	176	171	166	151	131	110	11.9	178	175	171	164	154	18.8
	⅝	9.22	1.20	1.86	150	145	140	128	112	93	12.0	150	147	144	138	129	18.6
	½	7.50	1.22	1.83	122	119	115	105	92	77	12.2	122	120	118	112	105	18.3
	⅜	5.72	1.23	1.81	93	91	88	80	71	59	12.3	93	91	89	85	80	18.1
	¼	3.88	1.25	1.79	63	62	60	55	49	41	12.5	63	62	61	58	54	17.9
3½×3½	¾	9.38	1.03	1.69	149	144	137	120	97		10.3	151	148	144	137	126	16.9
	⅝	7.96	1.04	1.66	127	122	117	102	84		10.4	128	125	122	115	106	16.6
	½	6.50	1.06	1.64	104	101	96	85	70		10.6	104	102	99	94	86	16.4
	⅜	4.96	1.07	1.61	79	77	74	65	54		10.7	80	78	76	71	65	16.1
	¼	3.38	1.09	1.59	54	52	50	45	37		10.9	54	53	51	48	44	15.9
3×3	⅝	6.72	0.88	1.46	104	99	92	75			8.8	106	103	100	92	82	14.6
	½	5.50	0.90	1.43	86	82	77	63			9.0	87	85	82	75	66	14.3
	⅜	4.22	0.91	1.41	66	63	59	49			9.1	66	64	62	57	50	14.1
	¼	2.88	0.93	1.38	45	43	41	34			9.3	45	44	42	38	34	13.8
2½×2½	½	4.50	0.74	1.24	67	62	56				7.4	69	66	63	56	47	12.4
	⅜	3.46	0.75	1.21	52	48	43				7.5	53	51	48	42	35	12.1
	¼	2.38	0.77	1.19	36	33	30				7.7	36	35	33	29		11.9

d Supports for roof signs and elevated tanks, radio towers, and similar structures are usually variations of a cantilever truss. Figure 10.6 shows the load and stress diagram of a truss of this kind. For the sake of comparison with the other diagrams, the truss is laid out horizontally with loads applied vertically. Normally this condition is reversed, with wind loads applied horizontally. For loads applied in the usual manner, from left to right, it will be noted that the stress diagram is laid out to the right of the load line instead of to the left as in the case of a standard truss. It is to be noted also that stresses in cantilever trusses for wind loads are subject to complete reversal, and that at the base of each leg anchorage must be provided in the foundation or structure on which it stands to carry the tensile stress or uplift under each leg. Failure to provide such proper anchorage is a common cause of failure of such cantilever trusses.

Table 10.3   Double Angle Members—Unequal Legs in Compression

Longer leg outstanding

Size, in.	t, in.	Area, sq in.	r x-x axis	r y-y axis	Axis x-x 4	5	6	8	10	12	14	Max. L	Axis y-y 6	8	10	12	14	Max. L
4 × 4	1	24.00	1.00	4.66	382	363	348	300	240			10.0	400	398	395	393	391	46.6
	⅞	21.22	1.01	4.63	338	326	309	268	216			10.1	354	352	349	347	345	46.3
	¾	18.38	1.02	4.61	293	282	268	234	189			10.2	306	304	302	300	298	46.1
	⅝	15.46	1.04	4.58	247	239	227	199	163			10.4	258	256	257	258	259	45.8
	½	12.50	1.05	4.55		193	184	162	134			10.5	208	207	205	204	203	45.5
8 × 6	1	26.00	1.73	3.78	432	428	420	404	382	355	323	17.3	437	434	429	424	417	37.8
	⅞	22.96	1.74	3.76	382	378	372	357	335	314	286	17.4	386	383	379	374	369	37.6
	¾	19.88	1.76	3.73	331	328	322	310	293	274	250	17.6	335	332	329	324	319	37.3
	⅝	16.72	1.77	3.72	278	275	271	261	247	231	211	17.7	282	279	276	272	268	37.2
	½	13.50	1.79	3.69	225	222	219	211	200	187	172	17.9	227	225	223	220	216	36.9
8 × 4	1	22.00	1.03	4.10	351	338	322	282	230			10.3	371	369	365	361	356	41.0
	⅞	19.46	1.04	4.07	310	299	286	251	206			10.4	328	326	323	319	315	40.7
	¾	16.88	1.05	4.04	270	260	249	218	180			10.5	285	283	280	277	273	40.4
	⅝	14.22	1.07	4.02	228	220	211	187	155			10.7	240	238	236	233	230	40.2
	½	11.50	1.08	4.00	185	179	171	151	126			10.8	194	192	190	188	186	40.0
7 × 4	1	20.00	1.06	3.54	320	300	295	260	216			10.6	336	333	329	324	318	35.4
	⅞	17.72	1.07	3.51	284	274	263	233	194			10.7	298	295	292	287	282	35.1
	¾	15.38	1.09	3.49	247	239	230	204	171			10.9	259	256	253	249	244	34.9
	⅝	12.96	1.10	3.47	208	202	194	173	146			11.0	218	216	213	210	206	34.7
	½	10.50	1.11	3.45	169	164	157	141	118			11.1	176	175	173	170	167	34.5
	⅜	7.96	1.13	3.42	128	124	120	107	92			11.3	134	132	130	128	126	34.2
6 × 4	⅞	15.96	1.11	2.97	257	248	238	214	181			11.1	267	264	260	254	246	29.7
	¾	13.88	1.12	2.95	224	216	208	187	159			11.2	232	229	225	220	214	29.5
	⅝	11.72	1.13	2.92	189	183	177	158	136			11.3	196	193	190	186	181	29.2
	½	9.50	1.15	2.90	153	149	143	129	110			11.5	158	156	153	150	146	29.0
	⅜	7.22	1.17	2.87	117	113	109	99	86			11.7	121	118	116	114	111	28.7
5 × 3½	¾	11.62	.98	2.48	184	177	167	143				9.8	193	189	184	179	172	24.8
	⅝	9.84	.99	2.45	155	149	142	122				9.9	163	160	155	150	144	24.5
	½	8.00	1.01	2.43	127	122	116	101	82			10.1	132	130	126	122	117	24.3
	⅜	6.10	1.02	2.40	97	94	89	78	63			10.2	101	99	96	93	89	24.0
4 × 3½	¾	10.12	1.01	1.94	161	155	147	127	104			10.1	165	160	153	145	135	19.4
	⅝	8.60	1.03	1.91	137	132	126	110	90			10.3	140	135	130	122	114	19.1
	½	7.00	1.04	1.89	112	108	103	90	74			10.4	114	110	105	99	92	18.9
	⅜	5.34	1.06	1.88	86	83	79	70	58			10.6	87	84	80	75	70	18.8
4 × 3	⅝	7.96	.85	1.99	123	116	108	86				8.5	130	126	121	115	108	19.9
	½	6.50	.86	1.96	101	95	89	71				8.6	106	103	99	94	88	19.6
	⅜	4.96	.88	1.94	77	73	67	56				8.8	81	78	75	71	66	19.4
	¼	3.38	.90	1.92	53	50	47	39				9.0	55	53	51	48	45	19.2
3½ × 3	⅝	7.34	.87	1.72	114	108	100	82				8.7	118	113	107	100	91	17.2
	½	6.00	.88	1.70	94	89	83	67				8.8	97	93	88	81	74	17.0
	⅜	4.60	.90	1.67	72	68	64	53				9.0	74	71	67	62	56	16.7
	¼	3.12	.91	1.65	49	47	44	36				9.1	50	48	45	41	37	16.5
3 × 2½	⅜	3.84	.74	1.48	57	53	48					7.4	61	57	53	48	41	14.8
	¼	2.62	.75	1.45	40	37	33					7.5	41	39	36	32	28	14.5
2½ × 2	⅜	3.10	.58	1.27	42	37						5.8	48	44	40	34		12.7
	¼	2.12	.59	1.25	29	25						5.9	33	30	27	22		12.5

Unbraced length in feet—⅜ in. back to back

Table 10.4 Double Angle Members—Unequal Legs in Compression

Shorter leg outstanding

Size, in.	t, in.	Area, sq in.	r x-x axis	r y-y axis	Axis x-x 4	6	8	10	12	14	Max. L	Axis y-y 4	6	8	10	12	14	Max L
9 × 4	1	24.00	2.84	1.55	405	403	395	387	378	367	28.4	397	383	364	338	308	271	15.5
	7/8	21.22	2.86	1.52	358	357	346	342	335	325	28.6	351	338	320	297	268	235	15.2
	3/4	18.38	2.88	1.50	310	307	303	297	290	282	28.8	304	292	276	255	230	201	15.0
	5/8	15.46	2.90	1.47	260	258	254	250	244	238	29.0	255	245	231	213	191	165	14.7
	1/2	12.50	2.92	1.45	211	209	206	202	198	192	29.2	206	198	186	171	153	131	14.5
8 × 6	1	26.00	2.49	2.52	437	432	423	413	400	384	24.9	437	432	424	414	401	387	25.2
	7/8	22.96	2.51	2.50	386	381	374	366	354	340	25.1	386	382	374	365	354	340	25.0
	3/4	19.88	2.53	2.48	335	330	325	317	307	295	25.3	335	330	324	316	306	294	24.8
	5/8	16.72	2.54	2.46	282	278	273	267	259	249	25.4	282	278	272	265	257	247	24.6
	1/2	13.50	2.56	2.44	227	224	220	215	209	202	25.6	227	224	220	214	207	199	24.4
8 × 4	1	22.00	2.52	1.61	370	365	359	350	342	327	25.2	364	353	336	315	289	258	16.1
	7/8	19.46	2.53	1.58	327	323	317	310	302	289	25.3	322	311	296	276	252	225	15.8
	3/4	16.88	2.55	1.55	284	280	276	269	262	252	25.5	279	269	256	238	216	191	15.5
	5/8	14.22	2.57	1.53	239	236	233	227	222	213	25.7	235	227	215	200	181	159	15.3
	1/2	11.50	2.59	1.51	194	191	188	184	179	172	25.9	190	183	173	160	145	126	15.1
7 × 4	1	20.00	2.18	1.67	336	329	321	311	298	282	21.8	332	322	308	290	268	242	16.7
	7/8	17.72	2.20	1.64	297	292	285	276	265	251	22.0	294	285	272	256	235	211	16.4
	3/4	15.38	2.22	1.62	258	254	248	240	230	219	22.2	255	247	236	220	203	181	16.2
	5/8	12.96	2.24	1.59	218	214	209	203	195	185	22.4	215	208	198	185	169	150	15.9
	1/2	10.50	2.25	1.57	176	173	170	164	158	150	22.5	174	168	160	149	136	120	15.7
	3/8	7.96	2.27	1.55	134	131	128	124	119	114	22.7	132	127	120	112	102	90	15.5
6 × 4	7/8	15.96	1.86	1.71	267	260	251	239	224	208	18.6	266	258	247	233	216	197	17.1
	3/4	13.88	1.88	1.69	232	226	218	209	197	183	18.8	231	224	214	202	187	170	16.9
	5/8	11.72	1.90	1.66	196	191	185	177	167	155	19.0	195	189	181	170	156	141	16.6
	1/2	9.50	1.91	1.65	159	155	149	143	135	125	19.1	158	152	146	137	126	113	16.5
	3/8	7.22	1.93	1.62	120	118	114	109	103	96	19.3	119	116	110	103	95	85	16.2
5 × 3½	3/4	11.62	1.55	1.54	192	185	176	164	149	132	15.5	192	185	176	163	148	131	15.4
	5/8	9.84	1.56	1.51	162	157	149	139	126	111	15.6	162	156	148	137	123	107	15.1
	1/2	8.00	1.58	1.49	132	128	121	113	103	92	15.8	131	126	119	110	99	87	14.9
	3/8	6.10	1.60	1.46	101	98	93	87	80	71	16.0	100	97	91	84	75	65	14.6
4 × 3½	3/4	10.12	1.20	1.63	164	155	141	123	101		12.0	168	163	155	145	134	120	16.3
	5/8	8.60	1.22	1.60	140	132	120	106	88		12.2	142	138	131	123	117	100	16.0
	1/2	7.00	1.23	1.58	114	107	98	88	73		12.3	116	112	106	100	91	81	15.8
	3/8	5.34	1.25	1.56	87	82	75	67	57		12.5	89	85	81	76	69	61	15.6
4 × 3	5/8	7.96	1.23	1.36	129	122	112	100	83		12.3	131	124	116	105	92		13.6
	1/2	6.50	1.25	1.33	106	100	92	82	69		12.5	106	101	94	85	74		13.3
	3/8	4.96	1.26	1.31	81	76	70	63	53		12.6	81	77	71	64	55		13.1
	1/4	3.38	1.28	1.29	55	52	48	43	37		12.8	55	52	48	43	37		12.9
3½ × 3	5/8	7.34	1.06	1.41	117	108	96	79			10.6	120	115	108	99	88		14.1
	1/2	6.00	1.07	1.38	96	89	79	65			10.7	99	94	88	80	72		13.8
	3/8	4.60	1.09	1.36	74	68	61	51			10.9	76	72	67	61	53		13.6
	1/4	3.12	1.11	1.34	50	47	42	35			11.1	51	49	45	41	36		13.4
3 × 2½	3/8	3.84	.93	1.16	60	54	46				9.3	62	58	53	45			11.6
	1/4	2.62	.95	1.13	41	37	32				9.5	42	40	35	30			11.3
2½ × 2	3/8	3.10	.77	.96	47	40					7.7	49	44	28				9.6
	1/4	2.12	.78	.94	32	27					7.8	33	30	26				9.4

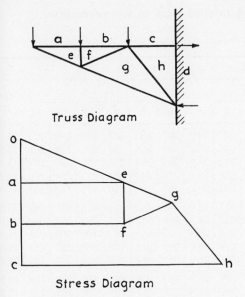

Truss Diagram

Stress Diagram

Fig. 10.6   Cantilever Truss

0.11   Steel trusses

a Steel trusses are not economical for roof spans below 60 ft if it is permissible to use flat-roof construction. Frequently, however, the roof pitch required (see Art. 10.40) makes flat construction undesirable, and if it is necessary to build up a two-way pitch, it is frequently advisable to take advantage of the condition and use steel trusses.

b Allowance must be made for the weight of the truss itself in selecting the dead load. Since this weight constitutes only a small portion of the total weight, a sizable error between actual and assumed weight will not materially influence the design. A simple way of approximating the weight of the truss is to compute the weight of a steel beam or girder which will carry the design load as a uniform load, and use a truss weight of 60 per cent of the beam weight.

For instance, assume a 40-lb per sq ft total load on trusses with 60-ft span, spaced 16 ft.

$$W = 40 \times 60 \times 16 = 38.4K$$
$$S = \frac{38.4 \times 60}{13.33} = 173 = 24 \text{ WF } 76$$

Use a truss-weight allowance of $0.6 \times 76 = 46$ lb per lin ft. (Actual trusses on this span weigh 43 lb per ft for a Fink truss and 48 lb per ft for a Warren truss.)

c Stresses are computed by the methods described in Art. 10.10, either graphically or by the application of Table 10.1. The computation of truss members is usually simplified by setting the truss up as shown in Table 10.5.

The computation of member sizes is a problem in the application of simple stresses, as described in Arts. 2.10, 2.12 (as modified by Art. 7.10), and 2.13 and Table 2.2. For carrying ordinary stresses without a combination of bending and direct stress, a pair of angles is ordinarily used because they lend themselves to economical connection to gusset plates and to use as stiff compression members. When a truss member carries bending between panel points, angles are not satisfactory because they are weak in bending. In this case, the preferable member is made up of a pair of channels. Channels, however, do not lend themselves economically to compression because the radius of gyration of two channels around a $\frac{3}{8}$- or $\frac{1}{2}$-in. gusset is not so high as a pair of angles, and the added depth to the neutral axis of a channel lowers the effective depth for a given maximum total depth.

For tension members the net effective area is taken as the net area of the connected leg plus half the area of the outstanding leg. On this basis members may be selected from Table 2.2.

Compression members are designed in accordance with Art. 7.10*b*. Table 10.3 lists the strength of various angles in pairs for various unbraced lengths. In the case of top-chord members, the spacing of purlins controls the unbraced length, in feet, about axis *x-x*, and the spacing of panel points controls the unbraced length about axis *y-y*. Usually they are the same.

As chord stresses are often too great to be carried economically by a pair of angles, wide-flange sections sometimes are used for truss members, with the flanges vertical. The members are usually kept to the same depth, and two gusset plates are used. Occasionally it is economical to use this type of truss even though the stresses could be carried by angle members, as in the irregular Warren truss shown in Fig. 10.4. Because columns are hung

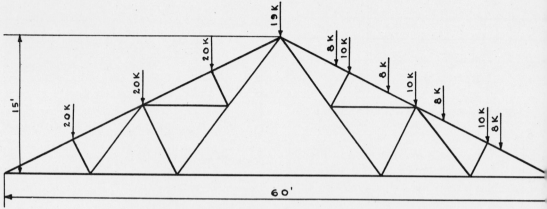

Fig. 10.7 Truss Load for Bending and Direct Stress

from the bottom chord, wide-flange sections lend themselves to better detail.

The selection of gusset-plate thickness to use throughout is a matter of detail. If stresses are light it is common practice to use a $\frac{3}{8}$-in. gusset plate with $\frac{3}{4}$-in. rivets. The AISC specification requires a minimum of two rivets, which would carry a stress of $2 \times 11.3 = 22.6$ kips (see Table 9.1).

Problem Design an eight-panel compound Fink truss on 60-ft span, 15-ft rise, with loads at panel points of 20,000 lb each (including the weight of the truss). Refer to Table 10.1 for the compound Fink truss, pitch, $h/L = 15/60 = \frac{1}{4}$. Since it is not economical to splice the chord members except at the center, the only chord stress it is necessary to design for is the heaviest one. Table 10.5 will use the same letters as in Table 10.1.

Assume that one truss in the building has eccentric loads on one side of the peak of the

Fink truss, so that the purlins from one sid are at panel points carrying 10 kips each while from the other panel the span from pea line to eave line is divided into five equa spans carrying 8 kips each. The load cond tion is shown in Fig. 10.7. The computatio of reactions indicated in Fig. 10.8 indicate that the loads for use in the stress diagran will closely approximate the original truss de signed above, so it will not be necessary t recompute the truss stresses. The top chor under consideration is a continuous beam and the moments may be computed by th moment-distribution methods of Art. 3.21 We shall consider the ends as freely supported Figure 10.9 shows the computation of moment

Since the negative moment is always great est in a continuous beam loaded in this man ner, we must design for the combination o greatest direct stress and moment. Referring again to Table 10.1, the direct stress in A is $7.83 \times 20 = 156.6$ kips, and the momen

Table 10.5 Design of Truss Members

Member	C	Stress, kips	L, ft	A	Section (all two angles), in.	Remarks
Top chord	7.83	+ 156	8.37		$6 \times 4 \times \frac{5}{8}$ S.L.V.	From Table 10.
Bottom chord	7	− 140		7.0	$8 \times 4 \times \frac{7}{16}$	From Fig. 2.3
BF	0.89	+ 17.8	4.19		$2\frac{1}{2} \times 2 \times \frac{1}{4}$ S.L.V.	From Table 10.
CF	1	− 20		1.0	$2\frac{1}{2} \times 2 \times \frac{1}{4}$	From Table 2.2
CG	1.79	+ 35.8	8.37		$3\frac{1}{2} \times 3 \times \frac{1}{4}$ L.L.V.	From Table 10.
CH	1	− 20		1.0	$2\frac{1}{2} \times 2 \times \frac{1}{4}$	From Table 2.2
DH	0.89	+ 17.8	4.19		$2\frac{1}{2} \times 2 \times \frac{1}{4}$ S.L.V.	From Table 10.
EH	3	− 60		3.0	$4 \times 4 \times \frac{5}{16}$	From Table 2.2

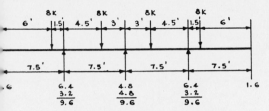

Fig. 10.8   Projected Load for Moment
Computation

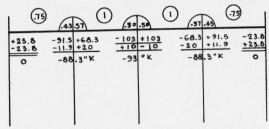

Fig. 10.9   Computation of Top-Chord Moment

rom Fig. 10.9 is 88.3 in.-kips; and in *BC* the
direct stress is $7.38 \times 20 = 147.6$ kips, and
the moment from Fig. 10.9 is 93 in.-kips.
Using the member selected in Table 10.5,
n *AB*

$$\text{Direct stress} = \frac{156.6}{11.72} = 13.36$$

$$\text{Eccentric stress} = \frac{88.3}{10.6} = \frac{8.33}{21.69}$$

which is excessive. Try two 12 channels, 20.7.

$$\text{Direct stress} = \frac{156.6}{12.06} = 12.98$$

$$\text{Eccentric stress} = \frac{88.3}{42.8} = 2.06$$

$$\frac{12.98}{15.25} = 85.2\%$$

$$\frac{2.06}{20} = \frac{10.3\%}{95.5\%}$$

which is allowable. Therefore the top chord
in question is two 12 channels, 20.7.

To compute the permissible stress in direct
stress given above, the method of Art. 1.31
for radius of gyration of a compound section
must be used.

$$
\begin{aligned}
I = 2 \times 3.9 \qquad\quad &= 7.8 \\
2 \times 6.03 \times 0.89^2 &= \frac{9.55}{17.35}
\end{aligned}
$$

$$r = \sqrt{\frac{17.35}{12.06}} = \sqrt{1.44} = 1.2$$

$$\frac{l}{r} = \frac{72}{1.2} \qquad\qquad = 60$$

The allowable stress from Table 7.1 is 15.25,
which is used in the foregoing problem.

10.12   Wood trusses

a   The design of wood trusses is primarily
a problem in the design of truss joints. In
compression members the *l/d* ratio will have
some effect on the size of the member, but in
tension members any member that will satisfactorily develop the connection will usually
take the tensile stress.

Many of the older wood trusses used wood
for compression members and wrought iron or
steel for tension members—usually in the
form of rods. The design of the joints of a
wood truss involve a complicated set of computations of inclined bearing, shear, and other
factors, as described in Art. 9.30.

b   With timber connectors available, most
trusses are designed using them as described
in Art. 9.33*d*. If decorative wood trusses are
used, the actual working truss may be built
up of 2- or 3-in.-thick members to develop the
connectors efficiently, and then boxed in with
thin enveloping material to give the appearance of a solid member.

In computing the loads to be carried by the
truss, an allowance must be made for the
weight of the truss itself. Formulae derived
from tabulated weights given by the Timber
Engineering Co. are:

For a flat-top wood truss, height $\frac{1}{8}$ to $\frac{1}{10}$ of
span, the weight of truss is $3 + 0.116S$ per-
cent of the live plus dead load, where S is the
span in feet.

For a pitched truss with $\frac{1}{5}$ to $\frac{1}{3}$ pitch, the
weight becomes $1.6 + 0.113S$ percent.

Figure 10.10 illustrates the design of a wood
truss using timber connectors. It has been
taken from the pamphlet of the Timber Engineering Co. entitled "Designing Timber Connector Structures."

c   *Procedure for the design of connector
joints.*   While this procedure will apply to
most structures, special cases may call for variations, but with the fundamental steps in
mind the variations can easily be made.

1. Determine stresses for structural members.

2. Form a tentative plan for framing the structure and select lumber species to be used.

3. Compute the sizes of the structural members.

4. Select the type and size of connectors which seem to be most suitable for the structure.

5. Determine the angle of load to grain for each member in the joint to get the ring capacity, required edge and end distances, and spacings for connectors.

6. Design those joints first which carry the greatest loads, since the sizes of the members required to space the connectors in these joints will be the determining factor in arriving at final member sizes.

7. Determine the amount of load in the joint which must be transferred between each two members to be joined and design for the largest load first. The positioning of the connectors for the smaller loads will usually not be a problem; it should, however, be checked.

8. Compute the number of connectors required to carry the loads and proceed to locate them on gage lines drawn with reference to the edges of the overlapped members. The spacings between connectors must also be checked.

9. If gage lines do not permit full spacings and the full capacities of connectors must be developed, the face widths of certain members must then be increased to provide the spacings required, or it may be that other sizes of connectors can be used without increasing the lumber size.

10. Check end distances and spacings for connectors in each member.

Problem A diagram for one-half of a 50-ft Fink roof truss with loads for each member is shown in Fig. 10.10. It is assumed that the roof loads are applied at the panel points.

Top chord. Since the greatest load is developed in the top-chord panels, the structural sizes should be designed for these loads first. To determine the size of the top chord in Fig. 10.10, it is assumed that (1) the chord will be composed of two members rather than

one, thereby providing greater surface are for placing connectors in the overlapped join members; (2) the members will be joined with connectors at the panel points to make i possible to take advantage of greater workin; stresses in compression due to the spaced column principle (see Art. 7.30b), and (3) lateral support will be provided at each pane point to prevent lateral buckling of the top chord.

When computing the sizes of spaced column members as for the top chord in question, it will usually be found that a larg value for d in the l/d ratio (l = length of pane in inches, d = least thickness in inches) i most suitable up to the point where the width of the member becomes too narrow to permi the placement of the necessary number of connectors. If the value for d becomes too small, greater overlapped area results but the working stresses of the lumber are rapidly reduced and the members become inefficient and uneconomical.

Reference to the top chord of the truss (Fig. 10.10) shows a panel length of 6 ft $8\frac{3}{4}$ in. and a maximum load of 38,100 lb. With members $1\frac{5}{8}$ in. thick the l/d ratio for this panel length is 50; with lumber $2\frac{5}{8}$ in. thick the ratio is 31; and with lumber $3\frac{5}{8}$ in. thick the ratio is 22. Then, for lumber with a modulus of elasticity E of 1,600,000 psi and a compressive stress f_c of 880 psi, the working stresses for the different l/d ratios will be 440, 820, and 880 psi respectively. Dividing the 38,100-lb load by the values for the different l/d ratios, the $1\frac{5}{8}$-in. thickness requires 87 sq in., the $2\frac{5}{8}$-in. thickness requires 47 sq in., and the $3\frac{5}{8}$-in. thickness requires 43 sq in. The $1\frac{5}{8}$-in. thickness is evidently impractical since two chord members 28 in. wide would be necessary. Chord members $3\frac{5}{8}$ in. thick take only a $7\frac{1}{2}$-in. width to carry the load but do not furnish sufficient surface area to accommodate the connectors. Members $2\frac{5}{8}$ in. thick require a $9\frac{1}{2}$-in. face width to carry the load and provide sufficient overlapped area for placing connectors and are therefore recommended for the top chord.

Bottom chord. The bottom-chord member L_0 (Fig. 10.10) has a tension load of 35,400 lb.

Assuming a lumber grade of 1,200 psi in tension or extreme fiber in bending (f), 29.5 sq in. of cross section are required. This is equivalent to approximately two pieces 3 × 6 in., nominal size, with a total net section of 29.54 sq in.

A thickness of 3 in. ($2\frac{5}{8}$ in. net) is selected primarily to maintain the same thickness as in the top-chord members, so that the splice plates will lie flat on the faces of the abutting members of upper and lower chords. The 6-in. width of lower-chord members is sufficient to accommodate the 4-in. split-ring connectors in this joint, but because of the necessity of an 8-in. nominal width to develop the load at an angle to grain in another bottom-chord joint for this truss, the bottom chord is made 8 in. wide throughout its entire length, thereby eliminating an extra splice joint in the bottom chord.

Web members in compression can best be handled as solid columns, with a relatively small l/d ratio, in contrast to web members in tension, which may be comparatively thin since their l/d is not a factor in their working stresses. This combination provides for efficient design and a symmetrically loaded joint by placing the compression members between the double chord members and the two tension members on the outside. Compression member $V2$, with a greater load than occurs in $V1$ or $V3$, is tentatively considered as having a 3-in. thickness ($2\frac{5}{8}$ in. net) to correspond to the appropriate 3-in. thickness of the center splice plates in the chord members. (The thickness of the center member of three splice plates used for joining a two-member chord should normally equal half the total thickness of the two members comprising the chord. The two outside splice pieces make up the remaining necessary section.) Using the same 880-psi grade of lumber as in the top chord and an l/d ratio of 25, the allowable working stress for member $V2$ is 680 psi. The load of 7,200 lb requires 10.6 sq in. of cross section. A 3 × 6-in. piece, with a cross section of 14.77 sq in., will accommodate this load and provide a 6-in. face for connectors.

Assuming a $2\frac{5}{8}$-in. net thickness for compression members $V1$ and $V3$, corresponding

in thickness to member $V2$, the l/d ratio is 12.3 for each of these two members. In the 880-psi grade of lumber, this gives a working stress of 880 psi, and for the 3,600-lb. load approximately 4 sq in. of cross section are required. A 3 × 4-in. piece, with a net cross section of 9.52 sq in., is the smallest size possible, since the $2\frac{5}{8}$-in. thickness must be maintained to fit between the chord members, and a $3\frac{5}{8}$-in. width of face is necessary for a $2\frac{1}{2}$-in. split ring. Therefore this size is recommended.

Tension members $D3$ and $D4$, with 15,000 lb maximum load and the 1,200-psi grade of lumber used in the truss, will require 12.5 sq in. of cross section. Two pieces 2 × 6 in., with a total of 18.2 sq in. of cross section, will provide more section than necessary. The other tension members, $D1$ and $D2$, with a load of 5,000 lb each, need less section than member $D4$, but 2 × 6s are recommended to keep the sizes uniform, and because smaller structural members are not generally recommended.

d　Design of timber joints. The order in which the joints in the Fink truss (Fig. 10.10) might logically be designed would be first the heel joint, because of the large loads to be transmitted; then the peak joint, with relatively large loads and with members entering the joint from three directions; and finally the remaining joints in any order desired, since they are comparatively simple. However, to present more clearly the design principles which apply to timber-connector joints, a few typical joints will be discussed first, and then the heel and peak joints of Fig. 10.10.

Load parallel to grain

Tension joint. In the tension joint loaded parallel to the grain (Fig. 10.12), consisting of two overlapped members and split rings placed in the contact faces, assume that the load to be carried is 14,000 lb and that the lumber is 1,200-psi grade of group B species.

Design the joint for the following conditions:

1. Full end distances and spacings for connectors

2. Permissible reduced spacings

3. Permissible reduced end distances

4. Permissible reduced spacings and end distances.

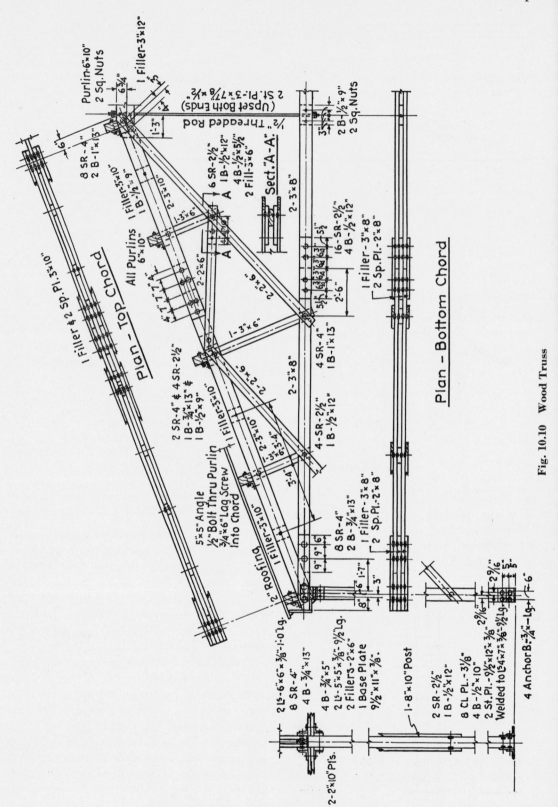

Fig. 10.10 Wood Truss

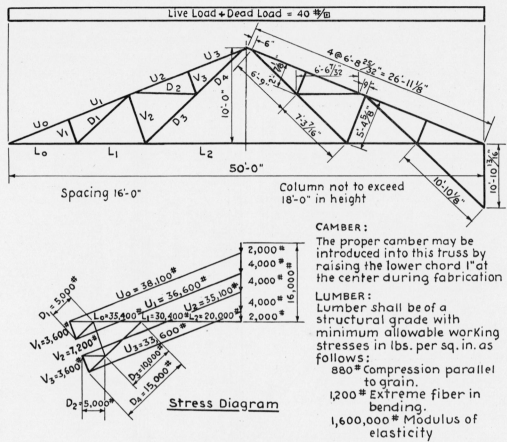

Live Load + Dead Load = 40 #/☐

Spacing 16'-0"

Column not to exceed 18'-0" in height

50'-0"

CAMBER:
The proper camber may be introduced into this truss by raising the lower chord 1" at the center during fabrication

LUMBER:
Lumber shall be of a structural grade with minimum allowable working stresses in lbs. per sq. in. as follows:
    880# Compression parallel to grain.
    1,200# Extreme fiber in bending.
    1,600,000# Modulus of elasticity

Stress Diagram

Fig. 10.10   Wood Truss (Continued)

The four conditions outlined are presented to show the different combinations possible and how substandard spacings and distances may be computed for reduced loads. In actual design, it is recommended that reductions for both spacings and distances be made, rather

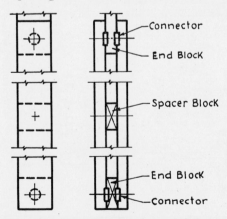

Fig. 10.11   Two-Member Spaced Column

than for one alone, thereby maintaining more uniform load reductions for all connectors.

1. *Full end distances and spacings.* Lumber Size: The 1,200-psi grade of lumber requires 11.7 sq in. of section to carry the 14,000-lb load. It will be found that a 2×8-in. member, with a sectional area of 12.19 sq in., and a 3×6-in. member, with a sectional area of 14.77 sq in., are the smallest nominal lumber sizes that will carry the load in tension.

Connector Size: Since split rings are specified for the joint, either one or two rows of $2\frac{1}{2}$-in. rings or one row of 4-in. rings could be used in the 8-in. width of lumber, or one row of 4-in. rings could be used in the 6-in. width of lumber. To keep the number of bolts at a minimum, 4-in. connectors are recommended, although in a structure where $2\frac{1}{2}$-in. split rings are used in other joints, it may be best to use them in this joint also.

Net Section: The net section of a member remaining after boring the bolt holes and cutting the grooves must then be checked to determine if it is adequate; it will usually be found adequate except where lumber of the higher stress grades is designed to nearly its full capacity. Checking the net section is readily done by referring to Tables 9.12 and 9.13. In Table 9.13 it will be found that the projected area of one 4-in. split ring and bolt in a member $1\frac{5}{8}$ in. thick is 3.09 sq in., and in a member $2\frac{5}{8}$ in. thick it is 3.84 sq in. These values subtracted from the sectional areas of the 2×8-in. and 3×6-in. lumber sizes leave 9.10 sq in. and 10.93 sq in. respectively. To

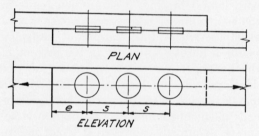

PLAN

ELEVATION

Fig. 10.12 Two-Member Tension Joint

determine if the net section remaining is sufficient, the actual square inches of net section required is computed from the table of constants (Table 9.11) by multiplying the load to be carried by the constant for standard loading for group B species in material less than 4 in. thick, which in this case is $14{,}000 \times 0.00046$, or 6.45 sq in. Therefore, either the 2×8-in. or 3×6-in. lumber sizes furnish adequate net section; the choice of size selected for a structure will be determined from the design as a whole.

Connectors Required: Working loads for split rings are given in Art. 9.33. A 4-in. split ring used in one face of a member $1\frac{5}{8}$ in. or more in thickness and loaded parallel to the grain has a load capacity of 5,500 lb for group B species, and to carry the 14,000-lb load 2.55, or 3, split rings are required. The standard spacing and end distance for these connectors for load applied parallel to grain (see Art. 9.33) are 9 and 7 in. respectively. With three bolts spaced 9 in. apart and a 7-in. end distance, the joint length from the

end of one piece to the end of the other piece in the joint is $7 + 9 + 9 + 7$, or 32 in.

2. *Permissible reduced spacings.* Assume that it is desirable to shorten as much as possible the spacing between bolts with 4-in. split rings in the tension joint discussed above and still carry the 14,000-lb load.

The total capacity of three 4-in. split rings is $3 \times 5{,}500$ lb, or 16,500 lb, but only 14,000 lb, or 85 percent of their capacity, need be developed. Therefore, instead of three connectors carrying 300 percent of the capacity of one connector, they need carry a total of only 255 percent. Since one connector in a row with reduced connector spacing is assumed to carry 100 percent capacity, the other two connectors need to develop 77.5 percent capacity each. By interpolation of spacing requirements from full spacing of 9 in. at 100 percent capacity to $4\frac{7}{8}$ in. at 50 percent capacity, as given in Art. 9.33, the spacing may be reduced from 9 to $7\frac{1}{8}$ in. The total joint length from the end of one member to the end of the other member in the joint is then $7 + 7\frac{1}{8} + 7\frac{1}{8} + 7$, or $28\frac{1}{4}$ in., a reduction of $3\frac{3}{4}$ in. from the length of the joint with full spacing and end distances.

3. *Permissible reduced end distance.* If the end distance only is to be reduced, the percentage reduction may be applied to the end ring up to the maximum of 37.5 percent allowed, which takes the minimum end distance permitted. Since the permissible reduction for the joint is 45 percent, it will be seen that the end distance may be reduced to the minimum allowed, or to $3\frac{1}{2}$ in. for the 4-in. split ring. The total joint length is then $3\frac{1}{2}$ in. for the 4-in. split ring. The total joint length is then $3\frac{1}{2} + 9 + 9 + 3\frac{1}{2}$, or 25 in.

4. *Permissible reduced spacing and reduced end distances.* It may sometimes be desirable to reduce both end distances and spacings. Such reductions are made by combining the two systems described under paragraphs 2 and 3 above. Assuming that the end distances are reduced, the full amount thereby reducing the capacity of the joint by 37.5 percent, it still leaves $45 - 37.5$, or 7.5 percent, which can be applied to reduced spacing. The 7.5 percent divided by the two bolts with

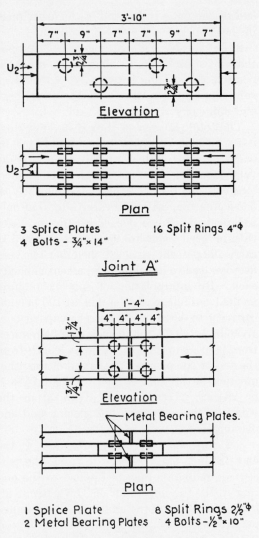

Elevation

U_2

Plan

3 Splice Plates   16 Split Rings 4"ϕ
4 Bolts - ¾"×14"

Joint "A"

Elevation

Metal Bearing Plates.

Plan

1 Splice Plate   8 Split Rings 2½"ϕ
2 Metal Bearing Plates   4 Bolts -½"×10"

Joint "B"

Details of compression splices: A—entire load of 35,100 lb carried by connectors; B—31 percent of load carried by connectors, 69 percent carried by end bearing of members against metal plates

Fig. 10.13 Details of Compression Splices

connectors (exclusive of the end bolt) gives 3.75 percent. By interpolation for reduced spacing, the 3.75 percent permits the spacing to be reduced from 9 to $8\frac{3}{4}$ in. The total joint length would then be $3\frac{1}{2} + 8\frac{3}{4} + 8\frac{3}{4} + 3\frac{1}{2}$, or $24\frac{1}{2}$ in.

Compression Joint. A compression joint may be designed similarly to a tension joint with all the load transferred by connectors, or it may be designed with part of the load

carried by connectors and part carried by end bearing of the members with a metal plate fitted snugly between them. It is frequently found more practical to design a compression joint with connectors carrying the entire load, since splice plates provide the necessary stiffness for the members joined and a minimum amount of labor is required to fabricate the joint. The design of the joint with part of the load carried by direct end bearing offers a convenient solution, on the other hand, when using comparatively large members with limited space for splicing and where lateral stiffness is provided by means other than the joint itself—such as placement near or in a joint with lateral bracing. Compression joints in the top chords of bridge trusses offer typical examples where this method of designing joints is found. As much as 100 percent of the bearing stress of the members may be developed by end bearing provided that a metal bearing plate is placed between the ends of members and that fabrication is accurate. Normally, however, it is not practical to count on more than 50 to 75 percent, since the joint must be held together by some means. This is handled advantageously by connectors and one or more splice plates for holding the joint in line and for carrying a portion of the load; the remaining portion of the load being transferred by end bearing of members against a snugly fitted bearing plate.

Another system sometimes used is that of filling with concrete the space enclosed by the metal gusset plates and the ends of the members, the concrete forming end bearing for all members entering the joint.

The joint in the top-chord member $U2$ in Fig. 10.10 will serve to explain the two design systems. Reference to the previous text, describing the method of finding the size of the top-chord members, will show that the top chord takes two pieces of lumber 3×10 in. nominal. For one condition assume that the entire load of 35,100 lb is carried by connectors, and for the other condition that part of the load will be transferred by end bearing of the chord members. See Fig. 10.13, joints A and B respectively.

With the entire load transmitted by splice plates, their combined sectional area must equal at least the total sectional area of the members joined. A center piece $2\frac{5}{8}$ in. thick and two side pieces $1\frac{5}{8}$ in. thick provide the necessary section. Both $2\frac{1}{2}$- and 4-in. diameter rings will be considered, since these are the most common sizes used in this type and size of truss. The 35,100-lb load for group B species required 12.3 split rings $2\frac{1}{2}$ in. in diameter on each side of the joint, or 6.5 split rings 4 in. in diameter. Twelve $2\frac{1}{2}$-in. split rings on each side of the joint will safely carry the load and will fit into the joint conveniently. It will be necessary to use eight split rings 4 in. in diameter to keep the joint symmetrically loaded. The cost of labor for the installation of rings of either size will be about equal, the single apparent advantage of one ring size over the other being that the $2\frac{1}{2}$-in. split ring takes slightly shorter splice plates. Joint A in Fig. 10.13 shows 4-in. split rings with end distances and spacings for full load capacity for the rings. The rings are placed off the center line to provide more even distribution of load to the members.

Figure 10.13 shows the same joint in joint B with the same load transmitted and member sizes as given in joint A, but with bearing plates between the ends of the members. The outside splice plates are omitted and $2\frac{1}{2}$-in. split rings are used instead of the 4-in. split rings. In this joint 31 percent of the load is carried by the rings and 69 percent is transferred through the abutting ends of the compression members.

Load at angle to grain

Most structural joints have members entering at an angle with reference to other members, and therefore produce bearing at an angle to grain. The several examples of joints in the following discussion are all of this type, with each one bringing out certain design features.

Chord members placed between web members. This is a type of joint commonly used in the design of pitched-roof trusses. By making the compression member the same thickness as the splice plates used between the chord members, a comparatively low l/d ratio is secured, and furthermore the compression member will also fit between the chord members. The tension members in the joint may be thinner, since their l/d ratio is not a factor and they are placed outside the chord members.

A joint of this type is formed by members $L1$, $L2$, $V2$, and $D3$ of Fig. 10.10 and is detailed to larger scale in Fig. 10.14.

In this joint each of the two tension members $D3$ exerts its load of 5,000 lb. (total 10,000 lb) at 45 deg to the grain in the two lower-chord members. At this angle of load to grain a 4-in. split ring in lumber $2\frac{5}{8}$ in. thick of group B series develops a safe working load of 4,590 lb. Two of these rings, one between each chord member and each diagonal, with a $\frac{3}{4}$-in. bolt will develop 9,180 lb. But this is not sufficient to carry the 10,000-lb load, and therefore to increase the load capacity without increasing the size of the members

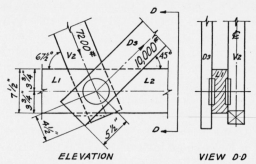

ELEVATION   VIEW D·D

Fig. 10.14   Detail of Lower Chord Joint

to accommodate an extra bolt or more rings, a 1-in. bolt is used in place of the $\frac{3}{4}$-in. bolt, thereby increasing the capacity of the connectors by 7 percent, giving a total of 9,800 lb. This is only 2 percent under the full connector capacity required, and the joint is adequate to meet good-design requirements. Since the load in the tension member is acting upward at 45 deg, the edge distance in the chord members must be $3\frac{3}{4}$ in. on the upper side of the ring where its outside surface is in compression against the wood.

The end distance required for the 4-in. split ring in tension member $D3$, where the load is acting parallel to the grain, is determined by the load it carries. The 4,590-lb load capacity of the 4-in. split ring is increased 7 percent for the 1-in. bolt, equaling 4,910 lb, or 85 percent of the capacity of a ring with a 1-in. bolt loaded to 0 deg to grain. This percentage capacity permits a $5\frac{1}{2}$-in. end distance.

Member $V2$ transmits the load to the lower chord at $67\frac{1}{2}$ deg to grain, at which angle the load per ring with a 1-in. bolt is 4,185 lb plus 7 percent, or 4,480 lb, and for two rings it is 8,960 lb. This is greater than the 7,200-lb load necessary. The load in this web member is acting downward, so that the compression side of the ring is toward the bottom edge of the chord; therefore this edge distance as well as that for the upper side must be $3\frac{3}{4}$ in., making a member with a $7\frac{1}{2}$-in. face necessary. It is this joint in the bottom chord which requires the widest face width and therefore determines the width of the member.

The standard end distance for a compression member with a 4-in. split ring is $5\frac{1}{2}$ in., but since only 80 percent of the load need be developed in member $V2$, the distance may be reduced to $4\frac{1}{2}$ in. The ends of both members $V2$ and $D3$ may be sawed off parallel to the edge of the bottom chord about $\frac{1}{2}$ in. below it, as shown by the dotted lines (Fig. 10.14), which still leaves sufficient end distance.

Chord member placed outside of web members. The lower-chord joint of a flat-top Pratt truss (Fig. 10.15) has the diagonal members placed between the vertical and the horizontal members. Advantages gained by this arrangement as compared to the diagonals being placed outside the chord members are (1) the diagonal members, which must transmit the greatest load, have two faces into which connectors may be placed, whereas if they are located outside the chord members, connectors could be placed in only one face of each diagonal; (2) the bottom chord, which is in tension, does not need to be the same thickness as the top chord to assemble the truss; and (3) the working load per connector between the vertical and the diagonal with a 42-deg angle is considerably greater than it would be between the vertical and the bottom chord with a 90-deg angle of load to grain.

An analysis of the joint in Fig. 10.15 with

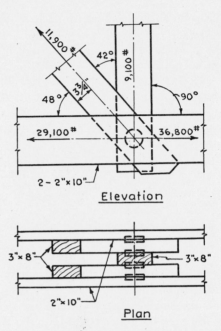

Fig. 10.15   Diagonals Between Vertical and Horizontal Members

axial loads in the members shows that where three overlapping members in a joint come together at different angles, it is the center member with connectors in both faces which has the load at an angle to the grain; the two side pieces are stressed only parallel to the grain. The side pieces (in Fig. 10.15 the horizontal chord and the vertical web member) must deliver their loads in the direction of their respective axes, thereby introducing stresses in the diagonal piece, which combine to produce the resultant force equal to the load carried by the diagonal member. Since the compression side of the ring in one face of the diagonal member applies to one edge and the compression side of the ring in the opposite face applies to the opposite edge, because of the direction of loads the diagonal must have a $3\frac{3}{4}$-in. edge distance on each side, resulting in a member with a face width of $7\frac{1}{2}$ in.

The vertical member (in Fig. 10.15) with a 9,100-lb load to transfer to the two diagonal members at 42 deg will take two 4-in. split rings, one on each side to carry the load, since at this angle, in group B species and for lumber $2\frac{5}{8}$ in. thick, one 4-in. ring will carry 4,645 lb and two will carry 9,290 lb. The two horizontal chord members must transmit a total of 7,700 lb to the diagonal members (36,800 − 29,100) at an angle to grain of 48 deg. Under the conditions presented, one ring will carry 4,540 lb and two will carry 9,080 lb, which is more capacity than necessary to carry the 7,700-lb load. Therefore, since the 4-in. split rings are sufficient to transfer the vertical and horizontal loads, they must also be sufficient to carry the load in the diagonal members.

Heel joint—Fink truss. The heel joint in the Fink truss shown in Fig. 10.10 is simplified by extending the top chord members to bear on the support, thereby transmitting directly to the support that portion of the load acting as the vertical component and eliminating the necessity of transferring this portion of the load by connectors through the bottom chord (see Fig. 10.16).

In the design of the heel joint, it is apparent that split rings may be used in this timber-to-timber connection. As previously noted it is usually more efficient to use the larger connector sizes since they keep the number of bolts and connectors to a minimum and facilitate fabrication. If the most appropriate connector size for the joint is not immediately evident, the number of connectors required for each size may then be computed and one selected which fits most advantageously into the members. The loads for split rings for the heel joint in Fig. 10.16 are dependent on the 22-deg angle of load bearing to grain of the connectors in the top chord, on the $2\frac{5}{8}$-in. lumber thickness as determined previously, and on the group B species of lumber. It is assumed that the truss will be used in a location where the lumber will reach an air-dry condition and, therefore, the moisture content of the lumber need not be considered as influencing split-ring loads. Based on the above conditions, the safe load for a $2\frac{1}{2}$-in. split ring is 2,640 lb and, for a 4-in. split ring, 5,005 lb.

The 35,400-lb horizontal load which must be transferred to the bottom chord will take 13.4 split rings $2\frac{1}{2}$ in. in diameter, or 7.1 split

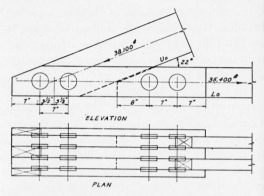

Fig. 10.16   Heel Joint of Fink Truss

rings 4 in. in diameter. With four contacting faces into which connectors must be placed to keep the joint symmetrically loaded, the number of rings must be rounded off to 16 $2\frac{1}{2}$-in. rings or 8 4-in. rings. This number of rings for each size can be located in the heel joint to carry the load. It will be noted, however, that the 4-in. ring is more efficient, because the number of connectors actually required in the joint approaches nearest the number which is recommended for a symmetrically loaded joint. Also, the 4-in. size requires only 2 bolts and 8 rings as compared to 4 bolts and 16 rings of the $2\frac{1}{2}$-in. size.

A further consideration in the design of a joint in which more than one bolt with connectors occurs is that if the full capacity of the connectors is not developed, as in this joint, it may be desirable to reduce their spacings and distances. The rule for permissible reduced spacing and reduced end distances may be applied, since the full capacities of the 4-in. rings are not developed. According to the rule, the 4 rings on one bolt will carry 400 percent of one ring capacity, or 400 × 5,005 lb = 20,020 lb. This amount subtracted from 35,400 lb leaves 15,380 lb for the 4 connectors on the second bolt, or 77 percent of their rated load. To develop 77 percent load capacity of the connectors in the second bolt, spacing between bolts may be reduced to 7 in. as determined by interpolation from design data given in Art. 9.33. End distance specified for the bottom-chord splice plates stressed in tension parallel to the grain is 7 in., and end distance for the top chord in compression is

$\frac{1}{2}$ in. measured parallel to the grain. Edge distance, since the angle of load to grain is less than 30 deg, remains at the $2\frac{3}{4}$-in. minimum for both members and is provided by the members used.

The load to be transferred between the two bottom-chord members and the splice plates is parallel to the grain, and for the conditions presented a 4-in. split ring will carry 5,400 lb. To carry the 35,400-lb load, 6 rings are required; 8 rings, however, are recommended to maintain a symmetrically loaded joint. The diagonal cut on the end of the bottom-chord member through a point giving a 7-in. standard end distance, measured along the center line, is not sufficient to provide the necessary $2\frac{3}{4}$-in. distance (equal to the edge distance for a 4-in. split ring) measured perpendicularly from the diagonal cut to the center of the bolt hole. Therefore, the end distance at the center line must be increased. Since the edge distance must be $2\frac{3}{4}$ in., the distance along the center line of the bottom chord is $2\frac{3}{4}$ in./sin 22 deg, or 7.2 required. In practice the end distance probably would be scaled and rounded off to $7\frac{1}{2}$ or 8 in. Spacing of the connectors may be taken as a full 9 in. as specified for full-load capacity where there is sufficient area to place them along the chord, or the spacing may be reduced following the practice discussed under Tension joint, page 384. Connector spacing is shown as 7 in. in Fig. 10.16 to correspond to the 7-in. end distance of the splice. A check of the net section required for the members, using the same procedure as that explained for the tension joint, will show that sufficient section is provided by the size of members used.

Peak joint. The design of the peak joint in the Fink truss (Fig. 10.10) demonstrates how two bolts with connectors may be located to accommodate three members entering the joint when the angle of load to grain is less than 30 deg for each two contacting members. In this joint, as detailed in Fig. 10.17, the 15,000 lb must be transferred from the two diagonals $D4$ to the two chord members $U3$, and the 20,000-lb horizontal component must be carried through the splice to the other half

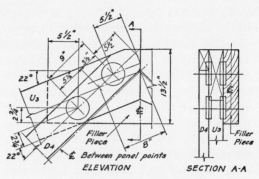

Fig. 10.17 Detail of Peak Joint

of the truss. (This horizontal component is equal to the tension in the bottom chord at the center of the truss—see Fig. 10.10.) In this joint connectors are located in the two overlapped areas between the chord members and the diagonals, also between the chord members and the filler piece. The larger load of 20,000 lb should be considered first in the design of the joint, since connectors placed on the bolts used for the larger load will quite probably provide spacings and distances to develop the smaller load. Part of the thrust between the two half trusses could be carried by end bearing of the top-chord members, requiring a fitting job for the metal bearing plates. However, the two half sections of the roof truss must be securely attached at this joint and, regardless of the means for absorbing the thrust, a splice is necessary, and can perform the functions of both a tie and a splice to carry the load.

In the top chord members a 22-deg angle of load to grain is made by the splice piece and also by web members $D4$. At this angle and with standard distances and spacings, the load per connector is 5,005 lb. With full distances and spacings, therefore, four connectors on two bolts will carry the 20,000-lb load to be transferred between the two chord pieces $U3$ and the filler piece. Since this part of the joint is in compression, the end distance for 4-in. split rings must be $5\frac{1}{2}$ in. This end distance for piece $U3$ then determines the gage line for the end connector, the gage line being parallel to the end cut and measured parallel with the grain in the chord. The required 9-in. spacing and $2\frac{3}{4}$-in. edge distances for all members joined must also be met. In order to locate the two bolts with connectors within the limits of the diagonal D4 and still have the specified edge distance for connectors in the chord member, it is necessary to offset the diagonal so that the intersection of the center lines of the diagonal and the chord members is 8 in. to the left of the panel point. The slight eccentricity introduced into the joint by offsetting diagonal D4 is of little importance and may be neglected. The filler piece must be of sufficient width and length to provide the specified edge and end distances for connectors in that piece. A splice piece 14 in. wide will provide the necessary width, and the length may be extended to meet the requirements.

The four 4-in. split rings between the chord and the web members must be investigated to determine if they develop sufficient load capacity to carry the 15,000-lb load. Since web members D4 are in tension, they take an end distance of 7 in. to develop full-load capacity for the connectors. The spacing of connectors is the required 9 in.; therefore the only reduction in load capacity is that due to the reduced end distance, from 7 to $5\frac{1}{2}$ in. (see Fig. 10.17). It will be noted that for these diagonal members there are two diagonal end cuts, and therefore the end distance is not measured to the extreme end of the member but to a point a short distance from the end, which gives approximately the required shear area for the connector. A reduction of $1\frac{1}{2}$ in. in end distance reduces the load capacity 17 percent (see charts). Therefore two connectors with full load carry 10,010 lb, and the other two connectors carry 83 percent of 10,010 lb, or 8,310 lb, which totals 18,320 lb, or 3,320 lb in excess of the 15,000 lb necessary to be developed.

10.13   Brackets, jib cranes, marquees

a   Although widely variant in use and construction, brackets, jib cranes, and marquees are classified together because as cantilever structures they present similar problems. The bracket may support a balcony, a sign, or other structure, but it usually consists of a

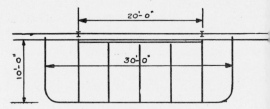

Fig. 10.18   Plan of Marquee

horizontal tension member supported from below by a diagonal compression member. A jib crane, a marquee, and some brackets have a horizontal compression member or members, and diagonal hangers above. The flagpole construction shown in Fig. 10.49 is a type of bracket.

Be sure that the structure to which a bracket or a marquee is attached can resist the resulting tension and compression. Almost always one, and frequently both, of these stresses are applied between two floors, and brick masonry is a poor material to resist bending. It is frequently necessary, even for comparatively light loads, to run a column from floor to floor as a vertical beam for attachment of the connections.

b   Figures 10.18 and 10.19 show a marquee which carries a gypsum roof on Ts, with a dead load of 30 and a live load of 30 psf. Design the marquee.

The three center beams each carry
$$W = 60 \times 5 \times 10 = 3{,}000 \text{ lb}$$
$$S = \frac{3 \times 10}{13.33} = 2.25$$

Use 5 channel 6.7.

The beam next to the wall carries three concentrations of 1,500 lb on a 20-ft span.
$$S = 4.5 \times 0.1 \times 20 = 9$$

Use 9 channel 13.4.

The facia beam is carried by the hanger at the column line, but cantilevers out to pick up another load 5 ft beyond the support. Because of lighting, and other factors, this load will be assumed the same as interior loads.
$$M_c = 1.5 \times 5 \quad = \quad 7.5$$
$$M = 5.25 \times 10 \ = 52.5$$
$$- 1.5 \times 20 = \underline{30}$$
$$22.5$$
$$S = 13.5$$

Architectural treatment suggests the use of a 12 channel 20.7 for a facia beam, bending it around to form the end beams. The bracket is made up of the beam on the column line and the hanger. The beam carries bending and direct stress. The bending is almost the same as that on the 5-in. beams, the load from the 9-in. channel coming in so close to the support as to cause practically no bending. The direct stresses in the marquee bracket are found by the stress diagram, Fig. 10.20. The beam carries a direct compression of 10.5 kips and a bending moment of 3.75 ft-kips, or 45 in.-kips.

Try two 5 channels 6.7, back to back with a plate between to which a clevis can be pinned for the hanger. The bending factor for a 5-in. channel is

$$\frac{A}{S} = \frac{1.95}{3} = 0.65$$

The bending converted into equivalent direct stress is

$$\begin{aligned} 45 \times 0.65 \quad &= 29.25 \\ \text{Direct stress} &= \underline{10.5} \\ &\quad 39.75 \text{ kips} \end{aligned}$$

Since it is stiffened throughout its length by the marquee roof construction,

$$A = \frac{39.75}{17} = 2.34 \text{ sq in.}$$

Therefore two 5-in. channels with an area of 3.9 sq in. may be used.

The hanger carries a stress of 11.76 kips, which will require an area at the root of the thread of

$$\frac{11.76}{20} = 0.588 \text{ sq in.}$$

Use $1\frac{1}{8}$-in. rod hanger.

The hanger should be furnished with clevises for each end, one with right-hand thread, the other with left-hand thread, for adjustment.

c A jib crane in its simplest form is a beam which is bracketed out from a column and carries a trolley on its lower flange by means of which loads up to several tons may be moved through an angle and a comparatively short distance. The jib crane is frequently supported on its own column, which rotates by means of pins, top and bottom,

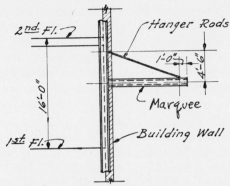

Fig. 10.19   Section Through Marquee

through brackets. Sometimes the brackets are on a building column, and the crane is supported by and pivots on the column brackets.

Figure 10.21 indicates a jib crane supported on its own column. Let us assume that it carries a load of 3,000 lb. Design the members. The sides of the triangle through which the stresses are figured are 2 ft 6 in., 9 ft. 8 in., and 10 ft 0 in.

The maximum direct stresses in the truss will occur when the trolley is at its extreme outermost point, and the load on the truss will be

$$\frac{10.5}{9.67} \times 3,000 = 3,260 \text{ lb}$$

The direct stress in the beam is

$$\frac{9.67}{2.5} \times 3,260 = 12,600 \text{ lb}$$

The direct stress in the tie rod is

$$\frac{10}{2.5} \times 3,260 = 13,040 \text{ lb}$$

The maximum bending will be in one of two positions—the end of the cantilever or the center of the simple span.

$$M_c = 3,000 \times 0.67 = 2,000 \text{ ft-lb}$$
$$M_s = \frac{3,000 \times 9.67}{4} = 7,250 \text{ ft-lb}$$

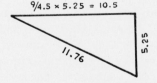

Fig. 10.20   Stress Diagram—Marquee

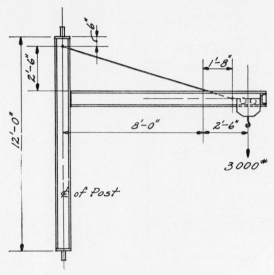

Fig. 10.21   Jib Crane

However, when the moment is 7,250, the direct stress is reduced to

$$\frac{1,500}{3,260} \times 12,600 = 5,800 \text{ lb}$$

Therefore, the beam must be designed for either a combination of 12,600 lb direct stress with 2,000 ft-lb bending moment, or 5,800 lb direct stress with 7,250 ft-lb bending moment.

Try 8 WF 17. The bending factor B is

$$\frac{A}{S} = \frac{5}{14.1} = 0.355$$

Equivalent direct stress for the first condition is

$$P_e = 0.355 \times 2,000 \times 12 = \quad 8,520$$
$$P_d = \quad 12,600$$
$$\overline{ 21,120} \text{ lb}$$

For the second condition this becomes

$$P_e = 355 \times 7,250 \times 12 = 30,885$$
$$P_d = \quad 5,800$$
$$\overline{ 36,685} \text{ lb}$$

The second condition therefore governs.

$$\frac{l}{r} = \frac{112}{1.16} = 96.6$$
$$f = 12,480$$
$$\text{Required area} = \frac{36,685}{12,480} = 2.94$$
$$\text{Area furnished} = 5$$

A spot check on the 7 I 15 shows that the l/r is in excess of 120 and it cannot be used.

The area required for the hanger is

$$\frac{13,040}{20,000} = 0.65 \text{ sq in.}$$

Use $1\frac{1}{8}$-in. round rod.

The post is subject to a vertical load of 3,000 lb and bending as indicated in Fig. 10.22. The maximum moment from this diagram is

$$2,625 \times 9 = 23,625 \text{ ft-lb}$$

Try 8 WF 24.

$$P_e = 0.339 \times 23,625 \times 12 = 96,100$$
$$P_d = \quad 3,000$$
$$\overline{ P = 99.1} \text{ kips}$$

The allowable load on 8 WF 24 = 93. Therefore use 8 WF 28 (see Table 7.3).

The pin at the top puts a pull of 2,625 on the column to which it is attached, and since this jib crane may be rotated, the pull may be against either axis.

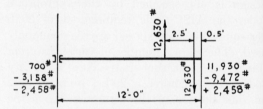

Fig. 10.22   Beam Diagram of Jib Crane

10.20   WIND STRESSES

a   In all or part of any structure, large or small, exposed to wind, wind pressure must be considered, and main structural members, anchorage, and other details must be designed accordingly. Although most structures built are satisfactorily stable and require no special investigation, there are also many which should be investigated, including (1) one-story, single-bay-width structures, such as churches, garages, and factories, (2) narrow multistory structures, even if only four or five stories high, and (3) roof structures, such as steeples, lanterns, cupolas, roof signs, high penthouses, high parapets, and roof tanks. Most building codes set up a minimum ratio of height to width, below which any investi-

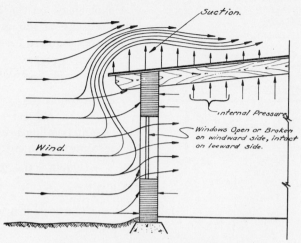

Suction.

internal Pressure

Windows Open or Broken on windward side, intact on leeward side.

Wind.

Fig. 10.23 Nature of Wind Stresses

gation for wind stresses in multistory buildings may be omitted. This ratio is never less than $1\frac{1}{2}$ to 1; in New York City and some other communities it is $2\frac{1}{2}$ to 1.

b If the wind pressure to be used in the design is not specified by the appropriate code, the AISC code requirement of 20 lb per square foot of exposed area is commonly used. There are a number of variations from this requirement, such as the New York City code, which requires a 20-psf pressure only on that portion of the structure above the 100-ft level. The Standard Code of the Pacific Coast Building Officials Conference requires 15 psf on the lower 60 ft of height and 20 psf for those portions more than 60 ft in height. Still other codes recommend 10 psf on the lower 60 ft and 20 psf on the portions above this.

c For roof structures, chimneys, tanks, and the like, it is common practice to use a pressure of 30 psf multiplied by a shape factor:

Square or rectangular	1.00
Hexagonal or octagonal	0.80
Round or elliptical	0.60

d The Factory Mutual Fire Insurance bulletins present the best summary generally available for wind stresses in factories. Although these are prepared primarily for industrial buildings, they will be applicable also to churches, schools, and other buildings. Bulletin 7.13 recommends that roofs with slopes of not over 20 deg be designed for a gross uplift of 30 psf and that walls and window supports shall resist a total horizontal force of 27 psf (see Fig. 10.23). The code of the U.S. Corps of Engineers requires that the details and method of attachment shall be designed to resist pressures as follows:

Wind on flat roofs—suction, 12 psf

Wind on windward side of sloping roofs for slopes of under 20 deg—suction, 12 psf

For slopes between 20 and 30 deg—suction decreasing uniformly from 12 to 0 psf

For slopes between 30 and 60 deg—pressure increasing uniformly from 0 to 9 psf

For slopes above 60 deg—pressure, 9 psf

For the leeward side of all sloping roofs—suction, 9 psf

Side walls should resist pressure or suction of 10 psf

e All members subject to stresses produced by a combination of wind and other loads or of wind loads alone may be proportioned for unit stresses $33\frac{1}{3}$ percent greater than those normally specified, but this allowance should never be used to reduce the normal design for live and dead loads only. In other words, if wind does not cause stresses greater than $33\frac{1}{3}$ percent of the original design for live and dead loads, it may be disregarded in the design of the member.

The overturning moment caused by wind pressure should never exceed two-thirds of the dead load resisting moment.

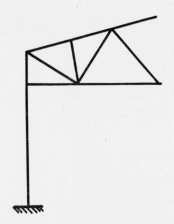

Fig. 10.24   Square End of Truss

10.21   Wind bracing—low steel buildings

a   As has been stated in Art. 10.20*d*, the design to resist wind on low steel-framed buildings applies to factory buildings and also to churches and other similar structures. The anchorage of steel or wood sash and its support should meet the requirements of the codes quoted. In buildings with wood siding, corrugated metal or asbestos-cement, and the like, the wind pressure is carried through the system of girts into the columns in the same manner as the application of floor loads to horizontal members. This design, although actually a wind-pressure design, is treated in Art. 10.41.

b   The wind pressure on a panel is divided between the two columns at either side of the panel, and the load is divided between reactions at the top and bottom of the column. The load going into the bottom of the wall or column is transferred directly to the foundation without causing any moment on the column. The load at the top of the column is considered to be distributed across the building, being divided roughly in proportion to the stiffness factor $K = I/h$. Thus for a simple two-column bent, half the eave load goes to each column.

c   The knee brace is designed as the support of a cantilever beam, to resist both cantilever load and uplift, and, since it is a sloping member, the stress is multiplied by the vector for the angle of the knee brace.

d   The design for one column is on the basis of a cantilever beam. The wind load on the column is applied as a shear load at the point of contraflexure. Obviously, as a cantilever beam, the top of the column must have two points of support—either the upper and lower chords of a truss, as in Fig. 10.24, or a knee brace, as in Fig. 10.25.

The length of the cantilever is taken to the point of contraflexure as determined from the amount of fixity at the base of the column. For a completely fixed base which may be obtained by means of building the steel column into the concrete foundation or by de-

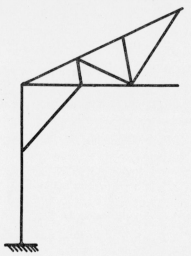

Fig. 10.25   Knee-braced End of Truss

veloping the full bending moment with anchor bolts, the point of contraflexure is midway between the knee or the lower chord, whichever forms the fulcrum, and the base. Otherwise the capacity of the anchors may be deducted from the cantilever of full height, as indicated in the following problem.

Problem   Assume wind at 10 psf acting on the structure shown in Fig. 10.26.

$$W \text{ per panel} = 10 \times 16 \times 20 = 3{,}200 \text{ lb}$$

The load at the top of the column is

$$\frac{3{,}200}{2} = 1{,}600 \text{ lb}$$

This load divided between the two columns *A* and *B* is (Fig. 10.27)

$$\frac{1{,}600}{2} = 800 \text{ lb per column}$$

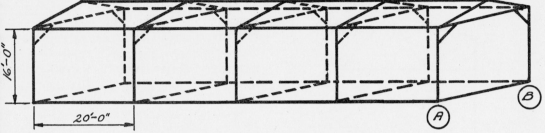

Fig. 10.26   Wind-braced Mill Building

Apply a knee brace as a fulcrum 3 ft below the bottom of the truss. If there were no contraflexure—that is, if the column were free to rotate about its base—the wind moment would be

$$M = 800 \times 13 = 10,400 \text{ ft-lb}$$

The knee brace is designed as a strut, as shown in Fig. 10.29.

To hold 800 lb in equilibrium, taking moments about c,

$$3P_b = 9.5 \times 800$$

Then

$$P_b = \frac{9.5 \times 800}{3} = 2,533 \text{ lb}$$

Assuming a knee brace at 45 deg,

$$P = \sqrt{2} \times 2,533 = 3,580 \text{ lb}$$

The length of knee brace at 45 deg is $\sqrt{2} \times 3 = 4.24$ ft. The knee brace to carry this load may be selected from Table 10.4 by dividing 3,580/1.33, or 2,690 on 4.24 ft length. The divisor 1.33 allows for increased stress for wind.

If we assume an 8-in. column with one $\frac{7}{8}$-in. anchor bolt 2 in. out from each face of the column and with the neutral axis of tension and compression at $d/7$ from the face of the column (see Fig. 10.28), which are safe

assumptions, the value of the anchorage may be computed thus:

$$d = 8 + 2 = 10$$
$$d/7 = 10/7 = \underline{1.43}$$
$$d - d/7 = \overline{8.57} \text{ (half lever arm of } M \text{ couple)}$$

The value of one $\frac{7}{8}$-in. bolt, under wind stress, is

$$0.419 \times 20,000 \times 1.33 = 11.2 \text{ kips}$$
$$M = 11.2 \times \frac{8.57 \times 2}{12} = 16$$

which is over half of the full moment. Therefore the point of contraflexure is at midheight, or $M = 10,400/2 = 5,200$ ft-lb. This moment is to be applied to the columns in accordance with the method of Art. 7.10e.

In addition to the column stress due to moment, there is a direct stress due to wind—a compression on the leeward column, and a tension on the windward column. The amount of this direct stress is found by taking moments about the base of one column. In the problem here stated, let us assume that the truss span is 40 ft and the dead load 10 lb per square foot of roof and 8 lb per square foot of side wall. The overturning moment due to wind load is $1,600 \times 16 = 25,600$ ft-lb. The direct stress in columns due to wind is

$$P = \frac{25,600}{40} = 640 \text{ lb}$$

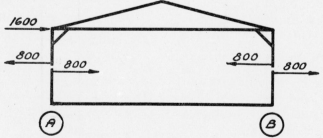

Fig. 10.27   Application of Wind Loads, Mill Building

The dead load on the windward column is

Roof: $20 \times 20 \times 10 = 4,000$ lb
Side wall: $20 \times 16 \times 8 = \underline{2,560 \text{ lb}}$
Total $= 6,560$ lb

The building is, therefore, stable against overturning because the uplift is only 9.8 percent of the dead load against $66\frac{2}{3}$ percent allowed (see Art. 10.20e).

In addition to the dead load, let us assume that there is a roof load of 30 psf. The load on each column is

Dead load $=\ \ 6,560$
Live load $= 30 \times 20 \times 20 = \underline{12,000}$
Subtotal $= 18,560$ lb
Wind, D.S. $=\ \ \ \ 640$ lb

Wind moment, equivalent
D.S. $= 5,200 \times 12 \times 0.333 = \underline{20,800}$
Total $= 40,000$ lb

To use Tables 7.1 to 7.4, divide by 1.33 because of wind allowance.

$$P = \frac{40,000}{1.33} = 30,000 \text{ lb}$$

Since the columns are braced the weak way by the girts, we may enter the tables at $13/2.12 = 6.1$ ft unbraced height; the 8 WF 24 is adequate to carry all stresses.

e Aside from proper design of columns,

anchorage, and other component parts, it is necessary also to cross-brace the entire structure properly against weaving. This is a matter of practical selection of size and location rather than of design, and is discussed more fully in Art. 10.40d.

f Article 10.20d states the requirements of several codes for anchorage of roof. The requirements of the Factory Mutual Fire Insurance Companies for a gross uplift of 30 psf seems rather severe, and it would seem satisfactory generally to use the U.S. Corps of Engineers' requirement that details for attachment be capable of resisting a net suction of 12 psf. Even this amount requires special anchorage of corrugated steel, asbestos-cement, or other lightweight roofing material —usually more anchorage than is ordinarily provided by the commonly used types, as is evidenced by the large number of light roofs lost in wind storms annually.

10.22   Wind bracing of multistory buildings

a The subject of wind bracing of high buildings may be best introduced by quoting from the final report of the Committee on Wind Bracing of the American Society of Civil Engineers, submitted in 1940.

Proper design of wind bracing involves provision for stability, strength and rigidity. The relative importance of these three factors varies considerably, but adequate consideration must be given to each.

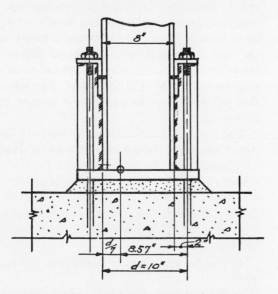

Fig. 10.28   Anchorage at Base of Column

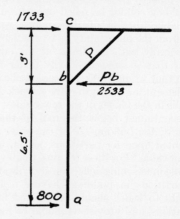

Fig. 10.29   Application of Wind Loads to Column

The frame of a building is made up, in general, of vertical members (columns) and horizontal members framed between the verticals (beams and girders). In tier buildings the horizontal members of the floors occur at fairly regular intervals throughout the height and, with floor slabs, form horizontal diaphragms uniting the columns at each floor level. The purpose of the wind bracing is to preserve this frame from undue distortion when subjected to horizontal forces.

In a building frame as described, the tendency of the panels formed by the columns and their connecting beams or girders to distort, due to horizontal thrust, is resisted by the connections at the columns and by the members in bending and direct stress Where several columns occur in a line, they form a bent which (to a degree depending on the rigidity of the beams, their connections, and the nature of the bracing utilized) tends to resist the horizontal thrust in the manner of a vertical truss with the columns forming multiple chords and the columns, beams, and girders forming the web. The columns on the windward side of the axis of the bent become tension chords and those on the leeward side, compression chords.

In successful design, the building must be assumed to act as a unit, and not distort appreciably when subjected to the applied lateral loads.

The floors of a building must act as horizontal diaphragms for the delivery of wind load increments that arise in each story to the braced bents that are provided to receive them. Bracing planes usually run in more than one direction and the floors must possess the necessary strength and rigidity under loads in their own planes to deliver these wind loads. If the floor is incapable of serving as a horizontal distribution unit, horizontal bracing should be provided between the braced bents. Most of the customary systems of floor construction used in fireproof buildings possess the requisite strength for this purpose.

As ordinarily constructed, the walls of a modern tall building cannot be relied upon to absorb any appreciable fraction of the applied wind force. Apart from the uncertainty as to whether the walls act integrally with the frame at the outset, it is obvious that if stressed heavily under horizontal loading they would crack and cease to be a dependable element of strength. In setback buildings, the walls in the planes of the tower sides, of course, are discontinued below the roof of the widened portion of the building. Nor can wind resistance be counted upon for partitions, which, in general, are removable. For these reasons, whatever may be their role in lessening deflection and vibration, walls and partitions in buildings having a high ratio of height to width should be ignored in strength calculations, and provisions should be made in the structural frame for the entire recommended wind load.

b There are a number of acceptable methods of distributing wind loads and computing bents for resistance of wind pressures. Judging from results, any one of these methods properly applied will give satisfactory results. The Miami hurricane of 1926 furnished a full-scale test of the wind bracing of tall buildings and proved that any building designed in accordance with the general principles of good wind bracing suffered little or no structural damage, even under stresses far in excess of those used in the design. On the other hand, several tall, narrow buildings which failed did not comply with the general principles, and although quite satisfactory for carrying vertical loads, were weak against lateral pressures.

c *The cantilever method* assumes that the entire bent acts as a cantilever beam or truss fixed at the base. There are many refinements of the simple method presented here, but this method has proven quite satisfactory and is recommended for the normal range of tall buildings up to about 30 stories high—that is, a height-to-width ratio from $1\frac{1}{2}$:1 up to 5:1. Beyond these limits, nobody but an experienced specialist on wind bracing should attempt the design.

In accordance with paragraph *a*, the loads applied against the outside wall are distributed by the floors as a diaphragm between the bents. Bents may be assumed at each column line and the wind stresses thus kept low, or, as is usually done, the bents are selected in the end walls and occasionally in interior bents where the projections of special details may be easily buried in partitions. The selection of wind-bent locations is a matter of experience.

The cantilever method assumes that (1) the direct stresses in the columns induced by wind are proportional to their distances from the center of gravity of the bent (similar to unit stresses in a beam); and (2) the point of inflection of beams and columns is at mid-span.

d The design of a wind bent by the cantilever method involves

1. The computation of coefficients for the bent.

2. The application of wind loads to the bent,

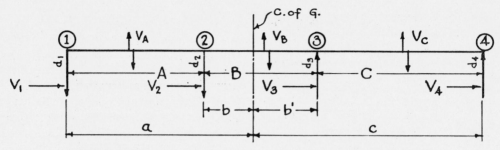

Fig. 10.30   Application of Wind Loads—Beam of Multistory Bent

and the computation of resultant shears and moments on the bent as a whole.

3. The computation of beam and column moments and direct stresses, from the coefficients found in step 1 and the shears and moments found in step 2.

4. The application of these shears and moments to the members already designed for live and dead load.

In detail, these steps are as follows:

1(a)   Lay out to scale a cross section of one floor only of the bent, as in Fig. 10.30.

1(b)   Locate the center of gravity of the bent, assuming the area of each column as unity.

1(c)   Compute the moment of inertia of the bent.

$$I = a^2 + b^2 + b'^2 + c^2$$

1(d)   For each column, compute the direct-stress coefficient.

$$d_1 = \pm \frac{a}{I}, \quad d_2 = \pm \frac{b}{I}, \quad d_3 = \pm \frac{b'}{I}, \quad d_4 = \pm \frac{c}{I}, \quad \text{and so on}$$

It will be noted that each stress may be compression or tension, depending on the direction of the wind.

1(e)   For each beam in the bent, compute the shear coefficient to apply at the center of the beam.

$$v_A = d_1, \quad v_B = d_1 + d_2, \quad v_C = d_1 + d_2 + d_3 \text{ (added algebraically)}$$

1(f)   For each beam, calculate beam-moment coefficient,

$$m_A = \frac{v_A A}{2}, \quad m_B = \frac{v_B B}{2}, \quad m_C = \frac{v_C C}{2}$$

1(g)   For each column, compute the shear coefficient.

$$v_1 = m_A, \quad v_2 = m_A + m_B, \quad v_3 = m_B + m_C, \quad v_4 = m_C$$

1(h)   Calculate the direct stress coefficients for each beam, working from each side and using the larger for design purposes.

$$p_A = 1.0 - v_1 \qquad\qquad p_C = 1.0 - v_4$$
$$p_B = p_A - v_2 \qquad \text{or} \qquad p_B = p_C - v_3$$
$$p_C = p_B - v_3 \qquad\qquad p_A = p_B - v_2$$

2(a)   Sketch the entire bent to scale, and on the right-hand side run a line of story heights (Fig. 10.32).

2(b)   Compute and apply the wind loads at each story, P_R, P_8, and the rest. Set these down at the left side of the bent. Where there are several wind bents of the same cross section, it may be advantageous to compute a bent for an applied load of 1 kip per foot of height and prorate the bents from the results obtained.

2(c)   At mid-story on the left side of the bent, indicate an arrow for the position of the shear load—the total load applied above this point—W_R, W_8, etc. Thus $W_R = P_R$, $W_8 = W_R + P_8$, $W_7 = W_8 + P_7$, etc. Set this shear value down above the mid-story arrow.

2(d)   Compute at each mid-story point the

total moment on the bent above this point, M_R below the roof, M_8 below the eighth floor, and so on, and set it down below the mid-story arrow. These moments are obtained as follows:

$$M_R = W_R \frac{h_R}{2}$$

$$M_8 = M_R + W_R \frac{h_R}{2} + W_8 \frac{h_8}{2}$$

$$M_7 = M_8 + \frac{W_8 h_8}{2} + \frac{W_7 h_7}{2}$$

Etc.

3(a)   For each story of each column, compute and set down in parentheses the direct stress due to wind,

$$P_{1'R} = d_1 M_R$$
$$P_{2'R} = d_2 M_R$$
$$P_{3'R} = d_3 M_R$$
$$P_{4'R} = d_4 M_R$$
$$P_{1'8} = d_1 M_8$$
$$P_{2'8} = d_2 M_8$$
$$P_{3'8} = d_3 M_8$$
Etc.

[The direct-stress coefficient for each column from step 1(d) multiplied by the moment from step 2(d).]

3(b)   For each beam in each story, compute and set down above the beam the moment for which to design the beam and the end connections.

$$M_{AR} = m_A M_R$$
$$M_{BR} = m_B M_R$$
$$M_{CR} = m_C M_R$$

[The moment coefficient for each beam from step 1(f) multiplied by the roof moment from step 2(d).]

$$M_{A8} = m_A(M_8 - M_R)$$
$$M_{B8} = m_B(M_8 - M_R)$$
$$M_{C8} = m_C(M_8 - M_R)$$
Etc.

[The moment coefficient for each beam from step 1(f) multiplied by the difference in moment above and below, from step 2(d).]

3(c)   Compute the moment at each floor of each column and set it down parallel with the column under the line below the floor.

$$M_{1'R} = v_1 W_R \frac{h_R}{2}$$

$$M_{2'R} = v_2 W_R \frac{h_R}{2}$$

$$M_{3'R} = v_3 W_R \frac{h_R}{2}$$

$$M_{4'R} = v_4 W_R \frac{h_R}{2}$$

$$M_{1'8} = v_1 W_8 \frac{h_8}{2}$$

$$M_{2'8} = v_2 W_8 \frac{h_8}{2}$$

$$M_{3'8} = v_3 W_8 \frac{h_8}{2}$$

Etc.

3(d)   For each beam in each floor compute the direct stress in the beam, and set it down below the beam in parentheses.

$$DS_{AR} = p_A P_R$$
$$DS_{BR} = p_B P_R$$
$$DS_{CR} = p_C P_R$$
$$DS_{A8} = p_A P_8$$
$$DS_{B8} = p_B P_8$$
$$DS_{C8} = p_C P_8$$
Etc.

4(a)   Check the beam sizes to carry the combined live- and dead-load moments plus the wind moment and wind direct stress (at the increased allowable stress). Figure 10.31 indicates the combination of live-, dead-, and wind-load moments in a beam of a wind bent. It will be noted that the maximum moment due to wind loads is at the end of the beam, whereas the maximum moment due to live and dead loads is at or near the middle of the beam, so that usually these moments are not additive. For the condition indicated in this figure, it is ordinarily necessary only to check the section modulus furnished for live and dead loads against the section modulus furnished for wind load at the increased stress. If the allowable stress increase for wind is $33\frac{1}{3}$ percent, the required section modulus becomes $S = 0.45M$, where M is the moment in foot-kips.

There are two types of end connection used to develop the end moment of the beam: (1) the simpler connection, of cap and seat connections to provide the necessary moment

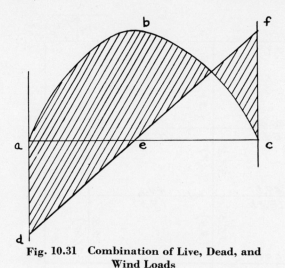

Fig. 10.31   Combination of Live, Dead, and Wind Loads

resistance without materially stiffening the joint; and (2) either a gusset-plate end connection or angle knee braces which will also furnish stiffness. If the bent is located in an outside wall, the stiffness may be provided by the masonry, and the cap and seat connection will be satisfactory. The knee braces or gussets may be buried in partitions.

If a knee brace or a gusset connection is used, the section modulus of the beam to be checked is that required for the combined moment at the inner end of the connection.

4(b) Having selected the beams to be used, design the end connections to transfer the moment to the column.

4(c) Having previously computed the live and dead loads and selected the necessary column to carry these loads, check the column section to carry the wind-load moments and direct stresses at the increased allowable stress.

e Applying the foregoing steps to the wind bent shown in Fig. 10.32, these results will be obtained:

1(b) $\bar{x}$ (from col. 1) $= \dfrac{18 + 30 + 44}{4} = 23$ ft

Therefore, $a = +23$, $b = +5$, $b' = -7$, $c = -21$.

1(c) $I = 23^2 + 5^2 + (-7)^2 + (-21)^2 = 1{,}044$

1(d) $d_1 = \pm \dfrac{23}{1{,}044} = 0.022$

$d_2 = \pm \dfrac{5}{1{,}044} = 0.0048$

$d_3 = \pm \dfrac{7}{1{,}044} = 0.0067$

$d_4 = \pm \dfrac{21}{1{,}044} = 0.0201$

1(e) $v_A = 0.022$

$v_B = 0.0268$

$v_C = 0.0268 - 0.0067 = 0.0201 \;(= d_4)$

1(f) $m_A = \dfrac{0.022 \times 18}{2} = 0.198$

$m_B = \dfrac{0.0268 \times 12}{2} = 0.1608$

$m_C = \dfrac{0.0201 \times 14}{2} = 0.1407$

1(g) $v_1 = 0.198$

$v_2 = 0.198 + 0.1608 = 0.3588$

$v_3 = 0.1608 + 0.1407 = 0.3015$

$v_4 = 0.1407$

(Note that within the limits of slide-rule accuracy, the sum of these coefficients equals 1. In the above example, it totals 0.999.)

1(h) $p_A = 1.00 - 0.198 = 0.802$

$p_B = 0.802 - 0.3588 = 0.4432$

$p_C = \;.4432 - 0.3015 = 0.1417$

or

$p_C = 1.00 - 0.1407 = 0.8593$

$p_B = 0.8593 - 0.3015 = 0.5578$

$p_A = 0.5578 - 0.3588 = 0.199$

Use $p_A = 0.802$, $p_B = 0.5578$, $p_C = 0.8593$.

2(b)   Applying a 1-kip load per foot of height,

$p_R = 4 \;(= \text{height of parapet}) + \frac{13}{2} = 10.5$

$p_8 = \frac{13}{2} + \frac{11}{2} = 12.0$

$p_7 = p_6 = p_5 = p_4 = p_3 = 11.0$

$p_2 = \frac{11}{2} + \frac{14}{2} = 12.5$

$p_1 = \frac{14}{2} = 7$

(There is no wind applied below grade, which is assumed in this problem as first-floor level.)

2(c) $W_R = P_R = 10.5$ kips

$W_8 = 10.5 + 12.0 = 22.5$

$W_7 = 22.5 + 11.0 = 33.5$

$W_6 = 33.5 + 11.0 = 44.5$

$W_5 = 44.5 + 11.0 = 55.5$

$W_4 = 55.5 + 11.0 = 66.5$

$W_3 = 66.5 + 11.0 = 77.5$

$W_2 = 77.5 + 12.5 = 90.0$

$W_1 = 90.0 + 7 = 97.0$

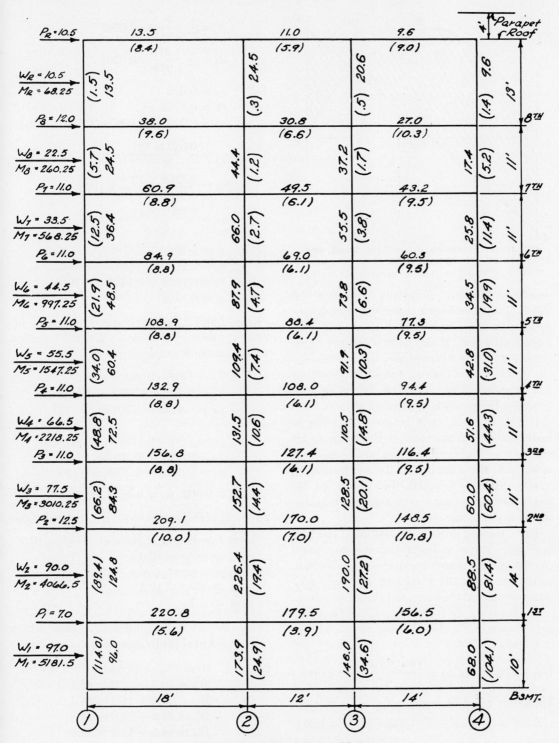

Fig. 10.32   Typical Wind Bent—Multistory

2(d)

$$M_R = 10.5 \times 6.5 = 68.25$$
$$M_8 = 68.25 + 68.25 + (22.5 \times 5.5) = 260.25$$
$$M_7 = 260.25 + 123.75 + (33.5 \times 5.5) = 568.25$$
$$M_6 = 568.25 + 184.25 + (44.5 \times 5.5) = 997.25$$
$$M_5 = 997.25 + 244.75 + (55.5 \times 5.5) = 1{,}547.25$$
$$M_4 = 1{,}547.25 + 305.25 + (66.5 \times 5.5) = 2{,}218.25$$
$$M_3 = 2{,}218.25 + 365.75 + (77.5 \times 5.5) = 3{,}010.25$$
$$M_2 = 3{,}010.25 + 426.25 + (90 \times 7) = 4{,}066.5$$
$$M_1 = 4{,}066.5 + 630 + (97 \times 5) = 5{,}181.5$$

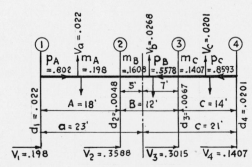

Fig. 10.33   Application of Coefficients—Beam of Multistory Bent

Steps 3(a), 3(b), 3(c), and 3(d) are set down in Fig. 10.32 directly from slide-rule calculations.

4(a)   In the bent shown in Fig. 10.32, assume that the columns below the second floor carry live- and dead-load direct stresses with negligible eccentricity, as follows:

Col. 1—261.5 kips   Col. 3—257 kips
Col. 2—297 kips   Col. 4—221.5 kips

The second-floor beams required would have the following section modulus for live and dead loads—

Cols. 1–2, $S = 41.5$
Cols. 2–3, $S = 18.5$
Cols. 3–4, $S = 25.1$

Assume that this bent carries 0.8 of the wind stress in Fig. 10.32. Then assuming that the columns and beams are in an end wall, the section modulus required to carry wind stresses in the beams are:

Cols. 1–2, $S = 0.45 \times 0.8 \times 209.1 = 75$
Cols. 2–3, $S = 0.45 \times 0.8 \times 170 = 61.2$
Cols. 3–4, $S = 0.45 \times 0.8 \times 148.5 = 53.5$

On this basis, we will select the beams as follows:

Cols. 1–2, 18 WF 50
Cols. 2–3, 16 WF 40
Cols. 3–4, 16 WF 36

It will be noted that the direct stress in the beams is negligible when spread over the area of the beams above noted.

4(b)   The moment to be provided at the ends of beams is as follows:

Cols. 1–2, $0.8 \times 209.1 = 167.3$
Cols. 2–3, $0.8 \times 170 = 136$
Cols. 3–4, $0.8 \times 148.5 = 119$

The stresses caused by moments in this range may be resisted by caps and seats built up from sections cut from wide-flange beams. For the beam at Col. 1–2, using the connec-

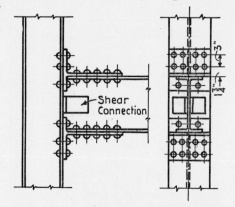

Fig. 10.34   Wind Bracing Connection

tion shown in Fig. 10.34, the moment couple between the top and the bottom of the beam would produce a stress of $167.3/1.5 = 111.5$ kips. The value of a $\frac{7}{8}$-in. rivet in single shear is $1.33 \times 9.02 = 12.03$ kips. This would require 10 rivets in each group between the beam and the T-type connections and would require a web thickness for the connecting member of at least 0.33 in. to develop this rivet capacity. The most economical connection would be cut from a 36-in. beam to make the most efficient use of materials.

In order to have ten $\frac{7}{8}$-in. rivets in the connection shown, it will be necessary to use two rows of four each and one row of two. It would be preferable to place them as shown in Fig. 10.34.

Since the entire group of rivets in the upper or lower T connection to the face of the column would fail as a unit, the load of the eight rivets above the flange would be applied at the center of gravity of the group of rivets in the determination of the thickness of metal, as described in Art. 4.13b.

The distance from the fillet to the center of gravity of the eight rivets is $1\frac{3}{4} + 1\frac{1}{2} - \frac{3}{8} = 2\frac{7}{8}$ in. = 2.88 in. To use the method of Art. 4.13b, the unit load per inch is $0.8 \times 111.5/12 = 89.2/12 = 7.4$, and to use this at the increased unit stress,

$$P = \frac{7.4}{1.33} = 5.56$$

$$M = 5.56 \times \frac{2.88}{2} = \frac{20t^2}{6}$$

or

$$t = \sqrt{\frac{5.56 \times 1.44 \times 6}{20}} = 1.55 \text{ in.}$$

Use 36 WF 280.

In the same manner, for the beam from Cols. 2 to 3, the stress developed by the moment couple is $136/1.33 = 102$, or nine $\frac{7}{8}$-in. rivets (use 10).

The thickness of the T connection is

$$P = 0.8 \times \frac{102}{1.33 \times 12} = 5.1$$

$$t = \sqrt{\frac{5.1 \times 1.44 \times 6}{20}} = 1.5$$

Use 36 WF 280.

For the beam from Cols. 3 to 4, the stress developed by the moment couple is $119/1.33 = 89.2 =$ eight $\frac{7}{8}$-in. rivets.

These can be put into a T-type connection using four rivets above and four below the center lines of the T. Using a $3\frac{1}{2}$-in. gage on the beam, the total lever arm is $1\frac{3}{4} - \frac{3}{8} = 1.38$ in. The load on the four rivets is $44.6/12 = 3.72$, and allowing for the increased fiber stress, this is equivalent to $3.72/1.33 = 2.8$.

$$t = \sqrt{\frac{2.8 \times 0.69 \times 6}{20}} = 0.58 \text{ in.}$$

Use 24 WF 76.

4(c)   The columns should have 12 in. width to take the connection used, and should be placed with the web parallel with the line of the bent to provide for the moment. Without considering wind stresses, the following columns could be used.

Col. 1, 261.5 kips—use 10 WF 60
Col. 2, 297   kips—use 10 WF 72
Col. 3, 257   kips—use 10 WF 60
Col. 4, 221.5 kips—use 10 WF 54

For col. 1, adding wind,

$$\text{D.S.} = 261.5$$
$$\text{Wind} = 89.4 \times .8 = \underline{71.5}$$
$$333.0$$

Using a 12-in. column, the equivalent direct load would be

$$124.8 \times 12 \times 0.8 \times 0.216 = 258$$

The equivalent total direct load to read from Table 7.3 would be $591/1.33 = 444$. Use 12 WF 99. Check for use of a 14-in. column.

$$124.8 \times 12 \times 0.8 \times 0.185 = 222$$
$$\frac{222 + 333}{1.33} = 417$$

Use 14 WF 95.

For col. 2, assuming a 14-in. column, the equivalent total moment and direct stress, reduced by 1.33 for use of the table, would be:

$$\text{D.S.} = 297.0$$
$$\text{Wind D.S.} = 0.8 \times 19.4 = 15.5$$
$$\text{Wind } M = 0.8 \times 226.4 \times 12 \times 0.185 = \underline{403}$$
$$\frac{715.5}{1.33} = 537 \qquad 715.5$$

Use 14 WF 119.

For col. 3, similarly,

$$\begin{aligned}
\text{D.S.} &= 257 \\
\text{Wind D.S.} = 0.8 \times 27.2 &= 21.8 \\
\text{Wind } M = 0.8 \times 190 \times 12 \times 0.185 &= \underline{337.} \\
&\ \ 615.8
\end{aligned}$$

$$\frac{615.8}{1.33} = 462$$

Use 14 WF 103.

For col. 4, similarly,

$$\begin{aligned}
\text{D.S.} &= 221.5 \\
\text{Wind D.S.} = 0.8 \times 81.4 &= 65.1 \\
\text{Wind } M = 0.8 \times 88.5 \times 12 \times 0.185 &= \underline{153.4} \\
&\ \ 440.0
\end{aligned}$$

$$\frac{440.0}{1.33} = 330$$

Use 14 WF 78.

10.30   SHALLOW BINS AND BUNKERS

a The general theory of lateral pressure of solids and the conversion of the load of ordinary level loads, sloping loads, and surcharges into equivalent fluid pressures has been discussed in Art. 8.30, Retaining Walls. A table of equivalent fluid pressures for various materials was given in Table 8.6. These rules in general will hold for the design of shallow bins, with certain modifications for sloping sides, and suspension bunkers. The designation "shallow bins" includes bins or vessels of all kinds in which the plane of rupture of the material intersects the open surface of the material, or a width, diameter, or side of square of about half the depth. If the depth exceeds this, the application of Janssen's formula will apply for granular material, and the bin will be classified as a deep bin and designed in accordance with Art. 10.31.

b For bunkers and bins in boiler rooms, two generally accepted cross sections of bins are used, the hopper-type bin (Fig. 10.35), and the suspension bunker (Fig. 10.36). The hopper-type bin may be square in plan, with the same cross section both ways, or it may be rectangular in plan, with the same cross section throughout its length, and with gates at intervals. For the design of the hopper-type bin, pressure on vertical side walls may be computed by the methods of Art. 8.30 for retaining walls. Pressure on the flat bottom is the weight per square foot of the total depth of material. The pressure on the diag-

onal sides is the vector combination of the vertical pressure and horizontal pressure.

Problem Find the pressure on the walls of the bunker shown in Fig. 10.35, level full, using coal with a weight of 50 lb per cu ft and equivalent fluid pressure of 12.5 lb.

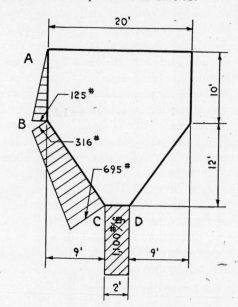

Fig. 10.35   Hopper Type Bunker

The pressure on vertical side AB varies uniformly from zero at the top to 125 psf at the bottom at B. On the bottom CD, the pressure is $22 \times 50 = 1,100$ psf.

The normal pressure on the diagonal plates is the vector sum of a vertical pressure of 1,100 and a lateral pressure of 22×12.5

= 275 psf. This may be obtained mathematically with sufficient accuracy as follows:

One square foot of sloping side carries $\frac{9}{15}$, or 0.6 ft, of vertical load, and $\frac{12}{15}$, or 0.8 ft, of horizontal pressure:

$$0.6 \times 1,100 = 660 \text{ psf}, \quad 660^2 = 435,600$$
$$0.8 \times 275 = 220 \text{ psf}, \quad 220^2 = \underline{48,400}$$
$$\sqrt{484,000} = 695 \text{ psf}$$

Therefore, the pressure at C normal to the sloping side is 695 psf. From C to B the pressure decreases uniformly in proportion to the total depth, so that at B this pressure is $\frac{10}{22} \times 695 = 316$ psf.

If the bunker were loaded with surcharge sloping with the angle of repose of the material, the equivalent fluid pressure would be increased in accordance with the slope pressure in Table 8.6. Moreover, the vertical loading would be increased and would be variable from the center to the edge of the bunker.

When the loads on the various plates of the bunkers have been determined, the design of plates, with the beams and the stiffeners that support them and carry the loads and stresses into the main building structure, is in accordance with ordinary moment methods if the plates are supported by beams in one direction only. Since continuity is usually developed, design is by the methods of Art. 3.21. If the stiffeners are used as supporting members from beam to beam, the method of determining the plate thickness is by one of the several flat-plate methods. The following formula by Grashof may be used for a rectangular plate of longer dimension a, shorter dimension b, and thickness t (all in inches), with a uniform load of w per square inch.

$$f_a \text{ in the longer direction} = \frac{a^2 b^4 w}{2t^2(a^4 + b^4)}$$

$$f_b \text{ in the shorter direction} = \frac{a^4 b^2 w}{2t^2(a^4 + b^4)}$$

$$\delta = \frac{w a^4 b^4}{32 t^3 (a^4 + b^4) E}$$

For a square plate this simplifies to

$$f = \frac{w a^2}{4 t^2}$$

$$\delta = \frac{w a^4}{64 t^3 E}$$

These formulae are for plates which are fixed at all edges, either welded, bolted, or riveted. Plates simply supported at the edges have a fiber stress that is approximately $1\frac{1}{2}$ times as great, or comparable to that obtained by ordinary moment theory of simple to continuous beams.

c The design of the suspension-type bunker shown in Fig. 10.36 is an entirely different type of problem. Here the plates are figured to carry direct tension in the manner of a suspension bridge. The upper portion of the bin side is treated as a plate girder with the web sloping in the plane of the top of the bunker side plates. If the bunker is too narrow in proportion to its height, there is a tendency to distortion of the plates under partial load. The distortion does not come out as the balance of the bunker is filled, thereby causing a lateral deflection of the plate-girder portion of the bunker between the end connections and the central portion where the distortion takes place. Because of the rigid connections, the bunker cannot distort there. The safest bunkers have a ratio of total sag S to width B of between 5:8 and 7:8.

The theoretical equation for the curve of the bunker is

$$y = \frac{2S}{B^2}\left(3x^2 - \frac{2x^3}{B}\right)$$

where x is the horizontal and y the vertical coordinate of any point on the curve.

The weight per running foot of length for the material contained in a level full bunker is

$$W_1 = 0.625 S B w$$

To this the triangle of surcharge W_2 must be added.

$$W = W_1 + W_2$$

The horizontal tensile stress at the bottom of the curve is

$$H = \frac{WB}{6S}$$

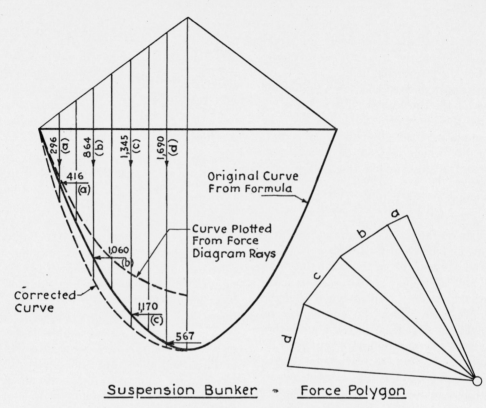

Suspension Bunker ⟶ **Force Polygon**

Fig. 10.36 Suspension Bunker

The maximum tension for which the plates must be designed is

$$T = W\sqrt{\frac{1}{4} + \left(\frac{2B}{3S}\right)^2}$$

It is not necessary to correct the tension or horizontal stress for the angle of the top girder, but it is advisable to lay out a corrected curve of the bunker to determine the angle with the vertical for the web of the girder. This is a graphical problem, as explained later.

The various steps required for the problem shown in Fig. 10.36 are partially worked out here and partially shown graphically.

Problem   Assume a bunker having a 16-ft width and a 12-ft sag, carrying coal weighing 50 lb per cu ft. Assume the upper 3 ft of the bin sides to act as a plate-girder web. Figure the required thickness of plate and the slope of the plate-girder web.

$$W_1 = 0.625 \times 16 \times 12 \times 50 = 6,000 \text{ lb per ft}$$

For an angle of repose of 1 on $1\frac{1}{3}$, the height of triangle W_2 is $8/1.33 = 6$.

$$W_2 = \frac{6 \times 16}{2} \times 50 = 2,400 \text{ lb per ft}$$

$$W = 6,000 + 2,400 = 8,400 \text{ lb per ft}$$

$$H = \frac{8,400 \times 16}{6 \times 12} = 1,867$$

$$T = 8,400\sqrt{\frac{1}{4} + \left(\frac{32}{36}\right)^2}$$
$$= 8,400\sqrt{1.04} = 8,560$$

The required net area of plate per foot is $8,560/20,000 = 0.428$ sq in., or 0.0356 per inch.

Even allowing for rivet holes, etc., it is obvious that $\frac{1}{4}$-in. plate will be adequate. The direct pull on the plate girder is therefore 8,560 lb per ft.

The coordinates for laying out the curve for the bunker, as obtained from the formula, are as follows:

$x =$	1	2	3	4	5	6	7	8
$y =$	0.269	1.03	2.22	3.75	5.56	7.58	9.75	12

Divide half the width of the bunker into equal parts (four have been used), and compute the load from the area of the intercepted parts. For the trapezoidal loads it is accurate enough to apply them at the center point; for triangles, at the third point. From Table 8.6 determine the equivalent fluid pressure. In this example it is the equivalent slope pressure, or 32, which is 0.64 of the vertical pressure. The pressure on the bottom section is

$$\frac{1,690}{2} \times 1.03 \times 0.64 = 567 \text{ psf}$$

Similarly on the second, third, and top sections, we find horizontal pressures of 1,170, 1,060, and 416 psf. From the combination of vertical and lateral loads, loads a, b, c, and d may be laid out on a force polygon, and the rays drawn from which the curve may be constructed, as shown in dotted lines within the bunker. This curve may be corrected by prorating the position of each point in the curve in proportion to the correct center depths. The revised end slope at the upper end is more nearly the correct slope for the web of the girder.

10.31   Deep concrete bins and silos

a As stated in Art. 10.30, when the dimensional proportion of a bin carrying granular materials, such as grains, sand, or coal, reaches a ratio for H/D of approximately 2, the rules of equivalent fluid pressure no longer are applicable, and Janssen's formula governs the design. This formula involves several variables for each material, and instead of giving the formulae, Table 10.6 is presented here, from which the vertical and lateral pressures may be obtained directly.

Problem Compute the lateral pressure 30 ft below the top of a 10-ft-diameter silo for storage of anthracite coal: Table 10.6 indicates the value for anthracite is 0.52 times the value selected from col. 1, or, for $H/D = 3$,

$$\frac{L}{D} = 0.52 \times 50.24 = 26.1$$

and

$$\frac{V}{D} = 0.52 \times 119.57 = 62.1$$

Therefore $L = 26.1 \times 10 = 261$ psf, and $V = 62.1 \times 10 = 621$ psf. Since the total weight of a column of coal at this point is $30 \times 52 = 1,560$ lb, it is obvious that the greater part of the vertical weight is carried into the side wall through friction, and in designing the footings this fact should be taken into consideration.

b In the design of silos, the stresses are carried by ring tension, as described in Art. 10.32, Pipe Design. The concrete not only is not given credit for carrying any of the tension, but because of concrete's low tensile value, the steel stress should be limited to 14,000 psi in design to prevent cracking of the concrete. The following method for the design of single reinforced-concrete silos has been in use successfully for some years. It is theoretical, but is governed largely by practical considerations. For example, at the base of the silo, the sides are doweled to the base or floor, and therefore cannot work in ring tension, but only by retaining-wall action from the base. It is therefore satisfactory to base the thickness design on stresses at the distance above the base determined in the following paragraph. Since the concrete is only an envelope for the material and the stresses are carried by the steel, the determination of thickness of concrete wall is dependent on good coverage for the steel, and may be assumed as 6 or 8 in., depending on whether heavy jack rods are to be used for raising slip forms.

The wall will carry a cantilever moment from the base which will resist pressure through a height of

$$H = \frac{20d}{\sqrt{L}}$$

where d is half the wall thickness and L is the unit lateral pressure as derived in Art. 10.31a. Thus, for the problem given in Art. 10.31a, use 8 in.

$$H \text{ carried from the base} = \frac{20 \times 4}{\sqrt{261}} = 4.96 \text{ ft}$$

We may start figuring ring tension 5 ft above the base and develop the dowels into the base to carry the full moment capacity of the 4-in. thickness.

Table 10.6 Pressure Factors for Various Materials in Concrete Bins

A = Area of bin, sq ft
H = Height of material in bin, ft
D = Diameter of bin, ft
V = Vertical pressure at depth H, psf
L = Lateral pressure at depth H, psf
P = Perimeter of bin, ft
$R = A/P$ = Hydraulic radius
$K = L/V$ = Ratio of lateral to vertical pressure
v' = Tangent of angle of friction of material on concrete wall

$$V = \frac{WR}{kv'}\left[1 - \left(1 \div \text{number whose common log is } \frac{Kv'h}{2.303\ R}\right)\right]$$

W = Weight of material, lb per cu ft

Values of constants and pressures

Material	W	K	v'	L/D and V/L
Wheat	50	.60	.4167	Col. 2
Cement	100	.42	.445	Col. 1
Raw mix	75	.42	.445	.75 Col. 1
Stone	100	.30	.767	Col. 3
Sand	100	.30	.52	Col. 4
Gravel	100	.30	.52	Col. 4
Anthracite	52	.42	.445	.52 Col. 1
Bituminous	50	.18	.695	Col. 5
Clinker	95	.30	.52	.95 Col. 4
Coke	30	.30	.767	.30 Col. 3

	1		2		3		4		5	
H/D	L/D	V/D	L/D	V/D	L/D	V/D	L/D	V/D	L/D	V/D
0.1	4.05	9.65	2.85	4.75	2.90	9.68	2.88	9.60	.88	4.88
0.2	7.74	18.42	5.43	9.05	5.58	18.59	5.62	18.72	1.71	9.52
0.3	11.24	26.75	7.77	12.94	7.92	26.40	8.16	27.20	2.51	13.93
0.4	14.56	34.65	9.90	16.49	10.16	33.88	10.61	35.36	3.26	18.13
0.5	17.42	41.46	11.80	19.67	12.18	40.59	12.82	42.72	3.98	22.12
0.6	20.15	47.96	13.54	22.56	13.99	46.64	14.98	49.92	4.67	25.92
0.7	22.93	54.57	15.10	25.17	15.71	52.36	16.99	56.64	5.32	29.53
0.8	25.35	60.33	16.53	27.54	17.16	57.20	18.86	62.88	5.94	32.97
0.9	27.54	65.55	17.81	29.67	18.55	61.82	20.64	68.80	6.52	36.24
1.0	29.56	70.35	18.97	31.61	19.87	66.22	22.27	74.24	7.08	39.35
1.1	31.47	74.90	20.02	33.36	20.99	69.96	23.86	79.52	7.61	42.30
1.2	33.27	79.18	20.97	34.94	22.06	73.54	25.39	84.64	8.12	45.12
1.3	34.98	83.25	21.83	36.38	23.00	76.67	26.69	88.96	8.60	47.80
1.4	36.47	86.80	22.60	37.67	23.91	79.70	27.94	93.12	9.06	50.34
1.5	37.90	90.20	23.31	38.85	24.68	82.28	29.18	97.28	9.49	52.76
1.6	39.23	93.37	23.95	39.91	25.41	84.70	30.29	100.96	9.91	55.07
1.7	40.46	96.30	24.52	40.87	26.07	86.90	31.39	104.64	10.31	57.26
1.8	41.54	98.87	25.04	41.73	26.73	89.10	32.40	108.00	10.68	59.34
1.9	42.63	101.46	25.52	42.52	27.26	90.86	33.31	111.04	11.04	61.33
2.0	43.61	103.79	25.94	43.24	27.76	92.53	34.18	113.92	11.38	63.21
2.1	44.51	105.93	26.33	43.88	28.22	94.05	35.02	116.72	11.69	64 93
2.2	45.36	107.96	26.67	44.45	28.63	95.43	35.85	119.49	12.01	66.71
2.3	46.14	109.81	27.00	45.00	29.04	96.80	36.55	121.84	12.29	68.30
2.4	46.87	111.55	27.28	45.47	29.37	97.90	37.27	124.24	12.58	69.88
2.5	47.55	113.17	27.54	45.90	29.70	99.00	37.92	126.40	12.84	71.35
2.6	48.10	114.48	27.77	46.29	29.99	99.95	38.61	128.70	13.09	72.75
2.7	48.75	116.03	27.99	46.64	30.24	100.79	39.07	130.24	13.33	74.05
2.8	49.28	117.29	28.18	46.96	30.50	101.66	39.63	132.10	13.56	75.34
2.9	49.88	118.71	28.35	47.25	30.71	102.38	40.13	133.76	13.78	76.57
3.0	50.24	119.57	28.51	47.51	30.91	103.04	40.61	135.36	13.98	77.69
3.2	51.07	121.55	28.78	47.96	31.25	104.18	41.48	138.27	14.37	79.81
3.4	51.78	123.24	29.00	48.33	31.56	105.20	42.24	140.80	14.71	81.70
3.6	52.39	124.69	29.18	48.64	31.80	105.99	42.92	143.06	15.03	83.47
3.8	52.93	125.97	29.33	48.88	31.99	106.65	43.51	145.04	15.30	85.00
4.0	53.38	127.04	29.45	49.09	32.17	107.23	44.05	146.82	15.52	86.47
4.5	54.26	129.14	29.66	49.43	32.47	108.24	45.11	150.35	16.10	89.46
5.0	54.86	130.57	29.80	49.66	32.67	108.90	45.88	152.93	16.52	91.79
6.0	55.57	132.26	29.93	49.88	32.87	109.56	46.86	156.21	17.10	95.02
8.0	56.06	133.47	29.99	49.98	32.98	109.93	47.65	158.83	17.67	98.17
10.0	56.17	133.69	30.00	50.00	33.00	109.99	47.91	159.70	17.88	99.13

At a point 5 ft above the base, $H/D = 2.5$, $L/D = 0.52 \times 47.55 = 24.7$, and $L = 247$. The ring tension at this point is, $P = 10 \times 247 = 2,470$ lb per foot of height. This is resisted by twice the steel areas of the section (once for each wall—see Art. 10.32). Therefore

$$A_s = \frac{2,470}{2 \times 14,000} = 0.088$$

The minimum steel should be $\frac{3}{8}$-in. round, 8 in. o.c. So the minimum steel may be used throughout the height.

The attention of the designer is called to the fact that for true fluids, such as oil, molasses, etc., and for shallow tanks or silos, whether of concrete or steel, the laws of fluid pressure still govern the design.

10.32　Pipe design

Under the internal pressure of water, steam, or any other fluid under pressure, a pipe has a tendency to rupture longitudinally. Figure 10.37 indicates the method of application of pressure on the inside walls of the pipe, and Fig. 10.38 indicates the method of solution. The internal pressure is considered to be applied uniformly on an area equal to a

Fig. 10.37　Application of Pressure—Pipe Design

unit length times the diameter. This is resisted by the two walls of steel or wrought iron pipe, by the hoops of wood-stave pipe, or by the reinforcement of concrete pipe. Therefore

$$P = \frac{wd}{2}$$

Problem　A water supply pipe is 6 ft in diameter and built of longitudinal wood staves held by hoops of 1-in. round steel rod. What spacing of hoops is required when the pressure is 50 psi?

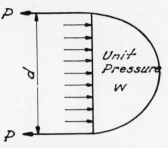

Fig. 10.38　Application of Pressure—Pipe Design

In this problem (from a state license examination),

$$P = \frac{50 \times 72}{2} = 1,800 \text{ lb per inch of length}$$

This would require a steel area of $1,800/20,000 = 0.09$ sq in per inch of length.

The area at the root of the thread of a 1-in. round rod is 0.55 sq in. (see Table 2.4), and through the body of the rod it is 0.7854 sq in. However, joints will be staggered so that two adjacent rods will never have the threaded area at the same point, and it is safe to reduce the area of one rod out of four, so that the average area to use is

$$3 \times 0.7854 = 2.3562$$
$$1 \times 0.551 \;\; = \underline{0.551}$$
$$\frac{2.9072}{4} = 0.7268 \text{ sq in.}$$

The spacing may be $0.7268/0.09 = 8.07$ in. Use 8-in. spacing.

10.33　Brick stacks

a　The design of a brick stack is a problem combining direct compression and bending due to wind stresses. The controlling factor normally is the net tension on the windward side of the stack. Usually the lower part of a stack is lined with firebrick, but since it is free from structural brickwork, firebrick may not be counted upon to resist stresses.

Large industrial and power-house stacks present specialized problems and should be designed and built by recognized chimney-construction companies. However, since there is a tendency to smaller-area higher stacks, particularly on schools and hospitals—stacks which will be neither designed nor built by chimney specialists—it is well to recognize the structural limitations of such stacks. Frequently the chimney design is left entirely to the heating engineer, and it is not referred to the structural engineer at all. As a result, although the stack does not blow over, it may become the object of excessive maintenance costs.

b As a code to govern the design of brick stacks, the requirements of the U.S. Corps of Engineers may be used:

Brick stacks shall be designed for a wind load of 30 psf multiplied by the shape factor listed below:

    Square or rectangular   1.00
    Hexagonal or octagonal   .80
    Round or elliptical   .60

The maximum unit tensile strength in pounds per square inch shall be 10 for ordinary brickwork and 35 for radial brick construction. The maximum unit compression shall be as set forth for ordinary brickwork, and 350 for radial brick construction.

c The maximum resultant compression on the leeward edge is

$$f_c = \frac{W}{A} + \frac{M}{S}$$

and the maximum allowable stress is the compression stress of the material. For normal brickwork, this should not be over 250 psi.

The maximum resultant tension on the windward side should be

$$f_t = \frac{M}{S} - \frac{W}{A}$$

The 30-psf wind pressure required by the U.S. Corps of Engineers should definitely be used in any area subject to high winds or in any tornado section. There are many areas, however, where a 20-psf wind pressure is sufficient.

Attached chimneys or chimneys within buildings need not be investigated below their point of attachment or the roof at which they are supported.

The worst condition for a square stack results from a wind blowing against a corner of the stack, on an area based on the diagonal dimension, but using a shape factor of 0.6. The section modulus of a brick stack of this shape is

$$S = 0.1178 \frac{D^4 - D_1{}^4}{D}$$

where D is the side of the square, in feet.

For an octagonal stack the section modulus is

$$S = 0.1095 \frac{D^4 - D_1{}^4}{D}$$

where D is the depth between any two parallel sides, that is, the short diameter.

For a round stack the section modulus is

$$S = 0.098175 \frac{D^4 - D_1{}^4}{D}$$

where D is the outside diameter of the circle.

Using the above formulae, with a 10-psi maximum tensile stress (1,440 psf), the maximum allowable height for a plain brick stack without reinforcement may be obtained by solving the following quadratic for height x (using foot units throughout).

$$\frac{M}{S} x^2 - 120x = 1,440$$

A close approximation of the maximum safe height, using 30-psf wind load, may be arrived at from the empirical formulae in Table 10.7. The section modulus of various square, octagonal, and round stack sections of smaller stacks is given in foot units in Table 10.8.

d The foundation for a free-standing stack must provide for eccentricity in any direction. Applying the load under the chimney walls, compute the eccentricity e by combining wind and dead loads. Compute the total load on

Table 10.7   Approximate Maximum Height of Brick Stacks

Wall thickness, in.	Square stacks	Octagonal stacks	Round stacks
8	$6.132D - 2.528$	$6.1D - 2.64$	$7.07D - 3.38$
12	$8D - 7.1$	$8.12D - 7.79$	$8.87D - 7.6$
16	$9.84D - 13.33$	$9.9D - 14.06$	$12.2D - 20.6$

Table 10.8   Section Modulus of Brick Stacks

Foot units

D	Square stacks			Octagonal stacks			Round stacks		
	8-in. wall	12-in. wall	16-in. wall	8-in. wall	12-in. wall	16-in. wall	8-in. wall	12-in. wall	16-in. wall
'0''	.93			.865			.775		
'4''	1.45			1.35			1.20		
'8''	2.09	2.22		1.94	2.06		1.74	1.85	
'0''	2.88	3.14		2.68	2.92		2.4	2.62	
'4''	3.8	4.25	4.36	3.53	3.95	4.05	3.16	3.53	3.62
'8''	4.86	5.56	5.77	4.51	5.16	5.37	4.04	4.62	4.8
'0''	6.05	7.07	7.45	5.62	6.57	6.92	5.03	5.88	6.2
'4''	7.4	8.8	9.39	6.86	8.16	8.72	6.15	7.3	7.8
'8''	8.85	10.7	11.6	8.21	9.9	10.8	7.35	8.86	9.63
'0''	10.5	12.8	14.1	9.56	11.9	13.0	8.72	10.6	11.7
'4''		15.2	16.8		14.1	15.6		12.6	13.9
'8''		17.7	20.0		16.4	18.6		14.7	16.6
'0''			23.0			21.4			19.2

the footing, and assume a footing at least 12 in. greater in each direction than the stack size. Check the footing for soil pressure, using the eccentricity computed above, and the formula for eccentric pressures,

$$f = \frac{P}{A}\left(1 \pm \frac{6e}{b}\right)$$

Problem   Check a square stack, 50 ft total height, attached up to 20 ft height. Use a 20-in. square inside stack with 1-ft walls (3 ft 8 in. square outside) and a 20-psf wind pressure.

The critical point in the masonry is at the top of the attachment, with a height of 30 ft above this point.

The load applied on the diagonal of the stack is

$$P = 20 \text{ lb} \times 3.67\sqrt{2} \times 30 = 3{,}111 \text{ lb}$$
$$M = 3{,}111 \times 15 = 46{,}665$$
$$\frac{M}{S} = \frac{46{,}665}{5.56} = 8{,}400 \text{ psf}$$
$$W = 120 \times 30 = 3{,}600$$

The net tension $= (8{,}400 - 3{,}600)/144 = 33.3$ psi, which is excessive.

The designer has two alternatives—to increase the thickness of wall or to put in steel rods. The amount of steel to be used as corner reinforcement may be determined partially by graphic means, as shown in Fig. 10.39. Computing:

Maximum tension	$= \dfrac{46{,}665}{5.56 \times 144} = 58.3$ psi
Reduction for direct compression	$= \dfrac{3{,}600}{144} \qquad = \underline{25.0}$
Net tension	$= 33.3$
Allowable net tension	$= \underline{10.0}$
Excessive net tension	$= \overline{23.3}$ psi

Length of excess tension triangle

$$\left(\frac{23.3}{58.3}\right) \times 31.1 = 12.4 \text{ in.}$$

$$\text{Total excess tension } 12.4 \times \frac{24.8}{2} \times \frac{23.3}{3} = 1{,}194 \text{ lb}$$

$$A_s = \frac{1{,}194}{20{,}000} = .06 \text{ sq in.}$$

Use one No. 3 bar at each corner ($A = .11$).

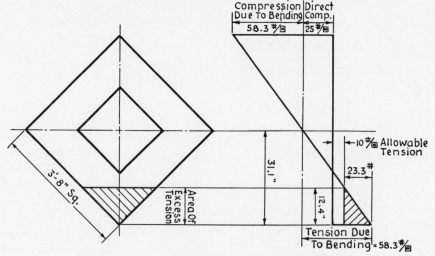

Fig. 10.39 Graphical Indication of Stresses in Stack

Spot checks will show that the stack does not need reinforcement within 20 ft of the top. The stresses due to wind moment theoretically do not increase below the roof line, but the compression forces increase at the rate of 120/144 or .83 psi per foot of height. The tension reinforcement is therefore required down to the foundation. The maximum compression at the footing level will be

$$58.3 + (50 \times 120)/144 = 100.0 \text{ psi}$$

which is well within the allowable compression value of the brick.

If this design is checked against a plain brick stack using 16-in. walls, it will become 4 ft 4 in. square and the moment at the point of attachment will be

$$M = 20 \times 4.33\sqrt{2} \times 30 \times 15 = 55,150$$
$$\frac{M}{S} = \frac{55,150}{9.39} = \quad 5,880$$
$$- \underline{3,600}$$
$$\frac{2,280}{144} = 15.7 \text{ psi}$$

This is still excessive, so the economical design would call for corner reinforcement of the smaller stack.

The total weight on the footing is

$$1,600 \times 50 = 80,000 \text{ lb}$$

Because the stack is attached, eccentricity on the footing due to wind can be disregarded.

Using a 12-in. overhang on all sides of the stack, the footing will be

$$3'8'' + 1'0'' + 1'0'' = 5'8'' \text{ square}$$

The soil pressure is

$$\frac{80,000}{5.67 \times 5.67} = 2,490 \text{ psf}$$

Allowing 12-in. footing thickness $= \dfrac{150}{2,640 \text{ psf}}$

The footing should have a minimum thickness of 12 in., and no reinforcement is required for bending stresses. However, because of temperature differentials, it is advisable to use a layer of bars in the bottom and a layer in the top of the slab, each layer of $\frac{3}{8}$-in. round, 12 in. o.c. in both directions.

10.40 MILL BUILDINGS

a Factory buildings, or as they are commonly termed, mill buildings, are treated separately because the attention of the designer should be called to a large number of design items scattered throughout this text which are particularly applicable to the design of this type of one-story building. Figures 10.40 and 10.41 indicate two of the common cross sections of mill buildings, but there are endless variations depending on such factors as use and location.

b The type of mill building illustrated by Fig. 10.40 is about the cheapest type of wide-

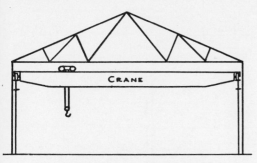

Fig. 10.40 Simple Mill Building

span structure, and is particularly applicable to the use of corrugated steel, aluminum, or asbestos-cement roofing and siding. If corrugated roofing of any kind is used, the minimum pitch of the roof should be $\frac{1}{5}$, or 1 on $2\frac{1}{2}$, if the sheets are cemented, and $\frac{1}{4}$, or 1 on 2, if the sheets are lapped and riveted, bolted, or nailed. This will determine the slope of the truss, and may even determine whether or not trusses should be used. If tar and gravel roofing on wood, concrete, or gypsum is used, the roof may be kept practically flat, and rolled beams will be cheaper up to spans of about 60 ft.

Trusses are used on spans of from 40 to 120 ft, and since they are heavily fabricated, it is preferable to space them from 20 to 25 ft apart, and thus to increase plain rolled steel in the purlins and save fabrication in the trusses.

A number of the articles in this text that have special application to mill buildings of the type shown in Fig. 10.40 are,

Art. 3.21*g*, Method of moment distribution (the indirect Hardy Cross method)

Art. 4.14, Unsymmetrical bending in purlins

Art. 4.23, Crane-runway girders

Art. 4.31, Corrugated siding and roofing

Art. 7.10*e*, Steel columns

Art. 10.10, Trusses

Art. 10.21, Wind bracing—low steel buildings

Art. 10.41, Girts

c The building shown in Fig. 10.41 is indicative of a better class of factory buildings, required where good working conditions are desirable—that is, where heat loss from the building is to be avoided. The flat roof shown requires the use of a roof covering over the main roofing material of concrete, wood, or gypsum. This type of building is usually used with masonry side walls to correspond in heat loss and other characteristics with the roof. Since the roof is flat, or relatively flat, it is not necessary to use trusses. This particular section shows the center bay as a monitor bay for the distribution of light more uniformly over the floor area.

d In addition to proper design of all the component parts of a mill building as discussed in other articles of this text, special care should be given to the bracing of mill buildings. The extent of the bracing is dependent on the type of construction and the use of the building. Obviously a building with corrugated siding and roofing, or even wood or precast-concrete roofing, must be braced much more rigidly than one with masonry side walls and poured-concrete roof. Unless the columns are unusually high without support, bracing may usually be omitted in the latter type.

In Fig. 10.42 a system of bracing is indicated for a seven-bay building of the type shown in Fig. 10.40. The end bays should be braced, and at least every third bay inside. Thus the bracing will work out as follows:

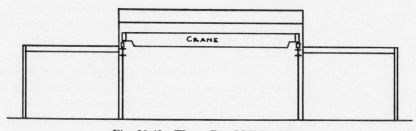

Fig. 10.41 Three-Bay Mill Building

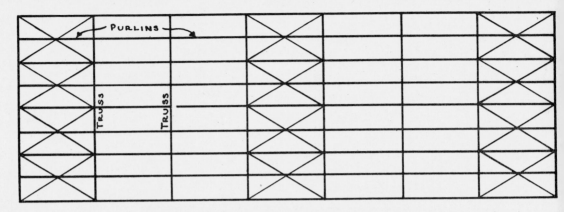

ROOF BRACING PLAN

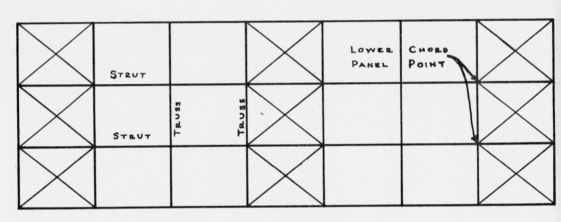

LOWER CHORD BRACING PLAN

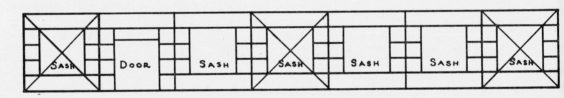

SIDEWALL BRACING

Fig. 10.42 Bracing of a Steel Mill Building

For three- and four-bay buildings, brace end bays only.

For five and seven bays, brace end bays and center bay.

For six bays, brace bays 1, 3, and 6.

For eight bays, brace bays 1, 3, 6, and 8.

For nine bays, brace bays 1, 4, 6, and 9.

For ten bays, brace bays 1, 4, 7, and 10.

In the roof framing or upper-chord system, the purlins act as struts. Formerly much of the cross bracing was rod bracing, usually $\frac{7}{8}$-in. rods, but nowadays there is a tendency

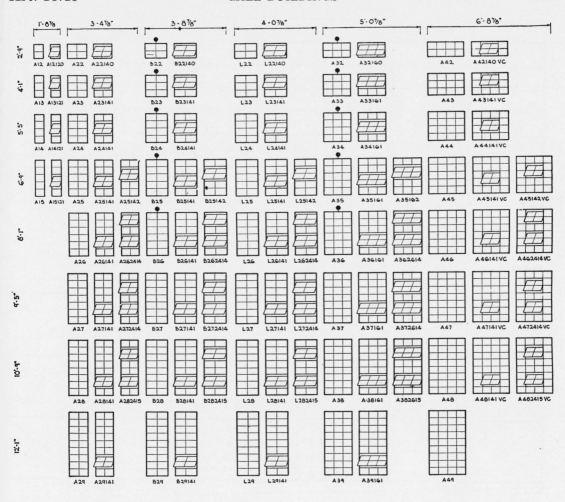

Fig. 10.43   Standard Commercial Type Steel Sash

toward light angles. The AISC Code specifies that for bracing members in tension, the least l/r ratio shall be 300.

The lower-chord bracing is made up similarly of angle cross bracing in tension and a continuous line of struts. These struts are required by the AISC specification to have a least l/r ratio of 200. A very satisfactory strut section is made up of two channels, one flatwise with the flanges turned downwards, on top of a channel with the web vertical. For this type of strut, a 6 channel 8.2 vertically with a 5 channel 6.7 horizontally is good to a span of 22 ft 10 in. Beyond this, to 26 ft,

Table 10.9 Combination of Standard Sash Units

WIDTH OF OPENING				TYPES AND ARRANGEMENT OF WINDOWS	NO. LIGHTS WIDE	NO. WINDOWS	NO. MULLIONS
COLUMN "A"		COLUMN "B"					
FROM	TO	FROM	TO				
		3'-7 7/8"	3'-8 7/8"	1-1	2	2	1
		5'-6 7/8"	5'-8 7/8"	1-1-1	3	3	2
8'-3 3/8"	8'-4 7/8"	6'-11 7/8"	7'-0 7/8"	2-2	4	2	1
7'-10 7/8"	8'-0 7/8"	7'-2 7/8"	7'-4 7/8"	1-2-1	4	3	2
10'-2 7/8"	10'-4 7/8"	8'-10 7/8"	9'-0 7/8"	2-1-2	5	3	2
		10'-3 7/8"	10'-4 7/8"	3-3	6	2	1
12'-6 7/8"	12'-8 7/8"	10'-6 7/8"	10'-8 7/8"	2-2-2	6	3	2
13'-6 7/8"	13'-8 7/8"	12'-2 7/8"	12'-4 7/8"	2-3-2	7	3	2
		13'-7 7/8"	13'-8 7/8"	4-4	8	2	1
15'-2 7/8"	15'-4 7/8"	13'-10 7/8"	14'-0 7/8"	2-4-2	8	3	2
16'-9 7/8"	17'-0 7/8"	14'-1 7/8"	14'-4 7/8"	2-2-2-2	8	4	3
		15'-6 7/8"	15'-8 7/8"	3-3-3	9	3	2
		17'-2 7/8"	17'-4 7/8"	3-4-3	10	3	2
18'-9 7/8"	19'-0 7/8"	17'-5 7/8"	17'-8 7/8"	2-3-3-2	10	4	3
21'-0 7/8"	21'-4 7/8"	17'-8 7/8"	18'-0 7/8"	2-2-2-2-2	10	5	4
		18'-10 7/8"	19'-0 7/8"	4-3-4	11	3	2
22'-0 7/8"	22'-4 7/8"	19'-4 7/8"	19'-8 7/8"	2-2-3-2-2	11	5	4
		20'-6 7/8"	20'-8 7/8"	4-4-4	12	3	2
		20'-9 7/8"	21'-0 7/8"	3-3-3-3	12	4	3
23'-0 7/8"	23'-4 7/8"	21'-0 7/8"	21'-4 7/8"	2-3-2-3-2	12	5	4
24'-0 7/8"	24'-4 7/8"	22'-8 7/8"	23'-0 7/8"	2-3-3-3-2	13	5	4
		24'-1 7/8"	24'-4 7/8"	3-4-4-3	14	4	3
25'-0 7/8"	25'-4 7/8"	24'-4 7/8"	24'-8 7/8"	3-3-2-3-3	14	5	4
27'-3 7/8"	27'-8 7/8"	24'-7 7/8"	25'-0 7/8"	2-2-3-3-2-2	14	6	5
29'-6 7/8"	30'-0 7/8"	24'-10 7/8"	25'-4 7/8"	2-2-2-2-2-2-2	14	7	6
		26'-0 7/8"	26'-4 7/8"	3-3-3-3-3	15	5	4
30'-6 7/8"	31'-0 7/8"	26'-6 7/8"	27'-0 7/8"	2-2-2-3-2-2-2	15	7	6
		27'-5 7/8"	27'-8 7/8"	4-4-4-4	16	4	3
29'-0 7/8"	29'-4 7/8"	27'-8 7/8"	28'-0 7/8"	2-4-4-4-2	16	5	4
29'-8 7/8"	29'-8 7/8"	27'-11 7/8"	28'-4 7/8"	2-3-3-3-3-2	16	6	5
31'-6 7/8"	32'-0 7/8"	28'-2 7/8"	28'-8 7/8"	3-2-2-2-2-2-3	16	7	6
		29'-4 7/8"	29'-8 7/8"	4-3-3-3-4	17	5	4
		31'-0 7/8"	31'-4 7/8"	3-4-4-4-3	18	5	4
		31'-3 7/8"	31'-8 7/8"	3-3-3-3-3-3	18	6	5
33'-6 7/8"	34'-0 7/8"	31'-6 7/8"	32'-0 7/8"	3-3-2-2-2-3-3	18	7	6
		32'-8 7/8"	33'-0 7/8"	4-4-3-4-4	19	5	4
		34'-4 7/8"	34'-8 7/8"	4-4-4-4-4	20	5	4
		34'-7 7/8"	35'-0 7/8"	4-3-3-3-3-4	20	6	5
		37'-11 7/8"	38'-4 7/8"	3-4-4-4-4-3	22	6	5
		41'-3 7/8"	41'-8 7/8"	4-4-4-4-4-4	24	6	5
		41'-6 7/8"	42'-0 7/8"	3-3-4-4-4-3-3	24	7	6
		44'-10 7/8"	45'-4 7/8"	3-4-4-4-4-4-3	26	7	6
		48'-2 7/8"	48'-8 7/8"	4-4-4-4-4-4-4	28	7	6
		55'-1 7/8"	55'-8 7/8"	4-4-4-4-4-4-4-4	32	8	7
		58'-8 7/8"	59'-4 7/8"	3-4-4-4-4-4-4-4-3	34	9	8
		62'-0 7/8"	62'-8 7/8"	4-4-4-4-4-4-4-4-4	36	9	8

ADJUSTABLE VERTICAL MULLION

OPENING DIMENSION 2⅛" MINIMUM

OPENING DIMENSION 3⅛" MAXIMUM

HORIZONTAL MULLION

FLASHING BY OTHER

1½ X 1½ X ³⁄₁₆

3X3X¼ TO 5X5X³⁄₁₆ AS REQUIRED

TYPICAL BAYS

1'-8 7/8" 6'-8 7/8" 4'-0 7/8" 6'-8 7/8" 1'-8 7/8" — 20'-0"

5'-0 7/8" 6'-8 7/8" 6'-8 7/8" 6'-8 7/8" — 20'-0"

6'-8 7/8" 6'-8 7/8" 6'-8 7/8" — 21'-0"

DIMENSIONS SHOWN IN COLUMN "A" ARE BASED ON A 24" NOMINAL GLASS WIDTH IN THE TWO LIGHT WIDE WINDOWS AND A 20" NOMINAL GLASS WIDTH IN ALL OTHER WINDOWS.

DIMENSIONS SHOWN IN COLUMN "B" ARE BASED ON A 20" NOMINAL GLASS WIDTH IN ALL WINDOWS.

IN MULTIPLE OPENINGS FOR ARCHITECTURAL AND INTERMEDIATE WINDOWS ADD 3⅛" FOR EACH PLATE MULLION.

we use an 8 channel 11.5 vertically with a 6 channel 8.2 horizontally, and up to 30 ft a 9 channel 13.4 vertically with a 7 channel 9.8 horizontally.

The side-wall bracing uses the girts for strut members, and the cross bracing of angles as already noted. The designer should remember that it is not possible to operate pivoted sash in the areas covered by side-wall cross bracing. If the cross bracing is placed tight against the inside edge of the girts and connected to them, the length to use in computing the l/r ratio may be greatly reduced and smaller members may be used.

Table 10.10   Combination of Standard Sash Units

SYMMETRICAL COMBINATIONS
OPENINGS FOR WINDOWS COMBINED HORIZONTALLY

WIDTH OF OPENING		COMPOSITION OF OPENING			
2⅛″ MULL'S	3⅛″ MULL'S	UNIT WIDTHS IN OPENING (ARRANGE SYMMETRICALLY)	UNITS WIDE	LIGHTS WIDE	NO. OF MULL'S
6′–11⅞″	7′–0⅞″	2 @ 3′–4⅞″	2	4	1
7′–7⅞″	7′–8⅞″	2 @ 3′–8⅞″	2	4	1
8′–3⅞″	8′–4⅞″	2 @ 4′–0⅞″	2	4	1
8′–10⅞″	9′–0⅞″	2 @ 1′–8⅞″ 1 @ 5′–0⅞″	3	5	2
10′–3⅞″	10′–4⅞″	2 @ 5′–0⅞″	2	6	1
10′–6⅞″	10′–8⅞″	3 @ 3′–4⅞″	3	6	2
11′–6⅞″	11′–8⅞″	3 @ 3′–8⅞″	3	6	2
12′–2⅞″	12′–4⅞″	2 @ 3′–4⅞″ 1 @ 5′–0⅞″	3	7	2
12′–6⅞″	12′–8⅞″	3 @ 4′–0⅞″	3	6	2
12′–10⅞″	13′–0⅞″	2 @ 3′–8⅞″ 1 @ 5′–0⅞″	3	7	2
13′–7⅞″	13′–8⅞″	2 @ 6′–8⅞″	2	8	1
13′–10⅞″	14′–0⅞″	2 @ 3′–4⅞″ 1 @ 6′–8⅞″	3	8	2
14′–1⅞″	14′–4⅞″	4 @ 3′–4⅞″	4	8	3
14′–6⅞″	14′–8⅞″	2 @ 3′–8⅞″ 1 @ 6′–8⅞″	3	8	2
15′–5⅞″	15′–8⅞″	4 @ 3′–8⅞″	4	8	3
15′–6⅞″	15′–8⅞″	3 @ 5′–0⅞″	3	9	2
16′–9⅞″	17′–0⅞″	4 @ 4′–0⅞″	4	8	3
17′–5⅞″	17′–8⅞″	2 @ 3′–4⅞″ 2 @ 5′–0⅞″	4	10	3
17′–8⅞″	18′–0⅞″	5 @ 3′–4⅞″	5	10	4
18′–9⅞″	19′–0⅞″	2 @ 4′–0⅞″ 2 @ 5′–0⅞″	4	10	3
19′–4⅞″	19′–8⅞″	5 @ 3′–8⅞″	5	10	4
20′–6⅞″	20′–8⅞″	3 @ 6′–8⅞″	3	12	2
20′–9⅞″	21′–0⅞″	4 @ 5′–0⅞″	4	12	3
21′–0⅞″	21′–4⅞″	5 @ 4′–0⅞″	5	10	4
21′–5⅞″	21′–8⅞″	2 @ 3′–8⅞″ 2 @ 6′–8⅞″	4	12	3
22′–0⅞″	22′–4⅞″	3 @ 3′–8⅞″ 2 @ 5′–0⅞″	5	12	4
22′–8⅞″	23′–0⅞″	2 @ 3′–4⅞″ 3 @ 5′–0⅞″	5	13	4
23′–3⅞″	23′–8⅞″	6 @ 3′–8⅞″	6	12	5
23′–4⅞″	23′–8⅞″	2 @ 3′–8⅞″ 3 @ 5′–0⅞″	5	13	4
24′–0⅞″	24′–4⅞″	2 @ 4′–0⅞″ 3 @ 5′–0⅞″	5	13	4
24′–4⅞″	24′–8⅞″	1 @ 3′–4⅞″ 4 @ 5′–0⅞″	5	14	4

OVERALL WIDTHS OF OPENINGS MAY VARY AS DESIRED BETWEEN DIMENSIONS SHOWN IN TABLE ABOVE, BY VARYING MULLION SPACINGS. SEE TYPICAL COMBINATION BELOW . WHEN MULLION COVERS ARE USED, MULLION SPACINGS MUST BE EITHER 2⅛″ OR 3⅛″.

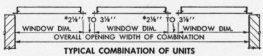

*2⅛″ TO 3⅛″   *2⅛″ TO 3⅛″
WINDOW DIM.   WINDOW DIM.   WINDOW DIM.
OVERALL OPENING WIDTH OF COMBINATION

TYPICAL COMBINATION OF UNITS
*NOTE: FOR MULLION DETAILS AND VARIATIONS SEE PLATE IND-112

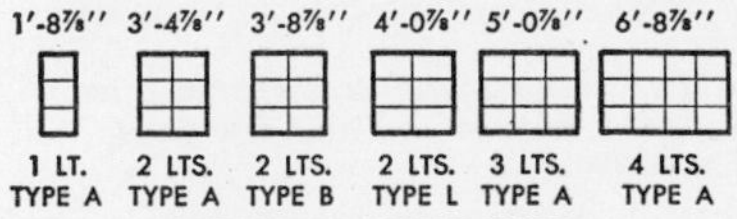

1′–8⅞″   3′–4⅞″   3′–8⅞″   4′–0⅞″   5′–0⅞″   6′–8⅞″

LTS.	DIM.	LTS.	DIM.
2	2′-9″	6	8′-1″
3	4′-1″	7	9′-5″
4	5′-5″	8	10′-9″
5	6′-9″	9	12′-1″

1 LT. TYPE A   2 LTS. TYPE A   2 LTS. TYPE B   2 LTS. TYPE L   3 LTS. TYPE A   4 LTS. TYPE A

WIDTHS OF SINGLE UNITS   **UNIT HEIGHTS**

NOTE: UNIT WIDTHS AND HEIGHTS SHOWN ARE WINDOW AND OPENING DIMS.

WINDOWS IN CONTINUOUS RUNS
SOME LAYOUTS FOR TYPICAL COLUMN SPACINGS

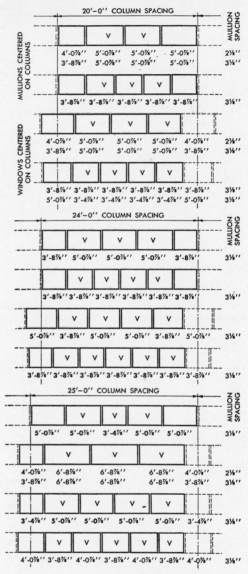

V —INDICATES UNITS WHICH MAY BE VENTED OR FIXED AS DESIRED. COMBINATIONS PRINTED IN HEAVY TYPE ARE LISTED ALSO IN TABLE FOR SYMMETRICAL COMBINATION OPENINGS.

e Commercial-type steel sash is practically standard in mill-building construction. Sash has been standardized in size by all sash companies, and the standard sizes are given in Fig. 10.43. The standard designation for steel sash is as follows: the letter A or L in-dicates the size glass as shown in Fig. 10.43. The first two figures indicate the number of lights in width and height respectively; the third figure is the number of ventilating units, the fourth figure is the number of lights in the ventilator or in each ventilator; the fifth

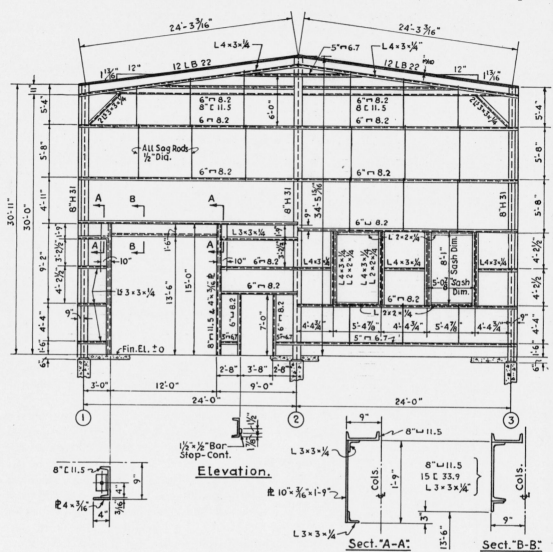

Fig. 10.44 Typical End Elevation—Mill Building, Framing

figure is the number of fixed rows below the ventilator; and if there are two ventilators, the sixth figure indicates the number of rows below the upper ventilator.

Steel sash is frequently used for continuous siding in a mill-type building. Tables 10.9 and 10.10 show the various combinations of standard units by means of which this can be accomplished.

10.41 Girts

Girts are defined in Art. 1.11 as secondary horizontal members in a side wall, designed to resist wind pressure. They are ordinarily

used with corrugated-steel siding and steel sash, although not necessarily. Other types of siding such as wood sheathing or asbestos-cement may be used instead of steel. (See Arts. 10.40 and 4.31 for further information on girt framing.)

Girts are ordinarily designed as angles or channels, depending on the span used. Since the main load to be carried is wind, normal to the face of the building, the main axis of the member is flatwise. To prevent deflection due to the weight of the girt and the siding, sag rods are used to carry the vertical weight back into the eave purlin, which is either vertical or at an acute angle with the vertical. The practical consideration of avoidance of dust pockets requires that as far as possible, channels be placed with the flanges downward. An end wall using girt framing is shown in Fig. 10.45. Details for framing around openings are shown in Fig. 10.46.

Problem Design a girt for the 24-ft span shown in Fig. 10.44. Assume that the building code requires us to design for a 20-psf wind load.

$$W = 24 \times 5.67 \times 20 = 2.72 \text{ kips}$$
$$S = \frac{2.72 \times 24}{13.33 \times 1.33} = 3.67$$

Use 6 channel 8.2.

To prevent sag of the girts due to their flatwise position, hang them by means of rods at the third points from the eave beam.

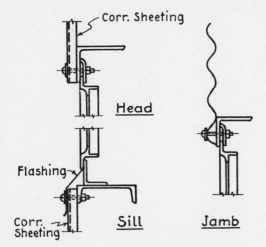

Fig. 10.45 **Details Around Openings in Buildings with Corrugated Siding**

10.50 POLES AND POSTS

a Poles and posts are frequently subjected to stresses in such a manner that it is necessary to compute (1) the size of the pole, or (2) the method of anchorage in the ground. Figure 10.46 indicates the application of loads to such a post, and the resultant passive soil pressures.

The applied loads may be from a hanging sign or pipe indicated by P, wind on the hanging member or on a flag indicated by H_1, wind

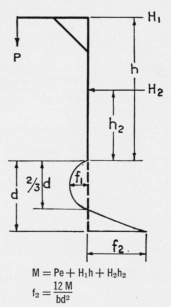

$$M = Pe + H_1h + H_2h_2$$
$$f_2 = \frac{12\,M}{bd^2}$$

Fig. 10.46 **Loads and Stresses on a Post**

on the pole itself, indicated by H_2, or a direct pull from a wire at H_1. The determination of these loads is probably more difficult than the solution of the structure itself.

b The loads to be used in computing the stresses to apply to such poles may be derived from the following. The weight of a sign may be given, but it is well to add 50 percent to this weight for wind gusts or for weight of sleet. Pipe lines and power lines should have added to their known weight an allowance for a coating of ice 1 in. thick. For the suspension of trolley wires, the amount of sag must be known to compute the tension H_1 at the top of the pole. The horizontal tension is

$$H_1 = \frac{wL^2}{8\Delta}$$

where w is the unit weight per linear foot including the weight of ice. A safe total load for a wire of this kind is 1.5 lb per linear foot.

The direct pull on a pole from a power line under equal tension on both sides of the pole

Fig. 10.47 **Foundation for Post or Pole**

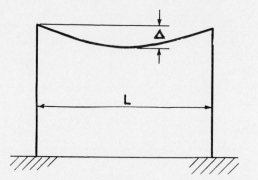

Fig. 10.48   Load on Cable Suspended from Poles

is zero as long as the line is intact. However, provision must be made for the stress created when the line on one side of the pole is broken.

In the design of flagpoles several U.S. government sources provide the best criteria for computing the pressure. The U.S. Navy standard formula for pressure H_1 applied at the top of the flag is

$$H_1 = 0.0003A V^{1.9}$$

where A is the area of the flag in square feet and V is wind velocity in miles per hour. For a 60-mile maximum,

$$V^{1.9} = 2,390$$

For U.S. Post Office buildings, the standard requirements for flag sizes and the resulting pressure computed by the Navy formula are, for a one-story building,

$A = 3.52$ ft $\times$ 6.69 ft $= 23.5$. $H_1 = 17$ lb

For two or more stories or for free-standing poles,

$A = 5.19$ ft $\times$ 9.77 ft $= 50.2$, $H_1 = 36$ lb

For exceptional buildings,

$A = 8.94$ ft $\times$ 16.99 ft $= 151.9$, $H_1 = 109$ lb

c The computation of the structure above grade is a simple matter of computation of moments as given by the moment formula in Fig. 10.46 and the resultant section modulus. Because the cantilever moment is reduced from the ground up, such poles, which are usually of pipe section, may be reduced by welding a smaller section into the lower section. The point of bending to be used in de-

termining the diameter of the maximum pipe and the passive pressure should be taken at a point about one-third of the depth d below grade.

d The maximum allowable soil pressure f_2 is the passive pressure discussed in Art. 8.30 as a resisting pressure to movement of sheet piling or retaining walls:

$$f_p = w_e \tan^2 (45 \deg + \tfrac{1}{2}\phi)$$

where w_e is the weight per cubic foot of the material at the bottom and ϕ the angle of repose of the material. This passive pressure is given for various types of soil in Table 8.6. For normal conditions, a value of 400 psf may be used.

Problem 1   Design an outdoor steel flagpole 60 ft high to carry a flag of 50 sq ft area. The flagpole is spliced 20 ft above grade and 40 ft above grade. Allow for a wind pressure of 10 psf on the diameter of the pole.

From Art. 10.50b, the pressure on the flag is 36 lb. At the first splice point the moment is $36 \times 20 = 720$. Assume 3-in.-diameter pole.

$$20 \times \tfrac{1}{4} \times 10 = 50 \times 10 = 500$$

$$720 + 500 = 1,220 \text{ ft-lb} = 14,640 \text{ in.-lb}$$

Since all moment is due to wind, all unit stresses may be increased $\tfrac{1}{3}$, or

$$\text{Required } S = \frac{14,640}{26,667} = 0.55$$

From Table 1.4 for 2-in. pipe,

$$S = \frac{0.666}{1.19} = 0.56$$

$$(\text{O.D.} = 2.375 \text{ in.})$$

At the next splice point, the moment is

$$36 \times 40 = 1,440$$

On upper 2-in. pipe,

$$20 \times \frac{2.375}{12} \times 10 = 39.4 \times 30 = 1,182$$

On assumed 4-in. pipe,

$$20 \times \frac{4.5}{12} \times 10 = 75 \times 10 \quad = \underline{\quad 750\quad}$$
$$3,372 \text{ ft-lb} = 40,450 \text{ in.-lb}$$
$$\text{Required } S = \frac{40,450}{26,667} = 1.515$$

For 3-in. pipe,

$$S = \frac{3.017}{1.75} = 1.72$$
$$(\text{O.D.} = 3.5 \text{ in.})$$

Assume the depth in ground at 8 ft. Then the point of maximum moment = 2 ft 8 in. below grade.

The moment on the flag is
$$36 \times 62.67 = 2,260$$

On the upper 2-in. pipe,
$$39.4 \times 52.67 = 2,075$$

On the middle section,
$$20 \times \frac{3.5}{12} \times 10 = 58 \times 32.67 = 1,900$$

And on the lower section, try 4-in. pipe.

$$20 \times \frac{4.5}{12} \times 10 = 75 \times 12.67 = \underline{\quad 950\quad}$$
$$7,185 \text{ ft-lb} = 86,400 \text{ in.-lb}$$
$$\text{Required } S = \frac{86,400}{26,667} = 3.23$$

For a 4-in. pipe,

$$S = \frac{7.233}{2.25} = 3.21$$

which is close enough.

Since stresses may be increased by $\frac{1}{3}$ for wind stresses, the allowable passive soil pressure is $1\frac{1}{3} \times 400 = 533$ psf and the formula for passive soil pressure in Fig. 10.46 becomes

$$533 = \frac{12 \times 7,185}{b \times 64}$$
$$b = \frac{12 \times 7,185}{533 \times 64} = 2.53$$

Therefore the pipe should be bedded in a concrete foundation 8 ft deep and 2 ft 7 in. square.

Problem 2 A flagpole is carried from the front of a building (Fig. 10.49). The supports *BD* and *BE* are not ordinarily designed to take any compression, so they may be rods. On the other hand, the pole from *B* to *C* carries compression, so *l/r* must be considered in design of this pole. Points *B*, *D*, and *E*

should be definitely supported into the steel structure of the building, and if they occur between stories, as they ordinarily do, vertical beams should be framed from spandrel to spandrel to carry the pull or thrust.

Assume a 50-sq ft flag, $P = 36$ lb. The can-

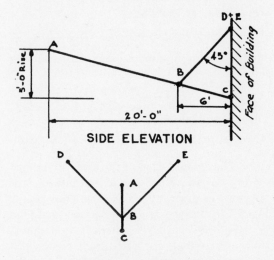

SIDE ELEVATION

FRONT ELEVATION

Fig. 10.49 Flagpole on Face of Building

tilever moment about B, assuming a 2-in. pipe pole is

$$36 \times 14 = 504$$
$$3.65 \times 14 \times 7 = \underline{358}$$
$$862 \text{ ft-lb} = 10,350 \text{ in.-lb}$$

Using a fiber stress of 26,667 psi

$$\text{Required } S = \frac{10,350}{26,667} = 0.388$$

For 2-in. pipe,

$$S = \frac{0.666}{1.19} = 0.56$$

For thrust on a 6-ft length, for $l/r \leqq 120$,

$$r = \frac{6 \times 12}{120} = 0.6$$

From Table 1.4 r of 2-in. pipe = 0.79
Since the wind load is horizontal and the

dead load vertical, the resultant pressure will approximate the angle of the diagonal tie closely enough to disregard the variation. The load at B parallel to the front wall is

$$36 \times 20 = 720$$
$$3.65 \times 20 \times 10 = \underline{730}$$

$$\frac{1,450}{6} = 242 \text{ lb}$$

On the line of BD or BE the stress is therefore

$$\sqrt{2} \times 242 = 342$$

The area at root of thread is

$$\frac{342}{26,667} = 0.0128 \text{ sq in.}$$

Therefore, minimum size rod, which is $\frac{5}{8}$-in. round, will be permissible.

Office Practice

11.10 STRUCTURAL CHECK LISTS

a No check list, however complete, can take the place of experience in the design and preparation of structural plans or in the checking of shop detail drawings. On the other hand, even for a thoroughly experienced designer or structural draftsman, the use of a check list frequently prevents the omission of details desirable for the benefit of bidders and calls attention to items which might otherwise be overlooked in the rush to complete the job.

No check list can be complete enough to cover every type of job. Each office must prepare its own check list as the result of experience. Included here are the various check lists used in the author's office, not in the single words on the check list, but expanded into the actual question to be answered.

b *Design information* (see also Art. 11.50):

1. Name, location, and general use of building.

2. Under what building code will the design be made?

3. Does this code have any unusual requirements or are they standard AISC, ACI, etc., codes?

c *Structural plan check list—Foundations:*

1. Are footings limited by lot lines or other restrictions, so as to require special shapes, combined footings, or other special treatment?

2. Is underpinning of adjacent structure required?

3. Does any adjacent excavation require footings to be dropped?

4. Are there old excavations on the site which will require the footings to be lowered?

5. Are stepped wall footings between different levels required?

6. Check comparative level of adjacent column footings.

7. Are all exterior footings below frost line?

8. Are retaining walls required outside the building?

9. Are building walls reinforced against earth pressure?

10. Are wall piers of sufficient area to take grillages?

11. Are area walls required?

12. Are pipe sleeves to be provided in foundation walls?

13. Do downspouts on interior columns require footings to be dropped to allow for pipe bend over the footing?

14. Are there any boiler pits, elevator pits, sump pits, or other pits, and are footings to be dropped for these pits?

15. Has provision been made in the wall design to permit installation or change of boilers or other mechanical equipment?

16. Is waterproofing of walls or floors required?

17. Is there sufficient hydrostatic head to require special reinforcement of the basement floor?

18. Show column numbers.

19. Show column center dimensions, wall thickness, and other necessary dimensions.

OFFICE PRACTICE Chap. 11

20. Show elevation of bottom of all footings.
21. Show detail wall sections on the drawing.
22. Indicate scale of drawing.
23. Include general explanatory notes.
24. Show footing schedule of reinforced column footings.

d   Structural plan check list—Floor plans:
(Go through this list for each floor.)

1. Are all slab designations noted?
2. Are all beam sizes shown?
3. Are all lintels provided for, interior as well as exterior?
4. Are radiator recess lintels provided?
5. Show column numbers.
6. Dimension column centers and special beam offsets, etc.
7. Include a general note covering beam levels, and note on the plan any exceptions.
8. Are all masonry piers of sufficient capacity for all loads?
9. Check architectural and mechanical plans for any wall chases in critical locations.
10. If there is a mail chute, it must carry through from top to bottom without any offsets. Check for interference by any beams.
11. Check interference of beams with water closet roughing.
12. Depress beams and slabs for floor-type urinals.
13. Frame for all shafts and other openings.
14. Provide double beams where floor elevation changes.
15. Note scale on drawings.
16. Show detail of floor construction.
17. Are there any beams across windows in stair wells (mid-story windows)?
18. Do beams provide sufficient stair clearance?
19. Are there any stair cantilever details to show?
20. In gypsum floors, are tie rods and end-span bracing shown?
21. In bar-joist floors, are sufficient details of general construction shown?
22. Are there any story heights over 13 ft 6 in. at elevator shafts? (If so, intermediate supports may be needed for elevator guides. Check with the elevator company.)

e   Structural-plan check list—Roof plans:

1. Check all applicable notes from check list for floors.
2. Note high and low points and all sloped beams so as to inform steel bidders of type of detail.
3. Include general notes on levels of roof beams and slabs.
4. Locate and detail ducts, skylights, and scuttles.
5. Are there any flagpoles or roof signs to be supported by roof steel?
6. If there is an overhanging cornice, provide anchorage.
7. Indicate scale of drawings.
8. Are there any elevator or stair penthouses?
9. In an elevator penthouse, is there a secondary framing level?
10. Are elevator trolley beams required in penthouse?
11. Indicate elevation of various elevator penthouse levels.

f   Structural plan check list—Miscellaneous schedules:

1. On column schedule, show all story heights, splice points, and top and bottom of all columns with relation to some given floor line.
2. Is a detail required for future extension of any columns, or future connections to any columns?
3. Is lintel schedule shown?
4. Is concrete-slab schedule shown?
5. Is concrete-beam schedule shown?

11.20   SURVEY

a   The survey required for proper structural design covers much more than an ordinary survey made for a property transfer.

Obviously, a structural-design survey should show the exact dimensions and angles of the property, the street lines, and the north pointer. It should also show all the old buildings or remains of old buildings on the site, together with the grades of the cellars. It should locate and give the size of all trees, and locate any public-utility right of way or easement on the property. Moreover, it should include the location, height, and, if possible, depth below grade of any building on the adjacent property within several feet of the property being surveyed, with a word or two of description.

If the building is to have a full basement, grades on the entire site are not necessary except where they will enable the contractor to bid more intelligently. Of course, grades at the building walls and outside the building walls are needed. If the lowest floor is at or above grade, the site should be completely cross-sectioned, the spacing of the cross sections being dependent on whether the site is comparatively level or full of humps and hollows. The location of rubbish fills, sloughs, water courses, springs, filled-in wells or cisterns, and deep holes should be given whenever possible.

If the site is nearby, there are certain facts which may be obtained directly from the public works department, although the author's experience has been that a surveyor can do a better job of obtaining data on the location, level, and size of water mains and tees, stormwater and sanitary sewers, gas mains, width of streets, and the like. Perhaps the surveyor can also advise on regulations governing projection upon city property of such elements as steps, belt courses, cornices, and open areas.

b If the building site is adjacent to one or more old buildings, or if foundation conditions are such that there is even a remote possibility of damage to other structures or claims for damage as a result of construction operations, it may be advisable to make a complete condition survey of all adjacent buildings to uncover existing defects before new construction is begun. Most old buildings have defects of some sort and unless a careful and systematic inspection is made, the builder may be saddled with false damage claims.

The inspection report should be systematic and should cover:

1. The type and location of building, date and time of examination, owner, parties making the examination, and whom they represent.

2. Condition of exterior, including photographs of all available fronts.

3. Sketch plans of all floors with notations of all rooms as a means of identification.

4. Complete description of all rooms, starting at the roof and working down to the cellar. Take the rooms in regular order to avoid omissions.

5. Divide stair halls at floor lines as "1st floor stair hall and stair to second."

6. In each room describe floor first, then ceiling, north wall, east wall, south wall, and west wall.

7. Whenever possible, examine girders in the cellar and their bearings. Also examine all floor beams whenever possible, especially under bathrooms and kitchens. If any defect or settlement is noted, check for resultant effects in floors above.

8. Record all separations between floors and baseboards if they exist. Note floors and heads of doors and windows out of level. Note stairs out of level and stairs pulled out of the mortises in the wall string.

9. Note wainscots, chair rails, or picture moldings where they indicate any settlement. Note also separations between wood mantels and chimney breasts and hearths cracked or sunk below adjoining floors.

10. In describing cracks, record them under the wall which appears to have moved, as "East Wall, crack at intersection with south wall open $\frac{1}{8}$ in. from base to 1 ft below ceiling, thence diagonally across east wall to ceiling."

11. Always state width of crack and length, as "hairline crack 3 ft long" or "crack $\frac{1}{32}$ in. full width of room."

12. Describe condition of wallpaper if it shows wrinkles or is cut diagonally across the corner, indicating a crack beneath.

13. Record water stains on walls or ceilings.

14. Where no defects are found, record "nothing noted."

Inasmuch as such a report might become an important document in court, it is well to have some representative of the owner accompany the person making the examination, and it might even pay to have a neutral party make the survey.

11.30 SOIL TESTS

a In order to determine satisfactorily the bearing capacity of the soil on which the foundation is to rest, it is necessary to have some knowledge of the materials both at the level of bearing and for some distance below it. This information is frequently available from former excavations, tests, or other data. If it is not available, test pits must be dug, soil samples taken and evaluated, or a soil load-bearing test must be made. There are a few soil-mechanics laboratories throughout the country that are now available to assist the designer in scientifically evaluating his data, and eventually this practice will probably be much more general.

b The drilling or digging of good test holes depends on a number of factors. For example: Is your building to be two stories or fifteen stories? Is it to be built in the downtown section of a city, in a small town, or out in the open country? Are there any neighboring conditions which might occasion distrust of the subsoil? Is the building designed for light occupancy or heavy loads? All of these points and many others should influence the decision about the number of test holes required, the depth below your lowest footing level to which tests should be carried, and the type of borings that should be made.

In or near a large city, there may be a local drilling company which specializes in such borings, and which for $3 to $5 a foot will drill as deeply as required with a 6-in. casing, and take dry samples of the soil. This service may be available in smaller towns and rural areas through a local well driller, but the main difficulty is that a well driller is likely to use a lot of water to make his drilling easier, and the presence of this water gives a false picture of the subsoil. Therefore, in outlying areas it is usually preferable to have test pits dug by hand, and these must be large enough to permit a man to work in them. On some jobs a local road contractor may come in with a power shovel and spend a day digging test holes for a reasonable cost. The practice of driving a small pipe and taking wash borings is unsatisfactory.

Obviously, it is not satisfactory to go only to the level of the footings. It is the material below the footings which is of the most importance. For high buildings it is advisable to carry several borings to rock, or at least 20 or 30 ft below the foundations, to be sure that there are no quicksand layers below the water line. For two- or three-story structures, it is usually satisfactory to go down about 4 to 6 ft below the footing with an open hole, then drive a bar down an extra 4 ft to be sure you are not too close to soft material. It is well to avoid location of a fairly large test hole under or near a column footing in the finished structure.

c After the test pit results have been obtained, they must still be interpreted. Here also there are factors aside from the actual test results which will influence interpretation. For example: In what season of the year were the tests made? Was it dry or wet? And finally, there is the ever-present human factor: the judgment of the man who makes the interpretation. Article 8.10 lists the recommended allowable bearing values on soils of different kinds.

d Although a soil-loading test is an expensive method of determining allowable soil pressure, it is good economy whenever there is doubt about the bearing capacity of the soil. Obviously, such a loading test should be made at the level where footings will be placed. The following extract from the Pacific Coast Uniform Building Code offers a good criterion to follow in making this test.

Where the bearing capacity of the soil is not definitely known or is in question, the Building Inspector may require load tests or other adequate proof as to the permissible safe bearing capacity at that particular location. To determine the safe bearing capacity of soil it shall be tested by loading an area not less than two square feet (2 sq ft) to not less than twice the maximum bearing capacity desired for use. Such double load shall be sustained by the soil until no additional settlement takes place for a period of not less than 48 hours in order that such desired bearing capacity may be used. Examination of sub-soil conditions may be required when deemed necessary.

The area specified must be a single area of 2 sq ft, and cannot be divided into four

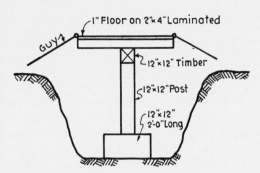

Fig. 11.1　Platform for Soil-loading Test

smaller areas. The platform which is built to carry the load therefore must be supported on a single central post as shown in Fig. 11.1. Since provision should be made for at least 20,000 lb load on the platform, consideration should be given to the material used for providing the load. If it is easily obtainable, pig iron is ideal, since it takes so little space. If a steel tank of sufficient capacity is available, it may be filled as required with water. Otherwise, cement in bags, or sand in bags is generally used. Obviously, the nature of the material used to make the test will influence the size of the platform that must be built. Probably the simplest way to hold the platform in horizontal position is by means of a guy cable at each of the four corners, although sometimes loose wedges against the sides are used.

11.40　COST DATA

a　Entire volumes are devoted to the subject of estimating and cost data, and it is impossible to give an adequate discussion in the few paragraphs that follow. There are, however, several points of general estimating practice which may be stated in this volume, including (1) a brief mention of rules of cubage and cubic foot costs and (2) the use of cost indices.

b　While cubage methods are not 100 percent accurate, the approximate cost of a building may be obtained quickly by multiplying the cubage of the proposed structure by the known cubic-foot cost of a comparable building. The method of finding cubage may be shown by the following "Rules of Cubage" of the New York State Education Department.

1. All horizontal areas shall be measured from the outside of the inclosing walls at the plane of the floor.

2. (*a*) The height of principal stories shall be measured from a horizontal plane two feet below the surface of the finished floor of the first story to the underside of the ceiling of the top story in that section of the building in which the cube occurs which is being calculated.

(*b*) In sections without finished ceilings, the perpendicular dimension shall be taken from a horizontal plane two feet below the finished floor of the first story to the mean height of roof surface of the section.

3. The height of developed basement areas shall be measured from the surface of the finished basement floor to a horizontal plane two feet below the surface of the finished floor of the first story.

4. Roof areas: (*a*) Parapet roofs (flat roof type) shall be measured from the underside of the ceiling of the top story to the high point of the finished roof surface.

(*b*) Sloping ridge roofs shall be measured from the underside of the ceiling of the top story to a horizontal plane at the mean height of the sloping roof.

(*c*) Sloping roofs with deck shall be calculated to obtain actual volume of the roof section above the plane of the ceiling of the top story.

5. Other areas: (*a*) The actual volume of towers, cupolas, penthouses, connecting passageways, boiler stacks, hoist shafts, area entrances and developed sub-basements shall be obtained. All measurements shall be taken from outside face to outside face of inclosing walls and from the surface of the floor through to the mean height of roof or inclosing surface.

Note: No cube shall be included more than once. If, for example, a boiler stack is within the principal walls of the building, only that volume which has not been included in 5, 6 and 7 shall be added under this classification.

(*b*) The actual volume of porticos and covered porches shall be obtained. Only one-half of this volume shall be included in computing the total cubage of the building. Horizontal measurements shall be taken from lines marking the outside of the faces of the frieze of the cornice, or wall structure above columns. Perpendicular measurements shall be taken from mean finished grade to mean height of roof.

6. Uncovered steps, stoops, approaches, buttresses, parapets, light courts, window areas, foundation walls, pipe trenches, cisterns, septic tanks, and retaining walls shall not be calculated nor included.

Table 11.1 *Engineering News-Record* Building Cost Index

1913 = 100

	1924	1925	1926	1927	1928	1929	1930	1931	1932	1933	1934
Av.	189.3	182.7	185.0	186.1	188.0	190.9	185.4	169.4	140.9	147.8	168.7

Month	1935	1936	1937	1938	1939	1940	1941	1942	1943	1944	1945
J	166.5	168.3	185.5	198.6	196.2	201.5	207.9	217.1	226.9	231.6	236.5
F	165.8	168.4	186.6	199.0	196.2	201.5	208.4	218.4	226.9	232.0	237.7
M	164.1	169.7	187.7	199.3	196.5	201.5	207.9	218.9	226.7	232.3	237.9
A	164.4	170.0	195.0	198.2	196.5	201.4	208.6	219.6	227.5	234.5	238.5
M	163.3	170.3	197.2	197.9	196.6	201.2	209.2	220.1	227.6	234.8	238.5
J	164.9	170.2	199.2	198.2	196.4	201.7	209.4	221.2	227.7	235.3	239.4
J	165.3	170.9	199.8	194.4	196.8	201.7	210.2	223.5	227.9	235.6	239.6
A	166.2	173.9	200.7	194.5	196.5	201.7	212.5	225.4	228.5	236.1	239.9
S	166.1	174.3	200.6	194.8	196.6	203.1	214.6	225.5	231.2	236.0	240.1
O	167.3	175.3	201.0	195.5	198.5	204.0	215.9	225.9	231.3	236.0	240.4
N	167.3	175.5	200.3	195.6	201.2	206.2	216.5	226.6	231.4	236.1	240.5
D	167.2	179.3	200.5	196.1	201.2	208.2	216.4	226.6	231.5	236.5	240.8
Av.	165.8	172.2	196.2	196.8	197.4	202.8	211.5	222.4	228.8	234.7	239.1

Month	1946	1947	1948	1949	1950	1951	1952	1953	1954	1955
J	242.2	294.6	333.6	354.9	356.2	393.0	405.8	425.0	436.4	458.8
F	243.9	301.6	335.5	352.9	356.5	398.2	406.2	425.2	437.1	459.4
M	245.4	303.3	334.2	352.5	360.0	399.3	407.4	424.9	436.7	459.6
A	254.4	305.2	334.6	351.4	362.8	400.1	407.9	426.4	437.5	460.6
M	258.1	304.6	333.9	348.9	364.3	401.1	410.3	426.2	438.2	462.6
J	265.3	307.4	339.3	349.3	373.4	400.8	412.5	426.2	439.7	464.8
J	267.2	308.9	342.4	349.5	377.7	400.3	414.5	435.2	444.1	467.5
A	272.3	317.8	355.5	350.9	383.1	401.2	422.4	436.9	455.5	478.0
S	272.4	322.6	355.5	352.0	392.8	400.3	424.4	436.0	454.3	479.2
O	273.0	327.3	357.1	353.0	397.4	403.4	424.8	436.0	455.3	480.0
N	274.0	329.2	355.9	352.9	390.2	404.5	426.0	436.0	456.3	479.3
D	280.0	333.1	355.6	353.2	391.4	405.7	424.9	435.5	456.8	
Av.	262.4	313.0	344.0	351.8	375.5	400.6	415.6	430.8	445.7	

7. Definitions: (*a*) The principal, or first story, is the lowest story the floor of which is wholly above finished grade to the building.

(*b*) The basement is that portion of the building immediately below the principal, or first story.

(*c*) A basement, sub-basement or a cellar shall not be termed a story.

(*d*) A sub-basement is that portion of a building which has been developed below the basement level.

(*e*) The mean height is the midpoint between the eaves and the peak of the roof.

c Obviously, cubic-foot prices are constantly changing, and consideration must be given to this fact. Cubic-foot costs of today may be compared with those of another date and current estimating costs prorated by the use of any one of a number of building-cost indices which are published regularly. Because it is easily obtained from any current issue of the magazine, included here is the *Engineering News-Record* Cost Index Table (Table 11.1). Unfortunately, this index makes no attempt to rate labor efficiency, but this is extremely difficult to do under any circumstances.

Problem Assume that a factory building 50 ft wide, 120 ft long, and 14 ft high cost

$35,000 when bid in the spring of 1940. The owner wished to build another similar building 40 ft wide, 180 ft long, and 16 ft high in 1953, when the *Engineering News-Record* Building Cost Index was 430. What was the estimated cost of the construction?

The volume of the original building was 84,000 cu ft and the cost was 41.6 cents per cubic foot. The cost index in 1940 was 201.5. The proposed new building will have 115,200 cu ft. The revised cost should be

$$\frac{430}{201.5} \times 41.6 = 88.8 \text{ cents per cubic foot}$$

and the total cost of the building would be $102,297.

11.50   DIMENSIONS AND CLEAR-ANCES

a Many of the dimensions and clearances given in this article are architectural rather than structural, but the engineer is frequently called upon to use them. Other dimensions and areas are given elsewhere in this book, particularly in Art. 11.60.

b For steel or concrete columns, with no other factors influencing spacing, 20 ft each way is a good spacing. For timber framing, the high cost of long timbers makes a shorter spacing more economical.

In general, it is cheaper to run the beams the long way of the span and the girders the short way.

For masonry buildings, most codes require that exterior columns be covered with 8 in. of masonry. In a two- or three-story building estimate on the basis of 8-in. columns; up to five stories, 10-in. columns; up to about nine stories, 12-in. columns; and above nine stories, 14-in. columns. In setting the centerline for wall columns, allow 8 in. for brick, 1 in. for splice plates and the like, and half the size of the column; thus it would be 1 ft 1 in. for an 8-in. column, 1 ft 2 in. for a 10-in. column, and so on. Some codes permit 4 in. of cover, which would reduce the above requirements. Consult code requirements before setting locations. Practically all codes require 8 in. of covering on beam webs, and 4 in. minimum

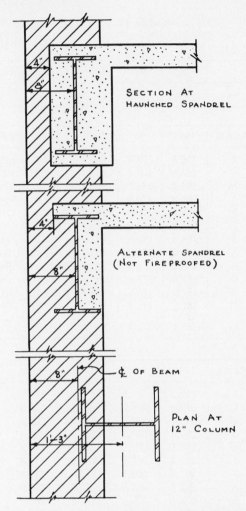

Fig. 11.2   Location of Wall Beams and Columns

on beam flanges in walls. Figure 11.2 indicates this requirement.

c For theater or church seating, allow 7 to 8 sq ft per person when using curved seats and 6 to 7 sq ft per person when using straight rows. These allowances are for the entire area, including aisles.

For dining-room seating, allow approximately 12 sq ft per person.

Toilet stalls are 2 ft 6 in. to 3 ft wide by 4 to 5 ft deep inside. Shower stalls are 2 ft 8 in. square to 3 ft 6 in. square. Urinal stalls are 2 ft to 2 ft 2 in. wide by 1 ft 8 in. to 2 ft deep (see Fig. 11.3 for further toilet-room clearances).

A telephone booth is 2 ft square inside.

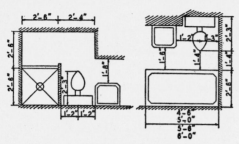

Fig. 11.3 Toilet-Room Clearances

Standard steel sash dimensions are given in Fig. 10.43.

Commonly accepted angles and pitches for ramps, stairs, and ladders are:

For pedestrian ramps, not over 20 deg, or $4\frac{3}{8}$ in. rise to 12 in. run. Preferred practice is 15 deg, or $3\frac{1}{4}$ in. rise to 12 in. run.

For stairs, not over 50 deg, or $14\frac{1}{4}$ in. rise to 12 in. run, with the preferred angle between 30 and 35 deg. The New York State Labor Department sets a maximum rise of $7\frac{3}{4}$ in. and minimum run of 10 in. exclusive of nosing, for each step. Vertical clearances are determined from Fig. 11.4.

Ladders should be used for slopes of over 50 deg. The preferred slope is 75 deg, with rungs ranging from $9\frac{3}{8}$ in. at 50 deg to $12\frac{3}{4}$ in. at 75 deg.

d Certain indoor sports require minimum clearances and lengths, the most common requirements being as follows:

Shuffleboard requires a court 6 ft wide by 52 ft long.

Bowling alleys require a width of 11 ft 6 in. and a length of 83 ft for a pair of alleys and the ball return.

A basketball court requires a floor area of 35 by 60 ft for elementary schools, 42 by 74 ft for junior high schools, 50 by 84 ft for senior high schools, and 50 by 94 ft for colleges, with 3 ft (ideally, 10 ft) clearance on all sides of the court.

A handball court requires an area of 20 by 44 ft, with 6 ft between courts or 8 ft from the side of the court to the nearest wall or construction.

The dimensions and contours of standard swimming pools are shown in Fig. 11.5.

e Standard railroad clearances are shown in Fig. 11.6. There may be local variations which will permit less clearance for certain switching railroads, but it is advisable to clear any variations from these figures with the railroad which will use the track.

Parking-garage spaces and clearances are given in Figs. 11.7 and 11.8. Where ramps are used, a 12 percent grade is desirable, with a preferred maximum of 15 percent. Curved ramps should have a 10 percent lateral slope. A one-way straight ramp should be 11 to 12 ft wide flared out at the ends, including 1-ft-wide curbs 6 in. high at each side. The outside diameter of the curve should be 60 ft.

Repair-garage dimensions are given in Art. 11.60*h*. Truck garages for the accommodation of trailer trucks or even large vans should have doors 12 to 14 ft in width, depending on directness of approach, and 13 ft high.

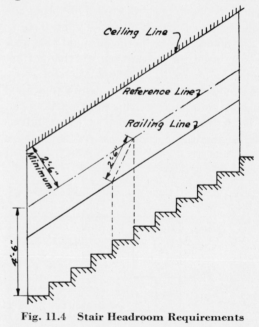

Fig. 11.4 Stair Headroom Requirements

11.60 ECONOMIC PROBLEMS OF LAYOUT

a Many of the problems of layout are architectural rather than structural, and, therefore, may be out of place in this volume. On the other hand, the problems of economics are largely engineering problems, and for the benefit of engineers who may have occasion

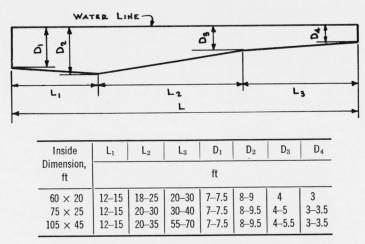

Fig. 11.5   Standard Rectangular Swimming Pools

Inside Dimension, ft	L₁	L₂	L₃	D₁	D₂	D₃	D₄
				ft			
60 × 20	12–15	18–25	20–30	7–7.5	8–9	4	3
75 × 25	12–15	20–30	30–40	7–7.5	8–9.5	4–5	3–3.5
105 × 45	12–15	20–35	55–70	7–7.5	8–9.5	4–5.5	3–3.5

to use such statistics, some of them are included here. Some points pertaining to these problems have been discussed in other articles, such as Arts. 1.40 to 1.42 and 5.10.

It should also be borne in mind that any economic data or comparisons will change from time to time with the fluctuation of costs. The following approximate figures may tend to guide the engineer in his thinking, however.

b A few years ago one of the country's large industrial corporations contemplated a large expansion program utilizing reinforced-concrete buildings. In preparation for this program it conducted a series of cost investigations, and the findings were as follows: Width and height have a greater effect on the cost of factory buildings than floor loads and column spacing. Width is affected by conditions of the site and by requirements for natural light. Height is affected by the intended use of the building and by land values. For buildings of the same width, on the

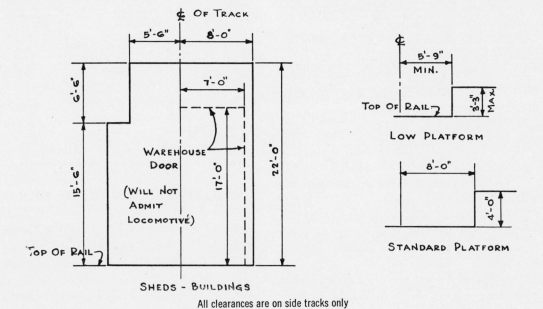

All clearances are on side tracks only

Fig. 11.6   Railroad Clearances

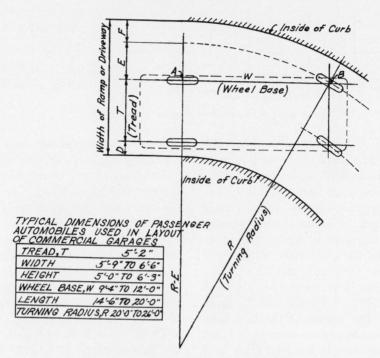

TYPICAL DIMENSIONS OF PASSENGER AUTOMOBILES USED IN LAYOUT OF COMMERCIAL GARAGES

TREAD, T	5'-2"
WIDTH	5'-9" TO 6'-6"
HEIGHT	5'-0" TO 6'-3"
WHEEL BASE, W	9'-4" TO 12'-0"
LENGTH	14'-6" TO 20'-0"
TURNING RADIUS, R	20'-0" TO 26'-0"

Fig. 11.7   Automobile Curved Ramps

basis of cost per square foot of floor a three-story building costs 96 percent as much as a two-story building, a four-story 89 percent, and a five-story 79 percent as much. On the basis of width alone, regardless of the number of stories from two to five, referring to the cost per square foot of floor as 100 percent for a building 60 ft wide, the cost for an 80-ft building would be 84 percent as great, for a 100-ft building would be 74 percent, and for a 120-ft building would be 66 percent.

Between limits of 16- and 25-ft spacing, using a 20-ft column spacing as 100 percent, the square-foot cost dependent on column spacing varies with the ratio $70 + 1.5s$, where s is the spacing in feet. As to live load, using a 200-psf load as 100 percent, the square-foot cost dependent on live load varies with the ratio $72 + 0.14w$, where w is the load in pounds per square foot. By applying these formulae to the ordinary range of spacings and loads, it will be seen that the effect of varying either spacing or load is relatively small.

In concrete structures with fairly heavy live loads, the rich-mix concretes show a considerable saving over a lean-mix concrete. For each 1,000 psi of unit strength provided, a 2,000-psi concrete costs about 45 percent more than a 3,000-psi concrete. Therefore, if load conditions and design are such that concrete can be used to anything like its economical maximum, it would pay to use a rich-mix concrete. This principle does not apply without reservations, however; it is suggested as one point in the cost picture where we do not ordinarily look for economy.

These ratios, of course, are prepared on the basis of concrete-building costs, but in general the same ideas would probably apply to steel construction.

c   Office-building design. The engineer or architect may be called upon to advise on the soundness of proposed projects as well as on their actual layout. With that idea in mind, the following is included.

In the ordinary office building there should be a reasonable expectation that the building should be 70 percent full within a year and 90 to 95 percent full in two years. A general rule used by many experts is that the ground floor of a tall building should earn enough to pay the taxes and a reasonable return on the

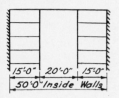 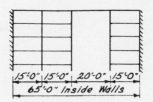 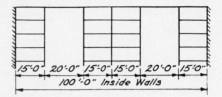

Fig. 11.8   Layout of Garage Parking Units

cost of the land. Some demand taxes on the first floor also. The shape of the lot is of vital importance. If the area is too small or the frontage too narrow, it is impossible to improve it intensively enough to secure proper return. The larger the lot and the more nearly it approaches a square in shape, the lower the unit cost and the greater the efficiency of the rental space. Ordinarily the net rentable area is from 60 to 70 percent of the total lot area, and from 70 to 80 percent of the gross building area. The rentals of the first floor and basement should pay a minimum of 5 percent interest, the taxes on the land alone, and the insurance on the building.

Investigations indicate that the average requirement of office space is 3.9 sq ft per capita in Detroit, 6.5 in Los Angeles, and 6.4 in Chicago. Another study based on 12 southern cities with a population of around 300,000 indicated $4\frac{1}{2}$ sq ft per capita. This is based on net rentable areas in buildings offering competitive office space.

Under normal conditions, in an office building column spacing should approximate 17 to 18 ft. This makes possible the most generally serviceable type of office unit, 17 to 18 ft in width and 25 to 30 ft in depth. In a building of 10 or more stories, the column spacing for offices should take precedence over that for stores. Offices facing an open park receive natural light to a much greater depth than those facing a narrow street. Best financial return is usually obtained by using the first floor for stores, and the available return from these stores may be the governing factor in determining the column spacing, rather than the spacing for offices. The ceiling height for offices should be 9 to 10 ft.

Each office unit should have two windows, about 4 ft 6 in. wide by 7 ft 6 in. high.

Corridors should be 6 ft 6 in. to 7 ft wide. No windows are necessary for corridors. Office doors should be 42 in. wide and doors between offices should be 30 in.

Population of office buildings may be estimated at 1 person per 125 sq ft.

d   Hotel design. The size of hotel bedrooms has become almost standardized. Rooms facing the street are usually about 10 to 12 ft wide by 16 ft in length; rooms facing a court are 9 to 11 ft wide by 14 ft long. Corner rooms are usually 15 to 16 ft wide by 18 to 20 ft long. It is well, if possible, to make hotel room sizes in multiples of standard carpet widths for economy.

Corridors should serve rooms on both sides and there should be ample linen-closet, slop-sink, and maid-room accommodations on each floor.

For dining rooms and cafeterias, provide 20 sq ft of dining space for each bedroom. For kitchens, provide the same amount.

Private bathrooms and closet room should be provided at the corridor end of each bedroom, and one ventilating shaft provided for each two bathrooms.

An article by Professors Randolph and Sayles of Cornell University published in *Architectural Record* gives a formula for approximate cubage as follows:

$$x = 0.41y + 0.013y^2 + 0.0002y^3$$

where y = hundreds of rooms

x = millions of cubic feet

Several other formulae give approximate areas as follows:

Lobby area in hundreds of square feet = $0.373y + 0.68$

Laundry area in hundreds of square feet = $2.12y - 5.59$

e School design. Much of the following on school design is from the regulations of the New York State Department of Education.

Classroom dimensions should be 22 ft wide and 27 or 30 ft long, or 19 ft wide and 30 ft long.

Classroom windows should be located on one of the broad sides on the left of the pupils, grouped with a space not exceeding 1 ft between windows. The glass area should be equal to one-fifth the floor area. The window near the forward end should be 6 ft from the corner if possible, and never less than 4 ft. A room 22 by 27 ft should have five windows 3 ft 4 in. wide and 8 ft 6 in. high, or four windows 4 ft wide by 8 ft 6 in. high, with the head of the window 11 ft or more from the floor. A room 19 by 30 ft should have either five windows 3 ft 4 in. by 7 ft 10 in. or four windows 4 ft by 7 ft 10 in., with the window head 10 ft or more from the floor. Windows for other rooms may be of any stock size. For toilet and coat rooms a window 2 ft 10 in. wide by 5 ft 2 in. high is satisfactory.

In smaller buildings, well-lighted and well-ventilated coat rooms having at least 50 sq ft of floor space should be provided for each sex.

In toilet rooms, provide one lavatory for each 50 pupils, one water closet for each 25 girls, and one closet and one urinal for each 40 boys.

Main corridors should be from 9 to 14 ft wide.

Recessed wardrobes for classrooms should be 2 to 3 ft deep with sliding or folding doors full width.

f Hospital design. For hospitals, the Veterans' Administration has set up criteria requiring a total area ranging from 432 sq ft minimum per person for a 1,000-bed hospital, to 595 sq ft for a 200-bed hospital. Corridors should be at least 8 ft wide. Single rooms should have a minimum size of 120 sq ft. Minimum height floor to floor is 11 ft.

g Warehouse design. Some years ago a committee of the American Railway Engineering Association made an investigation and report on the economics of various factors of warehouse design which are worth recording here. They recommended for warehouses where the turnover of goods is fairly rapid:

1. One elevator for each 40,000 sq ft of warehouse space
2. Shipping platform should be 4 percent of warehouse storage floor area
3. One car length of track siding for each 17,600 sq ft of storage area
4. One foot of tailboard frontage for each 1,100 sq ft of storage space
5. Tailboard frontage of 16 ft for each car length of siding

h Automobile salesrooms and service station design. Automobile sales and service stations are designed to fulfill requirements which have been established by the large manufacturers. Stalls are required for the following uses.

1. Service and repair stalls for regular customers
2. Used-car conditioning stalls
3. New-car conditioning stalls
4. Shop-storage stalls
5. Customer-reception stalls
6. Wash, polish, body, and paint stalls

The number of stalls required for the above uses is determined as follows: Take the average number of new cars sold per year for the past three years and divide by 28 for the number of service and repair stalls. Add one used-car conditioning stall for each 100 new cars sold, and one new-car conditioning stall for each 300 new cars sold. For shop storage, allow half the number of service and repair stalls. For customer reception, allow one-third the number of service and repair stalls. The number of stalls for work, polish, body, and paint must be based on past experience, since neighborhood competition is largely the governing factor.

For cars parked at right angles to the wall, allow 10 ft per car for service stalls and for customer reception, and 9 ft for shop-storage stalls. If diagonal parking is necessary add 15 percent. The stalls should be from 23 to 25 ft deep with a 25-ft aisle for diagonal parking. Lubrication racks require from 15 × 25 to 20 × 25 ft; wash racks, paint stalls, and body stalls, 15 × 25 ft; polish stalls, 12 × 25 ft. The minimum height if a lubrication hoist is used is 12 ft for passenger cars and 13 ft for trucks. Service doors should be 14 ft wide by 12 ft high for passenger cars and 13 ft high for trucks.

i Stair design. Since improper stairs constitute a fruitful cause of claims against public liability insurance companies, it is well to adhere very closely to accepted practice in their design.

The rise and run of a stair are determined by the following rules:

1. The sum of the rise and run should be not less than 17 in. nor more than 18 in.

2. Twice the rise plus the run should be not less than 24 in. nor more than 25 in.

3. The product of the rise and run should be not less than 70 nor more than 75.

For important stairs, a rise of 7 in. and a run of 11 in. will give satisfactory results. For less important stairs, 7 or $7\frac{1}{2}$ in. by 10 or even $9\frac{1}{2}$ in. may be used, and for basement stairs in residences, even 8 in. rise. The New York State Labor Department specifies a maximum rise of $7\frac{3}{4}$ in. and minimum run of 10 in. for exit stairs. The nosing may project $\frac{3}{4}$ to $1\frac{1}{2}$ in. beyond this.

The width of stairs is determined by their importance and by the number of persons that are expected to use them at one time. In general, stairs should be at least 3 ft wide. The New York State Labor laws specify a minimum of 3 ft 8 in. for exit stairs. The Building Code of the National Board of Fire Underwriters says that the width of stairs should be based on the number of people using the stairs, computed on the basis of 14 persons for each 22 in. width of stairway, plus 1 person for each 3 sq ft of hallway floor and stairway landings in the story height of each floor. Office buildings do not require as much stair area as other buildings, because the elevators are supposed to serve as proper exits. Many office buildings of large occupancy have only two 3-ft to 3-ft 8-in. stairways, and sometimes only one.

The New York City Code requires a minimum stair width of 3 ft 8 in., or a total of 22 in. width per person per $1\frac{1}{2}$ treads, plus one person for each $2\frac{3}{4}$ sq ft of floor area on the landings, platforms, and halls within the stairway. In small buildings, this width may be

cut to 3 ft. The occupancy is figured on the basis of one person for 10 sq ft of dance halls, restaurants, lodge rooms, and places of assembly; 15 sq ft in courtrooms and in classrooms in schools and colleges; 75 sq ft in work rooms, reading rooms, markets, showrooms, and stores; 50 sq ft in billiard rooms, bowling alleys, golf schools, and similar uses; 100 sq ft in office buildings and hospitals.

The New York State Labor law requires two enclosed fire stairways remote from each other for all buildings coming under its jurisdiction. This includes factories and loft buildings but not office buildings.

All stairways required as a legal means of exit shall run continuously from the roof to the ground floor and be connected by means of a fire enclosure to an outside exit at ground level.

j Elevators. The number and size of elevators are governed by:

1. The character of the building
2. The height of the building
3. The rentable area
4. The time interval between cars
5. The number of stories to be served
6. The average number and duration of stops per trip

No iron-clad rules can be given for all types of buildings, but office buildings and loft buildings have been sufficiently standardized in design to have developed some general rules. Good elevator service requires one elevator for each 20,000 to 30,000 sq ft of floor area. The elevator cabs should be at least as wide as they are deep, and, if possible, 20 to 50 per cent wider. Cabs should have from 28 to 30 sq ft minimum floor area and be at least 7 ft wide. Several moderate-sized cars of high speed are preferable to a greater number of large, slow cars.

Buildings equipped with both local and express cars should have the same number of cars for each. Express cars are not necessary up to about 18 floors. Express cars will not serve as many floors as local cars, because they must go a greater distance to reach their first stop, so local cars should serve to about three-fifths of the height.

It is advisable to consult the local representative of one of the reliable elevator manufacturers to assist in planning elevators.

11.70 CHECKING STEEL SHOP DRAWINGS

a Although the detailers in the employ of the steel fabricator are responsible for sizes taken from the designer's drawings, and for correct fitting of column-and-beam details, steel shop drawings should be checked by the architectural engineer to ensure general compliance, and to pick up interferences and discrepancies that may have been missed in the original design. The following check lists will indicate the general checking that should be done.

b *Anchor-bolt plan:*

1. Dimensions and angles
   a. Over-all dimensions
   b. Column centers
   c. Slopes of lines

2. Check column bases for:
   a. Column number
   b. Column turned right direction
   c. Elevation
   d. Billet or grillage sizes
   e. Interference of billet or grillage
   f. Size of pier to receive billet or grillage

c *Erection diagrams* (each checked individually):

1. Dimensions and angles
   a. Over-all dimensions
   b. Column centers
   c. Slopes of lines

2. Check columns for:
   a. Column section
   b. Column number
   c. Turned right direction
   d. Lateral supports

3. Check beams, girders, and trusses for:
   a. Section and general arrangement
   b. Location
   c. Elevation
   d. Clearance for stair wells, elevators, spandrels, fireproofing, etc.

4. Special sections
   a. Tie rods
   b. Shelf angles
   c. Special spandrels
   d. Lintels
   e. Hangers and struts

d *Beam details:*

1. Main material and over-all dimension
   a. Check for floor plan
   b. Clearance at ends
   c. Length of wall bearing

2. End connections
   a. Load capacity
   b. Eccentricity
   c. Material of connection
   d. Coped or blocked either end
   e. Square or sloping end
   f. Interferences
   g. Any countersunk rivets required

3. Connections into beam
   a. Location and size of beam connecting
   b. Elevation
   c. Beams framing opposite to use same holes
   d. Shelf angles, punching for nailers, knee braces, tie rods, etc.

4. General
   a. Size of rivets, open holes; exceptions
   b. Painting
   c. End marks, special marks, etc.

5. Special beams
   a. Hand holes for double beams
   b. Distance apart for double beams
   c. Separators or stiffeners
   d. Cover plates or web reinforcement

e *Column details:*

1. Main material
   a. Check from column schedule

2. Faces in right direction
   a. Faces noted

3. Dimensions
   a. Floor to floor
   b. Relation of ends to floor level

4. Base detail, splice detail, milled ends

5. Beam connections
   a. Elevation
   b. Size
   c. Interferences
   d. Clip angle loose
   e. Strength of seat connections

6. Miscellaneous connections
   a. Knee-brace connections
   b. Siding and girts
   c. Punch for nailers
   d. Bracing connections

7. General
   a. Column marking
   b. Size of rivets and open holes; exceptions
   c. Painting

f   Truss details:

1. Main material
   a. Compare with design
   b. Which leg of angle outstanding

2. Main dimensions
   a. Span
   b. Elevation of underside and depth
   c. Depth on gage lines
   d. Slope of members
   e. Panel spacing
   f. Monitor width and height

3. Joints
   a. Develop stress
   b. Eliminate eccentricity in connections

4. Miscellaneous connections
   a. Purlin clips
   b. Lower lateral bracing
   c. Top lateral bracing
   d. Tie rods
   e. Holes for nailers
   f. Attachment of beams to lower chords

5. General
   a. Truss marking
   b. Mark end
   c. Size of rivets, open holes; exceptions
   d. Painting

INDEX